COASTAL
FISHES
OF SOUTHERN AFRICA

PHIL & ELAINE HEEMSTRA

SOUTH AFRICAN INSTITUTE FOR AQUATIC BIODIVERSITY

NISC • SAIAB

© 2004 South African Institute for Aquatic Biodiversity and National Inquiry Service Centre

Published jointly by
the National Inquiry Service Centre (NISC), South Africa, and
the South African Institute for Aquatic Biodiversity (SAIAB).

Grateful acknowledgements are due to Sappi for donation
of paper and to Marine and Coastal Management
for their subvention of production costs.

NISC
PO Box 377, Grahamstown, 6140

SAIAB
Private Bag 1015, Grahamstown, 6140

www.coastalfishes.nisc.co.za

ISBN 1-920033-01-7

Printed by Paarl Print
on Avalon Supreme Gloss 300 g/m^2 and
115 g/m^2 produced and donated by Sappi.

Cover by Fuel Design.

Set in CG Omega 9 on 12 pt.

ACKNOWLEDGEMENTS

We are grateful to Paul Skelton, Managing Director of the South African Institute for Aquatic Biodiversity (SAIAB), for his patience, encouragement and support throughout the interminable endeavour that produced this book. We enjoyed the support of the entire staff of SAIAB and we were also fortunate to have access to the excellent resources, especially the library, image and fish collections, of SAIAB (formerly the JLB Smith Institute of Ichthyology).

Acknowledgements are also due to Margaret Crampton, our enthusiastic publisher at NISC. Many thanks to the skillful Project Manager, Michelle Willmers, for her well organised and tactful supervision of the production process. Thanks to Jenny Gon for her meticulous editing, to Charlene Bate for her imaginative and careful page layouts, and to Sue Abraham for her endless patience and help in preparing the graphic material.

We are grateful to Sappi Limited for providing the paper for printing the book and to the Marine and Coastal Management branch of the Department of Environmental Affairs and Tourism for their subvention of the production of this book.

We thank Wouter Holleman, Malcolm Smale, Jenny and Ofer Gon and Kate Moots for reading our manuscript and for their helpful suggestions to improve the text.

In writing the family and species accounts we used publications, advice and often unpublished data from Jerry Allen (Pomacentridae), Eric Anderson (Ambassidae), Tim Andrew (Stromateidae), Tony Booth (Sparidae), Jack Briggs (Gobiesocidae), Bruce Collette (Hemiramphidae, Belonidae and Scombridae), Leonard Compagno (Chondrichthyes), Paul Cowley (Dasyatidae and Sparidae), Pat Garrett (Molidae), Tony Gill (Pseudochromidae), Ofer Gon (Apogonidae), Marc Griffiths (Sciaenidae), Wouter Holleman (Tripterygiidae), Brett Human (Scyliorhinidae), Ken Hutchings (Sciaenidae), Barry Hutchins (Monacanthidae), Yukio Iwatsuki (Gerreidae, Leiognathidae and Sparidae), Les Knapp (Platycephalidae), Rudie Kuiter (Labridae), Helen Larson (Gobiidae and Microdesmidae), Jeff Leis (Diodontidae), Jackie Lockyear (Syngnathidae), Bruce Mann (Sparidae), Keiichi Matsuura (Balistidae and Tetraodontidae), Randy Mooi (Pempheridae and Plesiopidae), Monica Mwale (Syngnathidae), John Randall (Labridae, Mullidae, Acanthuridae and Scaridae), Bill Richards (Triglidae), Barry Russell (Nemipteridae), Kunio Sasaki (Sciaenidae), Bill Smith-Vaniz (Carangidae), James Stapley (Kuhliidae), Robin Stobbs (Latimeriidae), Rob Tilney (Ariidae), Niall Vine (Chaetodontidae suitable for aquaria), Steve Warren (fish suitable for aquaria), Gill Watson (Squalidae), Alan Whitfield (Monodactylidae), Jeff Williams (Blenniidae) and Rick Winterbottom (Pseudochromidae).

We are obliged to a host of friends, colleagues and fellow fish watchers for sharing their knowledge of fish, providing information, specimens and photographs or facilitating our work in various ways: Mark Addison, Neville Ayliffe, Andy Bentley, Greg Brett, Steve Brouwer, Simon Chater, Margot Collett, Allan Connell, Neil Deacon, John Dench, Greg de Valle, Lee-Ann Fargher, Sean Fennessy, Mike and Valda Fraser, Drew Grant, Tom Hecht, Mez Jiwaji, Roel Jonkman, John Keulder, Dennis King, Jerraleigh Kruger, Amanda MacPhail, Phumeza Mpambani, Vusi Mthombeni, Robin Palmer, Dennis and Sally Polack, Allon Poole, David Sandi, Ruth and Ginger Seipp, Margie Shaw, Kevin Smith, Pkee Stopforth, Les ter Morshuizen, Olav Weyl, Joan Wright and Punky Yose.

Guido Zsilavecz and Paul Cowley supplied fish photos; Ella van Tonder provided the cover photographs of the authors and Helen Randall did the drawing of a postlarval surgeonfish.

CONTENTS

v

The remarkable illustrations that are contained in the pages of this book provide a valuable opportunity to marvel at the sheer beauty and diversity of South Africa's marine fishes. So too do they remind us of the profound responsibility that we have to safeguard this natural heritage for generations to come.

It is perhaps fitting that *Coastal Fishes of Southern Africa* is published in 2004, at a time when our country is celebrating 10 years of democracy. For not only has democracy presented us with a unique opportunity to broaden access to our country's valuable commercial fisheries, but it has also opened the door for South Africans from all walks of life to explore the wonders of our coastal waters. This doesn't only mean visiting beaches that were previously out of bounds to the majority of our people, but rather, unlocking the wealth of opportunities that exist in the marine environment.

By way of example, the sighting by recreational divers of a living coelacanth off Sodwana Bay in October 2000 led to the establishment of the exciting African Coelacanth Ecosystem Resource Programme which was initiated in March 2002. The coelacanth, *Latimeria chalumnae*, is the focus of this programme which also has a strong emphasis on biodiversity conservation, capacity building and public understanding of science and technology. It is through programmes such as these that our government aims to make science and technology relevant and accessible to the youth in South Africa, with the ultimate goal of increasing the number of students pursuing careers in science and engineering.

One of the biggest challenges that we face in South Africa today is to strike a balance between meeting the food security needs of our coastal people, while at the same time ensuring that the resources upon which they depend are managed sustainably. Moreover, as a signatory to the Convention on Biodiversity, South Africa has a global responsibility to conserve endemic marine species, many of which are so beautifully presented here.

The role that information and education play in meeting these diverse challenges cannot be overstated. Not only do we need to ensure that our people are skilled to harvest marine resources responsibly – so that their children and their children's children will also have that opportunity – but we also need to encourage a new generation of marine scientists to discover the wonders of our country's marine environment. I believe that publications like this one have a vital role to play in meeting these objectives.

This book is sure to delight the many fishers, divers and nature enthusiasts who explore our shores, and I am quite sure that it will play an important role in educating and encouraging taxonomists and fisheries managers of the future. It is for all these reasons that the Department of Environmental Affairs and Tourism is proud to be associated with this impressive publication.

Mohammed Valli Moosa
Minister of Environmental Affairs and Tourism, 1999–2004

Marine scientists agree that the whole South African coast, sweeping down from the coral reefs of the Indian Ocean to the rich kelp beds of the Atlantic, is one of the richest, most biologically diverse and oceanographically complex marine environments on earth. The rich Benguela Current off the south-west coast of South Africa supports large quantities of fish, while the Agulhas Current off the east coast has a smaller quantity of fish but a greater diversity of species.

It is estimated that of the 1 800 fish species – excluding those below 200 m – identified along our coastline, 16% are endemic. Despite this richness, generally speaking, knowledge of our fish fauna is poor.

Coastal Fishes of Southern Africa helps to close the gap in our knowledge, providing a window into this fascinating underwater world. Increasing our foundation of knowledge is crucial, as oceans represent one of the most important life-support systems on earth, with people becoming increasingly dependent on the sea's natural resources. The sustainable use and management of these resources are critical to our future development.

'Where do I begin?' is usually the first question people ask when beginning to learn about a new subject. *Coastal Fishes of Southern Africa* makes it easy, not just to begin, but to learn more and more. Beautifully illustrated, it's an easy-to-reference, up-to-date guide to over 400 species of fish, which will appeal not just to the layperson, but also to fishery biologists and ichthyologists.

The authors' knowledge of and love for their subject is apparent on every page. The quality and accessibility of *Coastal Fishes of Southern Africa* will, I am sure, lead more and more people to become avid fish watchers.

Enjoy this wonderful book.

Jonathan Leslie
Chief Executive Officer
Sappi Limited

Coastal Fishes of Southern Africa provides illustrations and descriptions of over 400 species of coastal fish, as well as additional information on about 300 similar species. This book will help to identify the fish found around our coastline in tide pools, estuaries, along sandy beaches and rocky shores, on inshore reefs, as well as deep sea species of interest to sport and commercial fishermen.

IDENTIFYING YOUR FISH

- To find more information about a particular fish species, you will need to identify the family to which the fish belongs. The scientific names of families end in -idae (e.g. Labridae, Triglidae). If you know the family of the fish you want to identify, e.g. wrasses (Labridae) or seabream (Sparidae), you can go directly to the family account in the book using the index.

  If you don't know the family, start on p. xi at the illustrated guide to fish families which groups the families according to diagnostic features and look for an outline that matches your fish. Once you have identified a likely family, proceed to the family account.
- Each family account includes a set of small thumbnail images of the fish species described in this book. Once you find the image that appears to match your fish, turn to the species description for that fish. Bold text indicates features particularly useful for identification.
- On reaching the species description, compare your fish with the painting. If the colours of the species illustration do not match, read the colour description for variation within the species and check for similar species at the end of the species description. Highlighted distribution boxes based on current knowledge of fish distributions provide a further indication of whether you're looking at the right fish.

- To confirm your identification or find further information on a fish you are unable to identify, consult the recommended reading list at the end of this book for other authoritative sources.

READING FAMILY AND SPECIES ACCOUNTS

The families are in phylogenetic (evolutionary) order, in other words, the oldest, most 'primitive' cartilaginous fishes (Chondrichthyes) are first, followed by the more 'derived' (recently evolved) bony fish families. An advantage of the phylogenetic sequence is that similar fishes (e.g. all sharks [elasmobranchs] or snappers [Lutjanidae] or fusiliers [Caesionidae]), are grouped together, which facilitates comparisons and identification. Within families, species are arranged alphabetically by scientific names.

This book is divided into two sections – cartilaginous fishes (Class Chondrichthyes) and bony fishes (Class Osteichthyes).

Family accounts

- Each family account starts with a brief description of the family characteristics, size range of smallest and largest species in our area, and biology of the family.
- The family account includes a distribution box providing the worldwide geographic distribution of the family and an estimate of the number of genera and species within the family.

Species accounts

- Each species account begins with the common and scientific names. The scientific name comprises the genus name and the species epithet followed by the author(s) of that species. The author is the person who first identified that fish and gave it its scientific name and the author's name is usually accompanied by the year in which the species name and description was published. If the author's name is in brackets, the fish was originally named in a different genus to that currently in use. A few species are as yet undescribed (without a species epithet) and these are indicated by the abbreviation of species (sp.) after the genus name.

■ The description is accompanied by an illustration of the fish. There is often a great deal of colour variation between individuals within a species, as well as change in colour and body shape from juveniles to adults. Sexual dichromatism (males and females with different colour patterns) also occurs. Some species accounts are therefore accompanied by illustrations of two or more fish. In these illustrations, the smaller fish is usually the juvenile. The length measurement for each fish illustrated is given in the caption. Most colour sources are taken from southern African specimens, but where fish from other localities were used the localities are given in brackets.

■ The first paragraph of the species account includes counts, measurements, colour descriptions and other features useful for identification. Diagnostic data given for the family are not repeated for the species, and data not needed for identification are omitted. Measurements of body features are often given as a ratio of a larger measurement, such as standard length (SL) or total length (TL). The maximum sizes given for species are total length unless otherwise indicated. The introductory sections on fish anatomy and biology and the glossary at the back of the book will assist with understanding technical terms.

■ A distribution box provides details of worldwide and currently known southern African coastal distribution.

■ Most species accounts contain a paragraph(s) on the biology and ecology of the species, followed by general information, including edibility, suitability for aquaria and catch records.

■ Some species accounts include information on similar species. Page references are provided for similar species covered elsewhere in the book.

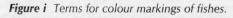

Figure i *Terms for colour markings of fishes.*

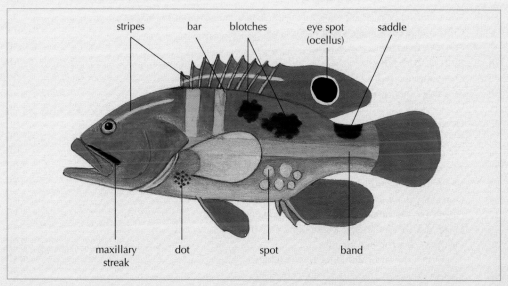

LIST OF FIGURES

This is a subjective guide to the fish and fish families in this book. Please note that a family may be represented in one or more diagnostic categories, depending on the character/s being highlighted. When trying to identify a fish pay particular attention to its gestalt (especially the shape and configuration of the head and mouth), the number of dorsal fins (one, two or three), the fin shapes (particularly the tail fin) and whether or not the fins have fin spines (a feature that is illustrated on the drawings). Please note that the fish are not drawn to scale.

DIAGNOSTIC FEATURE	TYPICAL FAMILY OUTLINE	
Shark-like	cow shark (p. 51)	catshark (p. 65)
	dogfish (p. 53)	hammerhead shark (p. 68)
	longtail shark (p. 54)	mackerel shark (p. 69)
	whale shark (p. 55)	thresher shark (p. 72)
	requiem shark (p. 56)	ragged-tooth shark (p. 73)
	hound shark (p. 63)	elephantfish (p. 89)

DIAGNOSTIC FEATURE	TYPICAL FAMILY OUTLINE

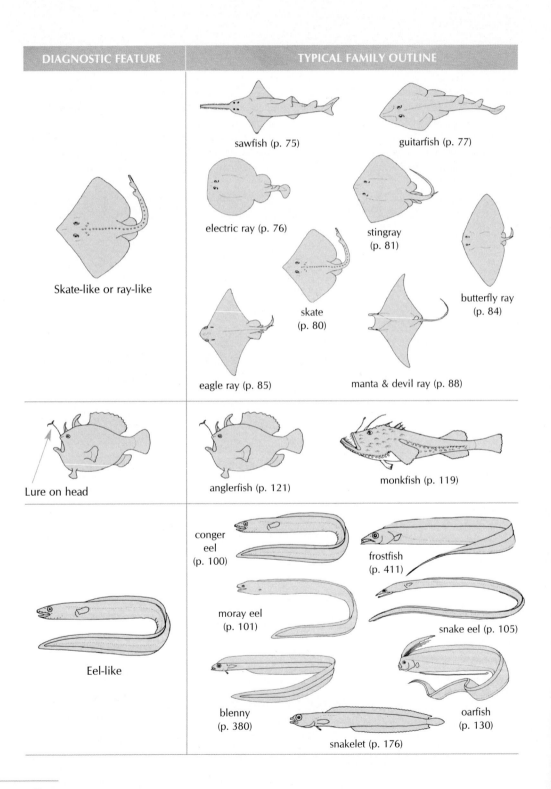

Skate-like or ray-like

sawfish (p. 75)

guitarfish (p. 77)

electric ray (p. 76)

stingray (p. 81)

skate (p. 80)

butterfly ray (p. 84)

eagle ray (p. 85)

manta & devil ray (p. 88)

Lure on head

anglerfish (p. 121)

monkfish (p. 119)

Eel-like

conger eel (p. 100)

frostfish (p. 411)

moray eel (p. 101)

snake eel (p. 105)

blenny (p. 380)

oarfish (p. 130)

snakelet (p. 176)

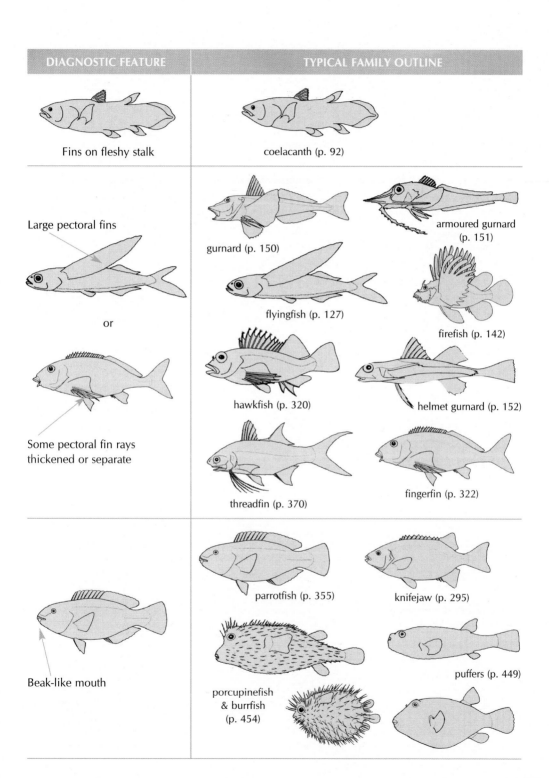

DIAGNOSTIC FEATURE	TYPICAL FAMILY OUTLINE
Fins on fleshy stalk	coelacanth (p. 92)

Large pectoral fins

or

Some pectoral fin rays thickened or separate

gurnard (p. 150)

armoured gurnard (p. 151)

flyingfish (p. 127)

firefish (p. 142)

hawkfish (p. 320)

helmet gurnard (p. 152)

threadfin (p. 370)

fingerfin (p. 322)

Beak-like mouth

parrotfish (p. 355)

knifejaw (p. 295)

porcupinefish & burrfish (p. 454)

puffers (p. 449)

DIAGNOSTIC FEATURE	TYPICAL FAMILY OUTLINE

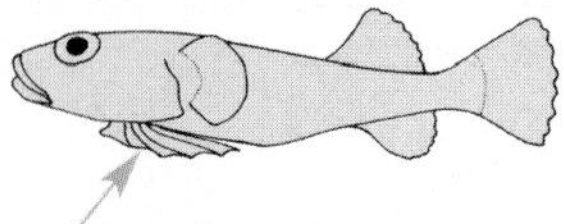

Pelvic fins joined into a sucker-like disc

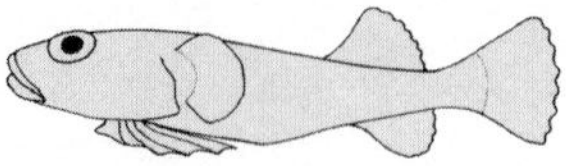

clingfish (p. 123)

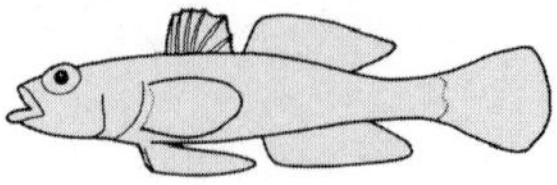

goby (p. 393)

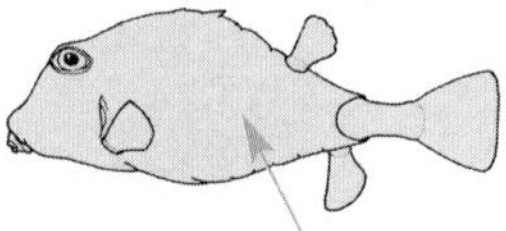

Body enclosed in a shell or carapace, or with armour-like body

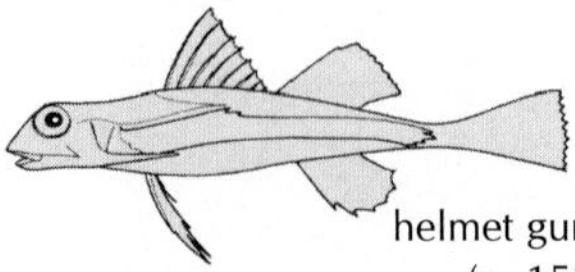

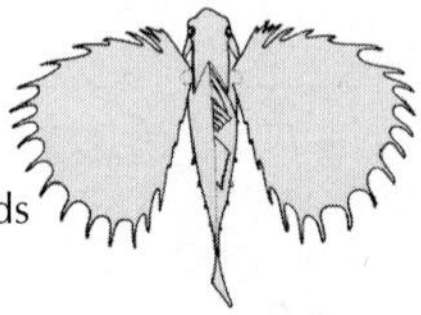

helmet gurnards (p. 152)

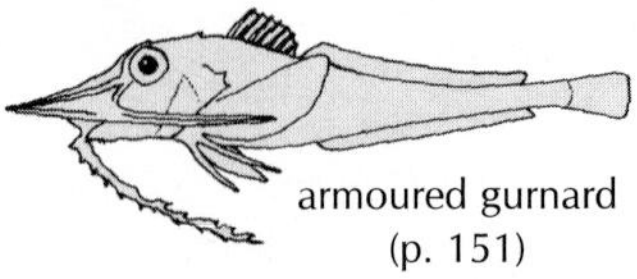

armoured gurnard (p. 151)

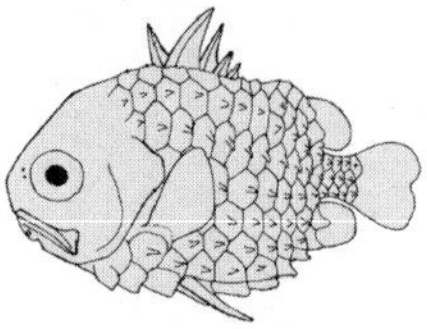

boxfish (p. 447)

pineapplefish (p. 132)

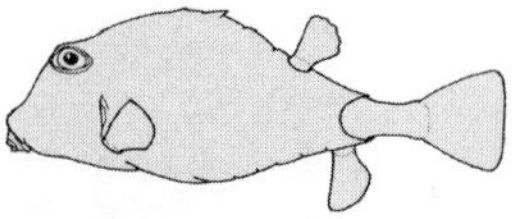

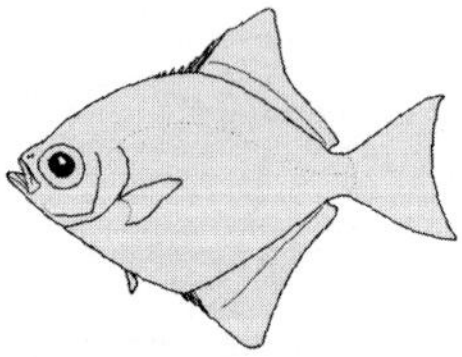

Diamond- or rhomboid-shaped body

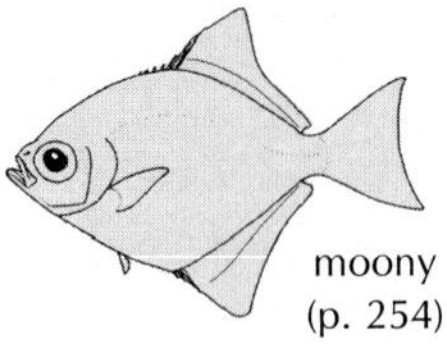

moony (p. 254)

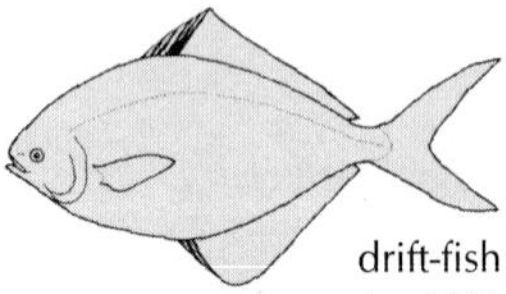

drift-fish (p. 428)

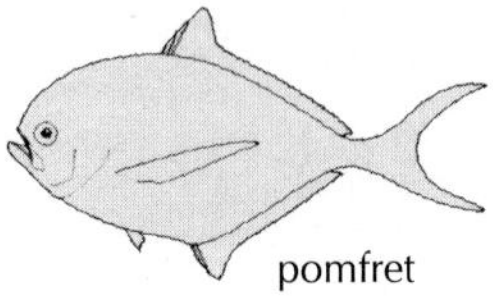

pomfret (p. 296)

coachman (p. 284)

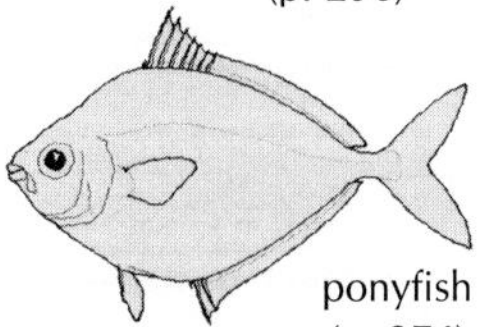

ponyfish (p. 274)

concertinafish (p. 259)

triggerfish (p. 439)

jutjaw (p. 249)

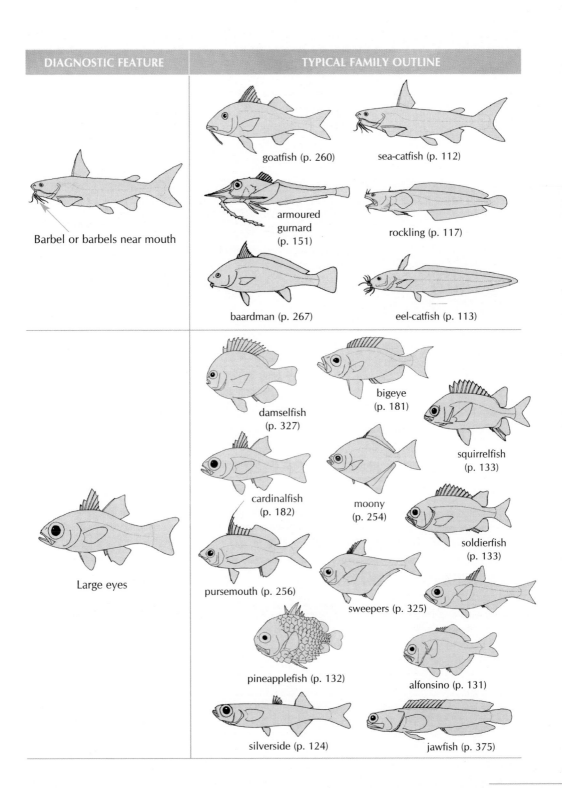

DIAGNOSTIC FEATURE	TYPICAL FAMILY OUTLINE

Barbel or barbels near mouth

goatfish (p. 260)

sea-catfish (p. 112)

armoured gurnard (p. 151)

rockling (p. 117)

baardman (p. 267)

eel-catfish (p. 113)

Large eyes

damselfish (p. 327)

bigeye (p. 181)

squirrelfish (p. 133)

cardinalfish (p. 182)

moony (p. 254)

soldierfish (p. 133)

pursemouth (p. 256)

sweepers (p. 325)

pineapplefish (p. 132)

alfonsino (p. 131)

silverside (p. 124)

jawfish (p. 375)

DIAGNOSTIC FEATURE	TYPICAL FAMILY OUTLINE

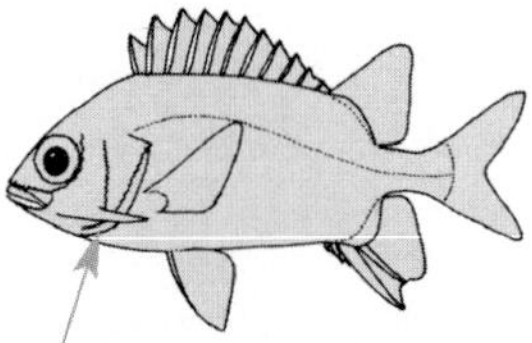

squirrelfish (p. 133)

armoured gurnard
(p. 151)

flathead (p. 148)

porcupinefish
& burrfish
(p. 454)

thornfish (p. 179)

**Prominent spine or spines
on head**

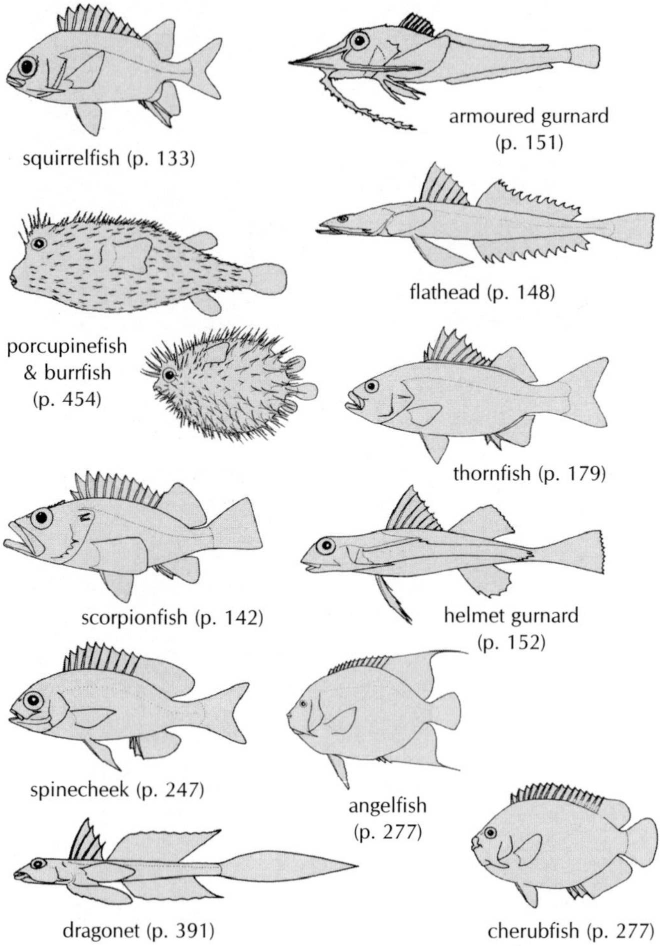

scorpionfish (p. 142)

helmet gurnard
(p. 152)

spinecheek (p. 247)

angelfish
(p. 277)

dragonet (p. 391)

cherubfish (p. 277)

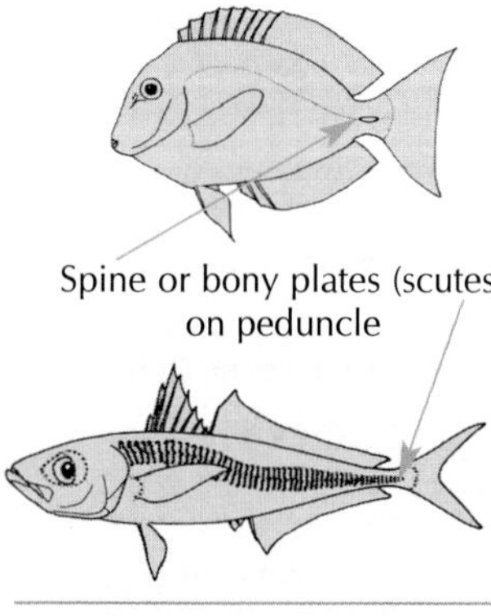

**Spine or bony plates (scutes)
on peduncle**

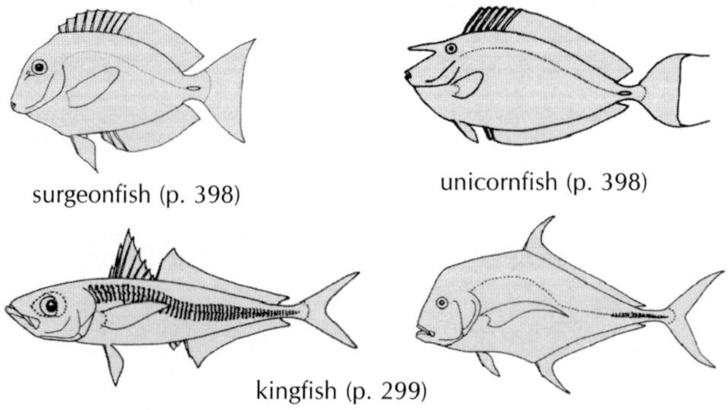

surgeonfish (p. 398)

unicornfish (p. 398)

kingfish (p. 299)

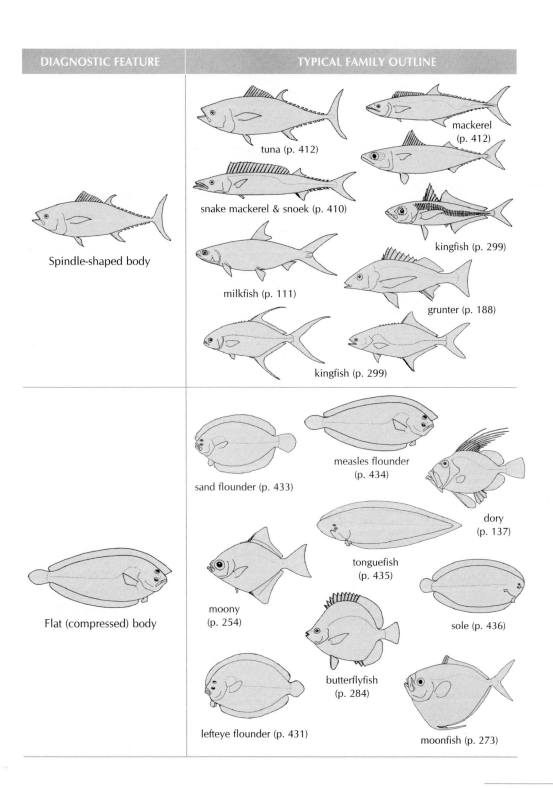

DIAGNOSTIC FEATURE	TYPICAL FAMILY OUTLINE
Spindle-shaped body	tuna (p. 412) mackerel (p. 412) snake mackerel & snoek (p. 410) kingfish (p. 299) milkfish (p. 111) grunter (p. 188) kingfish (p. 299)
Flat (compressed) body	sand flounder (p. 433) measles flounder (p. 434) dory (p. 137) tonguefish (p. 435) moony (p. 254) sole (p. 436) butterflyfish (p. 284) lefteye flounder (p. 431) moonfish (p. 273)

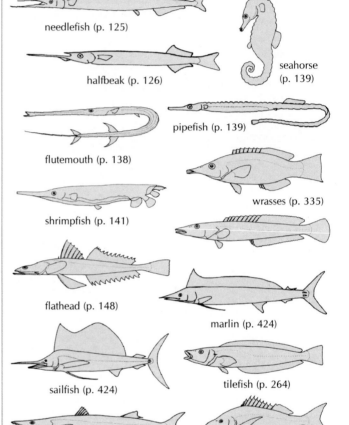

needlefish (p. 125)

halfbeak (p. 126)

seahorse (p. 139)

flutemouth (p. 138)

pipefish (p. 139)

shrimpfish (p. 141)

wrasses (p. 335)

flathead (p. 148)

marlin (p. 424)

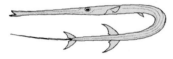

Elongated body and elongated head or snout

sailfish (p. 424)

tilefish (p. 264)

barracuda (p. 371)

grunter (p. 188)

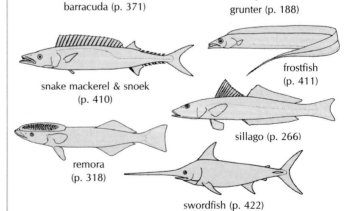

snake mackerel & snoek (p. 410)

frostfish (p. 411)

sillago (p. 266)

remora (p. 318)

swordfish (p. 422)

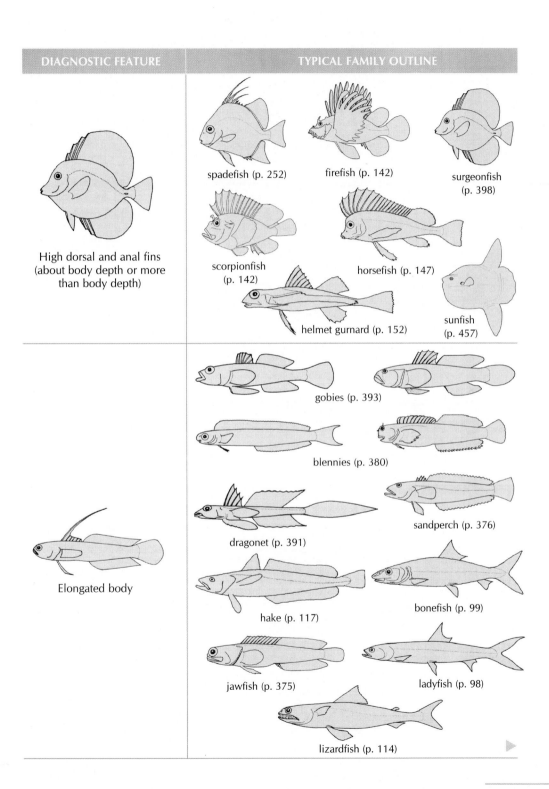

DIAGNOSTIC FEATURE	TYPICAL FAMILY OUTLINE

High dorsal and anal fins (about body depth or more than body depth)

spadefish (p. 252)

firefish (p. 142)

surgeonfish (p. 398)

scorpionfish (p. 142)

horsefish (p. 147)

helmet gurnard (p. 152)

sunfish (p. 457)

Elongated body

gobies (p. 393)

blennies (p. 380)

dragonet (p. 391)

sandperch (p. 376)

hake (p. 117)

bonefish (p. 99)

jawfish (p. 375)

ladyfish (p. 98)

lizardfish (p. 114)

DIAGNOSTIC FEATURE	TYPICAL FAMILY OUTLINE

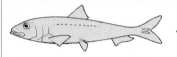

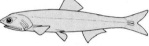

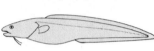

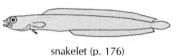

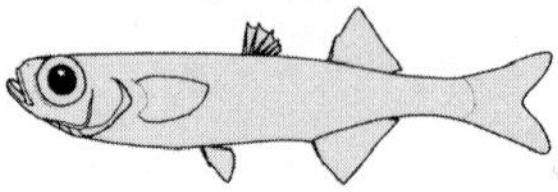

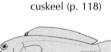

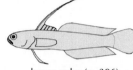

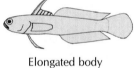

Elongated body (continued)

pilchard, herring & sardine (p. 107)

anchovy (p. 109)

hover goby (p. 396)

snakelet (p. 176)

silverside (p. 124)

cuskeel (p. 118)

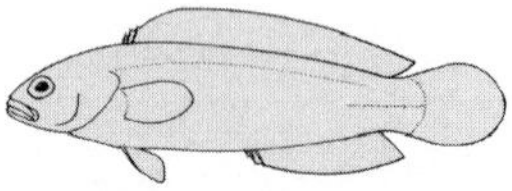

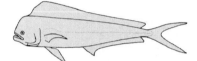

dottyback (p. 176)

dorado, dolphinfish (p. 316)

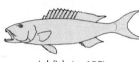

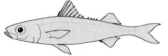

jobfish (p. 195)

rover (p. 298)

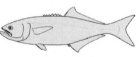

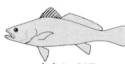

elf (p. 187)

kob (p. 267)

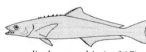

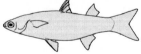

prodigal son, cobia (p. 317)

mullet (p. 363)

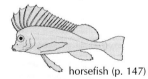

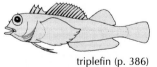

horsefish (p. 147)

triplefin (p. 386)

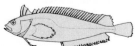

clinid, klipfish (p. 388)

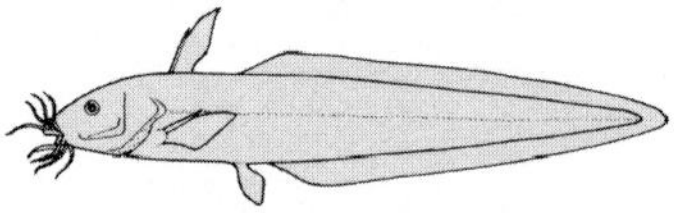

eel-catfish (p. 113)

DIAGNOSTIC FEATURE	TYPICAL FAMILY OUTLINE

Deep body

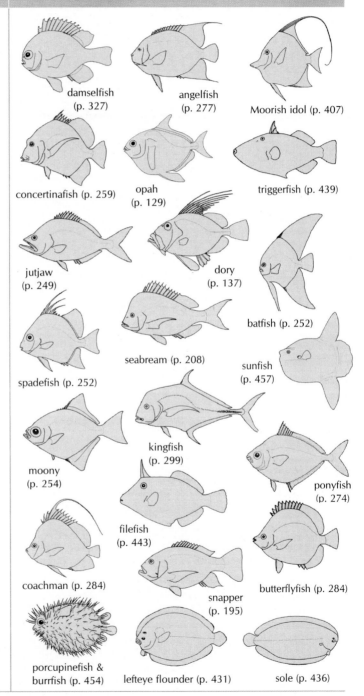

damselfish (p. 327)

angelfish (p. 277)

Moorish idol (p. 407)

concertinafish (p. 259)

opah (p. 129)

triggerfish (p. 439)

jutjaw (p. 249)

dory (p. 137)

batfish (p. 252)

spadefish (p. 252)

seabream (p. 208)

sunfish (p. 457)

moony (p. 254)

kingfish (p. 299)

ponyfish (p. 274)

coachman (p. 284)

filefish (p. 443)

snapper (p. 195)

butterflyfish (p. 284)

porcupinefish & burrfish (p. 454)

lefteye flounder (p. 431)

sole (p. 436)

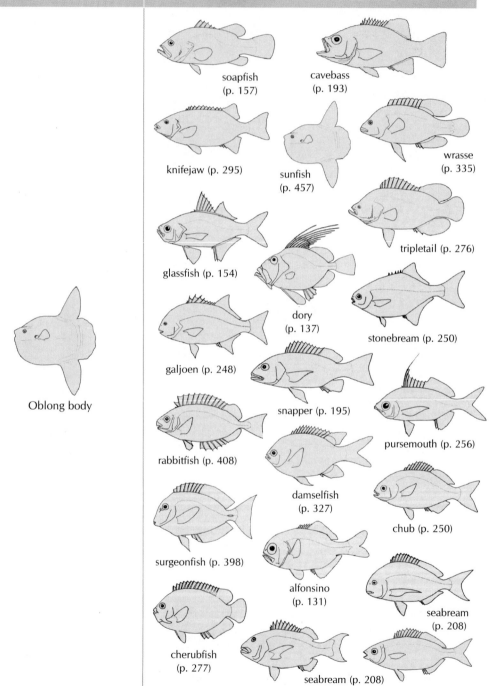

soapfish (p. 157)

cavebass (p. 193)

knifejaw (p. 295)

sunfish (p. 457)

wrasse (p. 335)

glassfish (p. 154)

dory (p. 137)

tripletail (p. 276)

galjoen (p. 248)

stonebream (p. 250)

rabbitfish (p. 408)

snapper (p. 195)

pursemouth (p. 256)

surgeonfish (p. 398)

damselfish (p. 327)

chub (p. 250)

cherubfish (p. 277)

alfonsino (p. 131)

seabream (p. 208)

seabream (p. 208)

Oblong body

DIAGNOSTIC FEATURE	TYPICAL FAMILY OUTLINE
Three dorsal fins	triplefin (p. 386)
Typical (perch-like) body	scorpionfish (p. 142) flagtail (p. 155) goldie (p. 157) rockcod (p. 157) rubberlip (p. 188) bigeye (p. 181) seabream (p. 208) cardinalfish (p. 182) spinecheek (p. 247) fusilier (p. 206) longfin (p. 178) elf (p. 187) thornfish (p. 179) wreckfish (p. 156) emperor (p. 242)

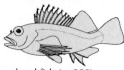

DIAGNOSTIC FEATURE	TYPICAL FAMILY OUTLINE
 Typical (perch-like) body (continued)	 hawkfish (p. 320) goatfish (p. 260) sweeper (p. 325) fingerfin (p. 322) baardman (p. 267) bluebottlefish (p. 429) wrasses (p. 335) snapper (p. 195) rockcod (p. 157)

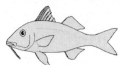

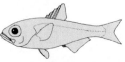

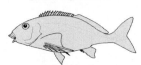

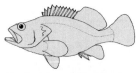

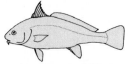

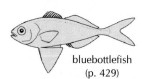

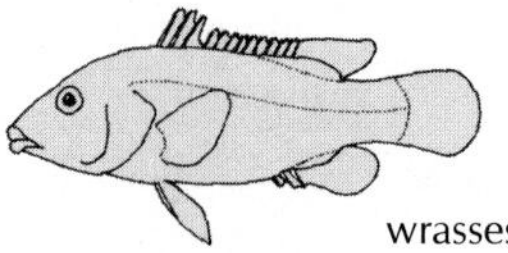

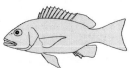

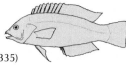

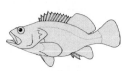

Fishes are the most abundant and diverse group of **vertebrate animals** in the world. According to recent estimates, there are some 27 000 species of fishes living in freshwater and in the seas of our planet. This is more than all other vertebrate species (amphibians, reptiles, birds and mammals) combined. About 250 new species of fish are described each year, and discoveries of new fish species are more common than discovery of new species in any other vertebrate group.

The name 'Earth' for our planet is a misnomer. With 75% of Earth's surface covered by oceans, we should name our planet, **Ocean**. The waters of planet Ocean abound with an immense variety of fascinating creatures that we call fish. These aquatic animals (fish) occupy every livable habitat in the seas, lakes and rivers of our aquatic planet. The southern African marine fish fauna comprises about 2 500 known species, nearly 16% of the total number of marine fish species in the world. In the past 10 years, more than 100 new (previously undescribed) species of marine fish have been found in the southern African region. This indicates that we still have much to learn about our marine fish fauna.

For the purposes of this book, the **southern African region** is bounded by the latitudes of 20° S and 35° S and the longitudes of 10° E and 40° E. On our west coast, the 20° S latitude is about midway between Walvis Bay and the Cunene River, the northern boundary of Namibia. Latitude 20° S intersects the east coast just south of Beira, Mozambique.

The vast majority of our marine fishes, some 1 800 species, are shallow water **coastal fishes**. By 'coastal fishes' we mean those species that occur in estuaries, near shore and on or over the **continental shelf**, which extends **from shore to depths of 200 m**. In view of the new records and new species of coastal fishes found in our area every year, we predict that the number of known coastal species will soon reach 2 000.

An indication of the great diversity of our shallow water fish fauna is that these 1 800 coastal species represent more than 200 families, or about 80% of the shallow water marine fish families in the world. Examples of some familiar coastal fish families in our area are the soles (Family Soleidae), moray eels (Family Muraenidae), damselfish (Family Pomacentridae) and butterflyfish (Family Chaetodontidae).

The richness (diversity and large number of species) of southern African marine fauna is due, in part, to the variety of habitats in our area: coral reefs, estuaries, sandy beaches, rocky shores, mud flats, mangroves, kelp beds and ocean depths of more than 5 km.

In addition to the differences in salinity, turbidity, substrate and plant growth that characterise different habitats, the other major physical factor affecting fish distribution and diversity in our region is temperature. The southern African coast includes a range of zoogeographic regions. Along the warm coast of Mozambique and northern KwaZulu-Natal (**KZN**), there are mangroves and coral reefs typical of tropical and subtropical conditions. This stretch of southern African coast forms the southern end of the range for many of the tropical fishes of the western Indian Ocean.

INTRODUCTION

The KZN coast south of St Lucia and the north coast of the **Eastern Cape** Province are a transition zone between the tropical and temperate regions and boast a mixture of tropical and warm-temperate species. South of the Kei River, the fish fauna of the Eastern Cape comprises mainly warm-temperate species and (during summer) juveniles of some subtropical fishes. This warm-temperate fauna is found along the south coast to False Bay (on the east side of the Cape Peninsula). The fish of the west coast of southern Africa (**Western Cape** Province, **Northern Cape** Province and **Namibia**) are mostly cool-temperate species.

An important aspect of our fish diversity is that the coast of southern Africa borders two great oceans and receives species from four separate faunas. About 73% of our coastal fish species come from the vast tropical Indo-Pacific fauna. Fish from the Atlantic Ocean (e.g. lyre gurnard, baardman, sand steenbras, etc.) comprise ~5% of our coastal fish fauna. Another 5% are worldwide coastal fishes (e.g. elf, dorado, giant yellowtail kingfish, etc.). The coastal fishes occurring in the temperate southern ocean (between 30° and 40° S) at South Africa, Australia, New Zealand and South America represent less than 1% of our fish fauna.

About 16% of our coastal fish are **endemic species**, known only from southern Africa. This relatively high level of endemism is due mainly to six families: clinids (all 40 species endemic), gobies (28 of 112 species), sparids (25 of 42 species), catsharks

Figure 1 *Marine zoogeographic zones and currents off the southern African coast.*

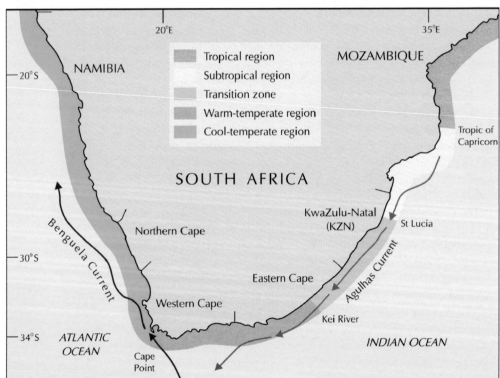

(11 of 16 species), bythitids (8 of 10 species) and toadfish (6 of 9 species). Most of our endemic species are restricted to the temperate zone from Namibia to the Kei River in the Eastern Cape.

Figure 2
Analysis of southern African fish fauna.

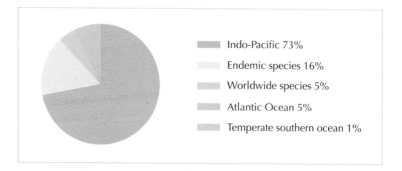

Indo-Pacific 73%

Endemic species 16%

Worldwide species 5%

Atlantic Ocean 5%

Temperate southern ocean 1%

WHAT IS A FISH?

Most people recognise a typical fish. But some sea snakes resemble eels, some small eels and pipefish are mistaken for worms and stonefish or some anglerfish look more like rocks than fish.

We can define fish (Superclass Pisces) as aquatic vertebrate animals with the following characteristics:

- ▣ jaws (the upper jaw being lost or fused to the cranium in some fish);
- ▣ gills that are present throughout life;
- ▣ internal ears with three semicircular canals;
- ▣ eyes that are usually well developed (but can be reduced or completely absent in some fish);
- ▣ median and paired fins usually present (absent in some fish);
- ▣ vertebral centra usually present (absent in coelacanths and reduced in some cartilaginous fish, e.g. sevengill sharks).

A major distinction is made between fish that have cartilaginous skeletons, sharks, batoids, chimaeras and elephantfish (Class **Chondrichthyes**), and fish with bony skeletons (Class **Osteichthyes**) which comprise the majority of fish described in this book.

FISH OR FISHES?

The word 'fish' in general conversation is both singular or plural, and applies to one or more specimens of one or more species. In scientific or technical publications, the term 'fishes' is used to indicate two or more species of fish. This book follows general usage, with the word 'fish' alluding to one or more specimens of one or more species; whether a singular or plural number of species is being referred to should be apparent from the context. If it is important to specify that more than one species is being discussed, the term 'fishes' is used. Note that the plural form of shark is sharks, and this may refer to more than one specimen of a single species or to two or more species of sharks.

FISH NAMES AND CLASSIFICATION

VERNACULAR ('COMMON') NAMES

When the Dutch settlers arrived in South Africa in 1652, they often gave names of well known European fishes to the similar fishes they found here. 'Snoek', 'steenbras' and 'kabeljou' are all names derived from these European names. The indigenous peoples of South Africa have contributed relatively few names to fishes, as only the early coastal people were fish eaters, and we know nothing of the fish names they used. Malay slaves and Indonesians brought a number of fish names with them, but many names were adapted or invented as the need arose.

The Afrikaans names for fishes of the Western Cape Province are relatively uniform. Only as distance increases eastwards from Mossel Bay (e.g. to Knysna, Plettenberg Bay and Port Elizabeth) do alternate names for the same species occur along our coast. English names for fishes exhibit a huge diversity, with many different names for the same fish in the Eastern Cape and KZN. In 1949, the South African ichthyologist JLB Smith listed 16 vernacular names (two English, nine Afrikaans, four hybrid [English/Afrikaans] and one local African language name) for the fish identified in this book as 'black musselcracker', *Cymatoceps nasutus*.

Eighty years ago the different vernacular names produced little confusion, as coastal communities were so isolated. In his book, *The Sea Fishes of Southern Africa* (published in 1949), JLB Smith listed all the vernacular names he could find, attached to the description and illustration of each fish. He argued that by referring to the illustration, everyone would be able to ascertain exactly which species was being discussed. While going a long way to unravel the confusion caused by several names for the same fish species, Smith's book did not resolve the problem.

Standard English names for fishes are important as substitutes for scientific names in ordinary discourse, popular and scientific publications and fishery regulations. Appropriate vernacular names for fish have proved to be more stable than scientific names. In the South African fish checklist published by John Gilchrist in 1902, for example, most of the scientific names in the list are now different, but many of the vernacular names are still in use today.

This book generally follows the vernacular names in *Smiths' Sea Fishes* (Smith & Heemstra 1986). In the case of widely distributed, commercially important species, we usually follow the internationally accepted English names used by the United Nations Food and Agriculture Organization.

SCIENTIFIC NAMES

A zoological species is a biological entity (plant, animal, bacteria, virus), comprising individuals that share a unique common gene pool and various anatomical (internal and external) features and colour patterns that enable us to recognise and name these particular organisms.

The scientific conventions applied to naming species can seem like a minefield to those unaccustomed to zoological nomenclature, and it is important to remember that each species of fish known to science has only one **valid scientific name**. This name consists of two Latin words, which together make up the unique binominal species name that applies only to this species. The valid name for the yellowbelly rockcod, for example, is *Epinephelus marginatus*. The first word in the scientific name (*Epinephelus*) is the **genus** name and it always starts with a capital letter. The genus category usually comprises two or more closely related species; a **monotypic genus** has only one species. The second word is the **species** epithet and it is always lower case, even if the word is a proper noun.

Scientific names are based on Latin, which was the international language of science until the 1700s. These Latin (or 'Latinised') names therefore follow the rules of Latin grammar. If the second term in a species name is an adjective or participle, it must agree in gender with the genus name it modifies. If a species is moved to another genus, it may have to change to agree with the gender of the new genus. For example, the adjective *striatus*, meaning striped, will have the '-us' ending if the genus name is masculine (*Pomadasys striatus*), '-a' ending for a feminine genus (*Argentina striata*), and '-um' ending for a neuter genus (*Pristipoma striatum*).

Although the system of **zoological nomenclature** was designed to promote the stability of species names, it is sometimes necessary to change names in the light of new discoveries or to rectify mistakes. Some species have been described (named as a new species) a number of times, in which case the oldest name (**senior synonym**) is usually the valid name, and the subsequent name (or names) are considered **junior synonyms**.

The case of the yellowbelly rockcod illustrates some of the problems involved in scientific naming. In *Smiths' Sea Fishes* (Smith & Heemstra 1986) and in many other publications up to 1986, *Epinephelus guaza* (Linnaeus 1758) was incorrectly used as the valid name for the yellowbelly rockcod, a common fish of the Mediterranean Sea and Atlantic and western Indian oceans. In 1758 Carl Linnaeus named a rockcod species *Labrus gvaza*. In *The Fishes of North and Middle America* (published in 1896), David Starr Jordan and Barton Evermann, thinking that they were looking at the same fish, ascribed it to another genus, *Epinephelus*, and gave the Linnaean name *Epinephelus guaza* to the yellowbelly rockcod. [The letters u and v were interchangeable in the Latin of Linnaeus' time.] *Epinephelus guaza* was used by numerous authors until research published almost 100 years later showed that this name was incorrect, since Linnaeus' original species description was copied from the description of a rockcod of the genus *Mycteroperca* that one of his students found in the Caribbean. The next available name

(oldest existing name) for the yellowbelly rockcod is *Serranus marginatus* Lowe 1834, from Madeira. However, this species is currently placed in the genus *Epinephelus* of the Family Serranidae, so the current valid name for the yellowbelly rockcod is *Epinephelus marginatus* (Lowe 1834). We indicate that a species is now assigned to a genus other than its original one by placing the author's name in parentheses. Citation of the author's name and date of publication should be given at least once in any publication that uses the scientific name.

CLASSIFICATION

Each species is included in a hierarchical scheme of **classification** that is based on the **inferred evolutionary (phylogenetic) relationships** expressed in a hierarchy of **taxa** (singular, '**taxon**') or categories, with each higher category being more inclusive than the one below. For the yellowbelly rockcod this hierarchy is as follows:

Fishes (Superclass Pisces)
Bony fish (Class Osteichthyes)
Ray-fin fish (Subclass Actinopterygii)
Modern bony fish (Subdivision Teleostei)
Higher teleosts (Infradivision Euteleostei)
Spiny-rayed fish
(Superorder Acanthopterygii)
Perch-like fish (Order Perciformes)
Rockcods, seabasses, anthiines & soapfish
(Family Serranidae)
Rockcods & soapfish
(Subfamily Epinephelinae)
Rockcods, groupers & hinds
(Tribe Epinephelini)
Rockcods (Genus *Epinephelus*)
Yellowbelly rockcod
(Species *Epinephelus marginatus*)

Additional categories, such as **subgenus** or **subspecies**, are sometimes used to denote finer distinctions in the classification. The subspecies concept is used for geographically isolated populations that are similiar to one another but different in what were deemed 'minor' features such as slight differences in colour pattern. The subspecies category is not employed in this book and valid subspecies are elevated to the level of species. We believe that the recognisable differences in these separate populations indicate that these populations are now on separate evolutionary tracks and justify their recognition as separate species.

The definitions of taxa are subject to modification in the light of new discoveries regarding relationships of the various species and also because there is a more or less subjective element in most taxonomic decisions. For example, some workers recognise the rockcod taxon *Cephalopholis* as only a subgenus of *Epinephelus,* whereas we consider it a valid genus. Differences between related genera may be slight or quite distinct, but a subjective element often comes into the evaluation of these differences.

THE SOUTHERN AFRICAN COAST

BOTTOM TOPOGRAPHY

In order to better understand the distribution of fish along the southern African coast, it is useful to examine the bottom topography of the ocean and the different ecological zones of the sea.

The **continental shelf** is the shallow seaward extension of land from shore to about 200 m. In places where the shelf is narrow, it drops rapidly to the deeper **continental slope** zone; in areas with a broad shelf, the gradient may be only 2 m in 1 000 m. On average, the depth of the continental slope increases by about 30–50 m in 1 000 m. The topography of the continental shelf and slope varies in the different coastal regions. On the west coast from Namibia to Cape Agulhas the continental shelf is generally broader (30–180 km) and the shelf edge deeper (300–400 m) than along the east coast. Between East London and Durban the edge of the shelf is close to the shore at the 200 m depth contour and the shelf is only 12.5 km wide in some places (e.g. Port St Johns). In this area the sea bottom slopes steeply from the edge of the shelf down to the abyssal plain at 4 000 m. Just north of Durban, the shelf widens to some 45 km, where sediments from the Thukela River are deposited as an undersea delta. There are a number of underwater canyons incised across the narrow shelf between St Lucia and Kosi Bay, the shelf in this area being only 2–4 km wide. Large slow-moving undersea sand dunes have been observed on the shelf south of Sodwana Bay.

Southwest of Port Elizabeth the continental shelf broadens into a large plateau, called the **Agulhas Bank**, which extends along the south coast and as far as 300 km offshore. This rich fishing area is frequented by trawlers and boat anglers.

ECOLOGICAL ZONES OF THE SEA

Estuaries, where rivers empty into the sea, are rich productive areas that support plant growth and provide shelter and nutrients for the larval and juvenile stages of many fish species. This estuary zone includes the intertidal and subtidal zones and is affected by ocean tides, freshwater input and frequent changes in temperature, salinity and turbidity. Our estuaries are populated by resident species (e.g. the estuarine roundherring, moonies, pipefish and Knysna seahorse) that spend their whole life in the estuary, as well as marine fish (e.g. mullet, dusky kob, sea-catfish, some clinids, gobies and leervis).

The **intertidal** (or **littoral**) **zone** is demarcated by the high and low tide marks. In areas with a large tidal range the broad intertidal zone is affected by wide fluctuations in temperature and salinity. Blennies, gobies and clinids are the most common littoral fish in our area. The colour patterns of these small sedentary fish are variable and blend in with the algae-covered rocks of this region. The intertidal zone is also productive, with an abundant population of invertebrate animals (molluscs, crustaceans, worms, sea urchins, etc.). These invertebrates provide food for many juvenile fish that use **tide pools** as a 'nursery area'. The fact that the intertidal zone is subject to wave action also makes it a turbulent habitat in some areas. Clingfish are well suited to this environment, with modified fleshy pelvic fins fused to form a strong sucking disc that is useful as an anchor in the wave-swept rocky surf.

Beyond the littoral zone, the ocean is divided into the **benthic** (bottom) and **pelagic** (open water) **zones**. The inshore component of the benthic zone, called the **subtidal** (or sublittoral) **zone** of the **continental shelf**, extends from the intertidal zone to ~200 m. Most of the fish that live in this habitat are benthic or **demersal** species that live on or near the bottom. Benthic fish are generally flattened (depressed or compressed), sedentary and their upper side is often coloured to blend in with various substrates. Stargazers and sand divers, for instance, have their eyes on top of their head and often bury themselves in the sand, with just their eyes exposed. The benthic **continental slope zone**, from 200–2 000 m, is a dark cold region with no plants and virtually no plankton. There are fewer fish in this deep sea zone and the fauna is beyond the scope of this book.

The pelagic habitat above the continental shelf is called the **neritic zone**. This zone is the most productive of all the marine habitats. Intense sunlight and plentiful nutrients from rivers and upwelling areas drive enormous production of algae, seagrass and **phytoplankton**. Consequently, much of the world's fishery resources are harvested from this rich zone. Typical neritic fishes are

Figure 3
Diagrammatic representation of the ecological zones of the sea.

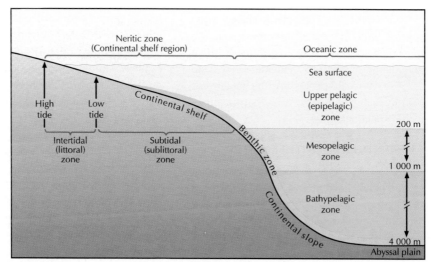

pilchards, elf, sparids, geelbek, galjoen and kingfish.

The pelagic realm beyond the continental shelf is called the 'open ocean' or **oceanic zone**. The **epipelagic region**, from the surface to about 200 m, is the uppermost component of the oceanic zone. Although it receives plenty of sunshine, the epipelagic region is (with a few localised exceptions) generally much less productive than the neritic zone, as it often lacks the nutrients necessary to support a large standing crop of phytoplankton. Exceptionally productive sites of the epipelagic region are the nutrient-rich upwelling areas off Namibia and the Western Cape, and in the eastern Pacific off California and Peru. These upwelling sites produce vast blooms of phytoplankton that support enormous populations of **zooplankton**, plankton-feeding fish and their predators (including humans). Fish typical of the epipelagic region are the blue shark, mako, whale shark, flyingfish, tunas, marlin, sailfish and dorado. At night, the epipelagic region is visited by vertically migrating fish from deeper waters.

The **mesopelagic zone** is the open ocean zone below the epipelagic zone. There are no visible boundaries for this zone, which extends from 200–1 000 m. It shares some species with the epipelagic zone, but the mesopelagic zone also harbours a huge community of small to moderate-sized deep sea fish. Typical species are the lanternfish (Family Myctophidae) and barracudinas (Family Paralepididae).

CURRENTS OFF SOUTHERN AFRICA

Along the east coast of southern Africa, the **Mozambique Current** is a series of spinning gyres that run southwards through the **Mozambique Channel** between Mozambique and Madagascar. The **East Madagascar Current**, flowing southwards along the east coast of Madagascar, curves westwards round the south end of Madagascar and joins the Mozambique Current just north of Durban to form the powerful **Agulhas Current** (see Figure 1). This deep fast current averages speeds of 4–7 km/h, with a maximum recorded speed of 13 km/h. The speed and volume of water transported by the Agulhas Current is comparable to the Gulf Stream of the western North Atlantic or the Brazil Current that runs southwards along the east coast of South America. Between Port St Johns and East London the Agulhas Current is only 5–10 km offshore, and the high speed of the current combined with gale-force southwesterly winds occasionally produce waves as high as 20 m, which result in dangerous seas.

The Agulhas Current usually follows the 200 m depth contour, and southwest of Port Elizabeth it turns away from the coast and begins to meander as the continental shelf merges with the Agulhas Bank. A portion of the Agulhas Current turns eastwards abruptly in a retroflection that eventually reaches Australia. Eddies also develop over the edge of the Agulhas Bank, and these spinning parcels of warm Agulhas Current water may be transported westwards past Cape Point and into the southeastern Atlantic Ocean. Inshore counter-currents often develop between the Agulhas Current and the coast and these northward-flowing inshore currents are important in the annual Sardine Run along the east coast.

Because of the tropical origin of the Agulhas Current, water temperatures on the east coast of southern Africa are usually considerably warmer than temperatures on the west coast. These temperature differences influence the fish fauna of these regions and account for the major disparities in the east and west coast fish faunas.

The slow cold ill-defined **Benguela Current** ('Benguela System' might be a better name) moves northwards along the west coast of southern Africa (see Figure 1). This complex system is enriched by the frequent upwelling of nutrient-rich deep water along this coast. The prevailing southerly and southeasterly winds of this region combined with the Coriolis effect of the earth's rotation, pushes the warm surface waters offshore and pulls the deep colder water (with higher concentrations of nitrates, phosphates, iron and silica) to the surface. This upwelling enrichment of the well-lit surface waters facilitates the growth of phytoplankton, and these microscopic plants form the base of the marine food pyramid. This increase in biomass is passed up the pyramid by zooplankton and filter-feeding fishes such as pilchards, anchovies, maasbanker, etc. and results in a rich harvest of the filter feeders and their predators (hake, snoek, giant yellowtail kingfish, etc.).

BONY FISH ANATOMY; FISH SHAPE, SIZE AND COLOURATION

A brief introduction to the anatomy of bony fishes is useful for identifying various species and provides some background to the biological information presented in this book. The external and internal anatomy of cartilaginous fishes is very different from that of bony fishes. For further details of cartilaginous fish anatomy, refer to the section on Chondrichthyes.

FINS

Fins are the organs by which fish steer, balance and swim. The **dorsal fin, anal fin** and **tail (caudal) fin** are called the **median fins**, as they lie in the median (middle) vertical plane of the fish. The **pectoral** and **pelvic** fins are called **paired fins**, as there are two (left and right) of each. Some species (pufferfish, pipefish, eels) lack pelvic fins; and some eels and some flatfish (flounders, soles, etc.) lack pectoral fins. Pelvic fins are also known as **ventral fins**. The **adipose fin** (seen on lizardfish, sea-catfish and a few deep sea fish) is a short fleshy median fin situated on top of the peduncle; it is not supported by fin rays. The **distal** part of a fin is the outer (marginal) part and the **proximal** or basal part is the portion nearest the body.

The rays that support the fins are of two kinds: **spines** or **soft-rays**. Fin spines are unsegmented, usually stiff and have a sharp tip, although some fish (e.g. blennies) have soft flexible spines. Soft-rays are segmented and, in most fish, branched. The cross-striations

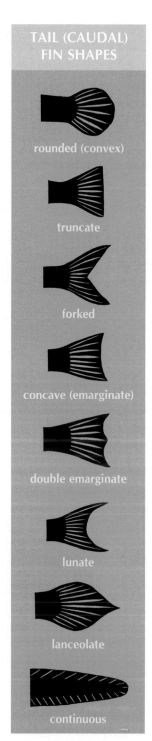

TAIL (CAUDAL) FIN SHAPES

rounded (convex)

truncate

forked

concave (emarginate)

double emarginate

lunate

lanceolate

continuous

Figure 4 *External anatomy of a bony fish. Above:* blue and yellow rockcod, Epinephelus flavocaeruleus. *Below:* rosy goatfish, Parupeneus rubescens.

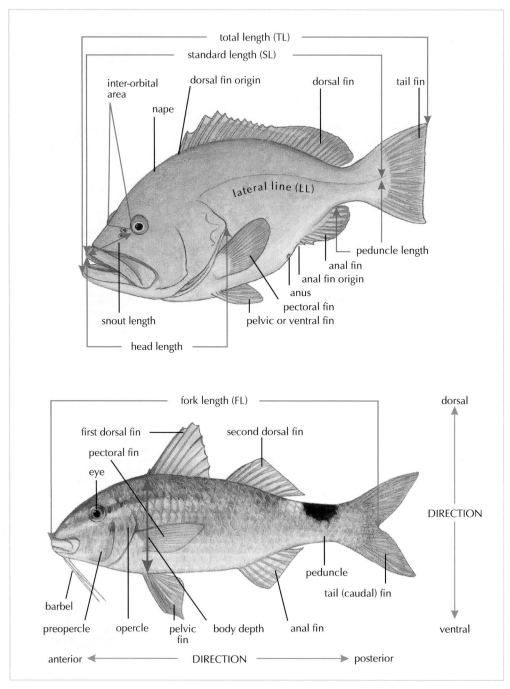

Figure 5 Dorsal fin spines and rays.

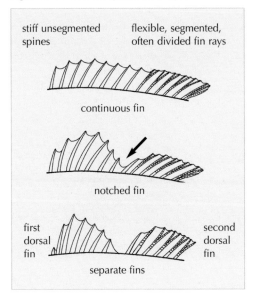

Figure 6 Scales from a bony fish.

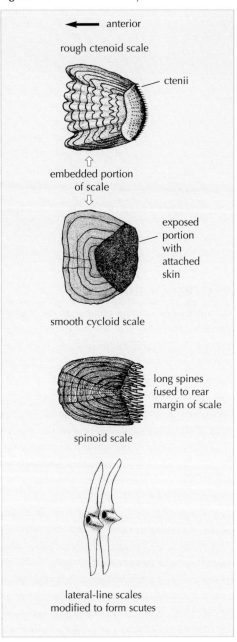

(segmentations) of the soft-rays are best seen with a light behind the fin.

In several families of bony fish there are no fin spines, and in bony fish with fin spines, the spinous dorsal fin may be joined to or separate from the soft-rayed dorsal fin. In a few species (some eels and pipefish) one or more of the median fins may be greatly reduced or even absent.

SCALES

The scales of most bony fish are **cycloid**, **ctenoid** or **spinoid**, with some fish having a mixture of different types of scales. Cycloid scales are smooth, but the rear (exposed) margin of ctenoid scales bears minute tooth-like spines (called **ctenii**) which give ctenoid scales their rough texture when the fish is stroked from the tail towards the head. Spinoid scales have long spines fused to the posterior part of the scale. In some kingfish the rear lateral-line scales are modified to form **scutes** (thick bony scales with a median ridge ending posteriorly in a sharp spine).

Most clupeid fish (herring, pilchards and sardines) and some dory fish have scutes along the ventral midline of the belly.

Figure 7 *Bones of a fish head.*

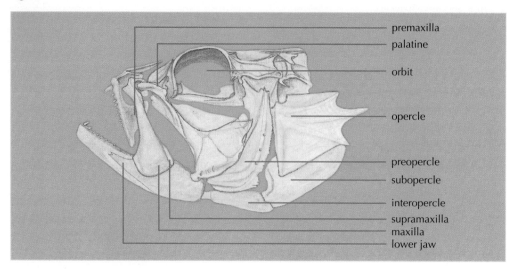

premaxilla
palatine
orbit
opercle
preopercle
subopercle
interopercle
supramaxilla
maxilla
lower jaw

ANATOMY OF THE HEAD

The upper jaw usually comprises two bones on each side of the jaw: the **premaxilla** at the front of the jaw and the **maxilla** on each side of the jaw. The left and right premaxillae are joined by a symphysis at the front of the upper jaw. In some fish, one or two little bones, the **supramaxilla**, are attached to the upper rear edge of the maxilla.

The gill cover or **operculum** (*pl.* **opercula**) comprises four bones: **opercle, subopercle, preopercle** and **interopercle**. The gill cover protects the gills, and in fish with a movable operculum the movement of this structure assists in pumping water through the gills.

On the underside of the head, the **branchiostegal membranes** of bony fish are supported by a series of slender curved bones called **branchiostegal rays**. The membranes are attached ventrally to the operculum and the **isthmus** or joined to one another, forming a free fold across the isthmus. They can also be attached posteriorly to the body, in which case the gill opening is more or less restricted to the rear edge of the gill cover.

GILLS

Most fish have four gill arches on each side of the head, just behind the mouth cavity. Each gill arch comprises an upper and lower limb, with a long series of soft **gill filaments** along their outer (posterior) edge. The scarlet gill filaments of a live or fresh fish are filled with blood capillaries as they are designed for gas exchange and are the respiratory organs of the fish. On the other (inner) side of the gill arches, most fish have a series of **gill rakers**. fish that feed on microscopic phytoplankton

Figure 8 *Underside of head of a bony fish.*

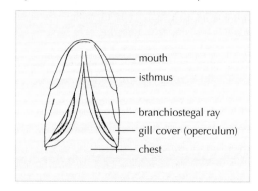

mouth
isthmus
branchiostegal ray
gill cover (operculum)
chest

or zooplankton, have many elongate gill rakers that act like a screen to collect the plankton from the water current that streams through their gills. Most fish have slender finger-like gill rakers, but some fish (e.g. great barracuda) have no gill rakers. **Gill raker counts** are often useful for identifying species and are usually done on one side (left or right) of the first (outermost) gill arch, unless otherwise stated. The raker in the angle of the gill arch is included in the count of the lower-limb rakers (see Figure 9). Gill raker counts are given as a ratio X / Y, where X is the number of rakers on the upper (dorsal) limb and Y the number of lower (ventral) limb rakers of the same arch. In counts of gill rakers from several specimens of one species, there is usually a range of two or more rakers on each limb. Thus a gill raker count of 7–9 / 23–26 indicates that the upper limb has 7 to 9 rakers and the lower limb 23 to 26 rakers. Gill raker counts may include small **rudimentary rakers** (with base wider than height of raker) at the upper and lower ends of the gill arch. Gill raker counts usually do not include rudiments, unless they are mentioned in the family or species account. **Developed rakers** are higher than wide.

INTERNAL ANATOMY OF A BONY FISH

The heart comprises four chambers and is located in a membranous cavity below and behind the gills. Venous (de-oxygenated) blood from the muscles and various organs (stomach, brain, kidneys, gonads, liver, spleen, etc.) enters the heart and is pumped to the gills where it picks up oxygen and releases carbon dioxide. The oxygenated blood from the gills is carried to the rest of the body via the dorsal aorta which runs along the underside of the vertebral column and sends off branches to the various muscles and organs. Most fish predators (like the halfmoon rockcod) have a distinct stomach, which is connected to a short J-shaped intestine. Herbivorous fish (e.g. surgeonfish) and detritivores have a very long coiled intestine. At the juncture of stomach and intestine there

Figure 9

Gill chamber of a rockcod exposed by lifting the operculum. In rockcods, gill raker counts include the rudimentary gill rakers. Gill raker count for this specimen: 2 gill rakers + 2 rudiments on upper limb of first gill arch and 6 gill rakers + 3 rudiments on lower limb = gill rakers 4 / 9.

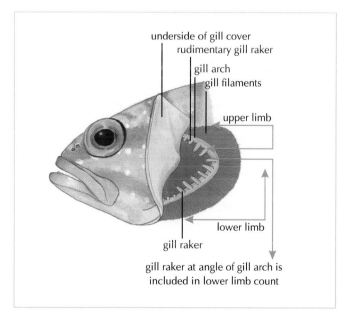

underside of gill cover
rudimentary gill raker
gill arch
gill filaments
upper limb
lower limb
gill raker
gill raker at angle of gill arch is included in lower limb count

Figure 10 *Internal anatomy of a bony fish, the halfmoon rockcod,* Epinephelus rivulatus.

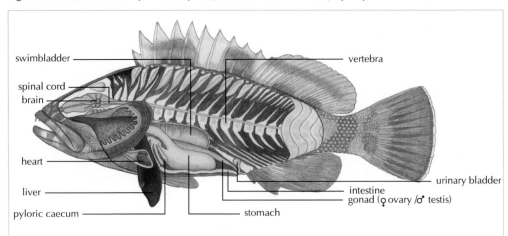

may be one or more finger-like appendages called pyloric caeca. The **pyloric caeca** have no obvious function and may, like the human appendix, be a useless remnant from some functional ancestral organ. The **liver** produces bile which aids in digestion, stores fat (as various lipid oils) and is rich in vitamins A and D. In some fish, the liver is actually toxic due to high concentrations of vitamin A. The gall bladder (not shown in our simplified drawing), which stores bile produced by the liver, is connected to the intestine near the pyloric caeca. The pancreas is incorporated in the liver of rockcods and most other spiny-rayed fish, but in cartilaginous and soft-rayed bony fish it is a distinct organ. The pancreas secretes various digestive enzymes as well as some hormones. The **urinary bladder** may be conspicuous in some species and very small in others. Likewise, the **gonads** are enlarged in adult fish during the spawning season and much smaller (even difficult to find) during the rest of the year or in juveniles. The **swimbladder** is well developed in some fish and rudimentary, or even absent in other species.

FISH SHAPE AND SIZE

Fish come in all shapes and sizes: **compressed** (laterally flattened from side to side, as in John Dory, flatfish and butterflyfish); **depressed** (vertically flattened, like monkfish and stingrays); **elongate** (eels, pipefish, needlefish and barracuda); **robust** and streamlined (kingfish and marlin); **spherical** (puffers and porcupinefish); **boxshaped** (boxfish); **triangular** in cross-section (cowfish) and **disc-shaped** (ocean sunfish).

The whale shark, which may grow to ~14 m and weigh 36 tonnes, is the largest fish in the sea. The tiny goby, *Trimmatom nanus* Winterbottom & Emery 1981, which attains 1 cm, is the smallest adult fish known, and occurs only at the Chagos and Maldives islands in the western Indian Ocean.

COLOURATION

In the surface waters of the sea, most fish are dark above and pale below (**counter-shaded**) to hide their shape against the well-lit background of open waters. Seen from above, the dark dorsal surface of a counter-shaded fish blends in with the colour of the ocean, and from below these fish disappear against the ocean's silvery surface. Most of the fish that live in water deeper than ~400 m are black and some species are scarlet, which is seen as black because the red rays of sunlight are absorbed in the first 20 m of water. A novice scuba diver is often surprised to see green blood from a cut or to notice that some fish appear a different colour in deep water compared to their colour at the surface.

Unlike silvery pelagic fish, the demersal (benthic) fish have complicated multicoloured patterns. Coral reef fish are renowned for their beautiful, bold and intricate patterns. **Sexual dichromatism** (with males and females coloured differently) is common amongst reef species and facilitates mate recognition. Changes in colour patterns between juveniles and adults are also seen in many territorial fish (e.g. some damselfish and large species of angelfish). Since the juveniles of these territorial adults do not directly compete (for food or mates) with their adults, the juveniles can be tolerated within the adults' territories. This strategy reduces the stress caused by territorial aggression.

The beautiful iridescent colours of fish are caused by the refraction of light from guanine crystals in special skin cells, called **iridocytes**. The guanine crystals are stacked in layers that reflect various colours of light depending on the angle of the incoming light and position of the observer.

Non-iridescent colours of fishes are produced by the reflection of light from various pigments (red, yellow, green, etc.) contained in **chromatophore** cells. In most fish the skin has several different types of chromatophores, but each chromatophore has only one colour of pigment. These colour cells are irregular, with multiple branches extending outwards from the centre. Colour changes of the fish result from movements of pigment granules inside the chromatophore.

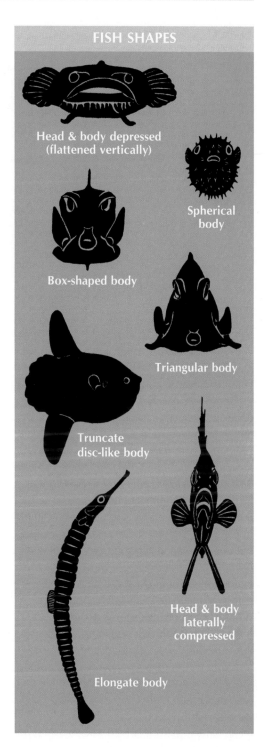

FISH SHAPES

Head & body depressed
(flattened vertically)

Spherical body

Box-shaped body

Triangular body

Truncate disc-like body

Head & body laterally compressed

Elongate body

Figure 11

Natal wrasse showing true colour at the surface or when illuminated by a photographer's flashlight (above) and without extra illumination, as seen by a diver at 20 m (below).

When the pigment is spread throughout the cell, the colour is intensified; when the granules are concentrated at the centre of the cell, the colour is paler.

Some fish change colour almost instantaneously, and such changes are controlled by the central nervous system. If a dark galjoen swimming over dark rocks swims into a well-lit sandy area, it immediately becomes paler. This quick change is effected by rapid contraction of the **melanophores** (black colour cells). Some colour alterations, such as the transition from juvenile to adult patterns, or from one sex to the other, also result from the increase or reduction in the number of different chromatophores. These slower, long-term type of colour changes are mediated by hormones.

Fish often change colour to match their habitat. Some fish (e.g. anglerfish, stonefish) are incredibly well camouflaged and easily mistaken for sponges or algae-covered rocks. The venomous stonefish lies half-buried in the sand and is also often covered with algae and various encrusting organisms that grow on the fish's warty skin. Flatfish are masters of disguise and are often invisible on the bottom until they move. Clinids (klipfish) are also difficult to see, as they are coloured like the seaweed in which they live.

The colour patterns of many coral reef fish are examples of **disruptive colouration**. The bold black bars of a sergeant major damselfish break up the general outline of the fish; and the irregular patches of contrasting colour of the clown triggerfish distract the eye from its overall shape. When cruising over the multi-hued coral reef, these boldly patterned fish are more difficult to see. Butterflyfish often have a broad black vertical band on the head to hide the eye. Some butterflyfish with a black eye band also have a prominent 'false eye spot' (**ocellus**) on the body or the dorsal fin. This false eye spot is thought to confuse predators that usually target the head.

Fish also change colour to facilitate species or mate recognition. Sexual dichromatism is common in hermaphroditic fish (e.g. wrasses, parrotfish and some sandperch), but some rockcods show sexual dichromatism only when they are about to spawn. Colour

Figure 12
Bluespot clinid
(klipfish) concealed
in seaweed
(photographer
G Zsilavecz).

patterns are important for finding a mate, guarding a territory, 'advertising' a fish's services (see cleaner wrasse species account, p. 347) and 'advertising' the distasteful nature of a fish's toxic mucus. Colour patterns are also used for deceptive mimicry of other fish (see mimic blenny species account, p. 381).

FISH BIOLOGY

FOOD AND FEEDING

Fish exploit a vast range of foods, from micro- and macro-plankton to algae, detritus, an array of invertebrate animals, fish, marine mammals, birds, turtles, sea snakes and, occasionally, human beings. One is usually able to tell a great deal about a fish's diet by examining its teeth. Large canines are typical of predators that feed on fish or cephalopods; incisors are typical of herbivores. Small villiform teeth occur in piscivores and planktivores, while molars indicate a diet of hard-shelled prey (crabs, gastropods or bivalves).

Herbivores (surgeonfish, angelfish, some damselfish, parrotfish, etc.) feed on algae, seagrass or detritus. These fish are active by day and are usually seen near the bottom, where they spend most of their time grazing. Their small mouths with small incisors and

their long intestines make them well suited to this diet.

Planktivores are divided into **filter-feeders** and **plankton pickers**. Bony fish filter-feeders (pilchards, sardines, anchovies, maasbanker, Indian mackerel, etc.) have numerous long gill rakers projecting between the gill arches. The mouth is moderate in size, the teeth minute or absent. The filter-feeding whale shark and manta ray have a grid-like structure between the gill arches and, like bony fish filter-feeders, they swim through concentrations of plankton with their mouths open. As the water current passes through the gills, the minute planktonic animals (copepods, amphipods, mysids, arrow worms, fish larvae, crustaceans, molluscs,

Figure 13 Types of fish teeth.

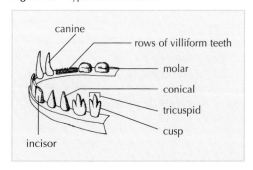

17

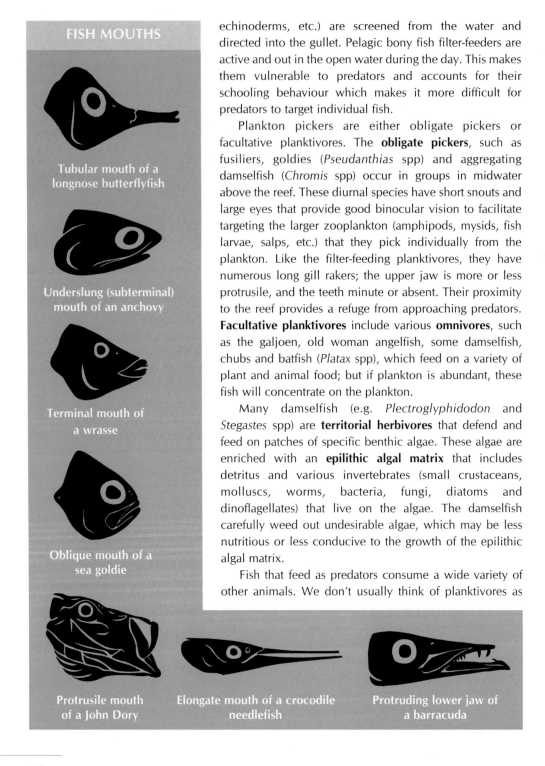

FISH MOULTHS

Tubular mouth of a
longnose butterflyfish

Underslung (subterminal)
mouth of an anchovy

Terminal mouth of
a wrasse

Oblique mouth of a
sea goldie

Protrusile mouth
of a John Dory

Elongate mouth of a crocodile
needlefish

Protruding lower jaw of
a barracuda

echinoderms, etc.) are screened from the water and directed into the gullet. Pelagic bony fish filter-feeders are active and out in the open water during the day. This makes them vulnerable to predators and accounts for their schooling behaviour which makes it more difficult for predators to target individual fish.

Plankton pickers are either obligate pickers or facultative planktivores. The **obligate pickers**, such as fusiliers, goldies (*Pseudanthias* spp) and aggregating damselfish (*Chromis* spp) occur in groups in midwater above the reef. These diurnal species have short snouts and large eyes that provide good binocular vision to facilitate targeting the larger zooplankton (amphipods, mysids, fish larvae, salps, etc.) that they pick individually from the plankton. Like the filter-feeding planktivores, they have numerous long gill rakers; the upper jaw is more or less protrusile, and the teeth minute or absent. Their proximity to the reef provides a refuge from approaching predators. **Facultative planktivores** include various **omnivores**, such as the galjoen, old woman angelfish, some damselfish, chubs and batfish (*Platax* spp), which feed on a variety of plant and animal food; but if plankton is abundant, these fish will concentrate on the plankton.

Many damselfish (e.g. *Plectroglyphidodon* and *Stegastes* spp) are **territorial herbivores** that defend and feed on patches of specific benthic algae. These algae are enriched with an **epilithic algal matrix** that includes detritus and various invertebrates (small crustaceans, molluscs, worms, bacteria, fungi, diatoms and dinoflagellates) that live on the algae. The damselfish carefully weed out undesirable algae, which may be less nutritious or less conducive to the growth of the epilithic algal matrix.

Fish that feed as predators consume a wide variety of other animals. We don't usually think of planktivores as predators, but they also eat other animals, including fish larvae. Some fish concentrate on invertebrate prey (tunicates, jellyfish, live coral, echinoderms, crustaceans, molluscs, worms and sponges); others eat mainly fish (**piscivores**) or cephalopods. Most fish also change their diet with growth. Juvenile rock-cod eat mainly crustaceans, but many adult rockcod include a large portion of fish and cephalopods in their diet. Most fish are essentially opportunists and will eat whatever is plentiful and easy to catch.

REPRODUCTION AND DEVELOPMENT

Most bony fish fertilise their eggs after they are released from the body of the female, but a few bony fish and all cartilaginous fish (chondrichthyans) fertilise their eggs inside the female. This **internal fertilisation** is usually accomplished with special copulatory structures called **intromittent organs**, but some species (e.g. the coelacanth) manage internal fertilisation without intromittent organs. In bony fish, the intromittent organ is usually called a penis; in chondrichthyans, males have paired intromittent organs (misnamed **claspers**) that are modified parts of the pelvic fin skeleton. The claspers are inserted, one at a time, into the oviducts of the female during copulation. Male sharks sometimes hold the female by biting her back or pectoral fins when they are mating.

The bony fish that use external fertilisation are **oviparous**. At **spawning** the eggs (spawn) are released in the sea where they are immediately fertilised by sperm from the male. In some fish, the eggs are **demersal** (deposited on the bottom) and guarded by one or both parents until they hatch. In most oviparous species (the '**broadcast spawners**'), a large number of small buoyant eggs are released near the surface and the eggs are immediately fertilised by one or more males.

Some oviparous fish are the most fecund of all vertebrates. A large codfish (*Gadus morhua*) of the North Atlantic produces some 9 million eggs per year, and a 25 kg ling (also Family Gadidae), was estimated to have 28 million eggs in its ovary. Whereas a tiny goby may produce fewer than ten eggs when it spawns.

Tropical fish often spawn more than once a year (some species spawn monthly or even every day) and usually in small groups or in pairs. The small **pelagic eggs** float near the surface and hatch after a day or two. Within a few days of hatching, the rapidly growing **larvae** have used up their small yolk supply and must find food. Tropical fish larvae may spend two months or longer drifting and feeding on plankton. In temperate waters, the larval stage may last five months (12 months or more for the eel, *Anguilla*). During their long sojourn in the plankton pelagic larvae may drift great distances, providing an excellent means of dispersal for shallow water fish. The wide distribution of many marine fish is attributed to their long-lived pelagic larvae.

Demersal eggs are generally bigger than pelagic eggs, usually adhesive and deposited on the bottom. Most fish with demersal eggs (damselfish, triggerfish and dottybacks) are also territorial and defend their eggs until they hatch. Larvae that hatch from demersal eggs are generally larger than larvae from pelagic eggs, and their larval stage is shorter or non-existent.

When seahorses spawn, the female deposits her eggs in a pouch on the belly of the male where the young develop until they hatch. Male seahorses go into labour with contractions of their pouch to expel the babies. After birth, the little colts and fillies are on their own.

Sea-catfish, cardinalfish and jawfish are **mouth brooders**; in these species the male carries the eggs in his mouth until they hatch.

In marine fish, it is usually the male that broods the eggs. In freshwater cichlids it is the female that does the mouth brooding.

Some cartilaginous fish (catsharks, skates and chimaeras) are also oviparous. The large eggs of these species are fertilised inside the female and deposited on the bottom in tough leathery egg cases. After several weeks, the fully developed embryos emerge as miniature copies of the adults and swim away. The egg case of the whale shark measures 30 × 15 cm, and the pup apparently breaks out of its case just before birth.

Most elasmobranchs and some bony fish (e.g. clinids) are **viviparous**. These species have **internal fertilisation**, the embryos develop within the body of the mother, and relatively few, well developed young are born via the oviduct. The newborn juveniles are left to fend for themselves.

During the gestation period, the developing pups of most viviparous elasmobranchs are provided with some extra nourishment (in addition to their original yolk supply) by the mother. Most carcharhinoid sharks (e.g. requiem sharks, smooth-hounds and hammerheads) have a **yolk-sac placental connection** between the pups and oviduct (uterus). After the initial yolk supply is exhausted, the flaccid yolk sac attaches to the inner lining of the oviduct; during the later months of the gestation period, the yolk-sac placenta absorbs nutrients and oxygen from the mother's blood. The uterine lining of some sharks and rays produces a nutritious secretion that is absorbed by enlarged gill filaments of the pups.

Mackerel sharks and ragged-tooth sharks are **oophagous**, with pups nourished by feeding on extra eggs supplied by the mother during the gestation period. With ragged-tooth sharks the largest pre-natal pup also feeds on its smaller siblings in the uterus, and there are only two survivors (one per oviduct) at the end of the gestation period. In the gravid female, the ovary swells to 9 kg and supplies small nutritive eggs to each uterus for the growing pups.

Viviparous fish with pups that receive no extra nourishment (e.g. spiny dogfish and coelacanths) are called **ovoviviparous**.

Many bony fish are **hermaphrodites**, with both sexes functional in one individual. There are two main types of hermaphroditism: **synchronous** and **sequential**. **Synchronous hermaphrodites** are fish that contain ripe eggs and sperm simultaneously. Although they have the ability to self-fertilise, synchronous hermaphrodites generally spawn with another fish and fertilise each other's eggs. **Sequential hermaphrodites** are fish that change sex during their life. Some fish species start their reproductive life as a female and after a year or more they change to male (**protogynous hermaphroditism**). See the account of the sea goldie (p. 160) for an example of a protogynous species. In the other type of sequential hermaphroditism, the species spawns as a male and later changes to female (**protandrous hermaphroditism**). See the nosestripe anemonefish (p. 330) for an example of a protandrous species. Hermaphroditism rarely occurs in freshwater fish, but it is known for many marine fish, particularly in coral reef species and mesopelagic fish. Most coral reef fish (e.g. wrasses, parrotfish, rockcods, emperors, threadfins, etc.) are protogynous hermaphrodites. Most mesopelagic hermaphrodites (lancetfish, barracudinas, greeneyes, etc.) are of the synchronous type.

GROWTH AND AGE DETERMINATION

Determination of the age and growth of fish is possible because of annual marks on the scales and other hard parts, such as vertebrae (for elasmobranchs) or the 'ear bones' (**otoliths**) of bony fish. In the shallow coastal waters of temperate areas, fish grow faster in summer than in winter because their metabolism and growth are affected by the temperature of their aquatic habitat. These annual growth variations are reflected in the form of alternate wide (faster) and narrow (slow) growth zones (**annuli**) on the hard parts of the fish. Ageing fish is thus similar to reading the age of a tree from the annual rings on a cross-section of its trunk. Determination of the growth of tropical or deep sea fish is more complicated, as their growth rate is more constant throughout the year.

Otoliths usually show the annual growth marks better than bones or scales. In long-lived mature fish, growth is slower than in juveniles and ascertaining the age of fish older than 10 years is therefore very difficult. Tetracycline, which is deposited as a visible mark on the scales or otoliths, has been used to mark the hard parts of live fish in order to estimate growth rates and validate the annual growth marks. A numbered tag is attached to a fish injected with tetracycline, and when the

Figure 14 Scanning electron micrographs of 'ear bones' (otoliths) from a white musselcracker (above) and dusky kob (below).

tagged fish is recaptured, examination of the otoliths show the age and growth that have occurred since the injection. Recent developments in the technology of age determination for fish involve measuring the ratio of radioactive isotopes of lead and radium in otolith sections. These studies confirm that some cold water species may live to an age of 80 years! The coelacanth, with its unusually low metabolism and slow growth, may live to an age of 60 years. One study estimated the maximum age for a whale shark at about 100 years, but some small estuarine or reef fish live for only one year. Dorado attain a length of 2 m and grow extremely fast. They are mature in one year at a length of 55 cm and only live four years.

RESPIRATION

Fish gills are equivalent to the lungs of other vertebrates, as it is here where oxygen is absorbed and carbon dioxide given off. The bright red colour of the gills of a live fish indicates the abundant blood supply within the thin walls of the **gill lamellae**, which are the sites of gas exchange. (On dead fish that are not fresh, the gills are reddish brown in colour.) In the lamellae, the blood is separated from the water flowing through the gills by a very thin membrane; oxygen diffuses from the water into the blood; and carbon dioxide moves from the blood into the water across this membrane.

Another adaptation to facilitate oxygen uptake by the gills is the **counter-current system of blood flow** in the lamellae, where the flow of blood in the lamellae is opposite to the water flow across the lamellae.

Fast active fish like tunas use a lot of energy and need a lot of oxygen. The gills of these fast-swimming fish have larger more numerous lamellae, providing a much greater surface area for diffusion, which enhances the

Figure 15 *Ram ventilation.*

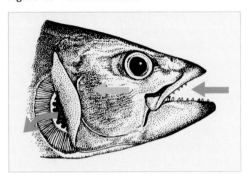

exchange of oxygen and carbon dioxide between blood and water.

Water is moved through the gills by **ram ventilation** or by a **branchial pump**. In ram ventilation, the fish swims with the mouth and gill openings wide open, and water flows straight through the mouth and gills and out through the gill openings. Ram ventilation is used by fast-swimming fish and by plankton filter-feeders (which swim about with their mouths open anyway).

Sedentary and slow-moving species use a muscular branchial pump to force water through the gills. Water is drawn into the mouth by expansion of the mouth and gill cavities, the mouth then closes, the operculum opens as the mouth and gill cavities contract, forcing water out through the gills. This can be observed in live fish as they alternately open and close their gill covers.

In water with low oxygen levels, such as the warm stagnant water of lagoons and closed estuaries, mullet jump more frequently than they do in well oxygenated habitats. They do this to take in air, which is then stored in bubbles in a chamber over the gills to provide an additional source of oxygen.

SWIMMING AND SPEED

Most fish propel themselves by using their peduncle and tail fin. In elongate flexible fish,

like morays and snake eels, the whole body is used for swimming in a serpentine motion. With swift tunas, mackerels and marlins the tail fin is the only means of propulsion.

The remarkable swimming speed of scombrids is attributed to several anatomical innovations. During the course of evolution, scombrids developed the rigid crescentic tail fin that allows rapid movements with minimal turbulence. A sprinting tuna can drive its tail fin at the incredible rate of 10 beats/second! The sides of the peduncle are equipped with fleshy horizontal keels which strengthen it and are also thought to reduce drag. The fusiform body also has grooves and recesses for the first dorsal and pectoral fins when they are folded to reduce turbulence.

Fish that swim at high speed use a lot of energy and this entails increased oxygen consumption. The surface area of scombrid fish gills is much greater than that of most other fish. Consequently, the gills of scombrids are much better at extracting oxygen than the gills of non-scombrids.

Some scombrids (bonitos and tunas) have an additional means to increase their metabolism. Most fish are 'cold-blooded', with their body temperature about the same as the ambient water temperature. But tunas and several other fast-swimming fish (e.g. marlin, swordfish, great white shark and mako) maintain the temperature of their deep muscles significantly above the ambient water temperature. Tunas have a circulatory system that includes a special network of capillaries functioning as a counter-current heat exchanger to transfer metabolic heat produced by the swimming muscles to the cold oxygenated blood running from the gills to the muscles. The warmer swimming muscles are then able to operate at the higher metabolic rate essential for sustained high-speed swimming. Of all scombrids, the bluefin tunas have the most efficient temperature regulation, which accounts for them being the only scombrids that are found in the cold waters off Norway and Alaska.

It is difficult to measure the speed of fast-swimming fish. Scombrids cruise at 2–10 km/h, but their sprinting (burst) speed, which is used to chase prey or flee predators, is much faster. Wahoo may be the fastest fish in sea, as one was timed doing 77 km/h in a 5-second burst. A yellowfin tuna has been timed at 74 km/h in a 5-second period.

Some other fast-swimming fish, e.g. marlin, sailfish, swordfish, dorado, mako and great white sharks, are reputed to rival tunas at their top speeds. The one feature common to all these speedy fish is a large rigid lunate tail fin. This fin design is most efficient for sustained high-speed cruising. The wide paddle-shaped tail of coelacanths or brindlebass is better for the fast start of a lunging predator.

Many reef fish (e.g. damselfish, parrotfish and wrasses) rely on their pectoral fins for swimming slowly over the reef, and they use their tail fin for fast starts, chasing prey or eluding predators. The oceanic opah has large rigid pectoral fins with enormous red muscles, and they are its main means of propulsion.

Some demersal batoids (rays and skates) use sinuous waves of their broad flexible pectoral fins for propulsion. The pelagic eagle, manta and devil rays use their stiffer pectoral fins like wings. Batoids with a substantial tail (electric rays, guitarfish and sawfish) rely on their tail fin for propulsion.

Ocean sunfish (Family Molidae) flap their large rigid paddle-like dorsal and anal fins synchronously from side to side as their primary means of

SWIMMING MODES

Tuna with streamlined body, stiff lunate tail fin and fleshy lateral keel on peduncle

Large pectoral and pelvic fins of the opah

Head on view of ocean sunfish swimming

Stingray using pectoral fins in cruising mode

propulsion. Puffers, burrfish and boxfish have short spatulate dorsal and anal fins which they use, as well as their pectoral fins, for slow swimming. They also use their tail fin when chased.

Triggerfish and filefish use sinuous waves of their long-based dorsal and anal fins for cruising and they rely on the tail fin for bursts of speed.

OSMOREGULATION

Osmoregulation is the physiological process by which the concentration of salt (sodium, chloride and other ions) in blood and other tissues is kept within the bounds essential for a living organism. The concentration of ions in the blood and tissues of marine bony fish is less than that of sea water; therefore these fish tend to lose water molecules by osmosis through their gills and skin. To compensate for this loss, bony fish swallow sea water and absorb water (along with ions which they do not need) through the gut. Excess ions are excreted mainly through special chloride cells in the gills and also in the faeces.

The ion concentration of the blood and tissues of cartilaginous fish is not much higher than that of bony fish; but the high concentration of urea in the blood and tissues of cartilaginous fish prevents water loss by osmosis. Cartilaginous fish (and the coelacanth, which also uses urea to osmoregulate) are somehow able to tolerate urea concentrations in their blood that would be fatal to most other animals. The influx of ions in chondrichthyans is countered by excreting ions (but not urea) via the gills, kidney and **rectal gland**. Water is resorbed in the kidney, and little urine is produced. Most of the excretion of sodium and chlorine ions by cartilaginous fish and the coelacanth is accomplished by the rectal gland.

In the elasmobranchs (sharks and rays) that live in freshwater, the concentration of urea and ions in the blood is much reduced compared to their levels in the sea. The freshwater stingrays (*Potamotrygon* spp) that live in the rivers of South America cannot retain urea in their blood and will die if placed in sea water.

Like other **euryhaline** fish, the Zambezi shark is able to cope with a wide range in salinity. This shark is common in coastal waters around the world, often occurs in rivers, and juveniles have been found as far inland as Malawi and the Kruger National Park! In view of the wide range of salinities in estuaries, it is understandable that the estuarine fish fauna comprises mainly euryhaline marine fish like moonies, mullet and dusky kob. The Mozambique tilapia, *Oreochromis mossambicus* (Peters 1852), is one of the few freshwater fish that can cope with estuarine salinities.

Stenohaline species are restricted to a narrow range of salinity; consequently, they are found either in freshwater or in the sea.

TEMPERATURE TOLERANCE AND REGULATION

The vast majority of fish are 'cold-blooded' animals, which means that the temperature of their body is the same as the temperature of the ambient water in which they live. However, some large fast-swimming fish (tuna, marlin, mako and great white sharks) keep their body temperature several degrees above the ambient water temperature (see the section on 'Swimming and Speed'). Most fish cannot survive rapid temperature changes of more than a few degrees Celsius. When a strong easterly wind blows over the Eastern Cape coast for two or three days, the warm surface water is pushed offshore and cold bottom water from the outer continental shelf and upper slope wells up to replace the warm surface water. This sudden cold upwelling may change the inshore water temperature by 5 or 6 degrees overnight, frequently killing fish or making them very sluggish.

BIOLUMINESCENCE

The ability of some organisms to produce light (**bioluminescence**), serves a multitude of uses for different species of fish. Patterns of photophores may be useful for species or mate recognition. Light organs are clearly used as lures on the end of fishing rods or barbels for deep sea anglerfish and scaly dragonfish. Some fish have bright headlight organs that are used to search for prey. The light from the numerous ventrally directed light organs of deep midwater fish matches the faint down-welling light from the surface and renders the fish invisible to predators or prey below.

There are two kinds of bioluminescent organs. Most bioluminescent fish produce substances that react chemically within a glandular photophore to produce light without heat. This light is controlled by the central nervous system via electrical impulses (for quick flashes) or via hormones (adrenaline) in the blood (for slower effects). In flashlight fish (Family Anomalopidae) and in several other families, the light from **bacterial light organs** is generated by symbiotic luminous bacteria that are cultured within the organ. Flashlight fish have two huge organs, one below each eye. These light organs (**photophores**) shine continuously and the Red Sea flashlight fish, *Photoblepharon steinitzi* (Abe & Haneda 1973), 'switches off' its light by pulling a black membrane up and over the light organ. The Pacific flashlight fish, *Anomalops katoptron* (Bleeker 1856), turns its light off by rotating the entire light organ down into a black pouch.

Red Sea flashlight fish also occur at Grand Comoro Island. During the day these fish are down in deep water (200–400 m) with the coelacanths, but at night flashlight fish come up to forage over the coral reef in groups of 10–20 fish. Their bright pale green lights are visible from the shore in 3–7 m of water. Underwater the lights are even more spectacular.

Bioluminescent organs occur in fish of many marine fish families, but no luminous freshwater fish are known. Bioluminescent fish are more common in the deep sea, but there are also a few shallow water species that are luminescent (e.g. pineapplefish, some cardinalfish and ponyfish).

Figure 16
Flashlight fish with a 'light' organ (photophore) under the eye containing luminous bacteria.

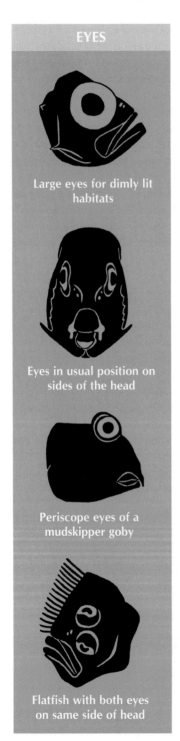

EYES

Large eyes for dimly lit habitats

Eyes in usual position on sides of the head

Periscope eyes of a mudskipper goby

Flatfish with both eyes on same side of head

The deep sea loosejaw, *Malacosteus niger* Ayres 1848, has a large photophore below each eye that produces red light. Since red rays of sunlight are absorbed in the first 20 m of sea water, most deep sea fish (including the prey of *Malacosteus*) are unable to see red light, but loosejaws have the retinal pigment essential to see red light and any prey illuminated with their red light. It seems that fish have developed their own infra-red night vision goggles.

MIGRATIONS

Fish migrations are regular mass movements from one place to another, usually for purposes of breeding or feeding. During the day, mesopelagic fish are found at depths of 200–1 000 m, and at night many of these deep sea fish (e.g. lanternfish) make vertical migrations of several hundred metres in order to feed on the abundant plankton near the surface. By feeding in surface waters at night, lanternfish are safe from birds and other predators that hunt their prey visually near the surface. The elf is one of many migratory coastal species. It moves from KZN to our south coast in late summer to feed, and returns to KZN waters to breed from September to December. Fish that must return to the sea to spawn, like the freshwater mullet, are called **catadromous**. This mullet spends most of its life in rivers, but spawns in the sea; damming of rivers and degradation of estuaries have reduced the available habitat for this vulnerable species. The annual Sardine Run, an epic fish migration along the east coast, is probably a feeding and spawning migration (see the pilchard species account, p. 108).

SENSORY FUNCTIONS
Vision

Fishes exhibit much diversity in development of their eyes and visual capabilities. The fish eye has a spherical inelastic lens, whereas most other vertebrates have an oval lens. The eye of humans and most other vertebrates is equipped with muscles that flatten an elastic lens to focus the eye. Focussing is also facilitated by the initial refraction of light rays by the cornea. The fish cornea is, however, optically non-functional, as it has a similar refractive index to water, and focussing is done by moving the lens back and forth in the eye.

Fish are usually long-sighted, especially in their lateral field of vision. Their greatest visual acuity is in the forward field of view, because it is the rear part of the retina that has the greatest density of visual receptor cells. Most shallow water fish have a retina with two types of receptor cells – rods and cones. The rods are sensitive to faint light, and the cones enable fish to see colour. Fish living in 500–1 000 m, where sunlight is very dim, usually have large eyes and mostly rods in their retinas.

Many sharks and also some bony fish (including coelacanths) have a *tapetum lucidum* at the back of the retina. This is a special layer of cells that reflects light back through the receptor cells and produces the 'eye-shine' that occurs when the fish is illuminated with a beam of light at night or in deep water where the light is dim. The eyes of a shark with a *tapetum lucidum* are, in effect, equipped with a 'light multiplier' that makes them more sensitive to the faint light at night or in deep water.

In low-light environments, such as ocean depths below ~2 000 m, many fish have tiny vestigial eyes. With little or no light, vision is of little use, and during the course of evolution some deep sea fish have lost their eyes completely. The loss of eyes and vision also occurs in animals that live in deep caves or underground rivers.

The retina of fish in shallow, well-lit habitats has many cone cells which enhance acuity of vision and also enable colour perception. The abundance of beautifully coloured butterflyfish, angelfish, wrasses, parrotfish, etc. on well-lit coral reefs indicates that colour and colour vision are important to these species. It is also obvious that in fish with differently coloured males and females, colour vision is linked to species and mate recognition.

Most fish, with movable eyes on the sides of their heads, have a wide field of view and can see in front, behind, above and below their bodies. The mudskipper goby, with its protruding eyes on top of its head enabling a 360° field of vision, spends much of its time out of the water, climbing about the roots of mangrove trees. The eyes can be retracted and rolled around in the eye socket to keep them moist, and erected again to scan the area for predators or possible prey. Mudskippers can see quite well in air, as anyone who has tried to catch one of these elusive little fish will attest.

Flounders, soles and other flatfish have adapted to a demersal (bottom-living) existence, with both eyes on the same side of the head. The head and body of these sedentary fish are usually in contact with the substrate, and an eye on the underside of the head would be of little use and subject to injury. Most flatfish are also camouflaged to match the substrate where they lie. If a flatfish is blinded it loses the ability to blend with its surroundings, hence vision is linked to alteration of **chromatophores** (colour cells) in the skin to produce an appropriate camouflage colour pattern.

Successful anglers know that the best catches are generally made when the water is not too clear – if they can see the fish, the fish can see them and is less likely to take their bait.

Hearing and lateral-line sense

The density of water is about 1 000 times greater than that of air; water is therefore much less compressible than air. This greater density and resistance to compression greatly affect the production and transmission of sound. In water, sound travels about five times faster than in air.

Fish perceive sounds with their **lateral lines** and their ears. The lateral lines are a system of minute perforated tubes or canals that run along the body just under the skin (usually in the mid-lateral region, hence the name 'lateral line') on each side of the fish. In most

Figure 17 *Inner ear (labyrinth) of a bony fish.*

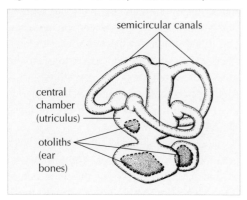

semicircular canals

central chamber (utriculus)

otoliths (ear bones)

fish the lateral lines continue onto the head, where they branch above and below the eye and onto the lower jaw. These branches on the head are known as **lateralis canals**. The lateral line tubes contain microscopic motion detectors called **neuromasts**. These sensory organs are exposed to the water surrounding the fish and are especially sensitive to the low-frequency swimming sounds (vibrations) produced by the movement of fish or other animals in their vicinity. This ability to detect the motion of other animals is useful to both predators and prey, especially at night or in the deep sea, where sunlight is non-existent. The greatly elongated lateral line of some mid-water fishes (e.g. the tube-eye, *Stylephorus*, with two greatly extended tail fin rays that carry the lateral-line tube well behind the fish, and the tapertail, *Radiicephalus*, with similar elongated tail fin rays) increases the effectiveness of these motion sensors. Sardines and anchovies lack a lateral line on the body, but the well developed lateralis canals of the head facilitate the co-ordinated swimming of these schooling fish.

Although fish have no external ears, they do have inner ears (**labyrinths**) which are convoluted fluid-filled organs enclosed in a bony chamber on each side of the cranium. The upper part of each labyrinth comprises

three curved interconnected membranous tubes (**semicircular canals**) that join a central chamber called the **utriculus**. Two of the semicircular canals lie in vertical planes approximately at right angles to each other; the third canal is located in the horizontal plane. Movements of the head generate displacements of the fluid (**endolymph**) in the semicircular canals and utriculus; and these fluid movements impinge on the sensory hair cells on the inner wall of the labyrinth. Stimulation of these neuromasts sends electric impulses to the brain to register movement and orientation of the fish. Gravity perception and balance are controlled by the utriculus.

The lower part of the labyrinth comprises two adjacent fluid-filled chambers, each with a dense calcareous 'ear bone' (**otolith**). The ears of fish are receptive to a wide range of sound frequencies, but the neuromasts, located within bony capsules of the skull, are mainly sensitive to higher frequencies. The sound-generated pressure wave is transmitted directly through the bones and muscles of the skull to the ear; or (in fish with a connection between swimbladder and ears) the sound wave causes vibrations of the gas-filled swim-bladder and these amplified vibrations are conducted directly to the ears. Fish with a swimbladder-ear connection are more sensitive to high-frequency sounds (up to 7 kHz). In the ear, sound wave vibrations are transmitted to the otoliths, and vibrations of the otoliths generate electrical activity in the neuromasts. The electrical impulses are conducted to the brain where they register as sounds.

Buoyancy, swimbladders and sound

In most fish, buoyancy is provided by a gas-filled **swimbladder** (or 'airbladder') situated in the upper part of the abdominal cavity, but sedentary benthic fish usually lack a swimbladder.

The swimbladder of most spiny-rayed bony fish, such as scorpionfish and fishes of the Order Perciformes, has no connection with the gut, and any change in the amount of gas in the swimbladder is a slow process of secretion or resorption. If a fish is pulled rapidly to the surface from a depth of 20 m or more, the volume of gas in the swimbladder cannot be adjusted to the sudden decrease in external pressure. The result is the rapid expansion of the swimbladder, which may rupture or push the everted stomach into the mouth.

Biologists who tag deep water fish to study their growth and movements use a large hypodermic needle to deflate the swimbladder before the fish is returned to the water. Aquarium fish collectors also use this technique to deflate fish caught below 10 m. Correctly done, this deflation procedure significantly improves the survival rate of fish caught in deep water.

Some species have developed a fat-filled swimbladder which provides buoyancy and prevents expansion of the swimbladder with changes in depth. Coelacanths have a fat-filled swimbladder and muscles rich in wax esters which are lighter than seawater and so provide buoyancy.

The oilfish (*Ruvettus pretiosus*) is marketed in the Comoro Islands for the laxative property of its flesh, which is a result of the abundance of wax esters in its body muscles. The coelacanth and oilfish share the same 200–700 m deep habitat at the Comoros; and in their search for prey, they experience large changes in depth. These two unrelated species have independently evolved the same solution (storage of light-weight wax esters in their swimbladder or body muscles) to the problem of buoyancy and depth changes.

Cartilaginous fish (sharks, rays and chimaeras) which do not have a swimbladder,

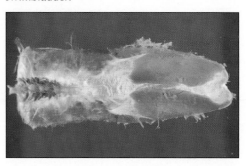

Figure 18 *Dorsal view of a cavebass swimbladder.*

also store lipids to provide buoyancy. In sharks, the lipids (mainly squalene, a light-weight oil and excellent lubricant) are stored in the liver. In some sharks, the liver may account for up to 25% of the shark's weight! (See also the section on buoyancy in the Chondrichthyes text.)

A gas-filled swimbladder is like a balloon filled with air and it can be used underwater to amplify or produce sounds. Some fish have muscles attached to the swimbladder, and contractions of these muscles produce vibrations that sound like drumming noises. The North American oyster toadfish (*Opsanus tau*) uses the well developed muscles that are attached to its large swimbladder to produce a variety of loud grunts, yelps, hoots and boat-whistle sounds when defending its territory or conducting courtship.

In kobs (Family Sciaenidae) drumming muscles run along the sides of the abdominal cavity. There are two very similar species of kob in our area; in the silver kob, only males have drumming muscles, but in the dusky kob both sexes have drumming muscles. The cavebass has a large thick-walled swimbladder with three pairs of muscles. This territorial fish is usually found beneath ledges or in caves, and it often produces a loud drumming sound to deter intruders.

Figure 19 *Fish nostrils. Dragon moray eel with two pairs of nostrils and a damselfish with a single pair of nostrils.*

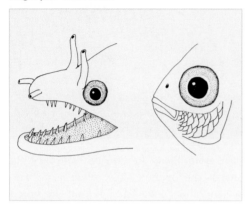

Smell

Most fish have a keen sense of smell. Their **nostrils** are paired, with a posterior and anterior nostril on each side of the snout. The **olfactory organs** are round to oval plates of folded sensory tissue enclosed in the **nasal capsules**. Water and odour molecules are drawn into the front nostril, pass over the olfactory organ, and then exit via the rear nostril. A few species have only a single nostril on each side of the head, and for these fish (e.g. cutlassfish, damselfish and wrasses) the sense of smell is apparently unimportant because they find their food and mates visually. The olfactory organs of these single-nostril fish are also rudimentary.

Sharks are renowned for their sense of smell, and their well developed olfactory organs enable them to follow scent trails for several kilometres. Smell is also important to Pacific salmon, which recognise the unique odours of the stream where they hatched and return to their original home after years at sea. Should their nostrils be blocked, these fish would not find their home streams.

Touch and taste

Although fish lack specialised touch receptors as found in mammals, they do have a network of **free nerve endings** in the skin which are able to register touch sensations. Fish taste by means of **taste receptors** in the mouth, on the lips, barbels and on certain modified fin rays (e.g. the thickened pectoral fin rays of gurnards).

The elongate barbels on the lower jaw and/or snout of catfish and goatfish have many microscopic taste buds and free nerve endings. These barbels are used like feelers, as the fish probes about the bottom when foraging for prey. Threadfins, gurnards and helmet gurnards have elongate thickened free pectoral fin rays which probably serve the same purpose.

An ichthyologist studying sharks in the Red Sea put out a hook baited with a live speckled sole, *Pardachirus marmoratus*, and a shark took the bait in its mouth. As it was about to bite or swallow the sole, it stopped abruptly, spat out the sole and swam away with its mouth wide open, shaking its head rapidly. This event revealed that the mucus of the sole contains a toxin that is distasteful to sharks and other predators.

A similar unexpected discovery involved the Atlantic soapfish, *Rypticus saponaceus*. Another ichthyologist speared a small soapfish that he wanted as a specimen but he had no bag in which to put the fish, so he tucked it into his swimming costume. After a few minutes he realised that this was a serious mistake, as the soapfish mucus also contains a bitter-tasting toxin that not only deters predators from eating them, but is also a powerful irritant to mucous membranes such as the lining of the urethra of an unsuspecting ichthyologist! Predators soon learn to recognise and avoid soapfish, which accounts for the conspicuous colour patterns of the sixstripe and arrowhead soapfish.

Electro-reception

Elasmobranchs and a few bony fish (e.g. eel-catfish) have **electro-receptors** that are able to detect the weak electric fields generated by the muscle contractions of living animals. Many elasmobranchs have well developed electro-sensory organs, called '**ampullae of Lorenzini**' (after the Italian anatomist who first described them), on the underside of the snout. Each small bulb-like sensory organ or ampulla has a slender jelly-filled canal leading to a pore at the surface of the skin. The conductivity of the jelly in the ampullae canals is twice that of sea water or body fluids and enables the ampullae to pick up the faint electric fields generated by the beating heart muscle of a buried animal. Laboratory experiments demonstrate that sharks and rays use their ampullae to locate prey hidden in the substrate. Elasmobranchs may also have the ability to sense electric fields produced as they move through the earth's magnetic field, and this sixth sense could be used to navigate during migration.

Pain

The question of whether fish experience pain is a complicated question, but it can best be answered from a scientific (physiological, behavioural, evolutionary, anatomical) approach. To say that this subject is a 'philosophical' question moves the issue into a realm beyond the scope of this book.

The common misunderstanding that fish feel pain is an **anthropomorphic** supposition that confuses the **nociceptive** (reflexive, unconscious) response of fish to predators or other noxious stimuli with the perception of pain in humans. Anthropomorphism (attributing human mental states or capacities to animals) is an impediment to understanding animal behaviour.

To understand the differences between **nociception**, the neural activity induced in sensory receptors (free nerve endings in fish) by an injurious stimulus, and **pain**, which is a subjective, unpleasant, psychological (sensory and emotional) experience of humans and other mammals, we must compare the neural anatomy of humans and fish; and we need to comprehend the relationship of brain structures to brain functions.

The difference between nociception of fish and pain in humans is clearly explained in an article by Professor James Rose (2002), who provides a convincing resolution to this controversial question.

As fellow **vertebrates**, mammals and fish have certain primitive nervous system features in common, such as a well developed brain enclosed in a cranium and attached to a spinal cord that is protected (in most species) by a series of vertebrae. Vertebrates also have various cutaneous sense organs that range from the simple free nerve endings (**nociceptors** that register noxious stimuli) of fish to the well developed encapsulated sense organs of mammals that register touch, temperature and pressure. The primitive features of our vertebrate nervous system can be traced back some 400 million years to the ancestral 'proto-bony fish' that gave rise to ray-fin fish (Subclass Actinopterygii) and fleshy-fin fish (Subclass Sarcopterygii). The Sarcopterygii includes the fossil fish ancestors of the living coelacanths and lungfish, as well as the highly modified group of vertebrates known as '**tetrapods**' (amphibians, reptiles, birds and mammals) which left the water to venture onto land as terrestrial vertebrates.

During their 300 million years of evolution, terrestrial vertebrates lost their fins and gills as they evolved lungs and four legs. About 200 million years ago, one group of small inconspicuous reptiles evolved hair, internal regulation of body temperature (**endothermy**) and a placental connection between the developing foetus and mother. This new branch of vertebrate evolution developed into the group known as the **mammals**. Along with endothermy, came improvements in sensory capacities, such as smell, vision and hearing, and a concomitant increase in the size and complexity of the brain, especially the **cerebrum** and its outer layer of tissue, called the **neocortex**.

Over the next 100 million years mammals flourished and diversified. Some mammals developed wings and took up flying (bats); others 're-invented' fins and returned to the sea (whales, dolphins and seals). About seven million years ago, in a small group of African mammals (**the primates**), locomotion shifted from walking on four legs to walking on the two rear legs; and the front legs and feet were slowly transformed into arms and hands useful for carrying things, climbing trees, and holding tools or weapons.

During the course of human evolution (from fish to mammal to man) the **cerebral hemispheres** increased enormously in size and complexity and acquired new information processing capacities. The uniquely human behavioural and psychological developments such as language, creativity, learning, art, science and culture are associated with the unprecedented expansion of the **human neocortex**, which is much larger than the neocortex of primates or other mammals.

Another function associated with the neocortex is conscious awareness, or **primary consciousness**, which is essential to perception of pain and the related experience of fear. A clinical definition of primary consciousness requires sustained awareness of the environment that is appropriate and meaningful, the ability to immediately follow commands to perform novel actions, and verbal or non-verbal communication indicating awareness of ongoing interaction. Examples of **unconscious states**, during which pain is not perceived, are deep sleep, concussion, coma and anaesthetic states. Note: anaesthetic drugs that block pain do not necessarily stop nociceptive motor (muscle) reactions to surgery, such as twitching or limb withdrawal; hence the use of additional nerve-muscle blocking drugs to prevent spasms or twitching during surgery.

The functions of the human neocortex are corroborated by injuries that cause destruction of the cerebral cortex, which results in a person in a permanent vegetative state with no conscious awareness. Although sleep-wake cycles and nociceptive reactions to noxious stimuli still occur, these behaviours are controlled by sub-cortical (brain stem and spinal) systems. Also, after damage to the frontal lobe neocortex, the perception and distress of pain in humans is greatly diminished. Another example of nociception in humans is seen in cases of injury where the spinal cord is cut. If a noxious stimulus (pin prick or electric shock) is applied to a limb below the cut, the nociceptive sensors are activated and send a signal to the spinal cord, which immediately causes limb withdrawal (if the muscles are still functional); but no nervous signal can be sent across the spinal cord gap to the neocortex, hence no pain is perceived.

Since the perception of pain and the related experience of fear occur in the cerebral neocortex, which is lacking in fish brains, pain and the awareness of fear are anatomically precluded in fish.

Based on current knowledge of fish brain anatomy and function, there is no evidence that fish have the mental capacity (information processing ability) to perceive pain as we

Figure 20 *Diagrammatic (simplified) illustrations of human and bony fish (salmon, Salmo salar) brains. The human brain shows the internal (medial) view of the right hemisphere, as if the brain were cut in half vertically between the eyes. The fish brain is shown whole, in left lateral view. The brain stems of each brain are shown up to the point where they connect with the spinal cord. Note the massive expansion of the human cerebrum and its outer layer (neocortex), which is associated with consciousness, language, learning, art, science, culture and perception of pain.*

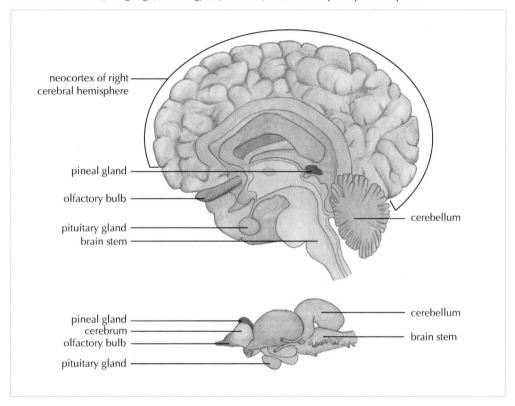

know it. If we redefine 'fish pain' as the neural activity induced in sensory receptors (free nerve endings in fish) by an injurious stimulus, we could then say, 'Yes, fish do feel fish pain.' But this conflates the useful physiological concept of nociception with pain, a different sensation.

Although fish brains are not able to perceive pain, they are well developed and support a marvellously complex sensory and behavioural repertoire in their aquatic environments. The senses of smell, vision, hearing and perception of water movements of fish far exceeds our human capacities. Some fish (e.g. sharks and most other elasmobranchs), can detect the weak electric fields produced by the muscular action of other animals. This electro-receptive sense is unknown in other vertebrates. Fish (and other animals) are capable of associative or implicit learning, but this does not require conscious awareness. Feeding and reproductive behaviours are exceedingly diverse in fish, although these behaviour patterns are highly stereotyped (rigid) within each species.

In spite of the inability of fish to feel pain, their nociceptive responses to harmful stimuli do cause stress in the fish. These stress responses, especially sustained or repeated ones, may be detrimental to the fish's health and well-being. In Professor Rose's words, the fact that fish cannot feel pain 'in no way devalues fishes or diminishes our responsibility for respectful and responsible stewardship of them. Fishes constitute a highly evolved, diverse, and complex life form whose history on Earth vastly eclipses the brief existence of humans. Our diverse uses of fishes have ancient historical precedents and modern justifications, but our increasingly deleterious impacts on fishes at the population and ecological levels require us to use our best scientific knowledge and understanding to foster their health and viability' (Rose 2002, p. 33).

PEOPLE AND THE SEA

THE EFFECTS OF FISHING

Catches of many sport and commercial fish have declined in recent years. These declines are due to a number of factors, foremost being an increase in the number of anglers and commercial fishermen harvesting our limited fish resources.

The slow growth and long life of some species (rockcods, red steenbras, large sharks, etc.) mean that it may take several years before they reach maturity and are able to reproduce. Because some species are territorial or resident in small areas (or even on a single reef) for many years, the larger species in a heavily exploited area will be quickly 'fished-out'.

In the 1970s records of fish caught in regular fishing club competitions in KZN showed that fewer and smaller elf (a.k.a. 'shad') were being caught. A commission of inquiry, called the Smith Committee (chaired by Margaret Smith), was appointed in 1980 to look into the matter, and recommended that:

- catching of elf be prohibited during their breeding season from September to November;
- during the rest of the year there should be a daily bag limit of four fish per angler;
- the sale of elf be prohibited.

As a result of the strict enforcement of these regulations (primarily in KZN), more large elf are now caught and the elf population has increased.

The Marine and Coastal Management (MCM) division of the South African Department of Environmental Affairs & Tourism conducts and funds research into the biology and fisheries of our marine fishes to formulate effective regulations and policies to ensure the sustainable use of these resources. One of the policies of MCM is the designation of Marine Protected Areas (MPAs) where fishing is restricted to enable the replenishment of exploited angling fish populations. In MPAs it has been observed that:

- the size of adults and the number of resident angling fish increase;
- because space is the limiting factor in reef fish populations, when an MPA reef fish population becomes crowded, some adults will move into areas outside the MPA;
- because the reproductive output of larger fish is greater than smaller fish of the same species, the production of young (larvae and small juveniles) by the fish population of the MPA is significantly increased, and some of these young are exported to other areas;
- fisheries are easier to monitor and manage within an MPA.

Despite the regulations put in place and the steps taken, populations of many of our angling and commercial fish species continue to decline. Enforcement of laws to restrict line fishing (which includes subsistence, recreational and commercial fishing), trawling and other commercial fisheries is not easy, particularly when we are dealing with some 300 species that are used for bait or human consumption. These species face exploitation by anglers, trawlers and spearfishermen. Conservation of the sea's resources relies on the co-operation of all who interact with it.

DANGEROUS FISH

Shark attacks

Although shark attacks are extremely rare, they are a reality off southern African coasts and a source of fear for many people. Each year far more people die from drowning than from shark attacks, but it is worth knowing what to do in case of an attack.

When treating a shark attack victim:
- send for medical help immediately;
- place the victim on the beach above the waves, parallel to the sea (not head downwards), and raise the legs to promote blood flow to the brain;
- it is most important to stop bleeding and keep the victim breathing;
- apply mouth-to-mouth resuscitation if necessary;
- serum, plasma or blood must be given intravenously as soon as possible, record pulse and blood pressure at frequent intervals;
- do not move patient for 30 minutes to avoid fatal secondary shock;
- if bleeding cannot be controlled, move the victim to the nearest medical facility;
- give no alcoholic or other drink, but water may be used to wet the lips;
- reassure victim and try to keep him/her calm.

Spearfishermen are at increased risk of shark attacks as spearing fish often results in blood in the water and the vibrations of wounded fish attract sharks. The practice of tying speared fish to a float towed by spearfishermen also attracts sharks. Spearfishermen are vulnerable to blackouts from breath-holding techniques, and an unconscious or drowned spearfisherman is easy prey for a shark.

Venomous and poisonous fish

The terms venom and poison are often confused. **Venom** is introduced through the skin and into the muscle and blood-stream by a wound (bite or sting), causing pain and occasionally death. **Poison** is a toxin that if eaten, may cause stomach or intestinal cramps, nausea, vomiting and, in severe cases, may result in paralysis and death.

Wounds from **venomous fish** (stingrays, catfish, rabbitfish, scorpionfish, stonefish and firefish) are painful and may even be fatal. Venoms produced by most creatures living in the sea are destroyed by temperatures in excess of 50° C, and first aid for all venomous injuries is to immerse the wound in hot (not scalding) water for at least 30 minutes. If one is out in a ski-boat with outboard motors, one can use the hot water from the cooling jet that spurts from the rear of the motor when it is running. First-aid chemical hot-packs (activated by adding water that reacts with a chemical to produce heat) can be applied to the wound and are available at some pharmacies.

DANGEROUS FISH

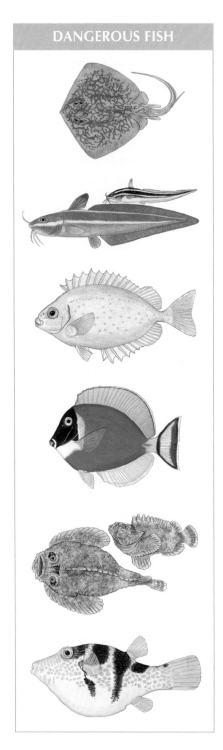

Stabs from the tail spine ('sting') of stingrays usually happen when someone stands on the ray. The ray then whips its tail forward to stab the victim's foot or leg with its serrated venomous spine. If you are wading in shallow sandy areas where stingrays may be found, watch out for stingrays and shuffle your feet along the bottom. Stingrays are sedentary non-aggressive fish that only use their spines for defence, and a touch from your foot will send it scooting off.

Catfish (a.k.a. 'barbel') have three hidden venomous serrated fin spines (one at the front edge of the dorsal fin and one on the front edge of each pectoral fin). These strong sharp spines can be locked to erect a spiky triangle that deters most predators. Jabs from these spines are extremely painful, and one should be very careful when handling these fish.

Rabbitfish, which are common in tropical waters, have a venomous mucus on their dorsal, anal and pelvic fin spines that causes pain similar to a bee sting.

Surgeonfish and unicornfish must be handled carefully. They have sharp spines or bony keels on the peduncle and this tail armature is covered with an anticoagulant. Wounds by these fish are not especially painful, but they bleed profusely and are easily infected by harmful bacteria.

Most scorpionfish have venomous dorsal fin spines. These sedentary species are more plentiful in tropical and subtropical areas, but a few deep water scorpionfish occur off our south coast. Small firefish (*Pterois* spp) sometimes occur in tide pools and attract the attention of children. These venomous fish may attack if a person tries to catch them (see firefish species account on p. 144). The stonefish is also renowned for the excruciating pain of its venom (see the species account on p. 146).

The only **poisonous fish** in our area are puffers and possibly boxfish and porcupinefish. The poison (called **tetrodotoxin**, from the puffer fish Family Tetraodontidae) of these fish is usually restricted to the skin and viscera, and the flesh might be safe, but it is still unwise to eat any of these fish. Symptoms include numbness of the mouth and lips, spreading to the face, neck and body; twitching, paralysis, impaired speech and swallowing, convulsions and breathing problems. Approximately half of all puffer poisonings are fatal. Unlike venoms, poisons are generally not affected by temperature and the best treatment is to induce vomiting as soon as possible and summon medical assistance. Cardiopulmonary resuscitation may also be needed.

The liver of many large fish predators (e.g. sharks, red steenbras and rockcods) may also be poisonous because of high concentrations of vitamin A. **Hypervitaminosis**, poisoning from excess vitamin A, may result in vomiting, stomach cramps, loss of hair and sloughing of skin from the palms and soles. This type of poisoning may be fatal, but there are no authenticated cases in our area.

We are also fortunate that there have been no incidents of **ciguatera poisoning** in our area. This tropical fish poisoning is caused by certain toxic dinoflagellates. These benthic micro-organisms are ingested by herbivorous animals (e.g. crustaceans, rabbitfish and surgeonfish) and the toxin may accumulate in the herbivore's body. As the toxin is passed up the food chain it is concentrated, and fish predators may be especially poisonous. Large piscivores notorious for causing ciguatera are the twinspot and humpback snappers, yellow-edge lyretail, marbled coralgrouper and barracuda. Ciguatera is known in the

Seychelles, Réunion and Mauritius, and is common at Caribbean and Pacific islands. Symptoms occur within 1–24 hours after eating the fish and usually include diarrhoea, abdominal pain, nausea, vomiting, muscle aches, burning sensation on skin from contact with cold water, tingling and numbness of mouth, lips and extremities as well as headaches. Neurological symptoms from a severe case of ciguatera may persist for years and the best treatment is to seek medical assistance. Cardiopulmonary resuscitation may be required.

Electric rays

Electric rays (Families Torpedinidae and Narcinidae) have a huge electric organ on each side of the head and can deliver a powerful shock to someone who inadvertently steps on them or tries to pick one up. Electric rays are common in estuaries and

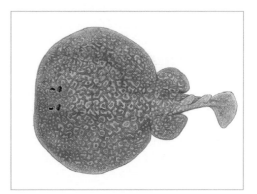

shallow sandy areas, and the shuffle suggested for avoiding stingrays may also be effective for avoiding electric ray shocks.

FISH WATCHERS BECOME FISH OBSERVERS

Once you have learnt how to recognise individual species and can confidently identify these fish, then you can become involved in the really interesting part of fish observing, which is seeing differences between species in the way they feed, react to divers and interact with other fish. As a '**fish observer**' you can discuss your observations and contribute to our knowledge of fishes. There are several useful ways that fish observers can organise their observations and increase their knowledge of fish:

■ Start a **life-list** of each species you identify, with notes on where (locality and habitat) and when you saw each species. Include notes on approximate size, sex (if obvious), state of maturity (juvenile or adult), and details of colour patterns for each species.

■ Compile a **biological/behavioural profile** of the species that you observe frequently. Are they solitary or shoaling? Active (free-swimming) or sedentary (usually observed sitting on the bottom)? Are they associated with the bottom (benthic or demersal) or are they pelagic (usually seen in midwater or near the surface)? Are they predators, herbivores (vegetarians) or omnivores? (Hint: herbivores [like parrotfish and surgeonfish] spend most of their time grazing on the bottom.) Are they territorial (like many damselfish)? Do they guard a nest (like damselfish and triggerfish)? Do they make sounds? Are they diurnal (more active during the day) or nocturnal (more active at night)?

■ Create a **site list** of all the species that occur in a particular place (e.g. Five-mile Reef at Sodwana Bay, a large tide pool at Clayton Rocks, Knysna Lagoon, etc.). Which species are common here? Which are present all year round? Do some species only appear seasonally?

■ Make a **checklist of species** from a particular locality (False Bay, Aliwal Shoal, Langebaan Lagoon, etc.) with notes on habitat, depth and seasonal occurrence for each species.

■ **Reality check**: confirm and compare your observations with a buddy or other fish observers. Consult books on fish, but don't believe everything you read. Just because something is printed in a book, doesn't mean it is necessarily true. Use the internet and consult FishBase (www.fishbase.org). If you can't find the answer there, send your question/observation to us or other scientists and education officers at coastal museums. (See list of contacts under 'Wanted: Rare and Interesting Fish' below.) But don't be disappointed if you are told 'Sorry we don't know the answer to that question.' We still have much to learn about fish. Learning about fish is a lifelong (and very enjoyable) activity, providing the opportunity to make interesting discoveries about these fascinating creatures.

■ **Underwater photography** is also a great way to record observations. Experienced underwater photographers can document the occurrence of particular species in certain habitats, depths and localities. This documentation is essential to determine the distributions of each species, and photographers can also record the variation in colour patterns of the species in our area.

HOW FISH OBSERVERS HAVE CONTRIBUTED TO OUR KNOWLEDGE OF FISH

South Africa has a proud tradition of amateur ichthyologists. In 1931, JLB Smith, a chemistry lecturer at Rhodes University and self-taught ichthyologist, published his first paper 'New and little known fishes from the south and east coasts of Africa'. Smith was a keen angler and soon developed an interest in the fish he caught. Identifying fishes with the scant literature available in South Africa at the time was a difficult task, and Smith eventually gave up his academic career in chemistry to devote himself to fish research. The discovery of the coelacanth in 1938 and its description as a new species by Smith made him world famous as an ichthyologist. In 1945 Smith was asked to produce a book on the sea fishes of southern Africa. With the help of his wife Margaret, and a team of artists, the book *The Sea Fishes of Southern Africa* was published in 1949. Smith continued his productive career in ichthyology until his death in 1968. Although lacking formal training in ichthyology, Margaret Smith had learned much in her role as research assistant/artist, and with the assistance of Rhodes University and the South African Council for Scientific and Industrial Research, she established the JLB Smith Institute of Ichthyology at Rhodes University.

As an angler, JLB Smith had a natural rapport with other anglers. Many anglers were encouraged to bring him interesting specimens. AR (Tony) Thorpe, a KZN attorney and avid angler, had a keen eye for identifying species and discovered three undescribed fish species in KZN waters. He supplied specimens and photographs for the description of these new species, which were named in his honour. Dave Bickell, a former angling correspondent for the *Eastern Province Herald*, discovered an unusual six-gill stingray on a beach in Port Elizabeth. This specimen was so different from all previously known stingrays that it was described as a new species, *Hexatrygon bickelli* Heemstra & Smith 1980, of a new genus and a new family. In 1981 Mark Pote, then a schoolboy, found an unusual puffer in a tide pool at Port Alfred and brought the fish to Margaret Smith in Grahamstown. It also represented a new species, *Pelagocephalus marki* Heemstra & Smith 1981. Jessica and Len Jones, active in the spearfishing community of KZN, found the previously unnamed Natal fingerfin, *Chirodactylus jessicalenorum*. Allan Connell, a marine biologist in Durban, collected specimens of the previously unknown harlequin

Figure 21 *A rare blackblotch swallowtail,* Holanthias caudicinctus *Heemstra & Randall 1986, known from eight specimens off Kenya, and one specimen each from KZN and the Eastern Cape; an undescribed sole,* Zebrias *sp., known only from Aliwal Shoal.*

goldie, *Pseudanthias connelli* (Heemstra & Randall 1986). Dennis King, engineer, underwater photographer and author of photographic books on South African fish, was involved in the discovery of the tiger angelfish, *Apolemichthys kingi*. Guido Zsilavecz, a computer specialist, enhanced his scuba diving with underwater photography and studies of the fish that he was observing. His detailed observations of the clinid fish of the Western Cape led him to describe a new species, the bluespot clinid, *Pavoclinus caeruleopunctatus*. Many other fish previously unknown in our area have been documented photographically by keen fish watchers. New range extensions of fish distributions have been recorded by fishermen or scuba divers with specimens and photographs. Sport divers Sally and Dennis Polack and dive charter operators Mark Addison and Neville Ayliffe have found several new records of fish not previously known for South Africa on their dives at Aliwal Shoal and Sodwana Bay. They, like many other self-taught ichthyologists, have made invaluable contributions to our knowledge of fishes.

WANTED: RARE AND INTERESTING FISH

If you catch or photograph a rare or unusual fish, or a fish species not previously seen in your area or the locality that you happen to be visiting, please send the specimen or a copy of the photograph – or better still, a photograph and the fish to the marine ichthyologists at SAIAB. Take a clear colour photograph of the fish as soon as possible after capture as colour fades or alters with stress and death. Please freeze the fish as soon as is convenient. Small fish are best frozen in water in a plastic container (margarine or ice cream tub).

You can leave the specimens and/or photographs at the South African Institute for Aquatic Biodiversity (SAIAB), Somerset Street/Private Bag 1015, Grahamstown. Tel (046) 603 5800.

If you cannot manage to visit SAIAB, you can hand in specimens at the following locations:

KZN:
- Oceanographic Research Institute (ORI) at uShaka Marine World, Point Precinct, Durban. Tel (031) 337 3536.

Eastern Cape:
- Port Elizabeth Museum at Bayworld, Beach Road, Humewood, Port Elizabeth. Tel (041) 584 0650;
- East London Museum, Oxford Street, East London. Tel (043) 743 0686;
- East London Aquarium, Esplanade, East London. Tel (043) 705 2637.

Western Cape:
- The South African Museum (Iziko Museums), 25 Queen Victoria Street, Gardens, Cape Town. Tel (021) 424 3330;
- The Two Oceans Aquarium, Dock Road, Victoria & Alfred Waterfront, Cape Town. Tel (021) 418 3823.

Please remember to supply the date, locality, collector or photographer, depth and method of capture. If you have any comments on the condition of the sea or observe any interesting fish behaviour, include that too. Along with the specimen, provide your contact name and details with a note asking that the specimen be forwarded to SAIAB in Grahamstown.

FISH TAGGING

There are many fish that have been tagged in South African waters as part of the Sedgwick's/ORI/WWF-SA national tagging programme. If by any chance you should catch a fish with a tag in it or see someone else catch a tagged fish, it is very important that you record the following information: the species of the fish, its length (specify total, fork or standard length), the tag number (printed on the tag), the locality where the fish

was caught, the name and address of the angler who caught it and the postal address on the tag if you wish to release the fish again. By recording this information and posting it to the Tagging Officer, ORI, PO Box 736, Durban 4000, you will be making a valuable contribution to this important programme that is helping us learn more about the movement patterns, growth and mortality rates of our line-fish species. In return you will be sent information about where the fish was originally tagged, how far it has moved during its time at liberty and how much it has grown. If you are a keen angler and would like to become involved in the tagging programme, you can contact the Tagging Officer at the above address for more information.

FISH TAGGING

Ichthyologist and keen angler Paul Cowley with a tagged black musselcracker. Note the yellow spaghetti tag near the dorsal fin. Fish tags range from simple numbered waterproof plastic discs or slender tubes with a barb at one end to sophisticated electronic tags that can record movements (distance and depth travelled, swimming speed, number of visits to a particular place, etc.), temperature of the water as well as the internal body temperature of the fish.

(Photograph P Cowley)

THE term 'Chondrichthyes' is derived from the Greek words for cartilage and fish. The chondrichthyan fishes (comprising sharks, batoids, chimaeras and elephantfish) are differentiated from the bony fishes by having a skeleton that is completely cartilaginous. The load bearing parts (jaws, fins, vertebrae, etc.) of cartilaginous fishes are calcified but differ from the porous bone in other animals. The eggs are fertilised inside the body of the female by means of paired intromittent organs (claspers) at the medial edge of the pelvic fins of the male. The term 'claspers' is a misnomer, as these organs are actually used to transfer sperm into the oviducts of the female during copulation.

The Class Chondrichthyes is divided into two subclasses. The sharks and batoids (Subclass Elasmobranchii) have 5–7 pairs of gill openings (slits), the upper jaw movably articulated with the cranium, and separate teeth (fused into tooth plates in a few species). The chimaeras and elephantfish (Subclass Holocephali) have one pair of gill slits, upper jaw fused to the cranium, and teeth fused into solid dental plates.

SUBCLASS ELASMOBRANCHII
Sharks & Batoids (Skates, Rays, etc.)

IDENTIFICATION

Many elasmobranchs are difficult to identify because they have few external features by which species may be distinguished, and these features change with growth. Colour is often uniform or variable in one species, and may change considerably from juvenile to adult. Many species are large and not easily captured, and few museums have facilities to accommodate them. Consequently, for many species, there are no adequate series of specimens to illustrate growth changes and sexual dimorphism.

CLASSIFICATION

There are about 1 100 living species of elasmobranchs. Our present concept of evolutionary relationships and classification of elasmobranchs has changed fundamentally in the past 15 years. The traditional scheme of two superorders, Squalomorphii (sharks) and Batoidea (rays, skates, guitarfish, sawfish, electric rays, etc.), has been replaced by a hierarchy of nine orders, with batoids assigned to the Order Rajiformes, one of five orders in the Superorder Squalomorphii.

Although higher-level relationships of the families, orders and superorders are important to understand the evolution of elasmobranchs (and bony fishes), the technical details of this aspect of ichthyology are beyond the scope of this introductory book.

For the pragmatic questions 'What fish (species) is this?' and 'How does it fit into the ecosystem?' we can focus on distinguishing species and families. For purposes of identifying elasmobranch species we can begin our query with 'Is this fish a shark or a batoid?' Sharks have 5–7 pairs of gill openings above or in front of the pectoral fins, 1 or 2 dorsal fins, and the anal fin may be present or absent. Batoids (skates, rays, etc.) are vertically flattened (depressed) fish with 5 or 6 pairs of gill openings on the underside of the head and the pectoral fins more or less fused to the head.

ELASMOBRANCH ANATOMY AND BIOLOGY

See introductory section (p. 17) for additional information on the anatomy and biology of cartilaginous fishes.

Scales

The skin of most elasmobranchs is densely covered with tiny scales called '**denticles**', although some batoid fish (electric rays and some stingrays) lack denticles. Teeth and denticles have a similar structure, with a core of dentine covered by a hard outer enamel layer. Most denticles, like teeth, do not grow larger after they are fully developed, and are continuously replaced by larger ones during the life of a shark. The shape and size of denticles vary from one place to another on the same shark, and also from one species to another.

A shark's skin feels very rough when it is stroked toward the head but smooth when stroked towards the tail. This is because the sharp tips of the denticles usually point posteriorly. Shark skin with the denticles removed has been used for leather, and the skin with denticles has been used as sandpaper.

Figure 22

Scanning electron micrograph of shark scales (denticles) from a hound shark. Magnification 60 X.

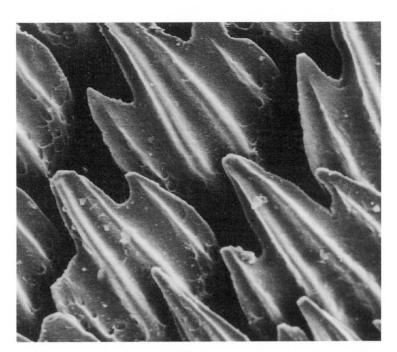

Figure 23 *Lateral view of a generalised shark to show external features.*

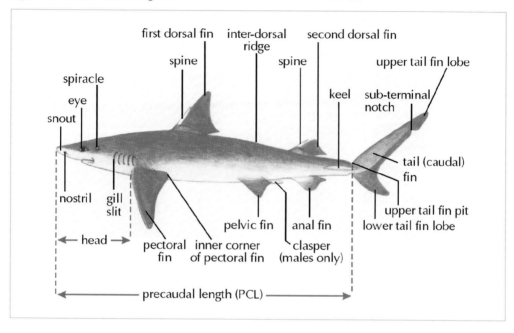

Figure 24 *Ventral view of smooth-hound shark head.*

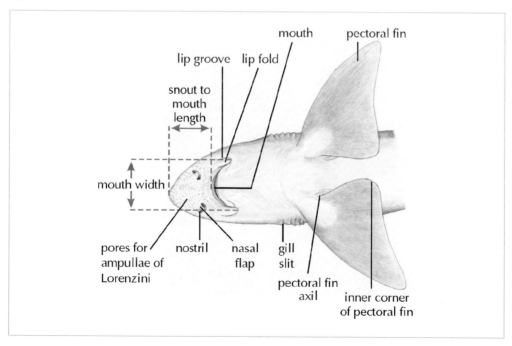

Figure 25 *Ventral (left) and dorsal (right) view of two male bluespotted ribbontail rays to show external features.*

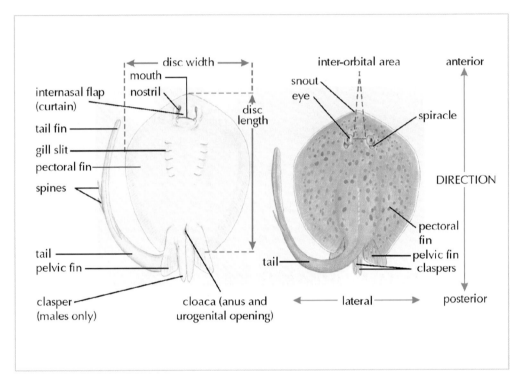

Teeth and feeding

Sharks have a life-long supply of teeth, as replacement teeth grow continuously on the inner surface of the jaws. If an outer tooth is lost, the next one in the row moves forward like a conveyor belt to take its place. Shark teeth are firmly anchored to a layer of tough connective tissue, not fixed in sockets in the jaws (as in most bony fishes). Tooth replacement rate has been determined to be about once a fortnight; thus a 20-year-old shark loses thousands of teeth during its lifetime. This accounts for the large numbers of shark teeth found near Raggies Cave at Aliwal Shoal in KZN.

The number and configuration of shark teeth are distinctive for each species and are useful for identification. Consequently, bite marks on a surfboard can usually be linked to a particular species, and some sharks can be identified from a single tooth.

Elasmobranch teeth come in three basic types:

■ broad compressed teeth (triangular in the great white shark, cockscomb-shaped in tiger sharks) well adapted for biting off pieces from large prey, e.g. seals;

■ long slender teeth (e.g. ragged-tooth sharks) suited for catching squid or fish that may be swallowed whole;

■ blunt molariform ('pavement') dentition (e.g. rays and smooth-hound sharks) useful for crushing the shells of molluscs and crustaceans.

Figure 26(a)

Three rows of shark teeth. The outer (first) functional series of teeth eventually falls out and is replaced by the second series in the line. New series of teeth are continuously forming on the inside of the jaws. Note that the rows of teeth run at right angles to the jaw.

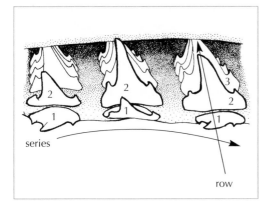

Figure 26(b)

Cross-section of a ragged-tooth shark jaw to show the 'conveyor belt' system of tooth replacement.

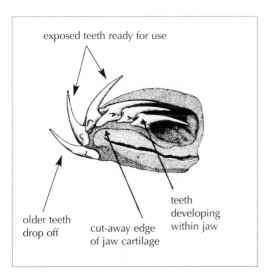

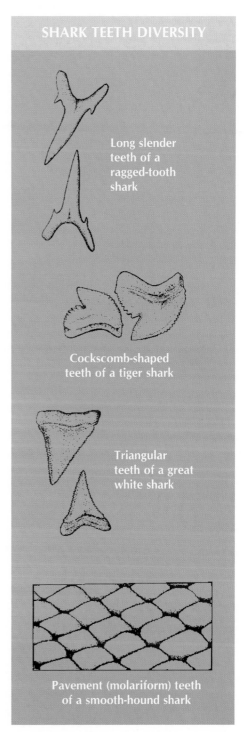

SHARK TEETH DIVERSITY

Long slender teeth of a ragged-tooth shark

Cockscomb-shaped teeth of a tiger shark

Triangular teeth of a great white shark

Pavement (molariform) teeth of a smooth-hound shark

Although the mouth of most sharks is on the underside of the head, it is unnecessary for them to roll over in order to bite their prey. When feeding, many sharks protrude their jaws, in some species beyond the snout, to bite their prey. Benthic-feeding sharks push their mouths down to grasp molluscs and crabs. For a shark that feeds on marine mammals or other large prey, the ability to open its mouth wide and protrude its jaws facilitates biting large pieces from its prey.

Fins

Shark fins are supported at the base by large, compressed, cartilaginous elements that articulate distally with **ceratotrichia**, slender filaments of an elastic protein similar to keratin and the principal ingredient of shark-fin soup. The ceratotrichia provide a strong flexible support for the fins. In most families of sharks and batoids there are no fin spines.

Reproduction

All elasmobranchs have internal fertilisation. At maturity, the claspers of males enlarge and become calcified, a visible sign that the fish is now an adult. Maturity in females is less obvious and usually requires dissection to check the state of the ovary. There are three different types of reproduction in elasmobranchs:

- **oviparous**, in which the embryo develops in a tough horny egg case after it is deposited on the bottom (e.g. catsharks);
- **ovoviviparous**, in which the embryos develop in membranous egg cases retained in the oviducts, and the pups (10 to 300 pups per litter) subsist on their own yolk until birth (e.g. tiger shark, whale shark, etc.);
- **viviparous**, in which the embryos develop in paired oviducts and receive additional nutrients from the mother; pups born at relatively large size (e.g. ragged-tooth sharks), and litters are small (~2–20 pups per litter) in most species.

Sensory abilities

Elasmobranchs have well developed senses of **smell**, **hearing** (including the related ability to detect low-frequency vibrations) and **vision**.

Most elasmobranchs also have a unique network of small flask-shaped sense organs called **ampullae of Lorenzini** on the underside of the snout. Each ampulla is connected to the sea by a small pore. Experiments with live sharks demonstrated

Figure 27
Catshark egg case.

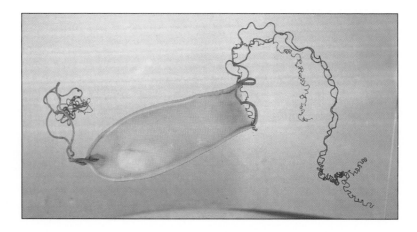

Figure 28
Birth of shortnose spiny dogfish pups. Note the cartilaginous cap on the tip of the fin spines to prevent damage to the mother during birth. The caps fall off soon after birth.

that the ampullae detect the weak electric field produced by contractions of respiratory muscles that are used to pump water over the gills of buried prey animals (e.g. crabs or fish). Benthic-feeding elasmobranchs are thus able to detect buried prey without being able to see or smell these animals.

Buoyancy

Although sharks and rays lack the gas-filled swimbladder that provides buoyancy in bony fish, they have developed other means to attain buoyancy. Sharks are less dense than most bony fish because their cartilaginous skeleton is not densely calcified; and they produce lightweight oils that are stored in the liver and provide buoyancy. The ragged-tooth shark also swallows air at the surface and uses its stomach as a buoyancy compensator.

Most rays do not have a buoyancy problem, as they spend most of their time on the bottom. The large active pelagic rays like mantas also do not have buoyancy problems, as their forward movement through the water provides lift to their wing-like pectoral fins.

Spiracle

Many elasmobranchs, mainly the benthic shark and batoid species, have an opening

behind each eye called a **spiracle**. This opening communicates with the gill chamber and is supposed to be the vestige of a gill slit of ancestral forms. The spiracle is absent or much reduced in pelagic species (e.g. mako, great whites, whale sharks, etc.), but well developed in demersal (bottom-living) sharks and batoids. In most benthic elasmobranchs, the spiracle is used to channel water over the gills as the mouth of these sedentary fish is usually in contact with sand or mud. A respiratory current coming in through the mouth of fish sitting on the bottom would soon cover the gills with sediment.

Spiral valve

All elasmobranchs have a **spiral valve** in their intestine. In most sharks the valve resembles a spiral staircase; in some elasmobranchs the

Figure 29 *Diagrammatic representation of a spiral valve in shark intestine.*

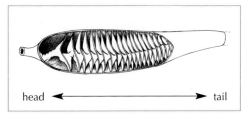

head ◄─────────────► tail

spiral valve is like a stack of elongated cones, one inside the other; and in requiem sharks, it looks like a scroll of rolled paper. Compared to a straight tubular intestine, the spiral valve provides a much greater surface area for the absorption of nutrients. This space-saving design allows sharks to consume more food at one time and also allows pregnant females to produce bigger litters with larger pups.

Movable eyelid

Pelagic sharks without a spiracle have a movable inner eyelid (**nictitans**) that can be pulled up to completely cover the eye. Sharks with a small spiracle, like the hound sharks (*Mustelus* spp), have a rudimentary nictitans that only partly covers the eye and is connected by a low groove to the lower eyelid. In sharks with a large spiracle, the nictitans is absent or replaced by a groove below the lower eyelid. The nictitans is not the same as the 'nictitating membrane' or movable third eyelid of birds.

Figure 30 Movable inner eyelids.

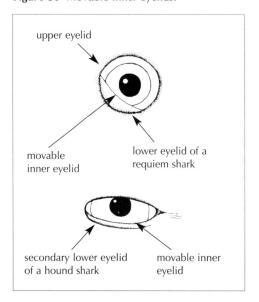

upper eyelid

movable inner eyelid

lower eyelid of a requiem shark

secondary lower eyelid of a hound shark

movable inner eyelid

ELASMOBRANCH FISHERIES

Sharks and rays are important resources exploited by trawlers, anglers and longline fisheries. Elasmobranchs are targeted and also taken as by-catch in some fisheries. The slow growth, late maturity and low fecundity (small litters) of most elasmobranchs make them vulnerable to over-exploitation and few species can support a sustainable fishery. Worldwide, elasmobranchs are threatened by overfishing. Many sharks caught in foreign longline fisheries are used for the lucrative shark-fin market. Catch statistics are often not reported in these high seas fisheries and the scarcity of many elasmobranch species is apparent but difficult to quantify. In southern African waters sharks and rays are caught in pelagic and bottom-set longline operations which are fished seasonally from tuna boats. Trawlers take elasmobranchs as a by-catch that may be discarded or marketed. Anglers also catch sharks and rays, but not all species are eaten.

SHARKS

Sharks (the non-batoid elasmobranchs) comprise ~500 diverse species, from a 25 cm adult dwarf shark, *Squaliolus laticaudus* Smith & Radcliffe 1912, to a ~14 m whale shark, the largest fish in the sea. Sharks occur in most habitats of the sea, from coastal waters to ocean depths of 4 000 m. Some sharks, e.g. Zambezi sharks and Ganges sharks, *Glyphis gangeticus* (Müller & Henle 1839), also occur in rivers and estuaries.

Sharks have 5–7 pairs of gill slits above or in front of the pectoral fins, 1 or 2 dorsal fins (with or without spines), the anal fin may be present or absent, and the eyeball is movable.

FAMILY HEXANCHIDAE ■ Cow Sharks

Body elongate, with **1 dorsal fin on rear part of body; anal fin present**; no fin spines; **6 or 7 pairs of gill slits extending onto underside of throat**; 1st pair of gill slits not joined ventrally; spiracles small, easily overlooked; no movable eyelid. Claspers sheathed by expanded inner margins of pelvic fins. Size range 1.4–5+ m.

Benthic sharks from shore to 1 900 m.

Circumglobal in tropical and temperate seas. Three genera, 4 species, all in our area.

Sixgill shark   Spotted sevengill shark

SIXGILL SHARK
Hexanchus griseus
(Bonnaterre 1788)

*97 cm immature
male (Japan)*

Six pairs of gill slits; snout short, its length 4–7% TL, 2.0–2.8 times in mouth width; dorsal fin base 1.1–1.4 times in distance from fin base to upper tail fin lobe; 6 rows of large comb-like teeth on each side of front of lower jaw plus ~14 rows of smaller teeth at rear of jaw, most of which are very small, probably not visible in live animals (especially if not sedated and participating willingly in the examination!). Brown to grey dorsally, slightly paler ventrally; eye lens luminous green. Attains 5+ m, 730+ kg.

Temperate and tropical waters of all oceans; eastern Atlantic to southern Mozambique; not in Red Sea.

Benthic species; juveniles inshore, adults usually near bottom in 100–1 900 m. Feeds on fish (sharks, dorado, swordfish, marlin, macrourids, hake, gurnards and monkfish), crustaceans, cephalopods and marine mammals. Adults in deep water are sluggish (probably because they are cold); juveniles from shallow water are more lively and may be dangerous. Females mature at 4.0–4.5 m, males at 3.5–4.0 m. Ovoviviparous, 22–108 pups per litter, 61–74 cm at birth.

Potentially dangerous, but not known to have attacked humans. Caught by trawlers, ski-boat anglers and occasionally by shore anglers; flesh edible. IGFA all-tackle record: 485 kg shark from the Azores.

The bigeye sixgill shark, *Hexanchus nakamurai* Teng 1962 [= *Hexanchus vitulus* Springer & Waller 1969], has snout length more than half mouth width and 5 rows of large teeth on each side of lower jaw. Attains 1.8 m, 36 kg. Known from 90–600 m in Atlantic, south-western Indian and western Pacific oceans, and off KZN.

SPOTTED SEVENGILL SHARK

Notorynchus cepedianus (Péron 1807)

1.8 m subadult female (Japan)

Seven pairs of gill slits; snout shorter than distance between lower ends of 1st pair of gill slits; **eye diameter less than inter-nostril distance**; 6 rows of large teeth on each side of upper and lower jaws; lower jaw teeth with 4–5 inclined cusps, upper teeth with 1–2 inclined cusps. Head and body russet to silvery grey or very pale, with **numerous black spots**. Attains 3 m, 182 kg.

Temperate waters of all oceans; Namibia to East London; not known from the Mediterranean or North Atlantic.

Benthic species from shore to 136 m. Feeds on elasmobranchs, bony fish, crustaceans, cephalopods, marine mammals and carrion. Generally cruises slowly near bottom, but is occasionally seen at surface; moves quickly when chasing prey, and may form hunting packs to catch seals. Females mature at ~2 m, 54 kg (11 years); males at 1.5–1.8 m,

17 kg (4–5 years). Ovoviviparous, 60–82 pups per litter, 45–53 cm at birth.

Caught by shore and boat anglers. SADSAA all-tackle record: 53.7 kg. Potentially dangerous but not known to attack humans. Has been kept in captivity. Excellent eating, although liver may be toxic due to high vitamin A content. Fished commercially in some areas; skin makes good quality leather.

The sharpnose sevengill shark, *Heptranchias perlo* (Bonnaterre 1788), has eye length greater than inter-nostril distance, mouth length subequal to its width and anal fin base much shorter than peduncle. Attains 137 cm. Worldwide in warm seas at depths of 50–1 000 m. Caught off Mozambique, KZN and Namibia.

FAMILY SQUALIDAE ■ Dogfish

Two dorsal fins with a spine at front of each fin; no anal fin; 5 pairs of gill slits; spiracles large; no movable eyelid; no fleshy keel on side of peduncle. Size range 20 cm to 1.2 m. Epipelagic and mesopelagic sharks from surface to near bottom in 600 m.

Worldwide in tropical to polar seas. Two genera with ~12 species, 5 in our area. (Several species that were included in the Squalidae in *Smiths' Sea Fishes* [Smith & Heemstra 1986] are now assigned to other families.)

SHORTNOSE SPINY DOGFISH
Squalus megalops
(Macleay 1881)

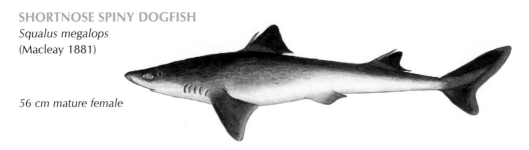

56 cm mature female

Second dorsal fin distinctly smaller than 1st dorsal fin; nasal flap with minute lobe; dorsal fin spines distinct and smooth (no lateral grooves); **1st dorsal fin spine over or in front of pectoral inner corner which is acute**; upper and lower jaw teeth similar with 1 cusp; distance from snout tip to inner end of nostril less than distance from inner end of nostril to lip groove; denticles lanceolate with single cusp. **Dark** brown or grey **above, paler below**; fins of juveniles dark grey with rear margins white; markings obscure in adults; eye lens luminous green. Attains 78 cm.

Southern Africa and Australia.

From shore to 500 m; usually near bottom; juveniles mainly pelagic over outer continental shelf. Feeds mainly on small bony fish, also crustaceans, cephalopods and worms. Occurs in large aggregations. Grows slowly; maximum ages of 32 years (78 cm) for females, 29 years (57 cm) for males. Females mature at 49–55 cm (15 years), males at 40 cm (9 years). Ovoviviparous, 2–4 pups per litter, 20–24 cm at birth; gestation period may be as long as 20 months. See p. 49 for photo of birth of the pups.

Probably the most abundant shark off southern Africa. Identification dubious, as South African specimens have not been critically compared with Australian material, which may be a different species. In Australia the fillets are sold fresh, dried, salted or smoked, but the liver may be toxic due to high vitamin A content. Taken in bottom trawls and by anglers.

SIMILAR SPECIES

The shortspine dogfish, *Squalus mitsukurii* Jordan & Fowler 1903, has distance from snout tip to inner end of nostril longer than distance from inner end of nostril to lip groove, and inner corner of pectoral fins more rounded. Worldwide, Namibia to Beira.

The piked dogfish, *Squalus acanthias* Linnaeus 1758, and the roughskin spurdog, *Cirrhigaleus asper* (Merrett 1973), have 1st dorsal fin spine behind vertical at inner corner of pectoral fin. *S. acanthias* has pointed snout and white spots. *C. asper* has a very rough skin, bluntly rounded snout, nasal flap with prominent lobe resembling a stubby barbel; 2nd dorsal fin subequal to 1st dorsal fin. *S. acanthias* occurs worldwide, Orange River mouth to the Eastern Cape. *C. asper* reported from western Atlantic and eastern central Pacific, Port Alfred to northern Madagascar.

FAMILY STEGOSTOMATIDAE ■ Longtail Shark

Tail fin longer than body, subequal to head plus body; 1st dorsal fin origin in front of pelvic fin origins; **anal fin larger than 2nd dorsal fin**; no fin spines; adult with prominent longitudinal ridges on body; mouth in front of eyes; 5 pairs of small gill slits, last 2 pairs close together; nostrils with barbels and joined to mouth by a groove; lower lip grooves separate; eye subequal to spiracle, which is behind eye; no movable eyelid. A single species.

LONGTAIL SHARK
Stegostoma fasciatum
(Hermann 1783)

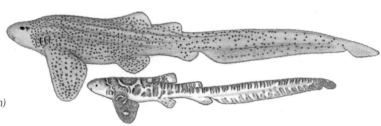

~ 1.2 m subadult
58 cm juvenile (Bahrain)

Adults with longitudinal ridges on body; juveniles 50–70 cm yellow or white with dark bars and spots, adults with dark spots. Attains 3.5 m.

Tropical Indo-West Pacific, Red Sea, Persian Gulf to Durban; rare south of KZN.

Coral and rocky reefs to 30 m. Feeds mainly at night on cephalopods, bivalves, gastropods, crustaceans and bony fish. Females mature at 170 cm, males at 150 cm. Oviparous, egg cases 13–17 × 8 cm, attached to substrate by hair-like fibres; young hatch at ~ 20 cm. Usually seen resting by day on the bottom. Juveniles in pursuit of prey swim fast, with eel-like undulations of body and tail.

Docile species that does well in captivity, and can be trained to take food from a diver's hand. Rarely eaten. Often called 'zebra shark' in allusion to the colour pattern of juveniles.

FAMILY RHINCODONTIDAE ■ Whale Shark

Head broad and flattened, with **huge terminal mouth** and minute teeth; **tail fin higher than dorsal fins**, lower lobe of tail fin more than half length of upper lobe; anal fin smaller than 2nd dorsal fin; no fin spines; eye behind corner of mouth; 5 pairs of large gill slits, last 2 pairs over pectoral fin bases; gill arches with internal filter screens; prominent **longitudinal ridges** on body of adult and distinct lateral keel along side of peduncle. A single species.

WHALE SHARK
Rhincodon typus
Smith 1828

3.5 m juvenile

Colour dark grey, bluish or brownish above, with grid-like pattern of white lines and spots. Largest of all fish, attains ~14 m, 36 tonnes.

Worldwide in tropical and temperate waters. Often seen along Mozambique and KZN coasts, rarely encountered off our south coast.

Coastal and oceanic, usually near surface. This huge pelagic shark is a suction filter-feeder that consumes macro-zooplankton, as well as schooling fish. Swims slowly, at or near the surface with its mouth open; sometimes assumes a vertical position and takes in huge mouthfuls of water (and prey) by bobbing up and down at the surface with its mouth open. In the mêlée of small tuna attacking a shoal of bait-fish surrounding a bobbing whale shark, some tuna were seen to leap out of the water and land in the open mouth of the shark! When feeding on dense concentrations of copepods at the surface, a juvenile whale shark was observed sweeping its head from side-to-side with its mouth wide open, almost as if it were vacuuming the surface of the water. Commercial fishermen sometimes use the presence of whale sharks as an indication of fish schools.

Adults usually solitary, occasionally in groups of 4 to 100. More often seen in summer in South Africa. Matures at ~9–10 m. Ovoviviparous, ~300 pups per litter. Egg cases are huge (30 × 14 × 9 cm) and resemble 'mermaid's purse' egg cases of catsharks, but lack tendrils for attaching the egg case to the bottom. A 10.6 m pregnant female with 300 pups was caught off Taiwan in 1996. The smaller pups (42–57 cm) were still contained in their egg case and had small yolk sacs attached to their chest. Some larger pups (58–64 cm), which had hatched from their egg case and had no external yolk sacs, were still alive, and a few survived their caesarean birth. Size at birth ranges from the 55 cm smallest free-living juvenile to 64 cm.

These enormous sharks are harmless. Divers often approach them but need to be careful that they are not hit by the powerful

tail fin, or are not inadvertently sucked into the mouth along with the shark's food. And divers should not touch their eyes (which are sensitive and movable).

Often accompanied by pilotfish, other juvenile kingfish, juvenile prodigal son and remoras. Some juvenile whale sharks have lived for several years in a large oceanarium in Japan; they are fed buckets of krill at the surface. The whale shark was fished commercially in Taiwan, where it was caught with harpoons and brought a high price.

The whale shark is listed as a Vulnerable species on the IUCN Red List. Killing of whale sharks is prohibited off the east coast of the USA, in the Maldives and Philippines. Recently listed on CITES Appendix II.

Figure 31
Anterior view of a whale shark head showing the slot-like half open terminal mouth.

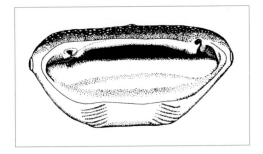

FAMILY CARCHARHINIDAE ■ Requiem Sharks

Two dorsal fins without spines; anal fin present; lower tail fin lobe $^1/_3$ to $^1/_2$ length of upper lobe; precaudal pits (depression in skin of peduncle at origin of upper and lower tail fin lobes) present; 5 pairs of gill slits, last pair over or behind pectoral fin origins; spiracles small or absent; movable lower eyelid well developed; mouth extends below eyes. Due to the upturned tail fin of some species, measurements of total length are less accurate than **precaudal length** (**PCL**), measured from tip of snout to origin of upper tail fin lobe. Size range 1.0–7.4 m TL.

Mainly neritic, a few species found in rivers and 2 species are truly oceanic.

Worldwide. About 12 genera, ∼50 species, 23 in our area.

Bronze whaler

Spinner shark

Zambezi shark

Dusky shark

Tiger shark

Blue shark

Milk shark

BRONZE WHALER
Carcharhinus brachyurus
(Günther 1870)

~1.8 m juvenile

First dorsal fin origin over inner edge of pectoral fin; 2nd dorsal fin height ~1/3 1st dorsal fin height; 2nd dorsal fin origin over anal fin origin; no inter-dorsal ridge; inter-dorsal distance more than twice 1st dorsal fin height; upper teeth with narrow oblique cusps and minute serrations; 15 teeth on each side of jaws; lip folds rudimentary. **Usually dark brownish grey or bronzy; fins plain or pectoral fins with slightly dusky tips.** Attains 2.9 m (females live 25 years and males 30 years).

Warm temperate waters of all oceans. Common from Namibia to KZN; follows the Sardine Run into KZN.

Coastal species, usually near bottom from shore to 100 m. Feeds on benthic and pelagic fish, also cephalopods. Often occurs in pairs. Females mature at 2.4 m, males at 2.0 m. Viviparous, 13–20 pups per litter, gestation ~12 months, born at 60–70 cm.

Reputed to be dangerous; no confirmed attacks on humans in southern African waters. Often caught by shore anglers and trawlers. IGFA all-tackle record: 242 kg shark from New Zealand. Juveniles excellent eating; produces good biltong. Also known as 'copper shark'.

SIMILAR SPECIES

The bignose shark, *Carcharhinus altimus* (Springer 1950), has 1st dorsal fin origin closer to pectoral axil than to inner corner of pectoral fin. Tropical waters, juveniles known from KZN and the Eastern Cape.

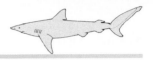

SPINNER SHARK
Carcharhinus brevipinna
(Müller & Henle 1839)

*1.8 m immature
male (Japan)*

Snout pointed, its length greater than mouth width; 1st dorsal fin origin over pectoral inner corner; 2nd dorsal fin origin over anal fin origin; no inter-dorsal ridge; **inter-dorsal distance more than twice height of 1st dorsal fin;** precaudal pits present; no keel on peduncle; upper jaw teeth with narrow, finely serrate, erect cusps; 16 teeth on each side of upper and lower jaws; upper lip folds distinct. Adults bronzy grey above, usually with clearly demarcated **black tips on fins,** but not on pelvic fins; newborn pups lack black fin tips. Attains 2.8 m.

Tropical and subtropical waters of Atlantic and Indo-West Pacific, Red Sea, Oman to the Eastern Cape. Common off KZN, extends south to Algoa Bay in summer.

Usually near surface; occasionally to 75 m. Feeds on elf, kingfish, mullet, kob and cephalopods and occasionally on benthic fish. Usually in fast-moving groups chasing schools of prey; renowned for their swift attacks, which sometimes result in the shark spiralling out of the water (hence 'spinner shark'). Females mature at 2.0 m, males at 1.8 m. Viviparous, 3–20 pups per litter, born in autumn at 65–75 cm after 12–15 month gestation. Pups are dropped along the KZN coast; juveniles are found off the Eastern Cape, rarely to Mossel Bay.

Unlikely to be dangerous to humans. Caught by anglers. SADSAA all-tackle record: 122.5 kg. Used for food, hides, fins and liver oil.

SIMILAR SPECIES

The blacktip shark, *Carcharhinus limbatus* (Müller & Henle 1839), has inter-dorsal distance less than 2.2 times 1st dorsal fin height and black fin tips not clearly demarcated. Tropical waters worldwide, KZN to the Western Cape.

ZAMBEZI SHARK
Carcharhinus leucas
(Müller & Henle
1839)

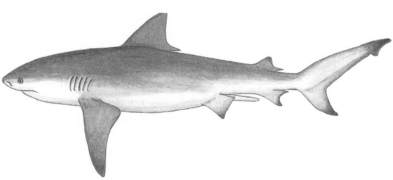

2.4 m mature male
(Australia)

Snout short, broadly rounded, its length about half mouth width; 1st dorsal fin origin over pectoral inner edge; 2nd dorsal fin origin over or in front of anal fin origin; 1st dorsal fin height about twice height of 2nd dorsal fin; no inter-dorsal ridge; body robust, depth contained ~4.5 times in precaudal length; inter-dorsal distance about twice height of 1st dorsal fin; precaudal pits present; no keel on peduncle; upper jaw teeth broad, triangular and distinctly serrate; 13 teeth on side of upper jaw, 12 on side of lower jaw; upper lip folds rudimentary. Juveniles with dusky fin tips, adult fin tips plain. Attains 3.4 m (50+ years).

> Worldwide in tropical and warm temperate waters; mainly continental coasts and large island groups; Red Sea, Oman to Cape St Francis; rare south of KZN.

Shallow water species, often found in surf; young in coastal lagoons, turbid estuaries and rivers, sometimes far from the sea. Feeds on variety of fish (including sharks and rays), crustaceans, echinoderms, molluscs, sea turtles, marine mammals, birds and occasionally garbage. Grows slowly, matures at ~1.9 m PCL (~20 years) for both sexes. Viviparous, 6–13 pups per litter, born at 75–80 cm after gestation of 10–11 months. A Zambezi shark lived in the oceanarium in Durban for over 20 years.

Large dangerous shark, a.k.a. 'bull shark'; known to attack humans. IGFA all-tackle record: 317 kg from Kenya. Used for meat, hides, fins, liver oil and fish meal. Also a valuable tourist attraction; seen by divers at Protea Bank off Shelly Beach, KZN.

SIMILAR SPECIES

The Java shark, *Carcharhinus amboinensis* (Müller & Henle 1839), has 1st dorsal fin height more than 3.1 times 2nd dorsal fin height. Indo-West Pacific, south to KZN.

DUSKY SHARK
Carcharhinus obscurus
(Lesueur 1818)

~2 m juvenile

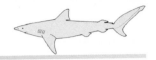

Snout length subequal to mouth width; **1st dorsal fin origin over pectoral inner corner; 2nd dorsal fin height distinctly less than least depth of peduncle, ~1/4 height of 1st dorsal fin**; 2nd dorsal origin over anal fin origin; precaudal pits present; no keel on peduncle; inter-dorsal ridge present; inter-dorsal distance more than twice height of 1st dorsal fin; upper jaw teeth broad, triangular and distinctly serrate; upper lip folds rudimentary. Fin tips of juveniles dusky, less apparent in adults. Attains 4.2 m (~32 years).

Continental coasts in warm temperate and tropical waters of all oceans; Western Cape to Mozambique and Madagascar.

Adults usually in 200–400 m; juveniles in shallow water and common in surf zone in summer. Predator/scavenger feeding on a variety of fish (including sharks and rays), crustaceans, molluscs and dead marine mammals. Females mature at 2.6–3.0 m, males at ~2.8 m. Viviparous, 6–14 pups per litter, gestation 8–16 months, born at 80–90 cm. Pups born in early winter off KZN. Migratory species, follows the Sardine Run northwards in winter and returns to the south coast in summer.

Potentially dangerous, but few verified attacks. IGFA all-tackle record: 347 kg from Florida, USA. Juveniles good eating and of commercial importance in Australia.

SIMILAR SPECIES

The bronze whaler (see p. 57) is darker grey, usually in larger groups and prefers colder water.

The sandbar shark, *Carcharhinus plumbeus* (Nardo 1827), has 1st dorsal fin height less than 2.2 times in distance from snout tip to dorsal fin origin. Worldwide in tropical and subtropical waters, south to Algoa Bay.

TIGER SHARK
Galeocerdo cuvier
(Péron & Lesueur 1822)

82 cm juvenile
3 m mature female
(Marshall Islands)

Head broad, snout bluntly rounded, very short, its length about half width of mouth; upper lip folds long, reaching forward to below eye; low keel along side of peduncle; pectoral fins shorter than head or upper tail lobe; teeth cockscomb-shaped (large, coarsely serrate with strongly curved cusp), similar in both jaws. Juveniles with numerous distinct irregular dark spots, becoming **vertical bars** in sharks up to 3 m and fading in larger adults. Attains 5.5 m, 900+ kg (at least 29 years). An unverified report (based on a photograph) of a 7.4 m tiger shark from Vietnam.

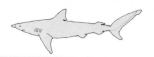

Worldwide in tropical waters; moves into higher latitudes in summer; rare off the Eastern Cape.

Ranges throughout water column, from shore to at least 350 m. Females mature at 2.5–3.5 m (11 years), males at 2.3–3.0 m (6–8 years). The tiger shark is the only ovoviviparous species (pups without placenta) in the family; 10–82 pups per litter, born at 51–76 cm, gestation 13–16 months; pups double their length in their first year. Notorious for the variety of edible and inedible items that it consumes. Feeds mainly on fish (including sharks and rays), sea snakes, sea birds, crustaceans, turtles, molluscs, marine mammals, carrion, garbage, etc.

Dangerous species, generally lethargic, but moves swiftly when attacking prey. Its large curved teeth leave identifiable wounds; responsible for several fatal attacks particularly in warm clear water around tropical islands. IGFA all-tackle record: 807 kg shark from South Carolina, USA. Tiger sharks are spectacular residents in large oceanariums, but usually die after a few months in captivity. Flesh edible, although liver may be toxic from high level of vitamin A. Skin makes excellent leather; jaws and teeth are often sold as curios. Tiger sharks are a valuable tourist attraction at Aliwal Shoal, where they are seen by divers in winter.

BLUE SHARK
Prionace glauca
(Linnaeus 1758)

2.8 m mature male

Head, body and pectoral fins elongate; **1st dorsal fin origin about midway between origins of pectoral and pelvic fins; pectoral fin length equal to or longer than head or upper tail lobe of adults**; teeth coarsely serrate, upper jaw teeth with broad curved cusp; no inter-dorsal ridge; no keel on peduncle; lip folds minute. Blue colour fades to grey soon after death. Attains 3.8 m, 250 kg.

Worldwide in tropical and temperate seas.

Favours water of 12–16° C; in tropical areas, blue sharks occur offshore in 80–350 m, but in temperate waters (off the Western Cape) they move closer to shore and near the surface. Matures at 2 m (~4–6 years); a 3 m blue shark is ~10 years old. Viviparous, 35–135 pups per litter, born at 40–50 cm, gestation 9–12 months. The thicker skin of females protects them from mating bites of males. Tagging studies show long distance movements (trans-Atlantic migrations and also Tasmania to Java). Feeds mainly on pelagic fish (including small sharks), squid, pelagic red crabs and dead cetaceans.

Potentially dangerous to man, but usually not aggressive. IGFA all-tackle record: 239 kg shark from Massachusetts, USA. Often taken in by-catch of pelagic longline fishery; fins marketed for soup; flesh and hide also used in some countries. Hardy species, usually survives stress of capture and tagging for study of its biology.

MILK SHARK
Rhizoprionodon acutus
(Rüppell 1837)

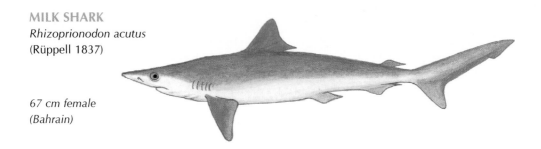

67 cm female
(Bahrain)

First dorsal fin origin over or behind inner corner of pectoral fins; **2nd dorsal fin origin over middle or rear half of anal fin base**; snout length greater than mouth width; lip folds subequal to nostril length; teeth similar in both jaws, usually smooth (weakly serrate in large adults) with oblique cusp; 12 teeth on side of upper jaw and 11 on side of lower jaw; no spiracles, inter-dorsal ridge or notch at rear edge of orbit. Bronze or greyish; dorsal and upper tail lobe tips dusky in juveniles and some adults. Attains 1.1 m.

> Tropical eastern Atlantic, Indo-West Pacific, Red Sea, Oman to Algoa Bay. Not at oceanic islands of Indian Ocean or central Pacific.

Continental shelf, from shore to 200 m; sometimes found in brackish water. Feeds on pelagic and benthic bony fish, cephalopods, gastropods and crustaceans. Matures at 70–80 cm. Viviparous, 2–8 pups per litter, gestation ~12 months, born at 35–40 cm.

Abundant species; the population off KZN has apparently increased in recent years as a result of the shark nets, which remove large sharks that are their major predator. Caught by shore anglers and from boats, also taken by trawlers. IGFA all-tackle record: 5 kg shark from West Africa. Used for food and fish meal in some countries. The name 'milk shark' comes from India, where this shark is eaten by women to promote lactation.

SIMILAR SPECIES

Very similar to *Rhizoprionodon terraenovae* (Richardson 1836) of western North Atlantic.

The sliteye shark, *Loxodon macrorhinus* Müller & Henle 1839, has a small notch in rear edge of orbit and inter-nostril distance subequal to mouth width. Indo-West Pacific, south to central KZN.

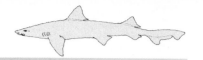

FAMILY TRIAKIDAE ■ Hound Sharks

Two dorsal fins without spines; 1st dorsal fin in front of pelvic fins; tail fin not lunate; precaudal pits and caudal keels absent; 5 pairs of gill slits, last pair over or behind pectoral fin origins; spiracles small; no barbel on front edge of nostrils; intestine with spiral valve. Size range 50 cm to 2 m.

Coastal species, usually near bottom.

Worldwide in tropical and temperate waters. Seven genera, ~38 species, 7 in our area.

Soupfin shark

Smooth-hound

Spotted gullyshark

SOUPFIN SHARK
Galeorhinus galeus
(Linnaeus 1758)

1.3 m
mature male

Snout pointed, length greater than mouth width; tail fin tip subequal to half length of upper lobe; 2nd dorsal fin height subequal to anal fin height and less than half length of tail fin tip; front edge of 2nd dorsal fin shorter than lower tail fin lobe; 1st dorsal fin origin over inner corner of pectoral fins; upper lip folds less than half mouth width; teeth blade-like, with large oblique cusp and some smaller cusplets along lateral (posterior) edge. Juveniles with black tips on fins. Attains 1.9 m (55 years).

Temperate waters of Southern Hemisphere, eastern North Atlantic and eastern North Pacific; Namibia to East London.

Benthic species occurring from shore to 500 m. Feeds on a variety of fish, cephalopods and crustaceans. Often schools by sex and size. Tagging studies indicate migrations of up to 2 500 km. Females mature at 1.3 m (8–10 years), males at ~1.2 m. Ovoviviparous, 6–52 pups per litter, gestation ~12 months, born at 30 cm. Females give birth near shore during summer, producing only one litter every 3 years.

Caught by anglers, commercial line-boats and trawlers. IGFA all-tackle record: 33 kg shark from New Zealand. Although the liver is toxic from high level of vitamin A, the meat is dried, salted and sold as shark biltong in

South Africa. Recent declines in catches from Argentina and southern Brazil indicate it is being overfished there. Also called 'tope'.

SIMILAR SPECIES

The lesser soupfin shark, *Hypogaleus hyugaensis* (Miyosi 1939), has 2nd dorsal fin height 1.5 times anal fin height and more than half length of tail fin tip. Attains ~ 1.3 m. This demersal species occurs in 40–230 m. Teeth similar in shape to those of the soupfin shark. Indo-West Pacific, Kenya to KZN. Not common in our area.

SMOOTH-HOUND
Mustelus mustelus
(Linnaeus 1758)

1.4 m mature female

Snout rounded, length slightly greater than mouth width; **2nd dorsal fin height greater than anal fin height and equal to length of tail fin tip**; origin of 1st dorsal fin over pectoral inner corner; 2nd dorsal fin origin distinctly ahead of anal fin origin; teeth with low, bluntly rounded cusp; length of upper lip folds 1.5–2.0% TL and 1.3–2.0 times in distance between nostrils; distance from 2nd dorsal fin base to tail fin origin 1.9–2.4 times in length of upper tail fin lobe. Usually grey, some sharks with a few scattered dark spots. Attains at least 1.7 m, 25 kg (~ 24 years).

Mediterranean and West Africa to Namibia, around our south coast to Durban.

From shore to 350 m; usually over sandy bottom. Benthic species, feeds mainly on crabs, lobsters, prawns, mantis shrimp, cephalopods and bony fish. Females mature at 1.3–1.4 m (12–15 years), males at 95 cm to 1.3 m (6–9 years). Viviparous, 4–23 pups per litter, born at 35–42 cm. In latter half of gestation period, pups are nourished by a placental connection with mother.

Caught by shore and ski-boat anglers. SADSAA all-tackle record: 25.4 kg. Good eating, but little used in South Africa; flesh exported to Australia, Europe and Africa; fins of large specimens are exported to Far East. This slow-growing, late-maturing species is vulnerable to overfishing.

SIMILAR SPECIES

The whitespotted smooth-hound, *Mustelus palumbes* Smith 1957, usually has small white spots on body, upper lip folds 2.0–2.4% TL and 1.0–1.4 times in inter-nostril distance. Endemic, Walvis Bay to northern KZN.

The hardnosed smooth-hound, *Mustelus mosis* Hemprich & Ehrenberg 1899, has distance from 2nd dorsal fin base to tail fin origin 1.7–2.0 times in length of dorsal tail fin lobe. Western Indian Ocean, Red Sea to Durban.

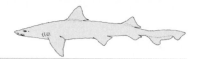

SPOTTED GULLYSHARK
Triakis megalopterus
(Smith 1839)

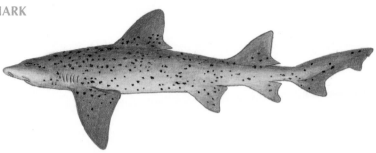

1.5 m
mature female

Robust heavy-bodied shark with large fins; 2nd dorsal fin almost at large as 1st, and its origin well in advance of anal fin; snout bluntly rounded, its length less than mouth width; lip folds prominent; mouth length less than half its width; teeth small with a narrow erect cusp; spiracles and inter-dorsal ridge present. **Usually with numerous small black spots**, but small juveniles and some adults with few or no spots. Attains 1.8 m, 50 kg (~21 years).

Endemic, Walvis Bay to Coffee Bay, rarely to southern KZN.

Sandy and rocky bottom from shore to 50 m; occasionally in estuaries. Feeds on crustaceans and fish (including small sharks). Females mature at 1.3–1.5 m (~16 years), males at 1.2–1.4 m (~13 years). Ovoviviparous, 6–12 pups per litter, born at 30–31 cm.

Commonly caught by shore anglers, but rarely eaten. SA angling record: 40 kg. The slow growth, late maturity, low fecundity and accessibility of its inshore habitat make the spotted gullyshark vulnerable to overfishing.

FAMILY SCYLIORHINIDAE ■ Catsharks

Two dorsal fins without spines; 1st dorsal fin origin over or behind pelvic fin origins; anal fin base longer than 2nd dorsal fin base; lower tail fin lobe indistinct; no precaudal pits or pairs of keels; 5 pairs of gill slits, last pair over or behind pectoral fin origins; nictitans rudimentary; spiracles small, close behind eye; teeth multi-cuspid, in several functional series and alike in both jaws. Most species oviparous. Size range 30 cm to ~1.6 m.

Usually found on or near bottom from shore to depths below 2 000 m. Small sluggish sharks, most species restricted to the shallow, cool water, benthic habitats of our south coast; the warm subtropical habitats to the north act as a barrier to dispersal of catsharks and account for the high degree of endemism in this family.

Worldwide in tropical and temperate waters. About 17 genera, ~100 species, 16 in our area and 11 species are endemic.

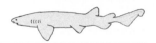

| Tiger catshark | Puffadder shyshark | Pyjama shark |

TIGER CATSHARK
Halaelurus natalensis
(Regan 1904)

44 cm mature female

Snout depressed, with distinct upturned knob at tip; anal fin origin well behind 1st dorsal fin; upper and lower lip grooves well developed; nostrils without barbels, separate from mouth; jaws with 3–4 functional series of small tricuspid teeth; inter-dorsal distance less than 3 times 1st dorsal fin height. **Pale with dark dorsal saddles.** Attains 48 cm.

Endemic, known only from False Bay to East London. The KZN type locality (indicated by the name) appears to be in error.

Benthic species found from shore to 172 m. Feeds on small fish (including sharks and rays), crustaceans, molluscs and worms. Matures at 37–41 cm. Oviparous, with 12–22 egg cases found in gravid females. Embryo ~45 mm when egg case is laid, but size at hatching is unknown. Egg case 40 × 15 mm, with tendrils for attachment to sessile organisms on the bottom.

Abundant species caught by anglers and trawlers.

SIMILAR SPECIES

The banded catshark, *Halaelurus lineatus* Bass, D'Aubrey & Kistnasamy 1975, has inter-dorsal distance 3.1–3.6 times height of 1st dorsal fin, lower edge of tail fin concave, and numerous small dark spots on body. Endemic, East London to Beira.

PUFFADDER SHYSHARK
Haploblepharus edwardsii
(Schinz 1822)

48 cm mature female

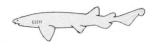

Dorsal fins of equal size; anal fin origin well behind 1st dorsal fin; nostrils connected to mouth by deep groove covered by broad nostril flap; no barbel on nostrils; snout short and thick, length equal to half mouth width; lip grooves continuous round corners of mouth; teeth with 3–5 sharp-pointed cusps; upper jaw teeth of adult males longer and narrower than in females and immature males. Dorsal surface with several **dark-edged orange-brown saddles** and numerous white spots; sharks from KZN with dark brown saddles and irregular pale spots represent an undescribed species. Attains 60 cm.

Endemic, Langebaan Lagoon (Saldanha Bay) to Storms River; abundant along southwestern coast.

Benthic species, often seen sitting on sand near rocks in 3–15 m. Feeds on bony fish, crustaceans, squid and polychaete worms. Matures at 40–50 cm. Oviparous, with 2 egg cases laid at a time. Egg cases 30–50 × 15–30 mm, dark brown with faint lateral striping and velvet-like surface. Embryos ~10 cm at hatching.

Also known as 'happy Eddie'.

SIMILAR SPECIES

The endemic dark shyshark, *Haploblepharus pictus* (Müller & Henle 1838), occurring from Lüderitz to East London, is tawny with several dark saddles bearing pale spots; large adults mostly dark brown with faint dorsal saddles. Often misidentified as *H. edwardsii*, but *H. pictus* has a broader, more bluntly rounded snout and a more depressed head than *H. edwardsii*.

PYJAMA SHARK
Poroderma africanum
(Gmelin 1789)

72 cm mature female

Second dorsal fin smaller than 1st dorsal fin; anal fin origin below 1st dorsal fin; nostril barbels short, not reaching mouth; no groove from nostrils to mouth; snout length equal to half mouth width; lip grooves short; teeth tricuspid, no marked sexual dimorphism. **Head and body with dark longitudinal stripes dorsally**; stripes with pale centres in some subadults and adults. Attains ~1 m.

Endemic, Saldanha Bay to East London.

Benthic species on rocky reefs from shore to 100 m. Feeds mainly on crustaceans, molluscs, bony fish and worms. Nocturnal species resting in rocks and caves by day. Females mature at 65–72 cm, males at 58–76 cm. Oviparous, with 2 egg cases laid at a time. Egg cases 5 × 10 cm; embryo 14 cm at hatching.

Harmless shark, often taken by shore anglers and trawlers.

SIMILAR SPECIES

The leopard catshark, *Poroderma pantherinum* (Smith 1838), has long nasal barbels that reach to the mouth, and colour pattern of dark spots, rings or rosettes. Endemic, Western Cape to Eastern Cape, rarely in KZN.

FAMILY SPHYRNIDAE ■ Hammerhead Sharks

Head flattened and greatly expanded laterally, with eyes on ends of lateral expansions; 2 dorsal fins without spines; anal fin subequal to 2nd dorsal fin; lower tail fin lobe distinct, but upper lobe much longer; precaudal pits present; 5 pairs of gill slits, last 2 pairs over pectoral fins; nictitans well developed; no spiracles. Size range 0.9–6.1 m.

Neritic sharks occurring from surface to the bottom from shore to ~300 m.

Large hammerheads are dangerous, and will take speared fish from divers, but they are generally not aggressive. The widely expanded head provides greater manoeuverability and is used to bash stingrays and hold them against the bottom while the shark bites pieces from the ray. Hammerheads seem immune to stingray venom.

Worldwide in tropical and temperate waters. One genus with 8 species, 3 in our area.

SMOOTH HAMMERHEAD
Sphyrna zygaena
(Linnaeus 1758)

~70 cm
immature female

Front edge of head without median indentation; 2nd dorsal fin height less than peduncle depth; 1st dorsal fin height equals body depth; teeth with broad serrate cusps; 14 teeth on each side of both jaws. Attains 3.5 m.

Warm temperate waters of all oceans, rarely found in tropical areas; St Helena Bay to southern Mozambique.

Juveniles common along our south and east coasts where they occasionally enter estuaries; large adults offshore to 200 m. Feeds on pelagic and benthic fish, including pilchards, sea-catfish, rockcods, sharks, skates and rays; also cephalopods, shrimp and crabs. Females mature at ~2.6 m, males at 2.5 m.

Viviparous, 29–50 pups per litter, gestation 10–11 months, born at 50–60 cm.

Caught by shore and boat anglers and by trawlers. Adults uncommon inshore. IGFA all-tackle record: 165 kg shark from the Azores. Meat, fins, liver oil and hide are sold in some countries, but not used in our area.

SIMILAR SPECIES

The other two hammerheads in our area are worldwide tropical species, south to KZN. The great hammerhead, *Sphyrna mokarran* (Rüppell 1837), and the scalloped hammerhead, *Sphyrna lewini* (Griffith & Smith 1834), have a median indentation on front edge of head. The great hammerhead, which attains a length of 6 m, has a tall acute

1st dorsal fin (fin height > half length of upper tail fin lobe and > body depth); 2nd dorsal fin larger than anal fin, and rear edge of pelvic fins distinctly concave. The scalloped hammerhead has a lower 1st dorsal fin (fin height < half upper tail fin lobe); 2nd dorsal fin smaller than anal fin, and rear edge of pelvic fins straight.

Figure 32
Head profiles of
(1) smooth hammerhead;
(2) great hammerhead;
(3) scalloped hammerhead.

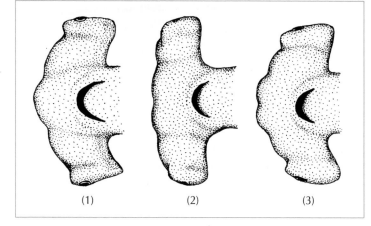

(1)　　　　(2)　　　　(3)

FAMILY LAMNIDAE ■ Mackerel Sharks

Tail fin lunate, lower lobe more than half length of upper lobe; peduncle flattened, with distinct lateral keels and precaudal pits; **2nd dorsal and anal fins much smaller than 1st dorsal fin**; no fin spines; 5 pairs of large gill slits, all in front of pectoral fins; no nictitans. The modified circulatory system of lamnid sharks keeps the body temperature warmer than the ambient water temperature and increases the metabolic rate, digestion of food and muscle power. Size range 3–7 m, 2 000 kg.

Swift, epipelagic and epibenthic sharks, occurring from surface to 1 280 m.

Worldwide. Three genera, 5 species, 4 in our area.

Great white shark

Shortfin mako

GREAT WHITE SHARK
Carcharodon carcharias
(Linnaeus 1758)

~ *4 m mature male*

Body robust, fusiform; 1st dorsal fin origin in front of pectoral inner corner; teeth large, triangular and coarsely serrate, but juveniles less than 1.5 m have lanceolate smooth-edged teeth with small basal cusps; snout bluntly conical, its length less than mouth width. Dark bluish grey or bronzy above, white below, with **sharp transition between dark upper colour and white underside**; pectoral fin tips dusky or black, often a black spot at axil of pectoral fins. Attains ~7 m (TL, with upper tail fin lobe bent to main body axis) and 2 000+ kg (females may live ~27 years).

> Worldwide in temperate and subtropical waters; rarely in tropical areas; mainly continental, with sporadic records from oceanic islands.

Usually inshore along our south and east coasts; occasionally offshore to depths of 130 m (exceptionally found at 1 280 m). Often congregates at seal or penguin colonies, offshore banks and estuary mouths. Juveniles less than 2.5 m feed on demersal and pelagic bony fish, cephalopods and crustaceans; adult white sharks prey on bony fish (numerous species, including tuna, marlin, barracuda and ocean sunfish), sharks, guitarfish, stingrays, eagle rays and marine mammals (mainly seals and dolphins).

Lacking a movable eyelid, the white shark protects its eyes by rolling them backwards when attacking its prey. Normally cruises at ~3 km/h, but can catch fast-swimming prey such as mako sharks, dolphins and seals. When chasing prey at the surface, this awesome predator sometimes erupts completely out of the water. The high metabolism and fast-swimming abilities of white sharks are (in part) consequences of their being warm-bodied fish, like the large tunas. A white shark was recorded with an internal body temperature of 27° C in water with an ambient temperature of 14° C.

Females mature at 4–5 m (12–14 years) and may attain 7 m; males mature at 3.5–4.0 m (9–10 years) and attain 5.5 m. Viviparous, with reports of 7–14 pups per litter, born at 1.2–1.7 m. Prenatal pups feed on nutritive eggs provided by the mother and this rich food supply accounts for their large birth size.

A bold and inquisitive shark that may attack people and has been responsible for several deaths of divers and swimmers. Although divers are often approached by white sharks, attacks are rare. In view of the slow growth and low fecundity of this species, unregulated angling and commercial fishing (such as open ocean gill-nets) threaten the future of white shark populations in some areas. Since 1991, the killing of white sharks

in South African waters has been prohibited; the species is also protected in Tasmania and New South Wales, USA (California and Florida) and Namibia. The white shark is listed as a Vulnerable species on the IUCN Red List. Tagging programmes are underway in South Africa to gather more information on white shark movements and population size.

SHORTFIN MAKO
Isurus oxyrinchus
Rafinesque 1810

~ 2.5 m immature female

Body fusiform; **1st dorsal fin origin behind or over pectoral inner corner; teeth lanceolate and smooth; pectoral fins distinctly shorter than head** (distance from snout tip to pectoral fin origin); snout conical, its length subequal to mouth width; mouth U-shaped; teeth at front of jaws with curved tips; teeth at front of lower jaw horizontal and protruding. Underside of head and body white. Attains 4 m, 600 kg.

Worldwide in tropical and temperate seas.

Pelagic, usually offshore from surface to 500 m; sometimes found just behind surf zone. Prefers water temperatures of 17–22° C. Females mature at 2.8 m, males at 2.0 m. Oviphagous (pups feed on eggs during gestation of 8–12 months); 2–16 pups per litter, born at ~70 cm. Feeds mostly on bony fish and squid; large adults also eat sharks, cetaceans and billfish. North Atlantic tagging studies revealed seasonal migrations and trans-Atlantic movements exceeding 3 920 km.

A famous game fish, readily jumping several times its length out of the water in pursuit of prey or when hooked (sometimes landing in the fisherman's boat). IGFA all-tackle record: 554 kg mako from Atlantic coast of USA. Dangerous when hooked or otherwise provoked, but seldom attacks swimmers or divers. Excellent eating, but most probably have dangerous levels of mercury in their flesh. Also used for oil, fins and hide; teeth used for curios.

SIMILAR SPECIES

The longfin mako, *Isurus paucus* Guitart Manday 1966, has pectoral fins equal to or longer than head, and teeth at front of jaw with straight tips. Worldwide in tropical waters, may be found off southern Africa.

FAMILY ALOPIIDAE ■ Thresher Sharks

Body fusiform; **tail fin upper lobe greatly elongate, 76–122% precaudal length**; 2nd dorsal and anal fins minute; no fin spines; pectoral fins longer than head; lower tail lobe short; pelvic fins large; teeth small, compressed and blade-like; 5 pairs of gill slits, last 2 pairs above pectoral fin bases; no movable eyelid. Size range 3.3–6.0 m.

Large active sharks of epipelagic and near-bottom habitats.

Worldwide. One genus, 3 species, all in our area.

THRESHER SHARK
Alopias vulpinus
(Bonnaterre 1788)

*~3.5 m mature
female (Australia)*

Body torpedo-shaped; **eyes small, not apparent in dorsal view of head**; inter-orbital area strongly arched; **no groove from eye to above gill slits**; eye diameter about half length of 1st gill slit; lip folds present at corners of mouth; teeth with single erect or slightly oblique cusp; pectoral fins falcate with narrow tip; tail fin upper lobe narrow, equal to or more than precaudal length. Brownish or blue-grey above; white on underside of body extending above pectoral fin bases. Attains 6+ m (~45 years).

Worldwide in temperate and tropical seas.

Coastal and offshore, adults from surface to 366 m; juveniles often found inshore. Feeds mainly on small schooling fish which are herded and stunned with the whip-like tail; also eats cephalopods, pelagic crustaceans and occasionally sea birds. Females mature at 3.5–4.0 m; males at ~3 m. Viviparous, pups feed on eggs during their 12-month gestation; 2–7 pups per litter, born at 1.2–1.6 m. Growth rapid, with 5 m attained at 9 years.

A fast powerful shark that sometimes leaps out of the water in pursuit of prey; often caught by anglers off the Western Cape. IGFA all-tackle record: 348 kg shark from New Zealand. Excellent eating, but little used in South Africa.

SIMILAR SPECIES

The smalltooth thresher, *Alopias pelagicus* Nakamura 1935, has upper tail fin lobe more narrow and longer (110–120% precaudal length), tooth cusp markedly oblique, with 1 or more small basal cusplets on posterolateral edge; teeth small, 41–45 rows in upper jaw; eyes large, orbit diameter subequal to length of 1st gill slit, inter-orbital area distinctly arched; no lip folds at corner of mouth. Head and body dark blue to grey dorsally, white ventrally, white not extending above pectoral fin bases. Indo-Pacific, south to KZN.

The bigeye thresher, *Alopias superciliosus* (Lowe 1840), has huge oval eyes, with orbits extending onto dorsal surface of head, interorbital area nearly flat; deep horizontal groove above gill slits; upper tail fin lobe ~75% precaudal length; no lip folds; head and body purplish grey or grey-brown dorsally, paler ventrally, pale colour of belly not extended above pectoral fin bases. Worldwide, Angola to KZN.

FAMILY ODONTASPIDIDAE ■ Ragged-tooth Sharks

Tail fin upper lobe much longer than lower lobe; 2nd dorsal and anal fins subequal; anal fin close to tail fin; body robust, depth about twice height of 1st dorsal fin; no fleshy keels on peduncle; upper precaudal pit present, lower absent; no fin spines; pectoral fins short and broad; 5 pairs of gill slits, last pair in front of pectoral fin origins; teeth narrow, awl-shaped, smooth; posterior teeth moderately compressed, blade-like; no spiracle or movable eyelid. Size range 3.1–4.3 m.

Benthic and epibenthic on continental shelf and slope, from shore to 1 600 m.

Worldwide in tropical and warm temperate waters. Two genera, 3 species, 2 in our area.

RAGGED-TOOTH SHARK
Carcharias taurus
Rafinesque 1810

1 m immature male

Dorsal and anal fins subequal; anal fin origin under middle of 2nd dorsal fin base; 1st dorsal fin closer to pelvic fins than to pectoral fin bases; snout length distinctly less than mouth width; most teeth with single small cusplet on each side at base of elongate central cusp; upper jaw with 3 rows of large teeth on each side of symphysis, then 1 or 2 much smaller teeth, followed posteriorly by 6 or 7 rows of large teeth and 3–15 rows of gradually smaller teeth. Head and body brownish or grey above, paler below; juveniles with dark brown spots which usually fade in adults. Attains 3.2 m (4.3 m in Australia).

Tropical and temperate waters of Atlantic, Indian and western Pacific oceans, mainly continental, including Canada, USA, southern Brazil to Argentina, Mediterranean, Canary and Cape Verde islands, west coast of Africa, Red Sea, Vietnam to China, Taiwan, Japan and Australia. Common off KZN and the Eastern Cape; rare off our west coast.

Benthic species occurring off sandy beaches, in estuaries and on coral or rocky reefs from shore to 190 m. Feeds mainly on fish which it can swallow whole; in addition to a variety of

demersal and pelagic bony fish, 'raggies' also eat sharks, skates, eagle rays, squid and crustaceans. Generally lethargic during the day (often retreating to caves and gullies), more active at night; occurs singly or in small groups or in aggregations of 20–80 sharks. Raggies sometimes work co-operatively to surround and concentrate schooling prey before attacking them. This shark swallows air at the surface to provide buoyancy and hang motionless in the water.

Seasonal migrations associated with reproduction; mating occurs off KZN in summer, pups born in Eastern Cape waters in spring and summer. Females mature at 2.4 m (6 years), males at 2.2 m (5 years). Viviparous, with 2 pups (one in each oviduct) in a litter. Fertilised egg is ~1 cm in diameter; the embryo's yolk supply is completely absorbed soon after it hatches in the oviduct at ~6 cm. At 10 cm, the pup has functional teeth, and it begins feeding on eggs and smaller siblings; at this stage, the mother's ovary increases production of nutritive eggs and swells to a massive 9 kg. During the rest of the 9–12 month gestation, the pup devours all siblings and nutritive eggs in its oviduct and grows to a birth size of ~1 m.

This docile, sluggish, slow-growing shark is ideal for public aquaria, and a male raggy has lived 17 years at the Durban oceanarium. The teeth are adapted for grasping and swallowing small prey, rather than cutting pieces from large prey (such as humans). Rarely bites swimmers or divers, but may be aggressive towards divers with speared fish.

Unregulated killing of ragged-tooth sharks by divers and anglers in Australia resulted in dramatic declines in the population off New South Wales. Despite protective legislation, the population has not shown signs of recovery (as of 2003). Raggies are eaten in Japan, and the liver oil and fins are also marketed. In Australia, the flesh was found to have mercury levels 10 times higher than permitted for human consumption. SADSAA all-tackle record: 191 kg.

SIMILAR SPECIES

The bumpytail ragged-tooth shark (a.k.a. 'smalltooth sandtiger'), *Odontaspis ferox* (Risso 1810), has snout longer than mouth width, 2nd dorsal fin noticeably smaller than 1st dorsal fin, anal fin origin below rear end of 2nd dorsal fin base, 1st dorsal fin origin over inner corner of pectoral fins; most teeth with 2–3 basal cusplets on each side of main cusp. Worldwide, found in 13–420 m; a few specimens trawled off KZN. Attains 4.2 m.

BATOIDS (SKATES, RAYS, ETC.) (ORDER RAJIFORMES)

The batoid group of elasmobranchs (skates, rays, guitarfish, sawfish, electric rays, numbfish, eagle rays, stingrays, sixgill stingrays and mantas) is a useful concept for identifying this group of depressed (vertically flattened) elasmobranchs. Most batoid species are benthic (demersal) fish that sit on the bottom or move close to the bottom when they are searching for food. Some batoids (e.g. manta rays, eagle rays and the pelagic stingray, *Pteroplatytrygon violacea*) have 'secondarily' adopted a pelagic lifestyle. (We assume that the first batoids were strictly demersal fish and that the pelagic species evolved later from these benthic ancestors.)

Batoids are distinguished by the following characters: head and body depressed, pectoral fins joined to head with 5 or 6 pairs of gill slits on the underside of the head, anal fin absent, and upper edge of orbit fused to eyeball.

FAMILY PRISTIDAE ■ Sawfish

Snout produced into a long saw with a row of stout teeth along each edge; head and front part of body depressed, flattened ventrally, rear half of body shark-like; 2 dorsal fins, 1st dorsal fin origin over or in front of pelvic fins; tail fin asymmetric, ventral lobe smaller; pectoral fins mostly fused to sides of head, inner rear tips free; 5 pairs of gill slits on underside of head; large spiracles behind eyes. Size range 3–7+ m (including saw).

Shallow coastal waters, usually over sandy or silty sand bottom; often in estuaries, occasionally in rivers. Feed on sea urchins, crustaceans, gastropods, bivalves and fish. The saw is used to scrape out buried prey and also to kill or disable schooling fish with rapid slashes through the school. Ovoviviparous, the saw of the prenatal pup is covered with soft skin to prevent injury to mother at birth. Good eating, but most species are rare. Populations are severely threatened by artisanal fisheries and habitat degradation (siltation and 'development' of estuaries).

Worldwide in tropical and warm temperate waters. Two genera, 6–7 species, 3 in our area.

LARGETOOTH SAWFISH
Pristis microdon
Latham 1794

3.6 m
(including saw)

Saw stout with 17–22 evenly spaced pairs of teeth; 1st dorsal fin origin about over rear tips of pectoral fins; tail fin with distinct lower lobe; space between last 2 teeth on saw less than twice distance between first 2 teeth; mouth small, transverse, with small crushing teeth. Attains 6.6 m, including saw.

Most identifications in literature records are uncertain due to lack of good photographs or important morphological information. Perhaps worldwide in tropical waters. Reported from northern Australia, Indonesia, northeastern Indian Ocean and Zanzibar, Mozambique to Port Alfred.

Inshore off beaches, in large estuaries, rivers, coastal lagoons and lakes. Males mature at ~3.5 m. Up to 13 young per litter, born at 40–70 cm.

Caught by anglers, trawlers and in gill-nets. Timid unless cornered. Little is known about this species; now rare and probably endangered. Photographs of the head may be sufficient for identification.

South African records of the smalltooth - sawfish, *Pristis pectinata* Latham 1794, are probably based on the green sawfish, *Pristis - zijsron* Bleeker 1851, which has 23–34 pairs of saw teeth, 1st dorsal fin origin above or behind pelvic fin origins, and no distinct lower tail lobe.

FAMILY TORPEDINIDAE ■ Electric Rays (Torpedos)

Head, body and pectoral fins forming a flabby circular disc, with large electric organ on each side of head (usually visible through skin on underside of disc); 2 dorsal fins; tail fin with large upper and lower lobes; mouth broadly arched and protrusile; eyes small; spiracles close behind eyes; skin naked; teeth small with low cusps; nostril flaps joined into broad short curtain in front of mouth; 5 pairs of gill openings on underside of head. Size range 0.6–1.8 m.

Generally benthic fish on sand or mud bottom, also on coral and rocky reefs, from shore to 457 m. Feed on small crustaceans, pelecypods, gastropods, worms, brittlestars and pelagic or demersal fish. The powerful electric organs can be used to deliver a shock of up to 220 volts which is used to deter predators or stun prey.

Worldwide in tropical and temperate waters. One genus with at least 17 species, 3 in our area.

MARBLED TORPEDO
Torpedo sinuspersici
Olfers 1831

19 cm DW

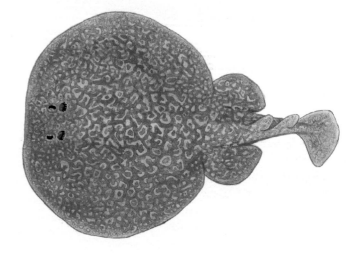

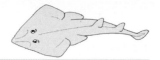

Margin of spiracles with short tentacles or papillae; tail fin height much less than distance from upper tail fin origin to 1st dorsal fin origin; teeth small with a sharp cusp. Dorsal surface russet to blackish with pale reticulated pattern. Attains 1.3 m.

Western Indian Ocean, Red Sea, Persian Gulf to Coffee Bay.

Benthic species found on sandy bottoms from shore out to 300 m; often in estuaries. Females mature at ~45 cm, males at 39 cm. Ovoviviparous, 9–22 pups per litter, born at 10 cm DW. Hunts for food at night, slowly sculling with its tail fin, a metre or so above the bottom. During the day, this ambush predator usually sits on the bottom (often covering itself with sand) waiting for unwary fish to approach; suddenly it lunges off the bottom, the pectoral fins (disc margin) are used to envelop the prey as a powerful shock is delivered to stun the fish. Movements of the disc margin then move the prey towards the flexible mouth.

Often seen by divers; also caught by anglers and trawlers. Edible, but rarely used for food.

South African specimens may represent a different species from the marbled torpedo of the Persian Gulf.

SIMILAR SPECIES

The blackspotted torpedo, *Torpedo fuscomaculata* Peters 1855, is grey or tan, often with numerous pale to dark brown spots. Southwestern Indian Ocean, Knysna to Mozambique.

The south coast torpedo, currently known as *Torpedo nobiliana* Bonaparte 1835, is uniform dark brown to black, with smooth spiracle margins and tail fin height about equal to distance from upper tail fin origin to 1st dorsal fin origin. Western Cape to Algoa Bay. This species may be undescribed.

FAMILY RHINOBATIDAE ▪ Guitarfish

Head and body flattened but rear part of body shark-like, body width at pelvic fin origins greater than inter-orbital width; pectoral fins broadly merging with sides of head, 5 pairs of gill slits on underside of head; 2 dorsal fins, 1st dorsal fin origin closer to pelvic fins than to tail fin; nostrils well in front of mouth; nasal flaps not expanded. Ovoviviparous. Size range 0.6–3.1 m.

Benthic neritic species, from shore to depths of 200 m.

Worldwide in tropical and temperate waters. Nine genera, ~53 species; 2 subfamilies in our area.

Subfamily Rhinobatinae ▫ Guitarfish

Head pointed with wedge-shaped, flattened snout; antero-lateral edges of head and pectoral fins straight or convex; tail stout, with 2 equal-sized dorsal fins and asymmetric lanceolate tail fin without distinct lobes; 1st dorsal fin behind pelvic fins, 1st dorsal fin origin closer to tail fin than to snout tip; pelvic fin origins under or in front of rear ends of pectoral fins. About 7 genera, ~44 species, ~5 species in our area.

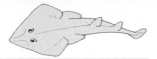

LESSER GUITARFISH
Rhinobatos annulatus
Smith 1841

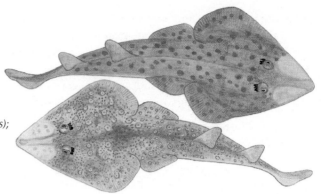

*38 cm; above: KZN pattern
(possibly an undescribed species);
below: Cape colour pattern*

Anterior nasal flap extending well past inner ends of nostrils and nearly meeting at midline of snout; 2 ridges on rear edge of spiracles; distance from snout tip to eyes 2–3 times interspiracle distance; distance from snout tip to mouth 2.5–3.2 times mouth width; interdorsal distance subequal to tail width at level of 1st dorsal fin origin. **Tan to dark brown dorsally with dark brown spots** (KZN) **or brown and white rings** (rest of South Africa); **snout with translucent pale area on either side of rostrum**. Attains 1.4 m (6 years).

Namibia to Sodwana Bay.

Sandy bottom from shore to 130 m; also in estuaries; common in Langebaan Lagoon (Saldanha Bay). Photographed on the bottom in 118 m in a canyon near Sodwana Bay. Feeds on small crustaceans, sand mussels, polychaete worms and bony fish. Females mature at 62–65 cm, males at 58 cm. Ovoviviparous. Mating occurs in April to June; 3–10 pups per litter, gestation 10 months, born at 23 cm; pups born in estuaries or in surf zone.

Often caught by surf anglers and trawlers. SA angling record: 28 kg. Good eating.

The brown spotted KZN form may represent an undescribed species.

SIMILAR SPECIES

The greyspot guitarfish, *Rhinobatos leucospilus* Norman 1926, has symmetrical bluish grey spots on snout; inter-dorsal distance greater than tail width at 1st dorsal fin origin. Known only from KZN.

The speckled guitarfish, *Rhinobatos ocellatus* Norman 1926, has brown dorsal surface with numerous dark-edged blue-grey ocelli on head, paired fins and tail; length from snout tip to mouth ~3.5 times mouth width, nostril width ~1.5 times inter-nostril width. Rare; 3 specimens known from Algoa Bay.

The slender guitarfish, *Rhinobatos holcorhynchus* Norman 1922, has anterior nasal flaps extending medially only to inner edge of nostrils; dorsal surface olive-green, sometimes with dark blotches; prominent black blotch on underside of snout. Kenya to Port Shepstone.

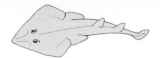

Subfamily Rhininae ▫ Giant Guitarfish & Bowmouth Guitarfish

Head pointed with wedge-shaped, flattened snout or front of head broadly rounded; **antero-lateral edges of head and pectoral fins distinctly concave; tail stout, with 2 equal-sized dorsal fins, 1st dorsal fin over pelvic fins, 1st dorsal fin origin about midway between tail fin base and snout tip; tail falcate with distinct upper and lower lobes**; pelvic fin origins behind rear ends of pectoral fins. Two genera, ~5 species, 2 in our area.

GIANT GUITARFISH
Rhynchobatus djiddensis
(Forsskål 1775)

1.5 m

First dorsal fin origin over or in front of pelvic fins; tail fin with distinct lower lobe; snout wedge-shaped, merging into concave lateral head profile; anterior nasal flaps restricted to nostril opening; 2 ridges on rear edge of spiracles; distance from snout tip to eyes 2–3 times inter-spiracle distance; inter-dorsal distance subequal to body width at level of 1st dorsal fin origin; teeth flattened, with low rounded cusp forming pavement-like crushing dentition. Dark olive-green dorsally, usually with **pale spots in longitudinal series** on body and pectoral fins, **dark eye spot ringed with pale spots at base of pectoral fins and dark polygonal mark between eyes**. Attains 3 m and at least 227 kg.

Indo-West Pacific, Red Sea, Oman to Algoa Bay (one record from Knysna); fairly common in KZN and Transkei area of the Eastern Cape in summer.

Mud and sand bottom down to 30 m; also caught in estuaries. Feeds on crustaceans, bivalves, squid and small fish. Females mature at 1.7 m, males at 1.2 m. Four pups per litter, born ~60 cm in summer.

Harmless but inquisitive species; does well in oceanariums. Often props itself up on tips of its pectoral fins. A powerful game fish; SADSAA all-tackle record: 92 kg. Flesh excellent, but small litters make this species vulnerable to overfishing. Anglers planning to tag this fish should avoid gaffing to increase its chance of survival.

Giant guitarfish identified as *Rhynchobatus djiddensis* may comprise a complex of 3 or more species.

─ **SIMILAR SPECIES** ────────────────

The bowmouth guitarfish, *Rhina ancylostoma* Bloch & Schneider 1801, has snout and front of head broadly rounded, sharply delimited from pectoral fins; 2–3 ridges of enlarged spiky denticles on dorsal surface of head and scapular area; jaws and tooth bands W-shaped, with 3 lobes on lower jaw fitting into 3 indentations on upper jaw; tail fin shark-like, upper lobe longer, lower lobe acute. Adult grey or brownish dorsally with scattered pale spots, white below; young with black spots or 2 black bands between eyes, body mostly black with white spots, dorsal fins and tail fin lobes blackish distally. Indo-West Pacific, Red Sea, Oman to Durban.

FAMILY RAJIDAE ▪ Skates

Head and body depressed, forming a flattened disc with pointed snout and wing-like pectoral fins; tail long and thin, usually with 2 small dorsal fins near tip and a medial row or rows of enlarged denticles or thorns; pelvic fins divided into anterior and posterior lobes; nostril flaps not fused to form median nasal curtain; 5 pairs of gill slits on underside of head; mouth small, but jaws are powerful with numerous small teeth. Adult males have enlarged hooked spines on the dorsal surface of the disc near the outer corners; these spines are used to hold the female during copulation. Size range 25 cm to 2.3 m TL, 1.8 m disc width (DW), 200 kg.

Benthic species on sand or mud bottom; most species on continental slope in 200–1 350 m, but some species occur near shore. Feed on crabs, shrimp, hermit crabs, amphipods, isopods, flatworms, polychaete worms, pelecypods, mysids, gastropods, octopus, squid, cuttlefish, bony fish and elasmobranchs. Oviparous, eggs laid in tough, flexible, dark brown, keratinous cases. Skates are good eating, and the pectoral fins of some species are marketed as 'skate wings'.

Worldwide in tropical to polar seas. Nine genera, more than 220 species; 4 genera, ~25 species in our area.

BISCUIT SKATE
Raja straeleni
Poll 1951

45 cm DW female

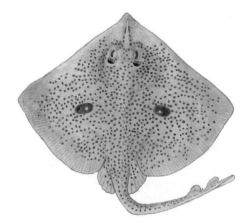

Anterior lobe of pelvic fin joined to rest of fin; snout stiff, supported by stout cartilage extending to tip of snout; upper surface of disc and tail with some enlarged denticles (thorns); **single row of thorns along mid-dorsal region of snout, disc and tail**; distance from mid anus to tip of tail more than distance from mid anus to tip of snout; snout length in front of eyes less than twice inter-spiracular distance; 35–45 rows of teeth in upper jaw. Adult brown to grey dorsally, covered with various sized **black spots forming whorls and blotches**; often with dark-edged eye spot at base of pectoral fins; mucous pores on underside of disc not pigmented. Attains 68 cm DW.

West Africa to East London.

Benthic species on sand and mud bottom from near shore to 690 m. Males mature at 40 cm DW. Feeds on bony fish (including some pelagic shoaling species), crustaceans and squid.

Caught by shore and ski-boat anglers and trawlers. Pectoral fins edible.

SIMILAR SPECIES

The spearnose skate, *Rostroraja alba* (Lacepède 1803), lacks small dark spots, but usually has small white spots and conspicuous thorns on tail. Eastern Atlantic to Mozambique.

The twineye skate, *Raja miraletus* (Linnaeus 1758), has 2 blue ocelli on disc; snout length not more than twice inter-spiracular distance. Mediterranean and eastern Atlantic to Durban.

The slime skate, *Dipturus pullopunctata* (Smith 1964), and the blackspot skate, *Dipturus campbelli* (Wallace 1967), have small black spots (mucous pores) on underside of disc. The slime skate occurs from Lüderitz to Bazaruto; the blackspot skate appears to be endemic to KZN.

FAMILY DASYATIDAE ▪ Stingrays

Head, body and pectoral fins forming flat, rounded or angular disc, the width 0.9–1.3 times its length; tail slender, usually longer than disc; tail fin absent; dorsal fins absent or reduced to low skin folds on tail; usually 1 or more large, serrate, venomous stinging spines on dorsal surface of tail well behind its base; head in front of spiracles not projecting from disc; 5 pairs of gill openings on underside of head. Size range 35 cm to 2.1 m DW, 300+ kg.

Most species inshore, in estuaries and along sandy beaches; some species in freshwater. Larger species more common offshore in 100–476 m. Feed on pelecypods, gastropods, crustaceans, worms and occasionally fish. Ovoviviparous.

Stingrays are not aggressive but they use their venomous tail spine in defence, when an unsuspecting wader steps on them. Wounds can be very painful or even fatal if the victim is struck on the body. The wound should be immersed in hot (50° C) water for half an hour to destroy the venom and stop the pain.

Worldwide in tropical and temperate seas. Six genera with ~70 species, 14 in our area.

Blue stingray

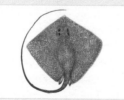

Honeycomb stingray

Bluespotted ribbontail ray

BLUE STINGRAY
Dasyatis chrysonota
(Smith 1828)

45 cm DW mature male

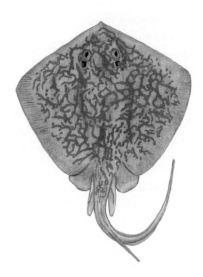

Disc rhomboidal, naked except for some denticles near front margin; snout angular; ventral finfold on tail falling well short of tail tip; preorbital snout longer than distance between spiracles. Golden brown dorsally, with irregular **finger-like blue markings**; underside white, occasionally with grey margins in juveniles. Attains 75 cm DW, 25 kg (males live at least 9 years and females 14 years).

Endemic to southern Africa, from central Angola to St Lucia, possibly to Maputo.

Benthic inshore species, usually caught in surf zone along sandy beaches and in river mouths; also trawled to depths of 109 m. Females mature at 50 cm DW (7 years), males at 41 cm DW (5 years). One to four pups per litter, born in surf zone at 17–20 cm DW; gestation 9 months. Mating probably occurs in surf zone before migrating offshore in winter.

An important sport fish, the blue stingray is edible, but most specimens are released. Although many are returned to the water alive, the survival rate appears to be low. Anglers should use landing nets rather than gaffs to land their fish, and avoid dragging the ray over dry beach sand, which removes the ray's protective mucous coating. SA angling record: 24.5 kg.

SIMILAR SPECIES

D. chrysonota differs from *Dasyatis pastinaca* (Linnaeus 1758) of the northeastern Atlantic and Mediterranean in colour pattern (*D. pastinaca* is uniformly greyish green to olive-brown).

Dasyatis marmorata (Steindachner 1892) is known from Senegal, with records from the Mediterranean, Morocco, Mauritania and the Congo. It differs from *D. chrysonota* in having a longer preoral snout (20–22 % DW) versus 18–19% DW in *D. chrysonota*.

The bluespotted stingray, *Dasyatis kuhlii* (Müller & Henle 1841), has small round blue spots and rear half of tail with black and white bands. Indo-West Pacific, south to Aliwal Shoal.

The short-tail stingray, *Dasyatis brevicaudata* (Hutton 1875), has tail length about equal to disc length; disc uniform greyish brown dorsally. False Bay to Maputo, Australia and New Zealand.

HONEYCOMB STINGRAY
Himantura uarnak
(Forsskål 1775)

76 cm DW male

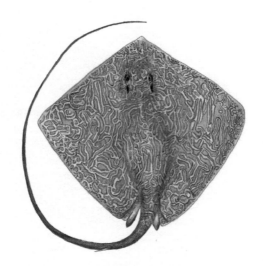

Disc rhomboidal, naked except for band of small flattened denticles along dorsal midline and onto base of tail; snout angular; tail elongate, whip-like, may be over twice disc length; no finfolds; preorbital snout length subequal to inter-spiracle distance. Dorsal surface of adults with intricate pattern of **dark spots and polygons** on pale background; juveniles pale brown, covered with dark brown spots. Attains 2 m DW, 120 kg.

Tropical Indo-West Pacific, Red Sea, Oman to East London; recently found in the Mediterranean.

Benthic on inshore sandy bottoms from shore to 50 m; also found in estuaries and lagoons. Feeds mainly on fish, especially ponyfish and anchovies; also crustaceans and molluscs. Matures at ~1 m DW (4–5 years). Three to five pups per litter, gestation 12 months, born at 28–30 cm DW.

Popular angling fish that puts up a strong fight. Commonly taken by surf anglers and beach seines, also caught by trawlers. SA angling record: 118 kg. Edible, but anglers usually release this ray. This species may comprise a complex of 2 or 3 similar species.

SIMILAR SPECIES

The dragon stingray, *Himantura jenkinsii* (Annandale 1909) [= *Himantura draco* Compagno & Heemstra 1984], has a conspicuous row of large, sharp, hooked denticles along dorsal midline from middle of disc to sting, and base of tail covered with large flattened denticles. Indo-West Pacific, south to Durban.

The sharpnose whipray, *Himantura gerrardi* (Gray 1851), has middle of disc densely covered with small flattened denticles; snout tip acutely pointed; tail much longer than disc width. Adults pale brown dorsally, white below; juveniles with alternating white and black bands on tail; bands fading in adults. Attains 90 cm DW, 65 kg. Commonly caught by shore anglers; fights strongly. Indo-West Pacific, Red Sea to the Eastern Cape.

BLUESPOTTED RIBBONTAIL RAY

Taeniura lymma
(Forsskål 1775)

25 cm DW male

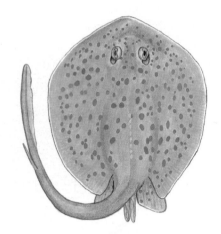

Disc oval, longer than wide; tail ~1.5 times DW; ventral finfold from below sting base to tip of tail; no dorsal tail fold; spine located on rear half of tail. Grey-brown, olive-green, reddish brown or tawny; **bright blue spots on disc and pelvic fins**; specimens from our area do not have blue stripes along each side of tail. Attains ~90 cm DW.

Tropical Indo-West Pacific, Red Sea, Oman to Durban.

Benthic in shallow sandy areas on or near coral reefs. Feeds on gastropods, bivalves, bony fish, crustaceans and worms. Mainly nocturnal, by day it hides in caves and under ledges. When foraging, the ray usually disturbs the sand to locate its prey; other fish (e.g. goatfish) often accompany it to catch any exposed prey that escape the ray. Litters of 7 pups.

Rarely caught by anglers, but often seen by divers at Sodwana Bay. This distinctive species may be a complex of 2 or 3 similar species.

SIMILAR SPECIES

The round ribbontail ray, *Taeniura meyeni* Müller & Henle 1841 [formerly *Taeniura melanospilos*], is larger (attains 1.6 m DW), has a more circular disc, slightly wider than long, and is bluish grey with scattered dark spots and blotches. Indo-West Pacific, Red Sea to KZN.

FAMILY GYMNURIDAE ■ Butterfly Rays

Head, body and pectoral fins forming a **broad diamond-shaped disc, much wider than long; tail less than half disc length; short spine at base**; snout blunt; head flattened, not raised above disc; 5 pairs of gill slits on underside of head; no dorsal or tail fins. Size range 1.0–2.5 m DW.

Coastal waters over sand or mud. Feed on fish, crabs, mole crabs and worms. Viviparous.

Worldwide in tropical and warm temperate seas. Two genera, ~12 species, apparently only one in our area. A previous report of *Gymnura japonica* (Temminck & Schlegel 1850) from the Agulhas Bank is unverified.

DIAMOND BUTTERFLY RAY
Gymnura natalensis
(Gilchrist & Thompson 1911)

1.8 m DW mature female

Disc smooth, front edge with broader median angle in adults than in young; small tentacle on rear edge of spiracle of juveniles, becoming smaller with growth and absent in large adults; tail about half disc length; jaws with 68–93 rows of small, sharply pointed teeth. Grey, brown or green dorsally, often with **darker mottling or faint dark spots**. Juveniles with dark and light bands on tail. Markings and colour match habitat. Attains 2.5 m DW and at least 90 kg.

Endemic, Namibia to southern Mozambique.

Common inshore benthic species, found along sandy shores and in estuaries; also on offshore banks to 75 m. Both sexes mature at ~1.1 m DW. Five to 10 pups in litter, born at ~40 cm DW. During the 12-month gestation, pups are nourished by uterine secretions ('milk') which is absorbed by accessory gill filaments projecting from the spiracles of the pups.

Often caught by shore anglers, usually after considerable effort. Trek-netters dislike this species because when caught, the ray lies flat against the net and makes it extremely difficult to retrieve. Also taken by trawlers. IGFA all-tackle record: 82.6 kg ray from Knysna Lagoon. Edible, but most are returned to the sea after capture.

FAMILY MYLIOBATIDAE ■ Eagle Rays

Head, body and pectoral fins form an angular (rhomboid) 'disc' much wider than long; fleshy snout and eyes projecting above and in front of leading edge of pectoral fins; spiracles not visible dorsally; 5 pairs of gill openings on underside of disc; tail slender, whip-like, with 1 small dorsal fin at base, followed by 1–4 serrate venomous spines; no tail fin or finfolds; jaws with large, plate-like, crushing teeth. Size range 1.5–2.3 m DW, 200 kg.

Coastal waters over sand, mud, coral and rocky reefs. Usually forage on bottom, using their fleshy snout to root out buried prey from the sediment. Feed on crustaceans and thick-shelled molluscs, with shell fragments ejected from the mouth. Swim well above bottom when migrating in enormous schools; sometimes leap high into the air. Ovoviviparous.

Worldwide in tropical and warm temperate waters. Five genera, ~32 species, 5 in our area.

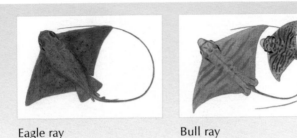

Eagle ray   Bull ray

EAGLE RAY
Myliobatis aquila
(Linnaeus 1758)

54 cm DW mature male

Snout projecting as a broad short lobe continuous with leading edge of pectoral fins; pelvic fins large, rear edge truncate; dorsal fin behind pelvic fins; tail (when intact) twice disc length; jaws with 7 rows of tooth plates: middle row of wide teeth and 3 rows of much smaller diamond-shaped teeth at each side. Males with small conical horn above each eye. Dark brown, black or olive-grey dorsally, occasionally with irregular dusky black spots; underside white. Attains 1.5 m DW.

Mediterranean, eastern Atlantic, and round our south coast to KZN.

Prefers temperate waters; often in shallow lagoons and estuaries. Taken by trawlers to depths of 95 m. Feeds on bivalves, gastropods, crustaceans (crabs, mole crabs and hermit crabs), worms, tunicates and bony fish. Females mature at ~60 cm DW, males at 54 cm. Four to seven pups per litter, 20–23 cm DW at birth, born in shallow water. Fast-swimming ray that occasionally leaps out of the water; often found in groups.

Provides good sport for anglers. SA angling record: 21.5 kg. Excellent eating.

Figure 33
Eagle ray head showing snout continuous with the leading edge of the pectoral fin.

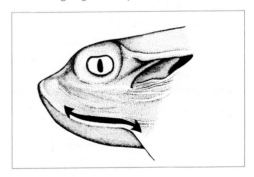

The circumtropical spotted eagle ray, *Aetobatus narinari* (Euphrasen 1790), has snout and pelvic fins narrowly rounded, dorsal fin over pelvic fins; prominent white spots on dorsal surface and 1 row of tooth plates in each jaw.

The Indo-West Pacific flapnose ray, *Rhinoptera javanica* (Muller & Henle 1841), found south to KZN, has forehead and snout with median indentation; disc plain brown above, white below.

The Indo-West Pacific ornate eagle ray, *Aetomyleus vespertilio* (Bleeker 1852), recently found off Maputo, has snout and pelvic fins narrowly rounded; dorsal surface brown with black transverse lines on front half of disc, forming a network posteriorly; rear margin of disc and pelvic fins with white spots; no spine at base of tail.

BULL RAY
Pteromylaeus bovinus
(Saint-Hilaire 1817)

86 cm DW female
22 cm DW unborn pup

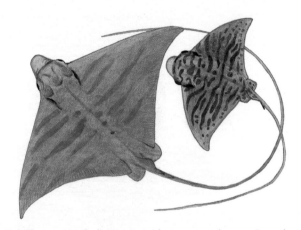

Snout resembles duck's bill; pectoral fins falcate, tips pointed; rear edge of pelvic fins rounded; dorsal fin over pelvic fins; tail (when intact) 1.6–1.8 times disc length, with 1–4 small serrated spines at base. Adult males with short conical horn above each eye. Jaws with 7 rows of tooth plates: a wide middle row and 3 rows of smaller diamond-shaped teeth at each side. Disc brown above, with pale blue-grey crossbars visible when ray is excited or injured; newborn pups with dark crossbars and spots. Attains 1.8 m DW, 85 kg.

Mediterranean and eastern Atlantic to Namibia and round our south coast to Mozambique.

In lagoons and estuaries, also over sand and mud bottoms to 56 m. Feeds on pelecypods, gastropods, crabs, hermit crabs, bony fish and squid. Females mature at 1.1 m DW, males at 95 cm. Three to seven pups per litter, born at 50 cm DW. Sometimes occurs in small groups.

Often caught by shore anglers; powerful swimmer that readily leaps out of the water and puts up a good fight. IGFA all-tackle record: 46.6 kg ray from Senegal. Excellent eating.

FAMILY MOBULIDAE ■ Mantas & Devil Rays

Head, body and pectoral fins form an angular rhomboid or chevron-shaped 'disc', much wider than long; head truncate in front, with 2 fleshy paddle-like cephalic fins that are normally curled while the ray is swimming, but unroll when fish is feeding to direct plankton (including small fish and crustaceans) into the open mouth; eyes and spiracles on sides of head; pectoral fin tips acute, the rear edge concave; 5 pairs of gill slits on underside of head; rows of fringed plates over internal gill slits to screen plankton from water flowing over the gills; dorsal fin on base of tail over pelvic fins; tail slender, shorter than disc length; bands of minute teeth on one or both jaws. Size range 1.1–6.7 m DW, 20 kg to 3 tonnes (~20 years).

Large to enormous, active, strong-swimming, filter-feeding planktivores of the epipelagic realm. Viviparous.

Worldwide. Two genera, ~11 species, 6 in our area.

MANTA
Manta birostris
(Walbaum 1792)

~4 m DW immature male (dorsal and ventral views)

Mouth at front of head; no teeth in upper jaw; **head width at spiracles greater than distance from middle of upper jaw to 5th pair of gill slits**; disc length ~40% DW; tail spine usually absent; dorsal and ventral surfaces rough, mostly covered with small denticles; tail of adults thick, rough and flexible only at base. Dark greyish blue, greenish brown or black dorsally, often with pale shoulder patches; underside white with grey margin sometimes with dark patches. Partial albino mantas have been found in Indonesia and off Malaysia. These rays were white dorsally (as well as ventrally), with a large Y-shaped black mark dorsally behind head and submarginal black bands dorsally along rear margins of wings. Largest of all rays, attaining at least 6.7 m DW and 3 tonnes.

Worldwide in tropical and warm temperate waters; Cape Point to KZN and probably Mozambique.

Epipelagic, usually near surface over continental shelf to 100 m. Matures at ~4 m DW. Two pups per litter, born at ~1.2 m DW. Births have been witnessed when the mother cart-wheels out of the water and the baby is ejected tail-first like a projectile with its

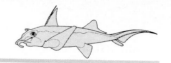

wings curled round its body. Usually seen singly or in pairs swimming slowly at the surface, but they can also swim at high speed, often cart-wheeling or 'flying' straight out of the water.

This gentle giant may approach divers near the surface, and is often seen with piscine hitchhikers (remoras [see p. 318]). Their trusting nature makes them vulnerable to man's cruelty. In the Bahamas, a 7 m manta towed an 8 m boat for more than 19 km, part of the time against the added resistance of an anchor dragging on the bottom; after 5 hours it was still alive, with 4 harpoons and a rifle bullet in its body.

SIMILAR SPECIES

The 5 species of devil rays (*Mobula* spp) known from our area have the mouth under and slightly behind front edge of head. Because of their large size, manta rays and devil rays are rarely preserved or deposited in museum fish collections. Measurements and photographs of fresh specimens are necessary for positive identifications.

SUBCLASS HOLOCEPHALI

Elephantfish & Chimaeras (Order Chimaeriformes)

Cartilaginous fishes with one external gill opening hidden by a soft gill cover on each side of head. Upper jaw fused to cranium, with two large tooth plates; lower jaw with a single tooth plate. Adult males with paired intromittent organs ('claspers') on the pelvic fins, a short claw-like appendage on the forehead and a retractable clasper resembling a chicken's foot in a pouch in front of each pelvic fin. The prepelvic claspers are protruded and grasp the female during copulation. First dorsal fin with a strong movable venomous spine. Reproduction oviparous, the keratinous (horny) egg cases are large and spindle-shaped.

Three families are represented in our area. The members of the Chimaeridae and Rhinochimaeridae are usually confined to depths of 400 m to more than 2 000 m, are rarely seen and are beyond the scope (depth) of this book.

FAMILY CALLORHINCHIDAE ■ Elephantfish

Fleshy hoe-shaped proboscis on front of snout; 1st dorsal fin with a strong serrate movable spine; 2nd dorsal fin short, high, falcate. The prepelvic and head claspers are used to hold the female while the intromittent organ is inserted into the oviduct. Oviparous. Skin smooth, without denticles. Size range 1.0–1.2 m.

Southern Hemisphere: South Africa, Australia, New Zealand and South America. One genus with ~3 species, one in our area.

ELEPHANTFISH
Callorhinchus capensis
Dumeril 1865

*49 cm (to rear of
2nd dorsal fin)
mature male*

Second dorsal fin higher anteriorly, its base subequal to distance from 1st dorsal fin; tail axis raised; anal fin high, the base narrow and adjoining tail fin. Silver or bronze, with dusky brown markings on flanks and head; fins brown. Attains 1.2 m (90 cm FL), 12 years.

Endemic, Namibia to Durban; common off our west and south coasts, rare elsewhere.

Soft bottom near shore and out to 374 m. Females mature at 50 cm FL (4 years) and males at 44 cm FL (3 years). At maturity, males display three distinct secondary sexual characteristics: the paired claspers on the inner edge of the pelvic fins enlarge to 9 cm and calcify; the paired retractable prepelvic grapplers enlarge; and a small frontal tentaculum (resembling a miniature door-knocker with little barbs) on the middle of the forehead. Egg case spindle-shaped, ~23 cm long, with broad flat ribbed flanges around edge.

Mating and egg laying occurs inshore. Adult males produce tiny spermatophores (1–2 mm in diameter). These sperm packets are carried in the green seminal fluid used to fertilise the female. Feeds on sea urchins, bivalves, crustaceans (stomatopods), gastropods, polychaetes and bony fish (especially the pelagic schooling goby, *Sufflogobius bibarbatus*, and the lightfish, *Maurolicus muelleri*).

Predators include Cape fur seals and sharks (bronze whaler, sixgill shark, spotted sevengill shark and soupfin shark).

Caught by anglers, beach seines, gill-nets and trawlers, usually in less than 100 m; egg cases and juveniles usually in less than 50 m. Flesh excellent when marinated with vinegar; sold commercially as 'silver trumpeter'; a.k.a. 'Joseph'. Relatively fast growth, early maturity and fecundity make this one of the few chondrichthyan fishes that may be able to support a moderately productive fishery.

O STEICHTHYES means 'bony fishes' and refers to the well developed bony skeleton of most species in this class. Most bony fish have a single gill opening on either side of the head. The majority of species are oviparous, with external fertilisation of the eggs taking place during spawning. The eggs are released into the water or attached to the bottom, and the male promptly ejects sperm to fertilise the eggs. Viviparous bony fish, which give birth to active (free-swimming) young, are much less common among marine fish. In our area we have only the bythitids (Family Bythitidae), klipfish (Family Clinidae) and the coelacanths (Family Latimeriidae) as viviparous fishes.

The Osteichthyes includes two subclasses: fleshy-fin fishes (Sarcopterygii) and ray-fin fishes (Actinopterygii).

SUBCLASS SARCOPTERYGII
Fleshy-fin Fishes & All Other Vertebrates

Vertebrate animals with pectoral and pelvic fins (or limbs) set off from body on a muscular pedicel containing a series of bony supports, with a single bone at the base articulating with bony pectoral and pelvic girdles; cranium divided transversely by an intra-cranial joint into a movable anterior (orbital) part and posterior (otic) part. The Subclass Sarcopterygii includes several groups of extinct fossil fish, two 'living fossils' (coelacanths and lungfish) and all of the vertebrate animals known as 'tetrapods' (a.k.a. 'four-legged' animals, such as amphibians, reptiles, birds and mammals). During the course of evolution, the intra-cranial joint is supposed to have been lost in the branches leading to lungfish and tetrapods.

COELACANTHS (ORDER COELACANTHIFORMES)

Second dorsal fin, anal fin, pectoral and pelvic fins with muscular pedicel projecting from body and containing several cartilaginous or bony skeletal elements; tail fin comprises 3 sectors: a small projecting central lobe containing tip of notochord and 2 larger (dorsal and ventral) lobes; 2 dorsal fins, each with a single basal skeletal element; 1st dorsal fin sail-like, supported by movable bony spines, fin rays unbranched; cranium divided transversely, with a joint between front (orbital) and rear (otic) parts of the head; 2 external nostril openings on each side of snout; no internal duct between nasal cavity and mouth; maxilla bone and branchiostegals absent.

The fossil genus name *Coelacanthus* (meaning 'hollow spine') refers to the long, hollow, posterior neural and haemal spines of the vertebrae that connect to the tubular bones supporting the tail fin rays.

The fossil record of coelacanths comprises ~120 species in ~47 genera and 5 families, extending from the Middle Devonian Period (~380 million years ago) to the end of the Cretaceous Period (70 million years ago), when the coelacanths were thought to have died out, along with dinosaurs and many other fossil groups. The first fossil coelacanth, described in 1822, was found in England. Others were discovered in Europe, North and South America, Greenland and Australia. Three extinct species are known from South African fossils, including one from Grahamstown (near Port Alfred). Fossil coelacanths range in size from 10 cm to a giant of 3.5 m; most species are known from marine deposits, but a few were adapted to freshwater. They attained their maximum diversity (in number of species) in the Triassic Period (~200 million years ago).

FAMILY LATIMERIIDAE ■ Coelacanths

Body robust, covered with large overlapping bony scales; the exposed part of each scale covered with small hard tubercles; **tail fin broadly rounded, with a small central supplementary fin projecting beyond the main fin margin with rays articulating directly to tip of notochord**; tail fin rays with minute spinelets; 1st dorsal fin movable, folding down into a recess, with 8 spinulose bony rays; skeleton mostly cartilaginous; vertebrae rudimentary. In place of the vertebral column of most adult fish, coelacanths have a large thick tube of cartilage called the **notochord**. In the early development of most fish, the notochord of the embryo or larva is gradually replaced by the bony vertebrae of the spinal column. In coelacanths, lungfish and some primitive sharks, transformation of the notochord into a segmented bony (or calcified) vertebral column does not take place. In coelacanths, the hollow notochord is filled with oil and provides a strong flexible support for the spinal cord. The vertebral neural and haemal spines are ossified (bony), fused with bony neural and haemal arches which protect the spinal cord and caudal artery respectively and are connected to the notochord; ribs absent; swimbladder large, filled with fat and running the length of the abdominal cavity; intestine with spiral valve; osmoregulation involves retention of urea and trimethylamine oxide in the blood, but urea is not resorbed by the kidneys and excess salts are excreted by a rectal gland.

Indian Ocean. Two living species, one in our area.

Some authors include *Latimeria* with its fossil relatives in the Family Coelacanthidae.

COELACANTH
Latimeria chalumnae
Smith 1939

~ 1.8 m

Head not scaly, opercular bones exposed; gill cover expanded as a thick flap of skin; 2 large overlapping gular plates on underside of lower jaw; jaws and tongue with conical teeth. The structure at the side of the upper jaw that looks like a maxilla is a thick ligament joining the front of the skull to the rear end of lower jaw. In adults the brain is simple (not much convoluted), occupying less than 2% of the brain cavity; and is confined to the rear part of the skull. In the late-term foetus, the brain fills the cranial cavity. A small brain placed at the back of the skull may cause less electrical interference with the electro-receptive sensor in the snout. Head and body dark metallic blue, covered with irregular white or pale bluish spots; after death, the colour becomes dark brownish black. Attains 1.8 m, 98 kg.

The discovery of the first living coelacanth near East London in 1938 caused quite a commotion in South Africa and in the zoological community of the world. Thanks to the work done by JLB and Margaret Smith, French anatomists, Hans Fricke, Mark and Arnez Erdman in Indonesia, and the recent amazing discovery of a resident group of coelacanths at Sodwana Bay we have learned much about the anatomy, biology and distribution of this fascinating fish.

A brief history of the coelacanth

In December 1938, the first living coelacanth known to science was caught near East London. The publication of JLB Smith's description of this specimen as the new species *Latimeria chalumnae* in the international journal *Nature* (March 1939) caused a sensation in the zoological world akin to finding a living dinosaur walking about the Karoo. Coelacanths were well known in the fossil record, but were thought to have gone extinct, along with the dinosaurs, 70 million years ago. The discovery and description of this 'living fossil' made JLB Smith and Marjorie Courtenay-Latimer familiar to ichthyologists all over the world. Miss Latimer, Curatrix of the East London Museum, recognised the fish as something quite unusual, and she went to considerable effort to preserve this strange 1.5 m long fish.

JLB Smith's 14-year search for the 'home' of the coelacanths was successful in December 1952, when a specimen was caught at Anjouan in the Comoro Islands, a group of four islands between the northern end of Madagascar and Africa. *Latimeria* was known to local fishermen as 'gombessa', but had no value as a food-fish and was not sold in the

local markets. The Comoros were then a French colony, and for the next 35 years, coelacanth research focussed on detailed anatomical studies by French scientists based on a series of specimens caught by Comoran fishermen. Since 1952, some 200 coelacanths have been caught with hook and line in depths of 35–600 m at Grand Comoro and Anjouan islands.

In the 1980s Hans Fricke and Jürgen Schauer supervised construction of a two-man research submersible christened *GEO* after the German *Geo* magazine (a major source of funds for the construction and operation of the new 'sub'). This submersible was specially designed to find and study *Latimeria* in its natural deep water habitat at the Comoros, a goal of Hans Fricke from when he was a teenager in East Germany and read JLB Smith's book *Old Fourlegs*.

In January 1987, after 22 unsuccessful dives at Grand Comoro, Jürgen was piloting the sub on their first night dive, when they finally found a coelacanth in 198 m, very near the lower safe-dive limit of 200 m for *GEO* dives. By 1990 Fricke had a new submersible

(*JAGO*) which could dive to 400 m, and the *JAGO* Team (now joined by Karen Hissmann) learned much about the biology, behaviour and ecology of coelacanths at the Comoros.

> A detailed account of the astonishing discovery of the first living coelacanth, of JLB Smith's 14-year search for the 'home' of the coelacanths, and of the dramatic recovery of a second specimen in the Comoro Islands is told in Smith's book *Old Fourlegs: The Story of the Coelacanth* (Longmans, Green & Co., London, 1956; 260 pp [this book is now out of print, but you may find a copy in your local library]). A more up-to-date version of the story and the 1998 discovery of coelacanths in Indonesia, is given by Samantha Weinberg in *A Fish Caught in Time: The Search for the Coelacanth* (Fourth Estate, London, 1999, 239 pp).

Behaviour

The *JAGO* Team found *Latimeria* to be a lethargic, nocturnal creature that spends most

Figure 34
JAGO, the two-man research submersible used by Hans Fricke and Jürgen Schauer to study the coelacanth. JAGO is 3.2 m long, 2.0 m wide, 2.5 m high; weight 3 033 kg; displacement 3 200 litres; maximum operating depth 400 m.

of the day resting in caves in groups of 2 to 16 fish. By doing this, the fish avoids currents (thereby saving considerable energy) and also hides from predators (deep water sharks). In the dimly lit caves, coelacanths are well camouflaged; with numerous irregular white spots on a dark background, they are difficult to see against the black basaltic cave walls, which are sparsely covered with white oyster shells.

At night, coelacanths emerge from their refuges to glide, cruise, drift or swim gracefully and slowly near the bottom, apparently searching for prey. On these nightly hunting forays, they may travel as much as 8 km; and before dawn, they retreat to the nearest cave.

Each coelacanth has its own distinctive pattern of white markings, and this allows recognition of individuals, tracking of their movements, and estimation of their population size.

Although several individuals occupy overlapping home ranges, no aggressive encounters between coelacanths have been observed. A single fish may frequent several caves within its home range, and three *Latimeria* were sighted within the same 7 km home range over a period of two years.

Swimming

Coelacanths appear to move in slow motion, drifting passively with the current, using their flexible fins to adjust their position. The principal means of propulsion is the synchronous sculling movements of the 2nd dorsal and anal fins. In slow swimming, the left pectoral and right pelvic fins move forward, while the right pectoral and left pelvic fins sweep backward. This co-ordinated tandem movement of alternate paired fins is similar to the gait of a lizard or mammal on land.

Contrary to Smith's name 'Old Fourlegs' and his idea that coelacanths stalked prey 'by crawling quietly along gullies and channels',

Latimeria do not use their paired fins for walking. Coelacanths seem to maintain a 'personal space'; even when resting in groups and slowly moving their fins, they rarely touch each other or the walls or bottom of the cave. Coelacanths, like some large rockcods, are able to lunge or make a quick start to catch prey by means of a powerful sweep of the tail fin.

Hunting for prey

When searching for prey, coelacanths often adopt a vertical position, with the head near the bottom and the tail fin curved at a right angle to the body. This head stand usually lasts for 2 or 3 minutes and may be used to scan the bottom for prey. The large sensory 'rostral organ' in the snout is thought to be an electroreceptive organ, like the ampullae of Lorenzini which assist sharks to find buried prey animals.

Coelacanths feed mainly on demersal and midwater fish. In addition to a swell shark and skate, various bony fish (synaphobranchid eel [*Ilyophis brunneus*], lanternfish [Family Myctophidae], barracudina [Family Paralepididae], beardfish [*Polymixia berndti*], alfonsino [*Beryx decadactylus*], *Symphysanodon* sp., deep water cardinalfish [*Coranthus polyacanthus*]) and a cuttlefish have also been found in their stomachs.

Based on their sedate behaviour and their relatively small gills, which imply a low oxygen consumption, *Latimeria* have one of the lowest metabolic rates of all fish. This energy-saving lifestyle is an advantage in their unusual deep water habitat where prey is scarce on the relatively barren volcanic slopes of the Comoros.

Reproduction

Unlike sharks which have obvious claspers for internal fertilisation, coelacanths (like birds) are somehow able to accomplish internal fertilisation without any obvious

copulatory organs. The pups (foetuses) are born when they have grown large enough (36–38 cm) to fend for themselves. The huge eggs are the size of an orange (9 cm in diameter and over 325 g in weight) and the largest eggs of all fish. The enormous yolk is sufficient for the development of the embryo. Contrary to previous speculation, recent information confirms that coelacanth pups do not practise 'embryonic cannibalism' or feed on eggs while in the uterus.

In August 1991 a 1.8 m, 98 kg pregnant coelacanth trawled off northern Mozambique was given to the Natural History Museum in Maputo. The specimen was dissected and found to contain 26 near-term pups, 31–36 cm in length. In view of the large size and advanced development of these pups, the size at birth is ~35–38 cm, which agrees with the age estimate of 6 months assigned to the smallest known free-swimming coelacanth, a 43 cm juvenile caught on hook and line at the Comoros. The gestation period has been estimated at ~13 months.

Profile of a 'living fossil'

So, what's the big deal? Why all the fuss about this strange primitive fish? The term 'living fossil' was coined by Charles Darwin (1859) for animals such as the South American lungfish and the Australian duck-billed platypus, which 'like fossils, connect to a certain extent, orders [species or families] now widely separated in the natural scale. These anomalous forms may almost be called living fossils; they have endured to the present day, from having inhabited a confined area, and from having thus been exposed to less severe competition.'

Latimeria fits two of Darwin's (1859) criteria for a living fossil:

- it is the sole surviving member of the coelacanths, which were common and diverse in the Permian and Triassic Periods 290–208 million years ago;
- it seems to have 'endured to the present day, from having inhabited a confined area, [barren rocky slopes that provide caves at depths of 100–300 m] and from having thus been exposed to less severe competition'.

Another characteristic of 'living fossils' is that they are similar anatomically to fossil species of the same group: *Latimeria* is very similar anatomically to *Macropoma*, a fossil coelacanth from the Upper Cretaceous Period.

Figure 35
A 35 cm coelacanth pup.

New Latimeria *populations*

In 1995 a coelacanth was caught in a gill-net set for sharks in 150 m off the southwest coast of Madagascar; three more *Latimeria* were subsequently taken in this deep gill-net fishery.

In 1998, two coelacanths were caught in a deep gill-net fishery at the Indonesian island of Sulawesi. Although it seems likely that all western Indian Ocean coelacanths are *Latimeria chalumnae*, a DNA comparison has indicated that the Indonesian coelacanths are a separate species.

In November 2000 and in May 2001, a group of scuba divers led by Pieter Venter filmed three coelacanths at 104–118 m in Jesser Canyon off Sodwana Bay, KZN. In 2003 a coelacanth was filmed by scuba divers at 54 m, also at Sodwana Bay.

The catch of an adult female coelacanth off Kenya in April 2001 demonstrated that we still have much to learn about the distribution of coelacanths and the biodiversity of the western Indian Ocean.

Coelacanth research in South Africa

In 2001, the JLB Smith Institute of Ichthyology (now the South African Institute for Aquatic Biodiversity) and Professor Hans Fricke developed a multi-disciplinary, internationally collaborative research programme to study the biology, ecology and genetics of South African coelacanths and the deep canyon community of which they are a part.

The German Science Foundation provided funding to bring the *JAGO* Team (Hans Fricke, Jürgen Schauer and Karen Hissmann) and their submersible to South Africa. The South African Department of Environmental Affairs and Tourism supplied the FRS *ALGOA* as a mother ship for *JAGO*. The first South African – German Coelacanth Expedition to

Sodwana Bay took place in March and April 2002.

The Expedition commenced with a geophysical survey of submarine canyons off the Greater St Lucia Wetland Park, KZN, using a multi-beam echo-sounder to collect bathymetric swath profiles for detailed contour maps of canyon topography. Of the 34 canyons mapped, 12 were new discoveries. The bathymetric maps were used to plan the research cruise and to guide *JAGO* to predetermined search areas.

The first survey dive with *JAGO* began in Jesser Canyon. The coelacanth that was filmed in a cave on this dive was also the first *Latimeria* photographed by the scuba divers in November 2000. Six other canyons were also searched. Ten different coelacanths were sighted during seven of the 13 survey dives. *Latimeria* were located at five different sites in two of the seven canyons searched off Sodwana Bay. These observations confirmed *Latimeria* as a resident member of the South African marine fish fauna. Scales were removed from three coelacanths for genetic studies. Further research off the KZN coast in 2004 found another five coelacanths in Jesser Canyon and two coelacanths in Chaka Canyon 50 km south of Sodwana Bay.

The deep demersal fish fauna of the canyons along the north coast of KZN is poorly known, difficult to sample and not easy to study. Fifty fish species were seen and photographed from the submersible *JAGO* or by the Discovery Team of scuba divers in the coelacanth habitat of the canyons off Sodwana Bay. An additional 85 fish species known in depths of 100–200 m along this coast are likely to occur in the canyons.

Latimeria chalumnae was added to the CITES Appendix I list of endangered species in 1989, and the catching or sale of coelacanths is prohibited.

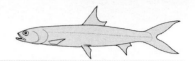

SUBCLASS ACTINOPTERYGII
Ray-fin Fishes

FAMILY ELOPIDAE ■ Ladyfish

Body cylindrical with small cycloid scales; **mouth terminal; upper jaw with toothed maxillary bone reaching past eye; large median gular bone behind chin**; no fin spines; pelvic fins abdominal; tail fin forked; adipose eyelid present. Leptocephalus larva similar to that of eels, but with forked tail fin. Size ~1 m.

Bays, coastal lagoons and estuaries.

Worldwide in tropical and warm temperate waters. One genus, ~6 species, 2 in our area.

LADYFISH
Elops machnata
(Forsskål 1775)

~75 cm

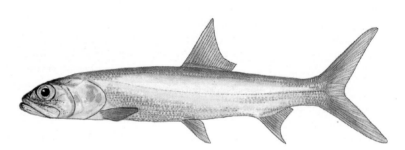

Dorsal fin rays 22–27; anal fin rays 15–18; pectoral fin rays 17–18; pelvic fin rays 12–16; **LL scales 90–103; gill rakers** 7–9 / **13–15**; branchiostegal rays 27–35. Head and body silvery; tip of dorsal fin blackish. Attains ~1 m.

Western Indian Ocean, Red Sea, Oman to Mossel Bay (south of Durban only in summer).

Inshore and in estuaries. Feeds on a variety of fish (mainly schooling species) and crustaceans (penaeid prawns and mysids). Large shoals congregate off Mozambique for spawning in winter. Tolerates a wide range of salinity and turbidity.

Crepuscular predator, renowned as a strong fighter; often jumps out of the water. Caught on various flesh baits and lures.

SADSAA all-tackle record: 12 kg. Not valued as a table fish, as the flesh is insipid and full of bones.

SIMILAR SPECIES

The Indo-West Pacific oxeye tarpon, *Megalops cyprinoides* (Broussonet 1782), is included in Elopidae by some authors. It has a compressed body with large scales (LL scales 36–40); last dorsal fin ray greatly elongated; anal fin rays 24–31; large forked tail fin. Mangroves, estuaries and rivers; breeds in the sea; rare south of KZN.

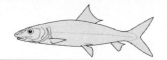

FAMILY ALBULIDAE ■ Bonefish

Body elongate, cylindrical, with small cycloid scales; **mouth below bluntly conical snout**; villiform teeth on premaxilla, vomer and dentary, but none on maxilla; 3 patches of small molars on palate and one on tongue; gular bone rudimentary or absent; branchiostegal rays 10–16; no fin spines; pelvic fins abdominal; tail fin forked; eyes nearly covered with clear adipose tissue. Leptocephalus larva similar to eel leptocephalus larva, but with forked tail fin. Size range 35 cm to ~1 m.

Worldwide in tropical and warm temperate waters. Two genera, several species, 2 in our area.

BONEFISH
Albula glossodonta
(Forsskål 1775)

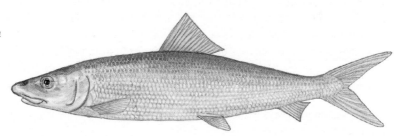

60 cm adult

Dorsal fin rays 15–19; anal fin rays 7–9; pectoral fin rays 17; pelvic fin rays 9–10; LL scales 62–75; gill rakers 8–10 / 8–12. Upper jaw 3.0–3.3 times, preoral snout 8.6–12.0 times in head length. Head and body silvery, dull green above, white below, with faint longitudinal lines along body, black blotch in front of nostrils; bases of paired fins bright yellow; yellow mark at corners of mouth. Attains 1 m.

Tropical and subtropical western Indian Ocean, Red Sea to Algoa Bay.

Shallow sandy bottom, also in mangroves and estuaries. Feeds mainly at night on crustaceans, worms and molluscs. Matures at ~30 cm (1–2 years). Spawns offshore.

Strong fast-swimming fish; superb fighter on light tackle. IGFA all-tackle record: 8.6 kg fish from northern KZN. Excellent bait when filleted fresh, but soon becomes too soft to use. Numerous small bones limit its use for food.

Previously known as *Albula vulpes* (Linnaeus), an Atlantic species.

— SIMILAR SPECIES —

The longfin bonefish, *Pterothrissus belloci* Cadenat 1937, of the west African coast, also has a forked tail and projecting snout, but it has a long dorsal fin (51–59 rays) from head to over anal fin; anal fin rays 12–14. Attains 35 cm. Occurs in 20–250 m. Known from Senegal to Walvis Bay, Namibia.

FAMILY CONGRIDAE   Conger Eels

Body eel-like; tail compressed; no scales; pectoral fins present in most species; rear nostril before or below front edge of eye; LL complete, pores continue onto head; **dorsal fin origin over or just behind pectoral fins; dorsal and anal fins continuous with tail fin**; branchiostegal rays 8–22. Size range 20 cm to 2.5 m.

Worldwide in tropical and temperate waters. About 32 genera, ~153 species, 14 in our area. Three subfamilies.

The Indo-West Pacific garden eel, *Heteroconger hassi* (Klausewitz & Eibl-Eibesfeldt 1959), was recently found at Sodwana Bay. This burrowing eel has dorsal and anal fin rays unsegmented, minute pectoral fins, body very elongate and slender, mouth and snout short, snout length subequal to eye diameter; lower jaw projecting. Head and body pale, covered with black spots; black blotch over gill opening and another larger blotch about 2 head lengths towards the tail. Occurs on sandy bottom in colonies, with front half of their bodies extending above their burrows as they pick plankton from the current.

Subfamily Congrinae   Conger Eels

Dorsal and anal fin rays segmented; pectoral fins well developed; snout length about twice eye diameter. Size range 37 cm to 2.5 m.
    Benthic eels from shore to 630 m. Some species attain more than 1.2 m and are good eating, but are not abundant enough to be commercially significant.

Worldwide in tropical and temperate waters. About 25 genera, ~100 species, ~9 in our area.

CAPE CONGER
Conger sp.

49 cm (Gough Island)

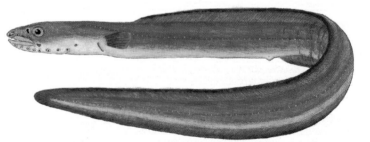

Tail longer than head and trunk combined; snout longer than eye; rear nostril in front of middle of eye; lips well developed; **teeth in 1–2 rows on jaws**, outer teeth longer, compressed, forming continuous cutting edge; **dorsal fin origin over or behind pectoral fin tips; sensory pore behind and in line with corner of mouth**; head 7.8–8.2 times in TL; LL

with 37–41 pores before anus. Brownish grey above, creamy white below; median fins with black margin. Attains 1.5 m, 15 kg.

Distribution uncertain; Knysna to southern Mozambique and Maldives; also Gough Island, South Atlantic.

Estuaries and soft bottom from shore to 30 m. Leptocephalus larvae live for ~12 months in the epipelagic plankton community of the open ocean before transforming to the benthic juvenile stage. Adult usually more active at night, when hunting prey (fish, cephalopods and crustaceans).

Flesh excellent. JLB Smith (1949, p. 392) wrote 'A dangerous fish. Large congers are much dreaded as they are difficult to kill and most vicious, and many a fisherman has been seriously mutilated. A large live conger hauled into a small boat in a rough sea by an inexperienced amateur created a situation full of intense action.'

The Cape conger was previously known as *Conger wilsoni*, but this name is not valid.

SIMILAR SPECIES

The moustache conger, *Conger cinereus* Rüppell 1830, has a dark streak below eye, dorsal fin origin over front half of pectoral fins, and a sensory pore behind and above the rictus. Western Indian Ocean, south to Knysna.

FAMILY MURAENIDAE ■ Moray Eels

Body eel-like, cylindrical or compressed; **no scales or pectoral fins; dorsal fin origin usually before gill opening, but fin is fleshy and origin may be difficult to see**; median fins continuous round tail; **rear nostril a slit or tube before or above eye**; head pores obvious or indistinct; **LL restricted to 1–3 minute pores** before gill opening. Size range 25 cm to 3.8 m.

Shallow water, coral and rocky reefs, estuaries, mud or silty sand or sandy bottom from shore to 70 m. Morays that feed mainly on fish have long powerful jaws, with numerous sharp canines and some long depressible fangs; species that prefer crustaceans have short jaws with nodular or molariform teeth. Details of reproduction are still unknown for most species, but we know that some morays are protandrous hermaphrodites and a few are synchronous hermaphrodites. Morays are not aggressive and rarely bite people, except when someone reaches into a hole or crevice where a moray is hiding.

Worldwide in tropical and warm temperate waters. About 15 genera, ~200 species, ~37 species in our area.

Floral moray

Lipspot moray

Honeycomb moray

Geometric moray

FLORAL MORAY
Echidna nebulosa
(Ahl 1789)

12 cm

Tail about half TL; **dorsal and anal fins distinct, beginning just ahead of gill opening and just behind anus**; front nostrils tubular, near tip of snout and directed forward; rear nostrils a small hole above front edge of eye; teeth short, conical, blunter with age; **no canines**; teeth at front of upper jaw in males blade-like, rear edge weakly serrate; front teeth of females bluntly conical. Colour pattern variable: white to creamy yellow, with **1–3 rows of numerous irregular brownish black blotches, usually with 1–3 yellow spots**; pale interspaces with irregular dark spots and flecks; snout and jaws pale. Attains 75 cm and has lived in an aquarium for at least 16 years.

Indo-West Pacific, Red Sea, Oman to East London.

Shallow water in rocks, seagrass beds and reefs. Usually nocturnal, but often seen during day. Feeds on crustaceans (mainly crabs) and small fish. When prey is too large to be swallowed immediately, the eel knots itself around the prey in order to manipulate it for swallowing or for tearing off bite-sized pieces. Spawning behaviour and larval development unknown, but this species appears to be a protogynous hermaphrodite.

In the aquarium, the floral moray seems near-sighted, and one has to wiggle the food close to its head before it seizes the food. Generally peaceful, but like most predators, this eel will eat any small unwary fish. Needs a large aquarium.

SIMILAR SPECIES

Juveniles of the barred moray, *Echidna polyzona* (Richardson 1845), are dark brown with 25–30 narrow greyish yellow rings, adults mottled dark brown. Indo-central Pacific, south to Sodwana Bay.

The whiteface moray, *Echidna leucotaenia* Schultz 1943, has uniformly dark brown body, with white fins and white patches on jaws. Indo-central Pacific, south to Sodwana Bay.

The zebra moray, *Gymnomuraena zebra* (Shaw 1797) [formerly placed in *Echidna*], also has blunt teeth and is dark brownish black with numerous narrow yellowish bars, much narrower than dark interspaces. Indo-Pacific, Oman to Durban.

LIPSPOT MORAY
Gymnothorax chilospilus
Bleeker 1865

20 cm

Dorsal fin origin well before gill opening; teeth uniserial to biserial, long fangs present; 3 rows of intermaxillary teeth, with 3 fang-like median teeth; maxillary teeth of juveniles and females biserial, of males uniserial; vomer teeth uniserial. Pre-anal length 2.0–2.3 times in TL; head length 7.0–8.6 times in TL; body depth at gill opening 14–22 times in TL, depth at anus 17–26 times in TL; snout 4.9–6.2 times in head length; upper jaw 2.6–2.9 times in head length; eye diameter 7.4–11 times in head length. Brownish with complex and variable pattern of irregular dark brown blotches and reticulations sometimes forming irregular vertical bars, occasionally nearly uniform brown; snout brown, posterior head pores in pale areas continuing around lower jaw, **bright white spot at rear of lower jaw just in front of dark brown rictus**; iris dark brown with gold ring around pupil. Attains 51 cm.

Indo-West Pacific, Oman to Aliwal Shoal and islands of western Indian Ocean.

Coral and rocky reefs in 2–45 m. Biology and distribution poorly known; previously confused with the undulated moray *Gymnothorax undulatus* (Lacepède 1803). This Indo-West Pacific species is known south to Inhaca and has been confused with an undescribed South African endemic moray. Neither of these 'undulated morays' has the white spot near the rictus of the lipspot moray.

HONEYCOMB MORAY
Gymnothorax favagineus
Bloch & Schneider 1801

55 cm

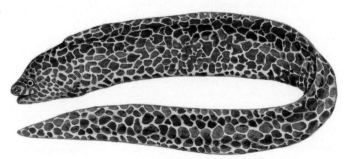

Body depth at anus 12–23 times in TL; dorsal fin begins ahead of gill opening; front nostrils tubular, near tip of snout and directed forward; rear nostrils a small hole above front edge of eye; 1 continuous row of sharp prominent teeth on jaws; several large depressible fangs at front of upper jaw; 1 or 2 rows of smaller teeth on vomer. **Dark honeycomb pattern** separated by network of pale lines; blotches on head not much bigger than eye,

pattern continues into mouth. One of the largest morays; attains 2 m.

Indo-West Pacific, Red Sea, Oman to Algoa Bay and islands of western Indian Ocean.

Shallow water in rocks and reefs; also out to 45 m and common on wrecks. Usually nocturnal, but often seen with its head protruding from the reef during day. Feeds on octopus and small fish. When prey is too large to be swallowed, the eel clamps its jaws on the prey, knots its tail and passes the knot towards its head, where the knot is pushed against the prey while the head is pulled back through the knot, thus ripping off a bite-sized piece of prey. Spawning behaviour and larval development unknown. Usually not aggressive; can be trained to take food from a diver's hand, but this practice is risky. The large size and strength of this moray make even an accidental bite a traumatic experience.

The reticulated moray, *Gymnothorax permistus* (Smith), is considered a synonym.

GEOMETRIC MORAY
Gymnothorax griseus
(Lacepède 1803)

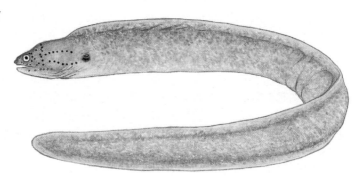

53 cm (Mauritius)

Body depth at anus 16–25 times in TL; tail (measured from anus) 1.4–1.6 times body length; dorsal fin distinct, beginning on head; front nostrils tubular, near tip of snout and directed forward; rear nostrils a small hole above front edge of eye; teeth numerous, short and stout. **Head with conspicuous lines of black dots**; body lilac-grey with brown mottling or mostly golden brown or yellowish with close-set brown dots; juveniles paler. Attains 65 cm.

Western Indian Ocean, Red Sea to the Eastern Cape.

Usually found on coral reefs. Feeds at night on small fish; hides in reef during the day. Appears to be a synchronous hermaphrodite, with ripe eggs and sperm developed simultaneously. Eggs and sperm are released (perhaps simultaneously) into the body cavity before they find their way out to the sea water via the urogenital pores on either side of the anus. Consequently, it may be difficult for this eel to avoid self-fertilisation. Eggs are nearly 3 mm in diameter, buoyant and released in batches of 8 000 to 12 000. Ripe fish are obvious from their large swollen bellies.

A small harmless species. Does well in an aquarium. Previously classified in the genus *Siderea*, which has recently been included in the genus *Gymnothorax*.

SIMILAR SPECIES

The paintspotted moray, *Gymnothorax pictus* (Ahl 1789), has tail subequal to body; head and body greyish, covered with irregular dark spots; juveniles yellow with irregular dark-ringed ocelli. Indo-Pacific, Oman to Sodwana Bay.

FAMILY OPHICHTHIDAE ■ Snake Eels

Body elongate, eel-like, without scales; **tail round in cross-section; 1 median sensory pore at rear of inter-orbital area**; pectoral fins present or absent; **rear nostril usually within or piercing upper lip**; branchiostegal rays numerous (15–49 pairs) and overlapping ventrally, forming a basket-like structure. Size range 15 cm to 2.5 m.

   Cryptic species, most hiding on reef or buried in sand or mud from shore to 200 m, but also found to 800 m; some species in estuaries. Rarely seen during day.

Worldwide in tropical and warm temperate waters. About 55 genera and more than 260 species, ~34 in our area.

Spotted snake eel

Serpent eel

SPOTTED SNAKE EEL
Myrichthys maculosus
(Cuvier 1816)

48 cm (Comoros)

Tail tip a hard finless point; body depth 33–46 times, head length 12–16 times in TL; dorsal and anal fin inconspicuous; dorsal fin origin on top of head; pectoral fins short; front nostrils a tube at tip of snout; rear nostril hidden in upper lip; 2 rows of small blunt teeth on jaws and vomer. **Head and body** pale, **covered with** large and small round to oval **brown/black spots**. Attains 1 m.

Indo-Pacific, Red Sea, Oman to the Eastern Cape and islands of the western Indian Ocean.

Often seen by day in sandy areas of coral reefs to 30 m; also in seagrass beds. Feeds on crustaceans and fish. Disappears in seconds by burrowing tail-first into the sand. If swallowed whole by a large fish, the snake eel can burrow through the predator's stomach wall with its hard-pointed tail. The unfortunate eel then seems trapped in the body cavity, as they are occasionally found mummified in the body cavity of predators.

   Does well in a large aquarium.

As implied by its name, the ringed snake eel, *Myrichthys colubrinus* (Boddaert 1781), is milky yellow with 25–32 narrow black rings; black spots between the rings in large adults. Indo-central Pacific, Oman to Maputo Bay.

SERPENT EEL
Ophisurus serpens
(Linnaeus 1766)

68 cm

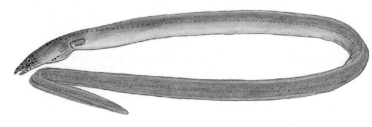

Body extremely elongate and slender; body depth at gill opening 40–60 times in TL; head length 11–13 times in TL; **snout and jaws elongate and slender, those of adults incapable of closing completely**; snout very long, less than 4 times in head length, snout tip slightly swollen (seen from above); tail tip a hard finless point; pectoral fins distinct; dorsal and anal fins inconspicuous; dorsal fin origin behind pectoral fins; front nostril a short tube on side of snout slightly closer to eye than tip of snout; rear nostril hidden by flap in upper lip; large fangs at front of jaws followed by 1–2 rows of smaller pointed teeth; a row of large and small slender teeth on vomer. Head and body olive-green or brown above, paler below; **head and LL pores in black spots**; juveniles silvery. Attains at least 2.5 m.

Eastern Atlantic and Indo-West Pacific in subtropical and temperate waters; extends all round the coast of southern Africa to Mozambique.

Inshore in sandy and muddy areas; common in estuaries; also offshore to at least 300 m. Feeds on crustaceans and small fish. Usually seen with just its head sticking out of the sand; strikes upwards to capture unsuspecting prey. Burrows either tail first or head first, and can disappear in seconds. Probably more active at night.

One of the longest eels; the slender body is deceptive as this is a powerful eel.

The bluntnose snake eel, *Ophichthus apicalis* (Bennett 1830), might be confused with juvenile serpent eels which are shorter snouted than adults. Bluntnose snake eels are yellow-brown with pale fins and lack black head and LL pores; their bodies are much less slender, depth at gill opening 26–33 times in TL. Attains 45 cm. Indo-West Pacific, Kenya to St Francis Bay and Madagascar.

The slender giant moray, *Strophidon sathete* (Hamilton 1822) [formerly *Thyrsoidea macrura* (Bleeker 1854)], also occurs in estuaries, but the snout is shorter, pectoral fins absent, and dorsal and anal fins continuous round tip of tail. Attains 3.8 m. Indo-central Pacific, south to St Lucia. The IGFA all-tackle record for the slender giant moray is a 5.35 kg moray from St Lucia.

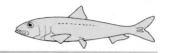

FAMILY CLUPEIDAE ■ Herring, Sardines & Pilchards

Moderate-sized silvery fish; body fusiform or strongly compressed; most species with a keel of scutes along belly. Mouth more or less terminal, upper jaw not reaching past eye; teeth minute or absent; gill rakers usually numerous, long and slender; no spines in fins. Scales cycloid, usually deciduous; no lateral line. Size range 6–28 cm.

Most clupeid fish occur in large schools near the surface and many are caught with huge purse seines. These vast catches make the clupeids of great economic importance in world fisheries. Usually salted or tinned for human consumption; also used for animal food. Juveniles of some species enter estuaries, and the estuarine roundherring can tolerate freshwater.

Vernacular names for clupeid fish (herring, sardine and pilchard) are confusing as they are often used interchangeably. To prevent misunderstanding one should include the scientific name when referring to these fish.

Worldwide in tropical and temperate seas. About 56 genera, ~190 species; ~50 species occur in freshwater. Thirteen species in our area.

Redeye roundherring

Estuarine roundherring

Pilchard

REDEYE ROUNDHERRING
Etrumeus whiteheadi
Wongratana 1983

22 cm

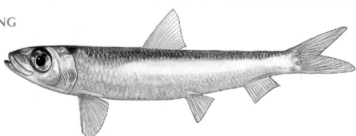

Belly rounded, ventral scutes absent or hidden; pelvic fin bases under or behind last 2 dorsal fin rays; anal fin rays 12–13, base short, well behind dorsal fin base; **gill rakers 16–18 / 35–40**. Head and body blue-green dorsally, flanks silvery. Attains 20 cm.

Endemic, Walvis Bay to Thukela River.

Females mature at 14–19 cm (~18 months). Juveniles occur in vast schools (often mixed with pilchards and anchovies) inshore in upwelling areas off the Western Cape. During the day, adults usually near bottom in 100–400 m, but at dusk they rise to surface where they can be caught with large purse seines. Spawns repeatedly on outer continental shelf and upper slope region in winter and spring. Feeds on zooplankton.

The name 'redeye' refers to the bleeding often visible in eyes of captured fish. Used for fish meal, fish oil or fish paste.

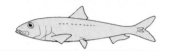

The east coast roundherring, *Etrumeus teres* (DeKay 1842), is known virtually worldwide in tropical and subtropical waters and is usually found north of Durban. It has 31–35 lower gill rakers; pelvic fin base half eye diameter behind last dorsal fin ray of adults.

The pilchard has longer anal fin (18–21 rays), operculum with bony ridges and a series of dark spots along the sides.

ESTUARINE ROUNDHERRING
Gilchristella aestuaria
(Gilchrist 1913)

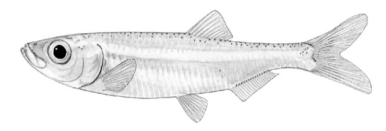

4 cm

Body fairly compressed; belly rounded, with rudimentary scutes (not visible without dissection); **pelvic fin origins in front of dorsal fin base**; pelvic fins reach halfway to anus. Gill raker counts highly variable. Body translucent; head and abdominal cavity silvery; top and sides of head and body sprinkled with black dots. Attains 65 mm (3 years).

Endemic, Olifants River north of Lambert's Bay to southern Mozambique.

Abundant in estuaries, coastal lakes and lower parts of rivers; rarely found in the sea. This roundherring completes its entire life cycle in estuaries. Seven-month-old fish (greater than 3 cm SL) are mature and spawn most of the year, with peaks in spring and summer. Feeds by day on zooplankton, either filter-feeding (in turbid estuaries) or by individually selecting larger zooplankton in clear water. In the turbid St Lucia system, where small copepods are abundant, *Gilchristella* have a deeper body and smaller head and eyes (head length less than body depth) than fish from estuaries with less abundant zooplankton. These different proportions appear to result from different growth rates in different habitats.

Usually found in shoals, this species is a major prey of estuarine bird and fish predators.

— SIMILAR SPECIES —

Differs from anchovies (which also have a silvery mid-lateral stripe on body) in its terminal mouth (mouth underslung in anchovies).

PILCHARD
Sardinops sagax
(Jenyns 1842)

18 cm

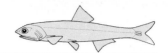

Body fusiform, not much compressed; **pelvic fins under dorsal fin at mid body; belly rounded with feeble scutes; radiating bony ridges on lower part of opercle**, even distinct in juveniles. Gill rakers ~120 in large fish; 2 enlarged scales at base of tail fin. **Body silvery with a series of dark spots**, some fish with a 2nd or 3rd series below. Attains 28 cm.

Subtropical and warm temperate waters of Southern Hemisphere and North Pacific; not known from southwestern Atlantic; in our area over continental shelf from southern Angola to Maputo. This schooling migratory species occurs in two populations: Namibian (Angola to Lüderitz) and South African (Orange River to Maputo). Mixing of these two populations is prevented by the cold water upwelling that occurs for most of the year off Lüderitz.

Two-year-old pilchards spawn repeatedly in spring and summer over the Agulhas Bank; and some spawning also occurs off southern KZN in winter and spring. Eggs and larvae from the Agulhas Bank spawning drift westwards. Juveniles congregate inshore in upwelling areas off the Western Cape coast during autumn and winter, eventually working their way to the south and east coasts where spawning occurs.

The numerous gill rakers of pilchards provide an efficient filter-feeding apparatus for microscopic phytoplankton (dinoflagellates and diatoms), and pilchards also feed on larger zooplankton (copepods and anchovy eggs). Pilchards are eaten by a wide variety of piscivores: snoek, tuna, yellowtail, garrick, geelbek, kob, bronze whaler, dusky shark, hammerhead, sixgill shark, hake, dolphins, seals, penguins, gannets, etc.

Following catches of 400 000 tonnes per year in the early 1960s, the South African pilchard catch crashed to ~70 000 tonnes in 1967. The Namibian pilchard catch increased to 1.4 million tonnes in 1968, fell to 300 000 tonnes in 1971, and stayed below 100 000 tonnes from 1978 to 1988. The population fluctuations of pilchard are monitored by Marine and Coastal Management (MCM) surveys to estimate the sustainable level of annual pelagic fish catches.

The annual Sardine Run off the east coast is controlled by changes in water temperature. In May and June, warm inshore water along the Eastern Cape coast is replaced by water less than 20° C. This cooler water allows enormous schools of pilchards and some other cool water clupeoids (anchovy and roundherring) to move inshore and northwards. These densely packed schools are chased into shallow water by dolphins and fish predators and become easy prey for birds, fish and humans. Rock and surf anglers catch many of the large fish predators from shore. The frenetic activity in the surf attracts people on shore and they jump in with baskets, skirts, buckets and nets to catch some of the abundant pilchards.

FAMILY ENGRAULIDAE ■ Anchovies

Body elongate, cylindrical or compressed; **snout projecting in front of mouth; maxilla reaching well past eye; teeth minute; gill rakers long and numerous**, typical of plankton-feeding fish. Size range 8–25 cm.

Pelagic fish, usually over continental shelf in huge schools. Anchovies are of great commercial importance in world fisheries.

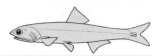
Worldwide in tropical and warm temperate waters. About 16 genera, ~139 species; a few species occur in freshwater, but most are marine. Six species in our area.

Japanese anchovy   Thorny anchovy

JAPANESE ANCHOVY
Engraulis japonicus
Temminck & Schlegel 1846

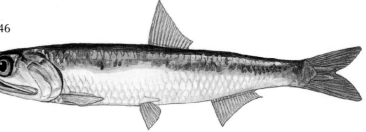

7 cm (no locality)

Belly rounded, **without scutes**; dorsal fin origin over pelvic fin bases; anal fin base well behind dorsal fin; **maxilla tip rounded, barely reaching edge of preopercle**. Silvery stripe along flanks in fish larger than 6 cm. Attains 13 cm (±3 years).

Distribution uncertain; Walvis Bay to Maputo in our area.

Pelagic from coast to ~200 m; abundant on Agulhas Bank. Feeds on zooplankton (mainly large copepods and krill). Although spawning occurs from Plettenberg Bay to Durban, most spawning takes place on the Agulhas Bank from October to January. One-year-old fish are mature and may release 10 batches (~10 000 eggs per batch at weekly intervals)

in a spawning season. Older fish can produce 20 or more batches per year. Unlike most fish eggs which are spherical, anchovy eggs are ellipsoidal. Eggs and larvae (which hatch 2.5 days after spawning) are carried towards the west coast, where dense plankton in upwelling areas supports rapid growth of juveniles.

Anchovies are a major component of the purse-seine fishery in South Africa. They are processed into fish meal, oil and paste. They also contribute to the winter Sardine Run that moves up the east coast to Durban.

The taxonomy and distribution of the *Engraulis* species are uncertain. The species that occurs off southern Africa may be endemic to our area.

THORNY ANCHOVY
Stolephorus holodon
(Boulenger 1900)

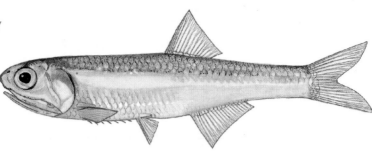

8 cm (no locality)

Body somewhat compressed, with **6–8 sharp needle-like scutes along belly in front of pelvic fins**; anal fin origin below dorsal fin; **maxilla tip pointed, reaching edge of operculum. Silver band along flanks**. Attains 8 cm.

Western Indian Ocean, Kenya to Algoa Bay.

An inshore species, often found in estuaries. Matures at 5 cm SL; spawns in summer, usually in the sea. Feeds on plankton, mainly copepods. No commercial value.

SIMILAR SPECIES

The Indian anchovy, *Stolephorus indicus* (van Hasselt 1823), has a shorter maxilla, not reaching the edge of the preopercle. Indo-central Pacific, south to KZN.

The buccaneer anchovy, *Encrasicholina punctifer* Fowler 1938, and Japanese anchovy (see above) have the anal fin origin behind the dorsal fin. The buccaneer anchovy has a diamond-shaped plate at anterior end of isthmus. Indo-central Pacific, south to St Lucia.

FAMILY CHANIDAE Milkfish

Body elongate, fusiform, covered with small grooved cycloid scales; head naked; **adipose eyelid well developed; mouth small, terminal; jaws toothless; gill membranes united, forming free fold across isthmus; no fin spines; dorsal fin over middle of body; tail fin deeply forked**; pelvic fins abdominal; anal fin close to tail fin. A single species.

MILKFISH
Chanos chanos
(Forsskål 1775)

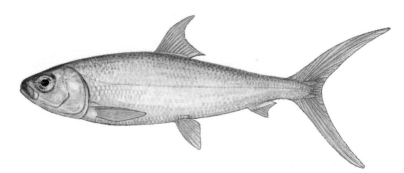

90 cm

Dorsal fin rays 13–17; anal fin rays 8–10; pectoral fin rays 15–17; pelvic fin rays 10–12; gill rakers more than 100. Head and body silvery blue-green above, white below. Attains 1.8 m (~15 years).

Tropical and warm temperate waters of Indo-Pacific, Red Sea to Swartvlei.

Occurs on soft bottom; abundant in estuaries of KZN. Feeds in shallow water on detritus and benthic invertebrates. A popular species for aquaculture. The hardy inshore larvae are easy to catch and have been reared in fish-culture operations for centuries in southeast Asia. Wild fish mature at 3–5 years of age (~50 cm, 4 kg), but in captivity may take 8–10 years to reach maturity. Spawns in sea at night in summer, sometimes more than once a year; eggs buoyant, but lack an oil globule. The ribbon-like larvae move inshore and into estuaries; some juveniles occur in freshwater, but do not mature there.

Shoals of milkfish in shallow water with dorsal fins exposed are sometimes mistaken for sharks. Caught with beach seines and by shore anglers; a vigorous fighter. SADSAA all-tackle record: 11.85 kg.

SIMILAR SPECIES

The ladyfish (see p. 98) is more slender (body depth distinctly less than head length), has a larger mouth (upper jaw reaches past eye) and a median gular bone on underside of lower jaw.

FAMILY ARIIDAE ■ Sea-catfish

Skin naked; 1st dorsal fin and pectoral fins with a large serrate venomous spine; no pelvic fin spine; 2 barbels on upper jaw, another 4 on lower jaw; teeth villiform, conical or granular; tail fin forked; adipose fin and swimbladder well developed; LL complete and branching onto head. Size range 30 cm to ~60 cm.

Shallow marine, brackish and freshwater. Edible; caught by anglers from shore or boats; also common in trawls.

Worldwide on tropical and temperate continental coasts. About 14 genera, ~124 species, 4 in our area.

WHITE SEA-CATFISH
Galeichthys feliceps
Valenciennes 1840

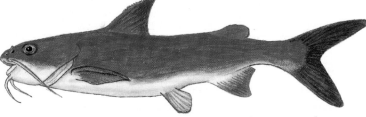

25 cm FL

Top of head smooth, covered with muscle and skin; **tail fin deeply forked, the lobes acute; distance from tail fin notch to tip of longest ray contained 1.4–2.2 times in head length**. Brown to grey or greenish brown above, paler below, midline of belly whitish. Attains 55 cm.

Endemic, Swakopmund to East London.

Benthic species, prefers inshore areas over soft bottom in bays and estuaries; also encountered offshore (to 102 m). Females mature at 24 cm SL, males at 26 cm. Spawning

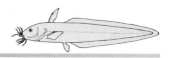

and mouth-brooding of young occur mainly in estuaries from September to December. The eggs are huge, 15–16 mm in diameter, and average brood size comprises 49 eggs. Males carry eggs and hatched embryos in their mouth for the 3–4 month incubation period, during which they do not feed, losing up to 24% of their total body weight. Eggs hatch after 75–80 days. In estuaries males are more common than females. Adults feed on crustaceans (mainly crabs), polychaetes, molluscs (including cephalopods) and fish; juveniles are primarily scavengers.

The dorsal and pectoral fin spines are venomous and cause painful wounds. Recommended treatment: immerse affected area in hot (50° C) water immediately, and keep wound in hot water for 30 minutes. Good eating and of some commercial importance in the Eastern Cape. A closed season from September to December would allow females to spawn before they are caught by anglers. SADSAA all-tackle record: 2.8 kg.

SIMILAR SPECIES

The black sea-catfish, *Galeichthys ater* Castelnau 1861, has tail fin lobes rounded, less deeply forked (distance from tail fin notch to tip of longest ray 2.7–4.0 times in head length). Head and body dark brown above and below. Western Cape to Margate.

FAMILY PLOTOSIDAE ■ Eel-catfish

Body elongate, **tail tapering to a point, with 2nd dorsal fin and anal fins joined to small tail fin; 1st dorsal fin and pectoral fins with a sharp serrate venomous spine; 4 pairs of barbels around mouth; skin naked**. Marine species have an arborescent organ (which may have salt-excreting function) in a pit behind anus. Moderate-sized (30 cm to ~60 cm) predators.

Shallow marine, brackish and freshwater. Feed on invertebrates and fish. Probably edible, certainly venomous.

Tropical and warm temperate Indo-Pacific region. About 9 genera, ~32 species, 2 in our area, one endemic.

STRIPED EEL-CATFISH
Plotosus lineatus
(Thunberg 1787)

6 cm juvenile (Comoros)
18 cm (Mauritius)

Gill membranes separate and attached to front end of isthmus; front nostrils a tube at edge of upper lip; teeth present on upper jaw; **total gill rakers 22–32**. Newly settled juveniles uniformly black; larger **juveniles dark brown or black above, with 2 pale stripes from head to tail; underside of head and body pale; pale stripes less obvious on large adults**. Attains 32 cm (~7 years).

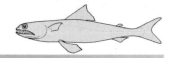

Tropical and warm temperate Indo-West Pacific, Red Sea to KZN; rarely south of KZN.

Inshore reefs, open coasts, tide pools; occasionally in estuaries. Oviparous, with demersal eggs and planktonic larvae. Feeds on benthic invertebrates, algae, molluscs and fish. Small juveniles occur in tight ball-like schools; large juveniles in swarm-like schools that contract at approach of predators. Adults solitary, usually in caves or under ledges. Juveniles can be seen busily carrying mouthfuls of sand when excavating a depression under a large rock. Males make a nest under a rock and guard the eggs.

Small juveniles are attractive aquarium fish, but grow rapidly and need a large aquarium; one must be wary of the venomous fin spines. Treat wounds in hot (50° C) water.

SIMILAR SPECIES

The endemic eel-catfish, *Plotosus nkunga* Gomon & Taylor 1982, usually lacks pale stripes (faint stripes sometimes visible on body but not extending onto head) and it has fewer gill rakers (total 16–21). Knysna to Kosi Bay.

FAMILY SYNODONTIDAE ▪ Lizardfish

Body cylindrical; fins with branched and unbranched rays, but no spines; small dorsal adipose fin above anal fin; pelvic fins abdominal with 8–9 rays; nostrils double; mouth extends well past eye; jaws with **numerous needle-like teeth**, teeth also present on palatines and tongue. Scale counts above and below the LL are of longitudinal rows of scales between the LL and origins of the dorsal and anal fin bases. Size range 15–53 cm.

Sandy or mud bottom, also coral or rocky reefs, from shore to ~ 200 m. These sedentary predators are usually well camouflaged, and are often buried in sand with just their eyes showing. When an unwary fish swims too close, the lizardfish rockets off the bottom and seizes the prey with its large jaws.

Worldwide in tropical and warm temperate waters. Three genera, ~ 56 species, 10 in our area.

Largescale lizardfish

Indian lizardfish

Redband lizardfish

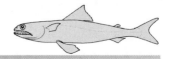

LARGESCALE LIZARDFISH
Saurida undosquamis
(Richardson 1848)

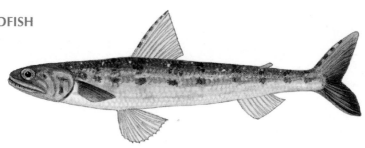

23 cm

Dorsal fin rays 11–13; anal fin rays 10–12; pectoral fin rays 14–15; **pelvic fin rays 9; tail fin mostly covered with tiny transparent scales**; front nostril flap short, reaches only slightly beyond nostril margin when depressed anteriorly; **upper jaw teeth needle-like and mostly exposed**; no teeth on vomer; scale rows above LL $3^1/_2$, below $5^1/_2$. Head and body brown dorsally, often with 8–10 faint dark bars joining row of dark spots along LL; **dark spots usually visible along front edge of dorsal fin and upper edge of tail fin**; lower tail lobe and rear margin of fin dusky. Attains 53 cm (6–7 years).

Figure 36 *Lizardfish (Saurida) showing closed mouth with upper jaw teeth exposed.*

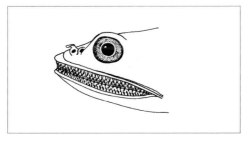

Tropical and warm temperate Indo-West Pacific, Red Sea to Knysna. Recently established population in the Mediterranean.

Common on sandy and mud bottom to 200 m. Seems to avoid estuaries. Feeds on fish and crustaceans. Literature reports of size at maturity are contradictory, with records of maturity at 11–12 cm FL (1-year-old males) or 25–36 cm FL (3–4 years). It seems that two species may be confused as *S. undosquamis*.

Common in trawls, but not highly regarded as a food-fish. Makes good bait for trolling.

— SIMILAR SPECIES —

The blotchy lizardfish, *Saurida gracilis* (Quoy & Gaimard 1824), has 9–12 dorsal fin rays, prominent dark blotches on body; dorsal, pelvic and tail fins with dark bars and spots; front nostril flap heavily pigmented. Attains 28 cm. Indo-West Pacific, south to Algoa Bay.

The greater lizardfish, *Saurida tumbil* (Bloch 1795), lacks dark spots along front edges of dorsal and tail fins and has teeth on vomer; attains 40 cm. Indo-West Pacific, Red Sea, Persian Gulf to Maputo.

INDIAN LIZARDFISH
Synodus indicus
(Day 1873)

12 cm

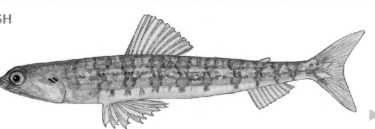

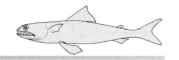

Dorsal fin rays 11–13; anal fin rays 9–11; **pectoral fin rays 12–13; pelvic fin rays 8**; tail fin mostly without scales; upper jaw teeth slender, compressed, mostly hidden by lip; **scales above LL 3¹/₂**, below 5; front nostril flap long and pointed; cheek covered with large scales. Body dusky pink dorsally, with pale blue-grey blotches and stripes; **2 short black streaks at upper edge of operculum**; tail fin yellow with blackish margin; some fish with ~9 dark blotches along LL. Attains 33 cm.

Indian Ocean, southern Red Sea to the Eastern Cape (occasionally to Mossel Bay).

Sandy or mud bottom in depths of 20–100 m. Common in by-catch of prawn trawlers, but not valued for human consumption. Aquarium specimens often try to leap out at night.

SIMILAR SPECIES

The variegated lizardfish, *Synodus dermatogenys* Fowler 1912, has 5¹/₂ scale rows above LL; body with 8–9 dark brown saddle blotches (upper half of alternate blotches may be reddish in life), no black streaks at upper edge of operculum and usually a bluish grey stripe along upper side. Indo-West Pacific, south to Algoa Bay.

The spotnose lizardfish, *Synodus binotatus* Schultz 1953, has 2 small dark spots on tip of snout; no black streaks at upper edge of operculum; body in front of dorsal fin pale, rear part of body with 3–4 dark saddle blotches. Indo-West Pacific, south to KZN.

REDBAND LIZARDFISH
Synodus variegatus
(Lacepède 1803)

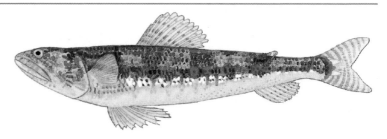

30 cm

Dorsal fin rays 11–13; anal fin rays 8–10; pectoral fin rays 11–13; pelvic fin rays 8; tail fin mostly without scales; front nostril flap short and rounded (rarely with slender point), not reaching middle of rear nostril; **scale rows above LL 5**, below 7. Two colour phases: **brown phase with broad dark brown midlateral band from head to tail, intersecting series of narrow dark brown bars and 4 broad saddle blotches; red phase with red band (or series of red blotches) running along scale row below LL and through series of vertical red (or dark brown) bars and blotches**. Tail fin with reddish brown spots or crossbars; paired fins yellow; dorsal fin pale yellow with reddish brown spots on rays. Attains 33 cm.

Indo-West Pacific, Red Sea to Aliwal Shoal.

Coral reefs and sandy areas near reefs; common in shallow water (5–60 m). Often seen in pairs on coral reefs. This well camouflaged ambush predator sits motionless, with only its eyes following movements of prey.

Makes an attractive aquarium fish, but cannot be kept in a communal tank with smaller fish.

SIMILAR SPECIES

The blacktail lizardfish, *Synodus jaculum* Russell & Cressey 1979, also occurs on coral reefs, but it has a distinct black blotch at tail base. Indo-West Pacific, south to KZN.

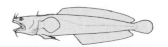

FAMILY PHYCIDAE ■ Rocklings

Body elongate; gill opening extends above pectoral fin base; 2 or 3 dorsal fins; 1 anal fin; no fin spines; swimbladder not connected to skull. A few species live in estuaries or freshwater, but most occur on continental slope. Size range 16 cm to 1.2 m.

Demersal fish on continental shelf and slope from shore to 980 m on rocky, mud, sand, shell or gravel bottom.

Worldwide in temperate seas. Classification unsettled, previously included in Family Gadidae or Subfamily Lotinae. Five genera, 27 species, 2 in our area.

CAPE ROCKLING
Gaidropsarus capensis
(Kaup 1858)

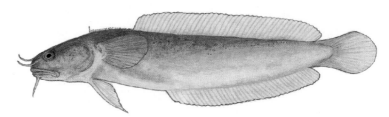

16 cm

Long 1st dorsal fin ray on nape, followed by a groove with a row of short fleshy filaments in front of long-based 2nd dorsal fin; pair of barbels on snout next to nostrils and single chin barbel; 2nd dorsal fin rays 43–52; anal fin rays 37–43; pectoral fin rays 18–21; pelvic fin rays 7. Head and body golden brown, belly and pelvic fins pale; median fins yellowish. Attains 18 cm.

Endemic, Walvis Ridge off Namibia, Lambert's Bay (eggs and larvae) to East London.

Rocky areas from shore to 50 m. A cryptic species usually hiding under rocks. Spawns all year; eggs buoyant with several oil globules; pelagic larvae transform to benthic juveniles at 21–25 mm (2 months old).

Too small to be of commercial importance.

SIMILAR SPECIES

The comb rockling, *Gaidropsarus novaezelandiae* (Hector 1874), has 2nd dorsal fin rays 62–64 and 50–54 anal fin rays. Known from tide pools of the Cape Peninsula and west coast. Reported from New Zealand, Tristan da Cunha and Gough, St Paul and Amsterdam islands.

FAMILY MERLUCCIIDAE ■ Hake

Body elongate, with cycloid scales; **V-shaped ridge on top of head**; mouth terminal, with sharp teeth on jaws and vomer; no chin barbel; 2 dorsal fins; no fin spines; pectoral fins mid-lateral; pelvic fin rays 7; tail fin separate from dorsal and anal fins; **swimbladder not attached to skull**. Size range 60 cm to 1.4 m.

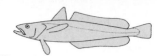

Continental shelf and upper slope. Hake are of great commercial importance.

Worldwide in temperate seas. One genus, 13 species, 2 in our area.

SHALLOW-WATER HAKE
Merluccius capensis
Castelnau 1861

44 cm

First dorsal fin rays 10–12; 2nd dorsal fin rays 38–43; anal fin rays 37–41; pectoral fin rays 14–16; gill rakers 3–6 / 11–15; **no pigment spots on gill arches**. Brownish dorsally, silvery-white ventrally. Attains 1.4 m, 19 kg (15 years).

Southern Angola to KZN, also on Valdivia Bank off Namibia.

During the day, adults rest near the bottom on the continental shelf and upper slope, to 550 m. Females grow faster than males and mature at 45–60 cm; spawning occurs in mid-water mainly from October to December. Young form schools at surface, but transform to benthic juveniles at 7–8 cm; 1-year-old fish are 16 cm; 10-year-olds are ~1 m. During the day, hake occur near bottom, but at night they move into midwater. Adults feed mainly on fish, including young hake; crustaceans and cephalopods comprise less than 10% of diet.

Abundant in trawl fishery, but catches have fluctuated widely from year to year due to overfishing and vagaries of recruitment. With proper management, annual landings of this most valuable fishery could be half a million tonnes.

— SIMILAR SPECIES —————

The endemic deepwater hake, *Merluccius paradoxus* Franca 1960, has 4–7 / 13–18 gill rakers and prominent pigment spots on the gill arches. Occurs from Angola to East London.

FAMILY OPHIDIIDAE ■ Cuskeels

Body tapering to a point, with **dorsal and anal fins long, low and joined to tail fin**; pelvic fins absent or of 1–2 slender rays. Scales small and cycloid. Oviparous. Size range 16 cm to 1.6 m.

Most species in deep water. The world depth record for fish is the ophidiid *Abyssobrotula galatheae* Nielsen 1977, recorded from 8 370 m in the Puerto Rico Trench.

Worldwide. About 46 genera, ~209 species, ~23 in our area.

KINGKLIP

Genypterus capensis
(Smith 1847)

1.2 m adult

Body depth ~7 times in TL; pectoral fin length 2.1–2.9 times in head; **pelvic fins on front of isthmus under eyes**; maxilla reaches past eye; no spines on preopercle or opercle. Scales minute, cycloid, in regular rows. Head and body **mottled pinkish brown**. Attains 1.6 m (~20 years).

Endemic, Swakopmund to Durban.

Rocky areas of continental shelf and upper slope in 50–550 m. Matures at 4–6 years when females are ~62 cm, males 48 cm; after maturity, females grow faster than males.

Nocturnal sedentary scavenger; juveniles occur inshore (< 200 m) and feed on a variety of benthic fish, crustaceans and squid; adults eat mainly fish.

The most sought-after species of the commercially important deep sea fishes. The longline fishery catches mainly large adults; juveniles taken by hake trawlers. Excellent food-fish; although the scales are very small and difficult to see without a lens, they are present, hence this fish should be considered kosher.

FAMILY LOPHIIDAE ▪ Monkfish

Head and anterior part of body flattened; dorsal surface of head with bony spines, knobs and ridges; skin thin, loose and naked; numerous fleshy flaps, tendrils and cirri on lateral margins of head and body; mouth enormous with long, slender and inwardly depressible teeth; lower jaw projecting well in front of upper jaw; soft dorsal fin over anal fin and near tail fin. **First dorsal fin spine at front of snout and modified as a fishing pole, with fleshy bait (*esca*) at tip; pelvic fins on underside of head.** Size range 30 cm to 1.2 m.

Continental shelf and upper slope in 70–600 m. Sedentary predators, mainly piscivorous. Excellent eating, marketed in South Africa.

Worldwide in tropical and temperate waters. Four genera with ~25 species, 5 in our area.

MONK
Lophius vomerinus
Valenciennes 1837

26 cm juvenile
1 cm postlarva

Dorsal fin with 3 isolated spines followed by 2–4 spines joined by a membrane and a soft-rayed fin of 8–13 rays; 1st and 2nd dorsal fin spines long, the rest short (3rd spine 5–8% SL); bait (*esca*) elongate, flattened, unbranched, often with long tassel arising from central fold; anal fin rays 7–11; pectoral fin rays 21–27. Upper surface mottled dark brown to pale greenish grey; underside white to dark brown; **peritoneum white**; dorsal fin spines 2–6 with dark brown tendrils. Attains 1 m.

Endemic, Namibia to East London.

Benthic fish in 67–485 m. One-year-old monks ~22 cm; matures at 40 cm (4 years); a 10-year-old monk is ~60 cm. Spawns in summer; eggs embedded in ribbon-like veils that float at surface. This well camouflaged predator sits on the bottom, waving its fishing lure over its mouth; when fish come within the strike zone, the monk lunges upwards using its muscular pectoral fins and sucks the prey into its cavernous mouth. The sedentary monk uses little energy and can go for long periods without feeding.

Monks are good eating, but it is usually just the tails (rear half of body) that appear in the markets. The flesh is often used in place of crayfish or prawns for seafood cocktails; perhaps these should be labelled 'seafood monktails'?

Monkfish should be handled cautiously, as the huge mouth, large needle-like depressible teeth and powerful jaws can cause serious injuries to the unwary fisherman. Previously identified as '*Lophius upsicephalus*' in *Smiths' Sea Fishes* (Smith & Heemstra 1986).

SIMILAR SPECIES

The northeastern Atlantic monk, *Lophius budegassa* Spinola 1807 [identified as '*Lophius vomerinus*' in Smith & Heemstra (1986)], extends south to northern Namibia. It has a dark peritoneum and 3rd dorsal fin spine 11–18% SL.

FAMILY ANTENNARIIDAE ▪ Anglerfish (Frogfish)

Body short, orbicular or globose, slightly compressed; **mouth large**, oblique or vertical, with bands of villiform teeth; **gill opening a small pore behind and below pectoral fin base. First dorsal fin spine at front of snout, modified as a fishing pole**, most species with a fleshy bait (*esca*) at the tip; 2nd and 3rd dorsal spines on head, in front of soft dorsal fin; pectoral fins with fleshy limb-like base; pelvic fins under head. Size range 3–36 cm.

Sedentary masters of disguise, anglerfish can assume various morphs to resemble unoccupied background or various inanimate structures (sponges, tunicates or algae-covered rock) in their habitat. This clever camouflage deceives large fish-eating predators (which are not interested in 'sponges') as well as potential prey (which see 'sponges' or 'algae-covered rock' as something to eat or hide under). As implied by the name, anglerfish often lure their prey within striking distance by means of their modified 1st dorsal fin spine, which is used like a fishing pole and bait; the striped angler may further enhance its allure by releasing a chemical attractant from the bait.

Prey capture can be divided into three phases:

▪ Stalking, accomplished by 'jet propulsion' (expelling water from the gill openings with a rapid contraction of the gill cavity) or a slow lumbering gallop using its pectoral and pelvic fins to clamber over the substrate. At a distance less than three body lengths from the prey, the angler slows its approach and crouches. When prey is within one body length, the angler turns so that its mouth is pointing towards the prey.

▪ Striking, in which, simultaneously, the mouth is thrown open, upper jaw protruded and oral cavity expanded 12 times in volume with lightning speed to suck in a large volume of water along with the prey. The entire strike phase, ending with jaw closure and prey capture, takes 6–7 thousandths of a second!

▪ Prey handling or swallowing, in which the gill openings are clamped shut with the pectoral fins, and the oral and gill cavities are contracted, forcing a large quantity of water and the prey into the expandable sac-like stomach.

With its large distensible mouth and enormous stomach, the anglerfish is able to swallow fish larger than itself. Watching an angler feed is amazing. When the prey enters the angler's strike zone, it suddenly disappears and a bulge appears in the belly of the angler. This strike is much faster than the strike of a cobra or mongoose or of other fish.

Reproduction of anglerfish is also unusual. The eggs are released with a mucous coating that expands into an 'egg raft' about 10 cm wide by 40–90 cm long with the edges rolled into a scroll. Presumably, the male fertilises the eggs as they are released by the female.

Most antennariids are sedentary fish of shallow water (1–300 m); the sargassumfish, *Histrio histrio* (Linnaeus 1758), lives in floating *Sargassum* weed and is often found out in the open ocean.

Worldwide. Fourteen genera with ~44 species, 9 in our area.

Pietsch & Grobecker (1987) produced a comprehensive monograph on the biology and systematics of these fascinating fish.

STRIPED ANGLER
Antennarius striatus
(Shaw & Nodder 1794)

15 cm adult

Fishing pole with fleshy bait (*esca*) **of 2–5 worm-like tentacles**; 2nd dorsal fin spine curved posteriorly, bound to head by narrow membrane; dorsal fin rays 11–13; anal fin rays 7, all rays divided; pectoral fin rays 9–12; peduncle distinct; some fish with scattered hair-like filaments on skin. Pale yellow to green, grey, yellow-brown or black; pale phases covered (except ventrally) with **dark streaks or elongate blotches usually radiating from eye**, some extending to pectoral fins and onto median fins. Some fish uniformly coloured (black, red, etc.); colour can change with habitat. Attains 22 cm.

Tropical and subtropical Atlantic, Senegal to Namibia; Indo-central Pacific, Red Sea to Knysna.

Soft bottom, seagrass beds, tide pools and reefs to 219 m. The striped angler makes an interesting aquarium fish, but this aggressive predator will eat any fish put in its tank, including those as large as itself.

SIMILAR SPECIES

The shaggy angler, *Antennarius hispidus* (Bloch & Schneider 1801), has a large *esca* with a dense tuft of fine filaments. Indo-West Pacific, south to Knysna.

The sargassumfish, *Histrio histrio* (Linnaeus 1758), has smooth skin and a fishing pole shorter than the 2nd dorsal fin spine. World-wide but absent from the Pacific east of Guam.

Figure 37
Fishing apparatus and dorsal fin spines of a striped angler.

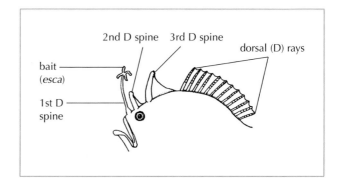

FAMILY GOBIESOCIDAE ■ Clingfish

Head markedly depressed; dorsal and anal fins small and close to tail fin; pelvic fins modified to form a thoracic suction disc that is also joined to lower part of pectoral fins; no fin spines except for reduced spine of pelvic fins; tail fin rays 8–14; skin smooth, naked, but covered with thick mucus; no swimbladder. Size range 3–30 cm.

Mostly small cryptic fish living in shallow water; some Australian clingfish act as cleaner fish and remove external parasites from larger species.

Worldwide in tropical and warm temperate waters. About 43 genera, ~150 species, 9 in our area.

ROCKSUCKER
Chorisochismus
dentex
(Pallas 1769)

17 cm (ventral, dorsal and lateral views)

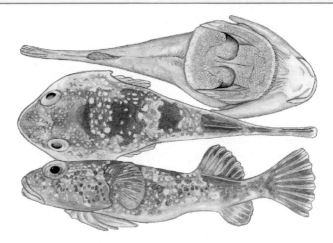

Dorsal fin rays 6–9; anal fin rays 6–7; pectoral fin rays 23–24; branchiostegal membranes attached to isthmus; **disc single**. Colour variable depending on habitat; usually greenish mottled with browns and pinks. After death, colour changes to reddish magenta. Attains 30 cm.

Endemic, Swakopmund to Durban.

Benthic fish common in tide pools; juveniles often attach to underside of seaweed. Rarely found deeper than 10 m. Female produces up to 500 eggs that she attaches to underside of rocks and shells; she is reported to guard and aerate the eggs by fanning with her pectoral fins. Adults feed mainly on limpets, sea urchins, chitons and gastropods; juveniles eat small crustaceans. The rocksucker has developed a clever strategy to capture limpets. The fish waits until the limpet raises its shell slightly in order to move, then lunges at the shell with open mouth and inserts its large upper teeth under the shell; the fish then pivots its body 180°, levering the limpet off the rock. The limpet is swallowed shell and all, and the shell is passed undigested in a mucoid capsule via the anus. The rocksucker can swallow surprisingly large limpets: a 12 cm fish contained a 3.1 cm pear limpet. The mouth and anus are capable of considerable distension.

Occasionally caught by anglers, but it holds so tightly to the rock that the line is

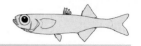

often broken. Can live for hours out of the water if kept moist and cool.

SIMILAR SPECIES

Gobies also have a ventral suction disc, but the pelvic fin rays are still apparent in the disc, and they have 2 dorsal fins (see p. 393).

The chubby clingfish, *Apletodon pellegrini* (Chabanaud 1925), has a double (divided) suction disc, 5–6 dorsal fin rays, small incisors at front of jaws and attains only 5 cm. Senegal to Port Alfred.

FAMILY ATHERINIDAE   Silversides

Body elongate, cylindrical or slightly compressed; **2 separate dorsal fins**, 1st with 4–8 slender spines; 2nd dorsal fin with 1 spine, 8–15 rays; **anal fin with** 1 weak spine, **11–18 rays**; pectoral fins shorter than head, mid-lateral; pelvic fins abdominal with 1 spine, 5 rays; scales cycloid; no LL; eye large, diameter subequal to or greater than snout length; mouth not reaching past vertical at middle of eye; teeth small, usually present on jaws, sometimes also on vomer, palatines and tongue. Size range 5–14 cm.

Shallow coastal waters; common in estuaries, some species confined to freshwater. Feed mainly on zooplankton (copepods, amphipods, ostracods, isopods, rotifers, veligers and phytoplankton). Usually in large schools. Not of commercial importance, but often used as bait; heavily exploited by a variety of fish and bird predators.

Superficially atherinids could be confused with clupeids or anchovies, but these latter fish have only a single dorsal fin set over or in front of pelvic fins. Juvenile mullet resemble silversides, but mullet have 3 anal fin spines (2 in small juveniles) and only 8 or 9 anal fin rays.

Worldwide in tropical and temperate waters. About 25 genera, with ~165 species, 5 in our area.

CAPE SILVERSIDE
Atherina breviceps
Valenciennes 1835

21 cm

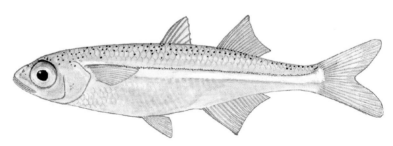

First dorsal fin with 5–8 spines; 2nd dorsal fin with 1 spine, 11–15 rays; anal fin with 1 spine, 15–18 rays; pectoral fin rays 13–16; LSS 44–50; body depth 4.7–6.3 times, head length 3.7–5.0 times in SL; **1st dorsal fin origin over pelvic fins**. Body translucent with brilliant **silvery mid-lateral stripe**; dorsal surface dusky yellow with small dark spots; head and abdomen silvery. Attains 11 cm.

Endemic, Walvis Bay to northern KZN.

Shallow sandy bottoms; common in bays and estuaries; also in freshwater and brackish coastal lakes. Juveniles feed on phytoplankton and small zooplankton; adults can filter feed or pick individual prey (larger zooplankton, benthic crustaceans, insects and small molluscs). Matures at 36–42 mm SL (8 months old); breeds during spring and summer. Eggs with long adhesive filaments usually attached to submerged plants and other objects. Tolerates salinities from freshwater to 40‰. Cape silverside are prey for most piscivores in our estuaries and inshore waters. Their habit of schooling at the surface makes them vulnerable to bird predators. Due to this heavy predation, less than 1% of the estuarine silverside population lives more than 2 years.

SIMILAR SPECIES

The hardyhead silverside, *Atherinomorus lacunosus* (Forster 1801), has 8–11 2nd dorsal fin rays and preopercle edge with notch. Indo-West Pacific, Oman to East London.

The pricklenose silverside, *Atherion africanum* Smith 1965, has minute denticles on outside of jaws and front of head and no notch in edge of preopercle. Western Indian Ocean, India to KZN.

FAMILY BELONIDAE ▪ Needlefish

Body greatly elongate, cylindrical or compressed; **jaws produced into a long slender beak** with needle-like teeth; gill rakers absent (except in the endemic Cape needlefish); dorsal and anal fins near tail fin; no fin spines; pelvic fins abdominal with 6 short rays; nasal organ a pit with protruding tentacle; LL begins on throat, runs along lower edge of body with a branch to pectoral fin origin; scales cycloid, deciduous. Head and body greenish blue dorsally, silvery below. Body length (BL) is measured from rear edge of operculum to tail fin base. Size range 4 cm to 1.3 m BL.

Mainly marine, epipelagic; some tropical species occur in freshwater. Feed mainly on fish. Eggs with sticky filaments which are attached to floating or demersal plants when the fish spawn. Belonids often leap and skitter along the surface. Flesh excellent, though some folks are put off by the green bones.

Worldwide in tropical and warm temperate waters. Ten genera, 33 species, 4 in our area.

CROCODILE NEEDLEFISH
Tylosurus crocodilus
(Péron & Lesueur 1821)

4 cm juvenile
54 cm adult

Head and body not compressed; dorsal fin rays 21–24; **anal fin rays 19–22**; pectoral fin rays 14–15; lower tail fin lobe longer than upper; no gill rakers. Body dark bluish dorsally, silvery on sides, white ventrally; black spot sometimes present on pectoral fins; dark fleshy mid-lateral keel on peduncle. Attains at least 86 cm BL.

Tropical and subtropical Atlantic, south to Angola; Indo-West Pacific, Red Sea, Oman to Knysna.

Pelagic, usually inshore, sometimes in estuaries; juveniles often offshore. Solitary or in small groups. Eggs large (~4 mm in diameter), demersal, with adhesive filaments that attach to floating or benthic plants; larvae pelagic.

At night crocodile needlefish often leap out of the water towards lights, and people fishing with lanterns have been impaled and seriously injured or killed by large needlefish.

─ SIMILAR SPECIES ─────────────

The endemic Cape needlefish, *Petalichthys capensis* Regan 1904, has tail fin lobes equal; 16–19 dorsal fin rays; 27–35 gill rakers. Schooling species; offshore, False Bay to Durban.

The barred needlefish, *Ablennes hians* (Valenciennes 1846), has head and body strongly compressed; 25–27 anal fin rays; and prominent black blotches or bars along body or just rear part of body. Worldwide, Red Sea, Oman to Algoa Bay.

The yellowfin needlefish, *Strongylura leiura* (Bleeker 1850), has 18–21 dorsal fin rays, dorsal and anal fin lobes yellowish, black bar on operculum behind preopercle. Indo-West Pacific, Persian Gulf to Durban.

FAMILY HEMIRAMPHIDAE ▪ Halfbeaks

Body elongate, cylindrical or laterally compressed; dorsal and anal fins near tail fin; no fin spines; pelvic fins abdominal with 6 rays; tail fin forked or emarginate, lower lobe longer than upper lobe; **lower jaw elongated into a slender, toothless, spear-like beak** (except in *Oxyporhamphus* and a few other genera); upper jaw triangular, projecting in front of snout; teeth minute, in several rows; gill rakers well developed on 1st and 2nd gill arches; nasal organ a pit with protruding tentacle; scales large, cycloid, deciduous; LL begins on throat, runs along ventral edge of body with a branch to pectoral fin origin. Size range 5–43 cm SL (from front of upper jaw to base of tail fin).

Most species marine, epipelagic, coastal and/or offshore; some species confined to freshwater. Feed on pelagic crustaceans, fish, zooplankton and floating seagrass. Eggs with sticky filaments that attach to floating or demersal plants when the fish spawn. Flesh excellent, but halfbeaks are not much used as food-fish. Like the needlefish and flyingfish, halfbeaks often leap and skitter at the surface; two offshore species have enlarged pectoral fins that enable them to glide in the air like a flyingfish.

Worldwide in tropical and temperate seas. Twelve genera with ~81 species, 6 in our area.

SPOTTED HALFBEAK
Hemiramphus far
(Forsskål 1775)

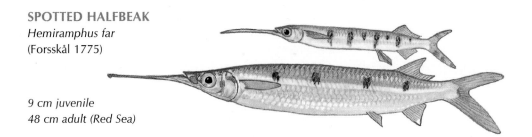

9 cm juvenile
48 cm adult (Red Sea)

Dorsal fin rays 13–15; anal fin rays 11–13; pectoral fin rays 11–12; gill rakers 6–8 / 17–23; front of upper jaw forming prominent triangular projection; body slightly compressed; **upper jaw naked**; no teeth on vomer or tongue; no preorbital ridge in front of eye. Adults blue-green dorsally, silvery below; **4–10 dusky blotches on upper flanks**; juveniles (6–9 cm SL) with 4–6 dark bars on body, 2 or 3 extending onto belly; pelvic fins black. Attains 43 cm SL.

Tropical and subtropical Indo-West Pacific, Mediterranean, Red Sea, common south to Knysna; a few records west to False Bay.

Epipelagic, common in estuaries and may be found far inland in rivers. Feeds at surface on algae, zooplankton, small fish and eggs. The elongated lower jaw is used to detect microscopic prey. Breeds in summer; eggs 3 mm in diameter, demersal and translucent with numerous short, adhesive filaments; female produces ~12 000 eggs per season. Spawning occurs over seagrass beds in estuaries. Adults leap from the water presumably to avoid predators. They can cover 3 m in a leap and they also skitter over water in a series of 6 or 7 leaps.

Spotted halfbeaks are caught by drifting a small baited hook at night and provide good sport on light tackle. Flesh excellent but the numerous fine bones are troublesome. Often used as trolled bait to catch scombrids and billfish.

SIMILAR SPECIES

The Cape halfbeak, *Hyporhamphus capensis* (Thominot 1886), has scales on upper jaw and a bony ridge just in front of the eye. Endemic, False Bay to southern Mozambique.

FAMILY EXOCOETIDAE ■ Flyingfish

Body elongate, subcylindrical to laterally compressed and usually flattened ventrally; **pectoral fins enlarged**, extending past dorsal fin origin; **no fin spines; dorsal and anal fins near tail fin; pelvic fins abdominal with 6 rays**; tail fin forked, lower lobe longer than upper; mouth small; jaws short, teeth microscopic or absent; gill rakers well developed; nasal organ a pit with protruding lobate tentacle; scales large, cycloid and deciduous; LL runs along ventral edge of body. Juveniles often with single or paired chin barbels and usually differ from adults in colour and size of fins. Size range 11–46 cm.

Epipelagic fish of the open ocean, also near shore. When disturbed by a ship or chased by predators, flyingfish leap from the water and glide over fairly long distances by means of their enlarged pectoral fins. The fish darts out of the water at a low angle, with a swimming

speed of about 24 km/h and spreads its large pectoral fins, the pelvic fins are closed and the lower tail fin lobe trails in the sea. The tail is vibrated rapidly (50 beats per second) to provide power for the take-off, and as air speed (~65 km/h) is attained, the pelvic fins are expanded to supply a lift force that raises the tail out of the water and trims the body. With both pairs of 'wings' fully expanded, the fish glides over the water for several seconds before dropping back into the sea. Some flights may be continued by the fish folding the pelvic fins, which drops the tail fin back into the water where it resumes the vibrating power phase to provide additional speed for another take-off. Most flights are single glides of 4–10 seconds covering 20–50 m, but repeated take-offs can extend a flight to 20 seconds and a distance of several hundred metres.

Flyingfish are prey for dolphins, sharks, tunas, billfish and dorado; juveniles are also taken by sea birds. Dorado feed heavily on flyingfish and have been seen to jump out of the water to catch them. They also swim rapidly below the airborne fish and catch them when the flyingfish drops back into the sea. Flyingfish are good eating and fished commercially in some areas. They can be caught with tiny baited hooks or drift nets or they can be attracted with night lights. Some artisanal fishers target spawning aggregations by attracting the fish with floating bundles of plants. When the flyingfish gather at the floating plants to deposit their eggs, the fish are quickly caught with long-handled dip nets.

Feed mainly on copepods, but will take any zooplankton (molluscs, siphonophores, arrow-worms and salps) when it is abundant.

Worldwide in tropical and temperate waters. Six or 7 genera, ~60 species, 12 in our area.

SMALLHEAD FLYINGFISH
Cheilopogon altipennis
(Valenciennes 1847)

39 cm adult
26 cm subadult
3 cm juvenile

Dorsal fin rays 11–14; anal fin rays 9–12; pectoral fin rays 13–15 (1st ray unbranched, rest branched), the fin reaching past anal fin base; pelvic fins enlarged, reaching past anal fin origin; anal fin origin under or behind 3rd dorsal fin ray; teeth conical; **head length**

4.4–5.0 times in SL; juveniles with fringed semicircular chin flap and blackish dorsal fin. Subadults with black spot in dorsal fin. Adults dark iridescent blue dorsally, silvery white below; **pectoral fins dusky** (20–30 cm SL fish with narrow pale band across fin); black dorsal fin spot reduced or absent. Attains at least 46 cm.

Worldwide in subtropical seas; often occurs at oceanic islands; generally avoids tropical areas. Cape Town to Kosi Bay; common over the Agulhas Bank.

Neritic species, prefers temperatures of 15–20° C. Eggs ~ 2 mm, demersal, with long sticky filaments. Spawning occurs in open ocean, ~ 24 000 eggs are released at one time.

SIMILAR SPECIES

The spotfin flyingfish, *Cheilopogon furcatus* (Mitchill 1815), and the blackwing flyingfish, *Cheilopogon cyanopterus* (Valenciennes 1847), have larger heads (head length 4.0–4.6 times in SL), 24–45 predorsal scales and the juveniles have a pair of elongate chin barbels. These two species are known in tropical and subtropical waters of the Atlantic, Indian and western Pacific oceans.

FAMILY LAMPRIDAE ■ Opahs

Body oblong-oval, compressed; scales minute, cycloid; mouth small, teeth absent in adults; upper jaw protrusile, the maxilla moving out with premaxilla as jaw is protruded; **pectoral and pelvic fins well developed**; anterior dorsal fin rays elongated, forming a high lobe; tail fin with 17 branched rays; pelvic fin rays 13–17; branchiostegal rays 6; gill rakers well developed; no fin spines. Size range 1.1–2.0 m.

Worldwide in tropical and temperate waters. Epipelagic in the open ocean. One genus with 2 species.

SPOTTED OPAH
Lampris guttatus
(Brünnich 1788)

95 cm

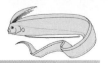

Body depth greater than head length, 58–68% SL; **pectoral fin length about half body depth**; pelvic fin origins under dorsal lobe; teeth rudimentary in 5 cm postlarva. Body bluish, darker dorsally, silver bluish below, with a pinkish tinge ventrally; **covered with round or oval white spots**; fins and front of snout reddish orange. Attains 1.8 cm FL, 150 kg.

Worldwide in subtropical and temperate seas; apparently avoids equatorial waters.

Open ocean from surface to 500 m. Opah feed on pelagic animals: squid, fish, jellyfish and small crustaceans. The well developed pectoral fins are the principal means of propulsion, but also uses the tail fin for acceleration.

Flesh excellent; the enormous pectoral fin muscles are dark red and resemble a fine beef steak in texture and flavour. Rarely taken in trawls, occasionally on hook and line. IGFA all-tackle record: 74 kg fish from California, USA.

SIMILAR SPECIES

The southern opah, *Lampris immaculatus* Gilchrist 1904, has a more elongate body (depth 43–53% SL), no pale spots, and pelvic fins well behind dorsal fin origin. Temperate southern ocean.

FAMILY REGALECIDAE ▪ Oarfish & Streamerfish

Body extremely elongate, much compressed, ribbon-like; scales absent; **dorsal fin extremely long**, origin on top of head, fin extends from head to tip of tail; tail fin rudimentary or absent; no anal fin; pelvic fins reduced to a greatly elongate stout ray or 1 short thick ray; pectoral fins short, their length 4–5 times in head length; upper jaw very protrusile. Size range 3–8 m.

Worldwide in temperate and tropical waters. Epipelagic in the open ocean. Two or 3 species, 2 in our area.

OARFISH
Regalecus glesne
Ascanius 1772

3.7 m

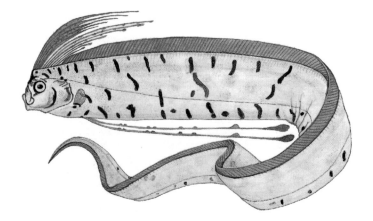

Dorsal fin origin on head, first 10–12 rays elongate (1–2 times body depth), first 5–6 rays bound together, the next 5–6 mostly free; total dorsal fin rays ~400 (or fewer, depending on injury); pectoral fin rays 13; tail fin of 4 rays in juveniles, absent in adults; pelvic fins represented by a single elongated stiff ray festooned with 3–4 short skin flaps; body depth more than head length; mouth toothless or with a few small teeth at front of lower jaw; small tuft of bristle-like teeth on vomer. **Head and body brilliant silver**, with bluish streaks when alive; body often with irregular blackish streaks and spots; **dorsal and pelvic fins crimson**; silvery pigment of body rubs off when touched. Attains 8 m, 150 kg.

Worldwide in tropical and temperate seas.

A fish of the open ocean, normally in depths of 15–500 m. Biology little known. Feeds on planktonic crustaceans. Adopts a vertical position in the water column to spot its food silhouetted against the light from the surface.

The 2.5 mm eggs have a thick reddish brown outer membrane and are produced in millions. Most specimens have been found washed up on the shore after stormy weather; rarely taken by trawlers. The elongate pelvic fins (the 'oars' of the oarfish) are not used for swimming, but have chemo-receptive organs ('tastebuds') that may be useful in prey selection. Swims vertically by means of undulating waves of dorsal fin rays. Flesh unpalatable, soft and watery, even when cooked.

Oarfish are a likely source of sea serpent myths.

SIMILAR SPECIES

The streamerfish, *Agrostichthys parkeri* (Benham 1904), has narrower body (depth $^1/_3$ to $^1/_2$ head length) and pelvic fins shorter than head. Known in our area from one specimen caught off the west coast. A live fish found off New Zealand was reported to produce an electric current. Attains 3 m.

FAMILY BERYCIDAE ■ Alfonsinos

Body oblong, oval, compressed; scales ctenoid (rough), extending onto cheeks and operculum; **dorsal fin with 4–6 spines, 12–20 branched rays; anal fin with 4 spines**, 12–30 rays; pelvic fins with 1 spine, 7 or 10–13 rays, set below pectoral fins; tail fin forked; jaws, vomer and palatines with villiform teeth. Size range 20–60 cm.

Rocky and coral reefs on continental shelf and upper slope in 10–800 m. Feed on zooplankton. Good eating and commercially important in some areas.

Worldwide (but not in eastern Pacific). Two genera with ~9 species, 3 in our area.

SHORT ALFONSINO
Centroberyx spinosus
(Gilchrist 1903)

20 cm adult
4 cm juvenile

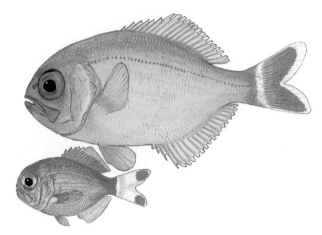

Dorsal fin with 5–6 spines, 14–15 rays; anal fin with 4 spines, 14–16 rays; **dorsal fin base about equal to anal fin base**; pectoral fin rays 13; pelvic fin with 1 spine, 7 rays; LL scales 43–47; gill rakers 10–11 / 20–22; body depth 1.9–2.0 times, head length 2.6–2.7 times in SL. **Body and head gold, reddish dorsally.** Attains 20 cm.

Known only from Knysna to Tongaat.

Found on reefs and rocky bottom in 15–120 m. This little-known benthic species probably feeds on small invertebrates (crustaceans, worms, etc.) and zooplankton. Too small to be of interest for food, but the beautiful colours would make it an attractive aquarium fish.

SIMILAR SPECIES

The slender beryx, *Beryx splendens* Lowe 1834, has dorsal fin base shorter than anal fin base and 25–30 anal fin rays. Occurs in 160–800 m. Worldwide, but not in eastern Pacific; Saldanha Bay to KZN.

FAMILY MONOCENTRIDAE ▪ Pineapplefish

Body oval, with **scales enlarged and fused to form a solid rough armour; dorsal fin with 5–7 strong spines, 11–12 rays; dorsal fin spines with no connecting membrane; anal fin no spines, 9–12 rays; pelvic fins with huge spine and 3–4 tiny rays**; tail fin with 17 branched rays. Villiform teeth on jaws and palatines, no teeth on vomer. Light organ containing luminescent bacteria on each side at front of lower jaw. Size range 17 cm.

Pineapplefish are found in the Indo-Pacific region at depths of 3–400 m. Two genera with 4 species, one in our area.

PINEAPPLEFISH
Monocentris japonica
(Houttuyn 1782)

13 cm
(arrow indicates
position of light organ)

Body orbicular; **dorsal fin with 5 or 6 spines without connecting membrane, canted alternately left and right**, and 11–12 rays; anal fin rays 9–11; pectoral fin rays 14; pelvic fin with 1 spine, 3 rays; the pelvic spines can be locked erect and fit into a groove along sides of belly when depressed; LL scales 12–15; each body scale with a flattened recurved spine. Attains 17 cm.

Indo-West Pacific, Red Sea to Mossel Bay.

Coral and rocky reefs, also in depressions on sand near reefs and wrecks in 10–400 m.

When juveniles attain adult size, they apparently move to deeper water.

Uses its light organs to find prey (benthic crustaceans) over open bottom at night. During the day, juveniles congregate in caves or under ledges; adults may be territorial, as they are found singly. Larvae have been raised from eggs fertilised in captivity. Eggs are 1.9 mm in diameter, and 21-day-old larvae are 6 mm.

A feeble swimmer; does well in aquaria but should be kept in a dimly lit environment.

FAMILY HOLOCENTRIDAE ■ Soldierfish & Squirrelfish

Body oblong to ovate, moderately compressed; **scales distinctly spiny**; eyes large; **villiform teeth on jaws, vomer and palatines; dorsal fin with 10–13 spines, 11–18 rays, the fin deeply divided before last spine; anal fin with 4 spines, 7–16 rays; pelvic fins with 1 spine, 7 rays**; fin spines strong; tail fin forked with 17 branched rays; head bones with grooves and ridges; suborbital and opercular bones with series of spinules. Size range 7–45 cm.

Demersal, on coral and rocky reefs from shore to 640 m. Usually in caves or under ledges by day, emerge at night to feed on benthic crustaceans, fish and zooplankton. Eggs and larvae pelagic. Adapt quickly to life in a large aquarium.

Worldwide in tropical and subtropical waters. About 70 species, 28 in our area.

Two subfamilies: Myripristinae (soldierfish, 5 genera) with no preopercle spine and 10–16 anal fin rays; and Holocentrinae (squirrelfish, 3 genera) with long spine at corner of preopercle and 7–10 anal fin rays.

Blotcheye soldier   Spotfin squirrelfish   Tailspot squirrelfish

Crown squirrelfish

BLOTCHEYE SOLDIER
Myripristis murdjan
(Forsskål 1775)

23 cm

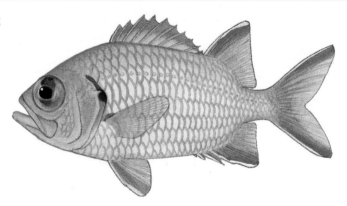

Dorsal fin 11 spines, 12–15 rays; anal fin rays 11–13; pectoral fin rays 14–16; LL scales 27–32; total gill rakers 36–43; numerous small scales on inner side of pectoral fin base; **pair of tooth patches at front of lower jaw just outside mouth**. Black on opercular membrane ends shortly below main spine; lower part of **spinous dorsal fin pale, outer part of fin red**; soft dorsal, anal and tail fins with or without dark pigment at tips of longest rays. Attains 27 cm.

Tropical and subtropical Indo-West Pacific, Red Sea, Oman to Sodwana Bay.

Coral reefs, 1–50 m. Feeds on zooplankton, fish, worms and cephalopods. Secretive species rarely seen during day. Matures at 12–14 cm FL.

The name 'blotcheye soldier' is misleading, as most soldierfish have a dark blotch on eye.

The epaulette soldier, *Myripristis kuntee* Valenciennes 1831, has spinous dorsal fin pale red basally, the outer part broadly yellow, tail fin dark red; 33–41 LL scales. Indo-central Pacific, south to Aliwal Shoal.

The bigscale soldier, *Myripristis berndti* Jordan & Evermann 1903, has outer half of spinous dorsal fin yellow, tail fin pale pink. Indo-Pacific, south to Aliwal Shoal.

SPOTFIN SQUIRRELFISH
Neoniphon sammara
(Forsskål 1775)

20 cm (Comoros)

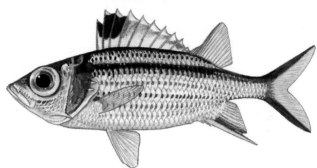

Body depth 3.0–3.6 times in SL; lower jaw projects when mouth closed; dorsal fin 11 spines, 11–13 rays; **anal fin rays 7–8, 3rd spine enlarged, reaching tail fin base**; pectoral fin rays 13–15; LL scales 38–43; 2$\frac{1}{2}$ scales from LL to middle dorsal fin spines. Body silvery, each scale with dark spot forming stripes on body; head reddish brown, cheek and lower jaw white; **spinous dorsal fin brownish, spine tips white, black blotch tinged with red on first 3 or 4 membranes**; tail fin yellowish with dark band along upper and lower margins. Attains 28 cm.

Indo-central Pacific, Red Sea, Oman to Aliwal Shoal.

Coral reefs in 1–30 m. Feeds mainly on crustaceans. Common in caves and under ledges in shallow water.

The blackfin squirrelfish, *Neoniphon opercularis* (Valenciennes 1831), has a submarginal black band covering most of the spinous dorsal fin. Indo-West Pacific, south to Bazaruto.

TAILSPOT SQUIRRELFISH
Sargocentron caudimaculatum
(Rüppell 1838)

21 cm (Red Sea)

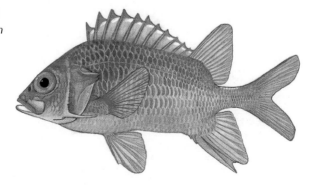

Dorsal head profile steep; body depth 2.5–2.9 times in SL; dorsal fin 11 spines, 13–15 rays, last spine about equidistant between 10th spine and 1st ray; anal fin rays 9; pectoral fin rays 13–15; LL scales 38–43; 2¹/₂ scales from LL to middle dorsal fin spines. **Head and body red, scales edged in silver; silvery white spot at front of peduncle**, often disappearing after death; white line along upper edge of opercle; some fish with entire rear third of body white. Attains 25 cm.

Tropical Indo-Pacific, Red Sea to the Eastern Cape.

Coral reefs, 2–30 m. A solitary fish, active by day and night; feeds on benthic crustaceans.

Excellent eating. Stout spines on fins and preopercle may cause injuries.

— SIMILAR SPECIES —

The sabre squirrelfish, *Sargocentron spiniferum* (Forsskål 1775), attains ~45 cm; has 3¹/₂ scales between LL and middle dorsal fin spines; spinous dorsal fin dark red, pelvic and anal fins yellowish. The huge preopercle spine is said to be venomous. Indo-central Pacific, Red Sea to Sodwana Bay. Most other species of *Sargocentron* have stripes on body.

CROWN SQUIRRELFISH
Sargocentron diadema
(Lacepède 1802)

18 cm

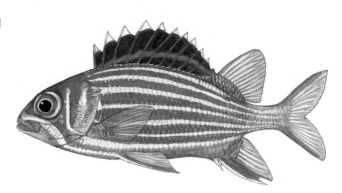

Body depth 2.7–3.2 times in SL; dorsal fin with 11 spines, 12–14 rays, last spine about equidistant between 10th spine and 1st ray; anal fin rays 8–10; pectoral fin rays 13–15; LL scales 46–50; 2¹/₂ scales from LL to middle dorsal fin spines; preopercle spine short, 2–3 times in eye diameter. **Body with alternating red and silvery white stripes; peduncle whitish; spinous dorsal fin dark red to black, membrane tips white, and usually a faint longitudinal white or pale red stripe along middle of fin.** Attains 21 cm.

Tropical and warm temperate Indo-Pacific, Red Sea, Oman to Algoa Bay.

Coral and rocky reefs in 2–30 m. Feeds on benthic invertebrates, mainly crustaceans, gastropods and worms. Often in aggregations during day, hiding in reef. Does well in large aquaria, given places to hide.

— SIMILAR SPECIES —

The samurai squirrelfish, *Sargocentron ittodai* (Jordan & Fowler 1902), has red and white stripes on body, short preopercle spine, but spinous dorsal fin red, with curved band formed by series of white spots along middle of fin. Indo-central Pacific, Red Sea to Aliwal Shoal.

FAMILY ZEIDAE ■ Dories

Body oval, distinctly compressed; body depth greater than head length; scales small, rudimentary or absent; head compressed; mouth large, oblique; upper jaw very protrusile; no spines or serrations on opercular bones; branched tail fin rays 11; dorsal, anal and pectoral fin rays unbranched; small spines or large bony plates called bucklers at base of dorsal and anal fins. Size range 22–90 cm.

Demersal fish but often make feeding excursions into midwater; feed primarily on fish, crustaceans and cephalopods. Adults usually solitary but congregate for spawning. Broadcast spawners with pelagic eggs and larvae. Common in trawls from 35–600 m.

Tropical and temperate regions worldwide. Seven genera with ~14 species, 5 in our area.

JOHN DORY
Zeus faber
Linnaeus 1758

3 cm juvenile (Angola)
39 cm adult

Dorsal fin with 9–11 elongate filamentous spines, 22–24 rays; anal fin with 4 spines, 20–23 rays; pectoral fin rays 13–14; **pelvic fin with 1 spine, 6–7 rays; 5–8 large bucklers (each with 1–2 spines) along soft dorsal and anal fin bases; 2 rows of 7–10 spiny scutes from pelvic fin base to anal fin.** Body silvery bronze, with wavy horizontal streaks and **large ocellus on flanks below LL and above pectoral fin.** Attains 90 cm, 8.2 kg (females ~15 years, males ~13 years).

Mediterranean and eastern Atlantic from Norway to South Africa and Mozambique; also Australia, New Zealand, South China Sea and Japan.

Continental shelf and upper slope; adults in 50–400 m. Small juveniles (<8 cm) feed on zooplankton, bigger juveniles also eat small demersal fish; adults feed mainly on fish, crustaceans and squid. The compressed head and body facilitates its slow stalking approach to the prey. Rapid extension of the protrusile upper jaw enables the fish to suck in a large volume of water and the unsuspecting prey. Males mature at ~26 cm (2–3 years); females mature at ~35 cm (3–4 years) and grow larger than males.

Excellent food-fish, commonly taken in trawls. Caught with live bait, but provides little sport (the bait probably puts up a better fight than the dory).

The Cape dory, *Zeus capensis* Valenciennes 1835, has a dusky spot (sometimes indistinct) surrounded by several smaller silver spots on or above LL and below anterior dorsal fin rays; 9–13 spines along base of soft dorsal and anal fins; dorsal fin spines not extended past fin membrane. Endemic, St Helena Bay to KZN.

The king dory, *Cyttus traversi* Hutton 1872, has a zip-like double row of enlarged scales along ventral edge of body from gill opening to anus; dorsal fin spines not longer than dorsal fin rays; anal fin has 2 small spines, 36–38 rays. Walvis Ridge off Namibia, Cape Town to Algoa Bay, Australia and New Zealand.

FAMILY FISTULARIIDAE ■ Flutemouths

Body and snout extremely elongate, snout tubular, head and body slightly depressed; scales absent or reduced to minute prickles; no fin spines; **tail fin forked, middle rays elongated into a filament;** pelvic fins small with 6 rays; anus close behind pelvic fins; LL continued on tail filament. Size range 1.2–1.5 m.

Flutemouths occur worldwide in shallow tropical and temperate waters. One genus with 4 species, 2 in our area.

SMOOTH FLUTEMOUTH
Fistularia commersonii
Rüppell 1838

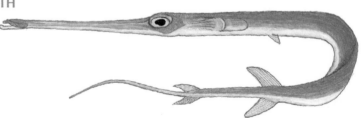

48 cm

Body smooth; **no bony ridges on dorsal midline in front of dorsal fin;** no spines on posterior LL plates; pupil pear-shaped; dorsal fin rays 15–17; anal fin rays 14–16; pectoral fin rays 14–16. Body **olive dorsally, silvery white below; pair of blue lines and/or rows of blue spots dorsally.** Also displays broad dark bars along body; this barred pattern may indicate stress or excitement (hunting mode). Attains 1.2 m SL.

Tropical and temperate Indo-Pacific, Red Sea, Oman to Mossel Bay.

Shallow reefs and seagrass beds, occasionally to 128 m. Often seen swimming over the reef top or back reef area; solitary or in loose aggregations of several individuals. Feeds almost exclusively on fish: morays, snake eels, halfbeaks, damselfish, cardinalfish, blennies, pilchards; and also on some squid and shrimp. Usually swims with undulating body movements; but when stalking prey, it moves slowly until within striking distance, draws its body into an 'S' shape and lunges forwards like a snake striking its prey. The flutemouth uses large herbivorous fish, like parrotfish, as a 'stalking horse' to approach prey.

Occasionally caught by anglers using prawn or squid bait. Flesh excellent.

The serrate flutemouth, *Fistularia petimba* Lacepède 1803, is red to orange-brown above, silvery below, with bony ridges along dorsal midline in front of dorsal fin, retrorse spines on rear LL plates, and a round pupil; it is usually found in deeper water (to 200 m).

Tropical Atlantic to Walvis Bay and Indo-central Pacific, Red Sea to Mossel Bay.

The trumpetfish, *Aulostomus chinensis* (Linnaeus 1766), has a more compressed (laterally flattened) head and body, small barbel at tip of lower jaw, a row of 8–13 short spines in front of the dorsal fin, and lacks the elongated tail filament of the flutemouth. Indo-Pacific, south to East London.

FAMILY SYNGNATHIDAE ■ Seahorses & Pipefish

Body armoured with dermal plates forming a tubular series of rings; no scales; mouth small, terminal, usually at end of tubular snout; no teeth; gill opening a pore above opercle, which is almost completely joined to head by skin; gills lobate. Head length is from tip of upper jaw to rear edge of opercle; snout length is from tip of upper jaw to front edge of eye socket. Sexually dimorphic: males carry the fertilised eggs exposed or concealed within a ventral pouch or folds of skin. Size range 2–65 cm.

Worldwide in tropical and temperate seas. Most species marine, but some also found in estuaries and freshwater. Fifty-two genera with ~215 species, 25 in our area.

Longsnout pipefish

Knysna seahorse

KNYSNA SEAHORSE
Hippocampus capensis
Boulenger 1900

8 cm (from crown to end of tail) mature female

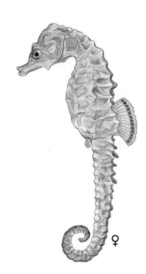

♀

Body with bulging belly; tail coiled distally (no tail fin); bony crown not well developed in adults; dorsal fin rays 16–18; pectoral fin rays 15–17; anal fin rays 3–4; **snout length 2.7–2.9 times in head length**; body rings 10–11 (last body ring includes anus); tail rings 32–34. Colour pale green, brown, black or speckled, depending on environment and mood of fish; dorsal fin with black submarginal band. Attains 8 cm.

> Known only along our south coast from Knysna, Keurbooms, Swartvlei and Klein-brak estuaries.

Silty sand estuarine areas with eelgrass. Sexually mature at 65 mm (1 year). During summer, the brood pouch of the male becomes silvery; mating occurs with the female depositing eggs in the male's pouch where they are fertilised. After 2–4 weeks, the male gives birth to 30–110 tiny (9 mm) young, and the same pair mate again immediately after the birth. Newborn seahorses look like miniature black adults, but tend to swim in a horizontal position; they use their prehensile tails to hold onto the eelgrass. At 20 mm, juveniles begin to change colour to match their habitat. It is not known whether the seahorse pairs for life or just for the summer mating season. The Knysna seahorse is adapted to temperate estuaries and will not survive in freshwater or hypersaline lagoons. Juveniles feed on small zooplankton; adults consume small crustaceans and fish larvae. Seahorses are eaten by fish and bird predators.

Because of their restricted distribution and low fecundity, the Knysna seahorse population is threatened. Capture of this species is prohibited by law. A captive breeding programme may provide juveniles for the aquarium trade, and thus reduce demands on the wild population. However, captive seahorses seem prone to tuberculosis and should be strictly monitored and kept isolated from the wild population.

SIMILAR SPECIES

The yellow seahorse (currently identified as *Hippocampus kuda* Bleeker 1852) has a longer snout (2.4–2.6 times in head length), 34–37 tail rings and is reported to attain 30 cm. Indo-central Pacific, south to Mossel Bay.

LONGSNOUT PIPEFISH
Syngnathus temminckii
Kaup 1856

13 cm

Body elongate and slender; **snout longer than rest of head**; dorsal fin rays 33–42; pectoral fin rays 10–14; anal fin rays 3; body rings 18–21, tail rings 36–43. Pale green to dark brown, variable depending on habitat. Attains 32 cm.

Endemic, Walvis Bay to at least Thukela Bank. The occurrence of the longsnout pipefish on the coast of Angola is dubious. Although reported (as *Syngnathus acus*) from the Seychelles, Réunion, Indonesia and elsewhere in the Indo-Pacific region, the identity of these populations is uncertain.

Common in estuaries, usually in eelgrass beds; also offshore to depths of 110 m. Sexually mature at 12 cm; breeding occurs in the sea or estuaries from November to March. Males carry developing embryos in a brood pouch on their belly. Feeds on zooplankton (mainly copepods), benthic amphipods and insect larvae.

The most common pipefish in South African estuaries. Previously identified as *Syngnathus acus* Linnaeus 1758 which is confined to the northeastern Atlantic and Mediterranean. Recent research has determined that the longsnout pipefish of southern Africa is a different species, which should be called *Syngnathus temminckii* (Monica Mwale, SAIAB, pers. comm.).

SIMILAR SPECIES

The rare river pipefish, *Syngnathus watermeyeri* Smith 1963, known only from the Bushmans and East Kleinemonde rivers near Port Alfred, has a shorter snout (3 times in head length) and 6–8 pectoral fin rays.

The belly pipefish, *Hippichthys heptagonus* Bleeker 1849, also has a shorter snout (1.9–2.8 times in head length) and 14 or 15 body rings. Indo-central Pacific, south to Durban.

FAMILY CENTRISCIDAE ▪ Shrimpfish (Razorfish)

Head and body extremely compressed, razor-like, with sharp ventral edge, encased by thin transparent bony plates; rear end of body twisted ventrally, so that the dorsal fin is in the normal position of the tail fin, which is displaced ventrally. Mouth very small, toothless. Fin rays unbranched. Maximum size ~16 cm.

This Indo-Pacific family comprises 2 genera with ~4 species, one in our area.

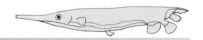

SHRIMPFISH
Aeoliscus punctulatus
(Bianconi 1855)

20 cm

Dorsal fin with 3 spines, 10–11 rays, 1st spine hinged at its base and slightly movable; anal fin rays 12–13; pectoral fin rays 11; pelvic fin rays 4. Body depth 5–7 times, head 2.5–2.8 times in SL. Distance from soft dorsal fin base to base of 1st dorsal fin spine less than body depth. Head and **body pale green or brown, with widely spaced small black spots**. Attains 20 cm.

Red Sea to KZN, occasionally to Algoa Bay.

Shallow coastal waters; often found among spines of the sea urchin *Diadema*. This bizarre little-known fish is usually seen in a head-down, vertical position; swims in small groups like a platoon of toy soldiers in formation. Reported to feed on crustaceans. Does well in aquaria if provided with live food.

FAMILY SCORPAENIDAE ■ Scorpionfish, Firefish & Stonefish

Body compressed or robust; scales present or absent; **head large, spiny; usually a row of spines below eye on bony ridge joined to preopercle and 3–5 spines on rear edge of preopercle**; dorsal fin with 7–18 spines, 4–14 rays; anal fin with 2–4 spines, 5–14 rays; pelvic fins with 1 spine, 5 rays; pectoral fin rays 11–23, the lower 1–3 rays separate in some species; last dorsal and anal fin rays double but counted as a single ray; tail fin rounded or truncate. Size range 5–50 cm.

Generally on or near coral and rocky reefs in 1–550 m. Sedentary ambush predators; feed on a variety of fish, crustaceans and octopus.

Worldwide in tropical and temperate waters. Family classification unsettled. About 60 genera, ~400 species, ~50 in our area.

Jacopever   Antenna firefish   False stonefish

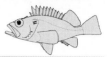

Stonefish   Paperfish

JACOPEVER
Helicolenus dactylopterus
(Delaroche 1809)

33 cm (Madeira)

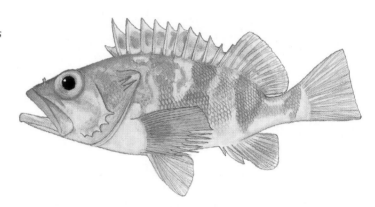

Body robust, oblong, with distinct overlapping scales; several small spines on top of head; 1 or no spines under eye; **dorsal fin with 12 spines** (shorter than half body depth), **12–13 rays; pectoral fin rays 18–20, upper part of fin truncate, lower rays free at tips**; anal fin with 3 spines, 5 rays. Head and body yellowish orange, with dark bars on body dorsally, belly white; inside of mouth blackish. Attains 40 cm.

Mediterranean and both sides of North Atlantic Ocean, from Norway to South Africa, round to Thukela River.

Offshore in rocky and soft-bottom habitats at depths of 55–550 m. Adults usually at depths below 250 m. Jacopever feed mainly on benthic fish and crustaceans, but will also take pelagic fish. Internal fertilisation, but the eggs are released before hatching; larvae pelagic. Spawns during winter. Juveniles are prey for sixgill sharks and hake.

Like other scorpionfish, the jacopever is presumed to have venomous dorsal fin spines, but it is edible and of some commercial importance as a by-catch of trawlers.

SIMILAR SPECIES

The false jacopever, *Sebastes capensis* (Gmelin 1789), has 13–14 dorsal fin spines, 6 anal fin rays, and 5–6 pale spots on body near dorsal fin. Western Cape; Gough and Tristan da Cunha islands in the South Atlantic.

ANTENNA FIREFISH
Pterois antennata
(Bloch 1787)

12 cm

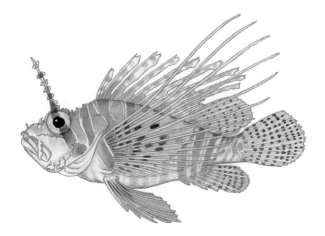

Body oblong; scales small and rough. **Dorsal fin with 12 separate spines**, the longest longer than body depth, 11–12 rays; anal fin with 3 spines, 6 rays; **pectoral fins with 16–17** elongate unbranched rays; long, conspicuously banded tentacles over eyes (resembling the antennae of some insects). Reddish to tan **mainly broad vertical bars on body and head, peduncle with oblique narrow bars** bordered by thin white lines; median fin rays pale with dark spots; dark bands on antennae correspond to width extensions; snout pale; white spot in upper pectoral axil. Attains ~20 cm.

Indo-central Pacific, Oman to Park Rynie, juveniles reach the Eastern Cape.

Rocky reefs, under overhangs and in caves, coral and sandy bottom from shore to 50 m. Crepuscular predator. Fish are engulfed with a swift lunge and lightning-fast thrust of the jaws. Despite venomous fin spines, juveniles are eaten by cornetfish. Adult firefish have no reported natural predators, and their slow conspicuous swimming over the reef implies they know that other fish will give them a wide berth.

Although often kept in aquaria, the firefish should be handled with great care. It quickly rotates its body to bring its venomous dorsal fin spines towards any intruder (fish, hand, net, etc.), and, within striking distance, it lunges forward, jabbing the spines into the victim. The stings from these spines are intensely painful; the anal and pelvic fin spines may also be venomous. The wound should be immediately immersed in hot water to stop the pain. Firefish feed avidly on any small fish and soon outgrow a small aquarium.

SIMILAR SPECIES

The plaintail firefish, *Pterois russelii* Bennett 1831, has no spots on median fins and only 13 pectoral fin rays. Indo-West Pacific, Persian Gulf to Sodwana Bay.

The common devil firefish of southern Africa, presently called *Pterois miles* (Bennett 1828), may be the same species as *Pterois volitans* (Linnaeus 1758) of the Pacific; and *P. miles* may be endemic to Sri Lanka. Scales smooth, pectoral fin rays 13–15. Distribution uncertain due to this confusion. Indo-West Pacific, Red Sea to South Africa.

FALSE STONEFISH
Scorpaenopsis diabolus
(Cuvier 1829)

12 cm (lower fish displaying a warning flash on inner side of pectoral fin)

Body with noticeable hump at nape, the depth 2.2–2.5 times in SL; scales small, ctenoid; chest (prepelvic area) distinctly scaly; dorsal fin with 12 spines (shorter than half body depth), 9 rays; pectoral fin rays 17–19, upper rays branched; anal fin with 3 spines, 5 rays; upper opercle spine bifurcate; snout longer than eye diameter; ascending process of premaxilla not reaching inter-orbital space; no teeth on palatines; snout length and inter-orbital width greater than eye diameter. Colour variable. **Inside of pectoral fins with a reddish orange band near margin, containing 2–7 black spots**, some fish with 1–4 black spots in the pectoral axil; broad reddish band near tail fin margin; pelvic fins mostly dark with pale margin. Attains 23 cm.

Indo-West Pacific, Red Sea, Oman to the Eastern Cape.

Coral reefs and rocky areas from shore to 40 m. When disturbed, false stonefish expose the bright warning colours of the inner side of the pectoral fins. Although its venom is not as potent as the true stonefish (see below), the false stonefish can inflict a painful wound.

SIMILAR SPECIES

The humpback scorpionfish, *Scorpaenopsis gibbosa* (Bloch & Schneider 1801), has inside of pectoral fins with several small black spots in the axil, large black blotch near base of upper rays, and a broad dark band near margin. Indian Ocean, Red Sea to the Eastern Cape.

The raggy scorpionfish, *Scorpaenopsis venosa* (Cuvier 1829), has no prominent dark markings on inside of pectoral fins and a distinct pit on top of head behind eyes. Indo-central Pacific, Persian Gulf to Aliwal Shoal.

The true stonefish has no scales on the body, a more flattened head and dorsal fin spines hidden by thick warty skin.

STONEFISH
Synanceia verrucosa
Bloch & Schneider
1801

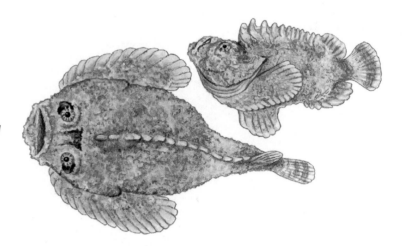

7 cm juvenile (lateral view; Taiwan)
35 cm (dorsal view)

Body globose, **head large, broad and flattened dorsally; eyes elevated, separated by a broad depression, also a pit below eye; mouth vertical; scales not apparent, the skin thick and warty, resembling a lump of coral rock; dorsal fin with 12–13 short stout spines, covered with thick skin and 5–7 rays**; anal fin with 3 spines, 5–6 rays; pectoral fins enormous, fan-like, with 17–19 fleshy rays. Colour variable, blending in with surroundings. Attains 36 cm.

Tropical Indo-Pacific, Red Sea, Oman to Aliwal Shoal, rarely to East London.

Shallow water on coral reefs to 20 m, coral rubble and sand; often seen under ledges or buried in sand. Sometimes exposed by low tide. This sedentary ambush predator feeds mainly on fish. Its excellent camouflage is enhanced by a coat of filamentous green and brown algae, hydroids and other organisms, and by its ability to bury itself in the sand. As implied by the name, the stonefish looks remarkably like a stone or bit of the reef and is, thereby, doubly attractive to little fish: open space is at a premium on the reef, and the space round the stonefish is kept vacant because all the small fish that mistake the 'open space' as a shelter site are eaten. Fish are attracted to the stonefish because of the luxuriant growth of algae and edible invertebrates on the stonefish and in the vicinity of the stonefish's ambush site. Gastropods and prawns have been observed to crawl over a stationary stonefish without its moving; however, any fish swimming in the vicinity are closely followed by movements of the stonefish's eyes. Once an unwary fish approaches within striking distance, it is caught with a lightning thrust of the very protrusile and capacious mouth. The stonefish is able to lift its head considerably more than other fishes can. High-speed cinematography has shown a stonefish bending its head 50° relative to the body axis, to catch a fish directly over its mouth. Nothing is known about the reproduction of stonefish.

The stonefish is the most venomous fish in the sea. The short sharp dorsal fin spines resemble a hypodermic needle, with a tubular venom duct that empties at the tip of the spine and is connected to a large venom gland covered by warty skin. When a hapless victim treads on the fish, the warty skin about the spine is compressed, squeezing the venom gland and injecting the venom into the victim's foot. Pain is immediate, soon becomes intolerable and wounds from stonefish may cause death within an hour. Soaking

the wound in water as hot as can be borne for at least half an hour relieves the pain and denatures the venom. An antivenom is available in Australia. When wading on or near coral reefs, one should wear thick-soled boots; thin-soled canvas shoes are not sufficient protection against stonefish spines. Despite the venomous spines, the flesh is delicious.

There are 4 or 5 species of true stonefish, but only one in our area. See false stonefish.

PAPERFISH
Taenianotus triacanthus
Lacepède 1802

4 cm juvenile
12 cm adult (Comoros)

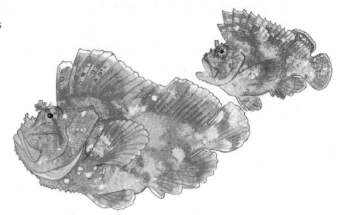

Body and head greatly compressed; scales reduced to small spiny papillae; dorsal fin high with 12 spines, 10–11 rays; anal fin with 3 spines, 5–6 rays; pectoral fin rays 14–15. Colour variable: tan to reddish, pink, purple, brown, yellow or blackish. Attains 12 cm.

Indo-Pacific, Kenya to Park Rynie.

Coral reefs and sand bottom from shore to 135 m. A sedentary species, often swaying from side to side imitating a bit of algae moved by the swell. Feeds on small fish and shrimp.

Periodically sheds its skin. Interesting aquarium fish, but needs protection from predators.

FAMILY CONGIOPODIDAE ▪ Horsefish

Body oblong, compressed; **dorsal fin prominent, fin origin above eye, front spines elongate, subequal to body depth; head shorter than body depth; front head profile concave with pronounced snout; single nostril on each side of snout; dorsal fin with 19–21 spines, 11–15 rays; no anal fin spines, rays 7–10**; pectoral fins slender, low on body, rays 9; pelvic fins with 1 spine, 5 unbranched rays; tail fin rounded to emarginate; skin naked (except for LL scales) and smooth or rough with modified scales forming minute prickles. Size range 45–76 cm.

Rocky reefs and sand or silty bottom in 10–500 m. Feed on small crustaceans, molluscs, sea urchins, brittlestars and worms. Sedentary species, sometimes taken in large numbers in trawls.

Southern Hemisphere. Four genera, about 17 species, 2 in our area.

SMOOTH HORSEFISH
Congiopodus torvus
(Gronow 1772)

22 cm juvenile

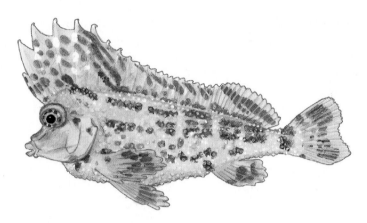

Body oblong, depth 2.9–3.3 times, head length 4.0–4.2 times in SL; dorsal fin 20–21 spines, 13–15 rays; **anal fin rays 7–8**; pectoral fin rays 9; pectoral and pelvic fins subequal, longer than head but shorter than longest dorsal fin spine; skin papillose in young, smooth in adult; **no spines above mouth**; LL obscure. Juveniles tawny with irregular darker markings; adults darker. Attains 76 cm.

Endemic, Walvis Bay to KZN.

Rocky reefs and soft bottom in 10–146 m. Sedentary, probably more active at night.

Edible, and abundant in some places, but rarely eaten.

SIMILAR SPECIES

The endemic spinynose horsefish, *Congiopodus spinifer* (Smith 1839), has spines on the snout above the mouth, 9–10 anal fin rays and a rough skin. Walvis Bay to KZN.

FAMILY PLATYCEPHALIDAE ▪ Flatheads

Body elongate; head markedly depressed; ctenoid scales present on body; head mostly naked, with various ridges and spines; mouth large, lower jaw projecting; villiform teeth on jaws, vomer and palatines; **2 dorsal fins, 1st with 8–10 spines; soft dorsal and anal fins with 10–15 branched rays (no anal fin spines); pelvic fins set far apart and behind pectoral fin base**, with 1 spine, 5 soft-rays; pupil variously constricted by intricate finger-like extensions of iris, which may expand or contract to protect the eye or increase visual sensitivity. Size range 12 cm to 1 m.

Sedentary, cryptically coloured fish, on sand or silty bottom and near coral reefs, from shore to 300 m. Feed mainly on fish and crustaceans. Ambush predators, rely on camouflage to hide from prey and predators. Large species are valuable food-fish.

Primarily Indo-central Pacific, 1 species in the Gulf of Guinea, 2 in the Mediterranean; strangely, none in the eastern Pacific. About 18 genera, ~63 species, ~12 in our area.

Longhead flathead   Bartail flathead

LONGHEAD FLATHEAD
Papilloculiceps longiceps
(Ehrenberg 1829)

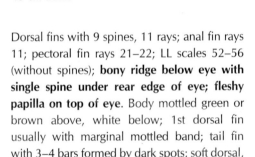

43 cm adult

Dorsal fins with 9 spines, 11 rays; anal fin rays 11; pectoral fin rays 21–22; LL scales 52–56 (without spines); **bony ridge below eye with single spine under rear edge of eye; fleshy papilla on top of eye**. Body mottled green or brown above, white below; 1st dorsal fin usually with marginal mottled band; tail fin with 3–4 bars formed by dark spots; soft dorsal, anal and pelvic fins spotted. Attains 70 cm.

Western Indian Ocean, Red Sea to Aliwal Shoal; recent immigrant into the Mediterranean.

Usually on sandy bottom near coral reefs in 1–20 m; occasionally enters estuaries. Caught in subsistence fisheries; often sold at main fish market in Maputo.

— SIMILAR SPECIES

The crocodile flathead, *Cociella punctata* (Cuvier 1829), has 3–4 spines on ridge below eye; 11 dorsal and anal fin rays; no papilla on eye. Indo-West Pacific, Red Sea to Durban.

The smaller yellowtail flathead, *Cociella heemstrai* Knapp 1996, is similar to the crocodile flathead, but usually has 12 dorsal and anal fin rays, no papilla on eye and middle third of tail fin yellow. Attains 50 cm. Western Indian Ocean, Oman to Durban and Madagascar.

BARTAIL FLATHEAD
Platycephalus indicus
(Linnaeus 1758)

23 cm

Dorsal fin with 9–10 spines, 13–14 rays; anal fin rays 13; pectoral fin rays 18–20; LL scales 68–82 (without spines); no spines on ridge below eye; 2 preopercle spines, lower slightly

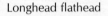

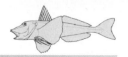

longer; inter-orbital width equal to or greater than eye diameter. Adult brown or grey above, white below; **tail fin white or yellow, with 2–3 horizontal black stripes**. Attains 1 m.

Indo-central Pacific, Red Sea, Oman to Mossel Bay; has migrated through the Suez Canal to the Mediterranean.

Estuaries and inshore waters on sandy or silty bottom to 25 m. Juveniles common in mangroves. Feeds on prawns, crabs, mysids, worms and fish. Sexually mature at ~36 cm SL; eggs pelagic; spawns in KZN, July to November. Often buried in sand with only its eyes exposed.

Good eating, but large specimens are less tasty. Handle large flatheads with care! Although not venomous, the sharp spines at the corner of the preopercle can cause serious injury. Takes flesh bait, also plugs and spoons. SA angling record: 3.7 kg.

— **SIMILAR SPECIES** —

Other flatheads in our area have distinct spines on head, larger scales, and lack the characteristic black bars on tail of this flathead.

FAMILY TRIGLIDAE ■ Gurnards

Body elongate; **head bones exposed; scales small, ctenoid and overlapping, or rudimentary and more or less embedded; a row of small spines along each side of dorsal fin bases; snout projecting in front of lower jaw; 1st dorsal fin with 8–10 spines; 2nd dorsal fin with 13–19 rays**; anal fin rays 14–18 (no spine); **pectoral fin rays 13–15, lower 2–3 rays free and enlarged**; tail fin with 9–10 branched rays; pelvic fins set wide apart, with 1 spine, 5 branched rays; maxilla covered by preorbital bone when mouth is closed. Size range 15–70 cm.

Sedentary fish of continental shelf, from shore to 480 m. The free pectoral rays are used as feelers to find prey and 'walk' on the bottom. Feed mainly on crustaceans, bony fish and cephalopods. Some species attain 60–70 cm and are commercially important as food-fish.

Temperate and tropical waters of all oceans. About 8 genera, ~125 species, 10 in our area.

CAPE GURNARD
Chelidonichthys capensis
(Cuvier 1829)

60 cm (lateral and dorsal views)

Dorsal fin spines 8–9, rays 15–17; anal fin rays 14–16; pectoral fin rays 10–11 + 3 free rays; **chest naked**, body scales more or less embedded; **lower gill rakers 13–18** plus rudiments; **inter-orbital width 0.5–1.7 times in eye diameter**; preorbital bones rounded at front of snout, with 4–6 short spines; **dorsal head profile convex** without transverse groove; pectoral fin reaches vertical line at base of 7th anal fin ray. Head and body **reddish dorsally, pale red below LL, white or pink ventrally**; pectoral fins dark green, **large black blotch with small white or pale blue spots on inner side**. Attains 70 cm.

Endemic, Cape Fria to Maputo.

Soft bottom in 10–390 m. Females mature at 35 cm (4 years); males mature ~37 cm (5 years). Eggs pelagic, spawns in summer. Juveniles feed on crustaceans; adults eat crustaceans, cephalopods and fish, mainly dragonets. The large swimbladder is used in sound production.

Excellent food-fish and important commercial species caught mainly by trawlers. SADSAA all-tackle record: 4.15 kg.

SIMILAR SPECIES

The bluefin gurnard, *Chelidonichthys kumu* (Cuvier 1829), has narrower inter-orbital area (width 1.5–2.2 times in eye diameter) and 8–10 lower gill rakers. Indo-West Pacific, south to False Bay.

The lesser gurnard, *Chelidonichthys queketti* (Regan 1904), has dorsal + anal fin rays = 34–36, large outer spine at front of preorbital bones, and pectoral fins lack black blotch. Endemic, Orange River to KZN.

The lyre gurnard, *Trigla lyra* Linnaeus 1758, has a long shoulder spine (spine length measured from edge of operculum greater than eye diameter), opercular spine reaches past margin of operculum; horizontal ridge on preopercle. This eastern Atlantic and Mediterranean species extends to Walvis Bay.

FAMILY PERISTEDIIDAE   Armoured Gurnards (Crocodilefish)

Head and body flattened ventrally, completely encased in armour of bony tile-like scales; front of snout with 2 flat bony processes projecting forward; pectoral fins with 2 ventral-most rays free and enlarged, used as feelers; dorsal fin divided into spinous and soft-rayed fins; pelvic fins wide apart, with 1 spine and 5 branched rays; tail fin with 9 or 10 branched rays; maxilla covered by preorbital bone; a series of barbels on lower jaw. Size range 15–70 cm.

Demersal fish usually found on sand or silty bottom in 58–550 m. Feed on benthic crustaceans, molluscs, brittlestars and worms.

Worldwide on outer continental shelf and slope. About 4 genera, with ~30 species, 3 in our area.

CROCODILEFISH
Satyrichthys adeni
(Lloyd 1907)

*16 cm (dorsal and
ventral views)*

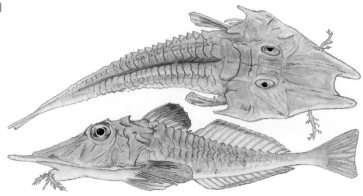

Head flattened; body elongate; chin with 2 large fleshy branched barbels, barbels not reaching pelvic fins; **preopercle with short stout spine; dorsal fin with 7–8 spines, 13–16 rays; anal fin rays 14–16**; pectoral fin rays 12–15 + 2 free rays; LSS 27–30; gill rakers 4–6 / 17–20; head length 2.1–2.4 times in SL; inter-orbital width 4.0–5.8 times in head length. Head and body orange to reddish brown; margin of dorsal and anal fins dusky brown; pectoral fins dusky brown. Attains 70 cm.

Indo-West Pacific, Gulf of Aden to Mossel Bay.

Sand and mud bottom in 58–295 m. This bizarre species is occasionally taken by trawlers. The thick bony armour plates are presumably highly modified scales.

SIMILAR SPECIES

Satyrichthys investigatoris (Alcock 1898) has 21–22 dorsal and anal fin rays, chin barbel and preopercle spine extend past pelvic fin base. Indian Ocean, south to Durban.

FAMILY DACTYLOPTERIDAE ▪ Helmet Gurnards

Body thick, elongate, covered with scute-like scales; **head large, blunt, with bones united to form bony helmet; preopercle spine elongate; pectoral fins greatly enlarged, reaching past dorsal fin**; spinous dorsal fin with 1–2 long isolated spines on rear part of head, followed by short fin of 5 slender spines and longer fin of 9 soft-rays; anal fin with 6 rays below soft dorsal fin; pelvic fins with 1 hidden spine, 4 rays; mouth small, on underside of head; teeth short and blunt; no teeth on vomer or palatines; no LL. Size range 30–60 cm.

Sand, coral rubble or silty bottom near or on coral and rocky reefs. Benthic fish sitting on or cruising slowly over the substrate. Feed on crustaceans, molluscs and benthic fish.

Tropical and subtropical waters of all oceans, but not in eastern Pacific. Two genera, with ~7 species, 2 in our area.

STARRY HELMET GURNARD
Dactyloptena peterseni
(Nyström 1887)

32 cm (Saipan)
6 cm juvenile (dorsal
and lateral views;
Comoros)

Dorsal fin with 1 spine on rear of head, then a wide gap to fin of 5 spines and short gap to soft-rayed fin of 9 rays; anal fin rays 6 (no spines); pectoral fin rays 32–34, lower 5 rays partly free and used as feelers to find prey and 'walk' on bottom. Body orange-red with scattered yellowish green spots, pale below; pectoral fins green at centre with yellow transverse lines and spots. Attains 56 cm, 1.5 kg.

Indo-central Pacific, Red Sea to Algoa Bay.

Usually on sandy or gravel bottom, often near reefs; adults trawled in 50–250 m; postlarvae and small juveniles pelagic near surface. Uses its front pectoral rays to crawl over the bottom and disturb small crustaceans (its prey) that hide in the sediment. This crepuscular predator also feeds on fish, and will take a hook baited with prawn or worms. When sitting with its huge pectoral fins folded back along the body, its mottled camouflage blends in well with the substrate. Although it usually proceeds at a slow pace when moving over the bottom, it can put on a sudden burst of speed and easily eludes capture. When swimming fast, it folds the pectoral fins back along the body and uses quick movements of the tail fin. The huge,

brightly coloured pectoral fins of some helmet gurnards may be used in courtship, warning displays or to assist in capturing prey.

Although these benthic fish are often called 'flying gurnards', they are unable to fly or glide out of the water. Superficially, their huge pectoral fins resemble the pectoral fins of flyingfish; and this has led to the mistaken assumption that helmet gurnards are able to fly. Unlike flyingfish (Family Exocoetidae, see p. 127), which have rigid pectoral fins supported by stiff fin rays, the fins of helmet gurnards are soft and delicate. If one lifts a helmet gurnard from the water, the pectoral fins collapse like a wet cloth.

Juveniles are interesting aquarium fish (but cannot share a tank with smaller fish); adults need an enormous tank, as they like to roam.

SIMILAR SPECIES

The oriental helmet gurnard, *Dactyloptena orientalis* (Cuvier 1829), has 1st dorsal fin spine on back of head, and the 2nd closer to spinous dorsal fin; it also has dark spots and beautiful blue lines on central part of pectoral fins. Indo-central Pacific, Red Sea, Oman to Algoa Bay.

FAMILY AMBASSIDAE ▪ Glassfish

Body oblong, compressed, covered with thin cycloid scales; cheeks and opercle also scaly; **dorsal fin deeply divided before last spine, with 7–8 spines, 8–11 rays; anal fin with 3 spines, 8–11 rays; tail fin forked; maxilla naked; no supramaxilla; small teeth on jaws, vomer and palatines; no spine on opercle**. Size range 9–16 cm.

   Small translucent silvery fish, usually in schools, common in estuaries and coastal lagoons, some species confined to freshwater.

   Tropical and subtropical Indo-West Pacific. Eight genera with ~40 species, 3 in our area.

SMOOTH GLASSY
Ambassis natalensis
Gilchrist & Thompson 1908

10 cm

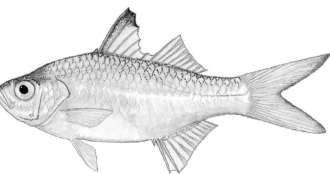

Dorsal fin with 8 spines, 9–11 rays; anal fin rays 9–11; pectoral fin rays 14–15; LL complete, with 27–29 scales; **predorsal scales 9–11**; 2 rows of cheek scales; **rear edge of preopercle smooth except for 1–5 spines at angle; preopercle ridge with 1–5 spines posteriorly. Membrane between 2nd and 4th dorsal fin spines blackish**; dorsal body scales with black margins. Attains 10 cm.

   Zambezi River to East London, Madagascar and Mauritius.

Estuaries and sheltered coastal waters. Matures at 35 mm SL; spawns from August to November. Feeds mainly during day and early evening on zooplankton, insect larvae and filamentous algae.

   No commercial importance, but often used for bait. Also suitable as an aquarium fish.

SIMILAR SPECIES

The longspine glassy, *Ambassis ambassis* (Lacepède 1802) [previously identified as *Ambassis productus*], has preopercle ridge completely serrate and 13–18 predorsal scales. Western Indian Ocean, Kenya to KZN and Madagascar.

   The bald glassy, *Ambassis dussumieri* Cuvier 1828 [previously identified as *Ambassis gymnocephalus*], has interrupted LL, lower preopercle ridge completely serrate, and distinct retrorse spine below front nostril. Indo-West Pacific, Red Sea, Oman to Algoa Bay.

FAMILY KUHLIIDAE ■ Flagtails

Body elongate-oval, compressed, covered with moderate, weakly ctenoid scales; cheeks and opercle scaly, top of head naked; **dorsal fin with 10 spines, 8–13 rays, fin margin notched before last spine; anal fin with 3 spines, 9–13 rays; tail fin forked or emarginate; LL complete; maxilla exposed, without scales or supramaxilla**; jaws, vomer and palatines with villiform teeth; preorbital and lower edge of preopercle serrate; opercle with 2 flat spines. Size range 12–45 cm.

Coral and rocky reefs exposed to surge; juveniles common in tide pools; some species in estuaries or freshwater. Most species are active schooling fish, feed on zooplankton and fish in open water at night.

Tropical and subtropical waters of Indo-Pacific. One genus, ~8 species, 2 in our area.

BARRED FLAGTAIL
Kuhlia mugil
(Bloch & Schneider 1801)

12 cm

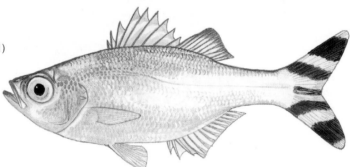

Dorsal and anal fin rays 9–11; pectoral fin rays 13–15; **LL scales 48–56**; gill rakers 9–12 / 23–27. Head and body silvery; **tail fin with 5 black bands**; dusky margin on front of soft dorsal fin. Attains 20 cm.

Tropical and subtropical Indo-Pacific, Red Sea, Oman to Cape Agulhas.

Shallow coastal waters; juveniles common in tide pools; adults often in large schools on reefs, in the surf and also in estuaries. Hyperactive schooling fish; not shy of humans. Spawns throughout year off KZN.

Flesh edible, but this species is too small to be of importance as a food-fish; often used for bait. Do well in aquaria, but keep the lid on and bear in mind that they will outcompete most other fish for food.

Kuhlia taeniura (Cuvier) is a synonym.

─ SIMILAR SPECIES ────────────

Juveniles of the rock flagtail, *Kuhlia rupestris* (Lacepède 1802), have tail fin with 2 dark blotches which merge to form a broad, vertical, submarginal dark band in adults; fish in freshwater have most scales with dusky spot; adults in sea more silvery; lower gill rakers 16–19 and LL scales 38–44. More common in freshwater, but spawns in the sea. Indocentral Pacific, south to Durban.

FAMILY POLYPRIONIDAE ▪ Wreckfish

Body oblong, robust, covered with small rough scales; head, except for snout, also scaly; dorsal fin with 11–12 spines, 11–12 rays (rays longer than spines); anal fin with 3 spines, 9–10 rays; pectoral fins shorter than pelvic fins; maxilla exposed, scaly, with large supramaxilla; jaws, vomer, palatines and tongue with villiform teeth; **opercle with distinct horizontal ridge ending in a short spine**; preopercle with large spines in juveniles, serrate in adults. Size 2+ m.

Adults demersal in 40–650 m on rocky bottom and around wrecks; often at oceanic islands and seamounts.

Tropical and temperate waters of all oceans. One genus with 2 or 3 species; apparently only one in our area.

WRECKFISH
Polyprion americanus
(Bloch & Schneider 1801)

11 cm juvenile
73 cm adult

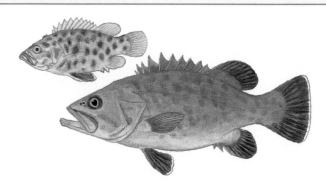

Body depth 2.3–3.1 times in SL. Small juveniles with spiny knobs and ridges on head and distinctly serrate pelvic fin spines. **Adults dark bluish grey with faint darker blotches**, ventral surface paler; juveniles brown, covered with large dark spots, tail fin pale. Attains 2+ m, 200+ kg.

Mediterranean and Atlantic Ocean (from Norway to South Africa and Canada to Argentina), Indian Ocean and South Pacific; along our coast from Walvis Bay to KZN; also Australia and New Zealand.

Juveniles (<50 cm) epipelagic and often associated with flotsam in open ocean; adults to 650 m. The wreckfish is not hermaphroditic. Matures at 67 cm (6.6 kg). A piscivore, feeding on hake and many other fish. Adults sometimes occur in large aggregations.

A 50 cm wreckfish kept in the Plymouth Laboratory Aquarium was unusually aggressive towards other large fish.

Excellent eating. The name 'wreckfish' alludes to its often being caught near wrecks in deep water. IGFA all-tackle record: 71 kg fish caught in New Zealand. Catches are supposed to have declined in South African waters in recent years, and the species is on the MCM protected list.

SIMILAR SPECIES

The two-tone wreckfish, *Polyprion oxygeneios* (Bloch & Schneider 1801), is widely distributed in the Indo-Pacific area and may be found in our area. It is bicoloured, the top half dark brown or grey and lower half abruptly white or silvery; the body is more elongate, with body depth 3.3–3.8 times in SL.

FAMILY SERRANIDAE ■ Rockcods, Goldies, Seabasses & Soapfish

Body robust or somewhat compressed, oblong to elongate; **dorsal fin with 7–13 spines, 10–21 rays; anal fin with 2–3 spines, 6–10 rays; pelvic fins with 1 spine, 5 rays; tail fin rounded, truncate to deeply forked; maxilla exposed; small slender teeth on jaws, vomer and palatines**; small canines usually present at front of jaws; **no molars or incisors; preopercle serrate (serrations reduced in adults of some species); opercle with 3 flat spines, upper and lower spines often indistinct** (covered by skin and scales); scales small to moderate, adherent, usually ctenoid; **cheeks and opercle scaly**; LL usually complete; branchiostegal rays 7, membranes separate, joined to isthmus far forward. Size range 4 cm to 2.7 m.

Coral and rocky reefs from shore to 500 m; some species occur in estuaries, tide pools, mangrove swamps and over sandy/mud bottom. All serranids are carnivorous, but the family includes a variety of ecological types (see subfamily texts below). Most species are proto-gynous hermaphrodites, but synchronous hermaphrodites are also common.

Worldwide in tropical and warm temperate waters. The Family Serranidae comprises 5 subfamilies (the subfamily not included in this book is the Liopropominae), ~48 genera, ~330 species; 77 species known or likely to be found in our area.

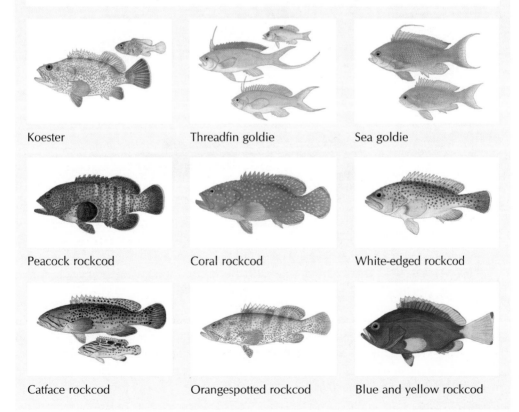

Koester

Threadfin goldie

Sea goldie

Peacock rockcod

Coral rockcod

White-edged rockcod

Catface rockcod

Orangespotted rockcod

Blue and yellow rockcod

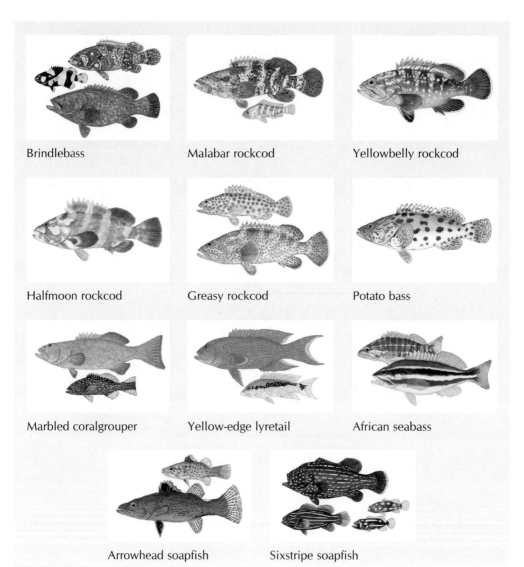

Brindlebass

Malabar rockcod

Yellowbelly rockcod

Halfmoon rockcod

Greasy rockcod

Potato bass

Marbled coralgrouper

Yellow-edge lyretail

African seabass

Arrowhead soapfish

Sixstripe soapfish

Subfamily Anthiinae ⬚ Anthiines, Goldies & Basslets

Dorsal fin with 10–13 spines, 13–19 rays; anal fin rays 6–9; branched tail fin rays usually 13.
Ecologically, there are three kinds of anthiines:

■ small (7–11 cm SL) schooling plankton-feeders with numerous long gill rakers; often associated with coral reefs in 5–30 m. Most sexually dichromatic anthiines are protogynous hermaphrodites, e.g. sea goldies;

- moderate-sized (15–37 cm SL) deep water (24 m to ~300 m) epibenthic fish with numerous long gill rakers; they feed on macro-zooplankton, crustaceans and fish. Sexually dichromatic and probably protogynous hermaphrodites, e.g. swallowtails (*Holanthias* spp);
- small to moderate-sized (4–35 cm SL) solitary, sedentary ambush predators, e.g. koester and basslets (*Plectranthias* spp), with gill rakers fewer and shorter than plankton-feeding anthiines. Feed mainly on benthic crustaceans, worms, cephalopods and fish. No sexual dichromatism; reproductive mode uncertain.

Worldwide in tropical and warm temperate waters. The Anthiines are a disparate assemblage of small to moderate-sized (4–40 cm SL) colourful serranids, comprising ~21 genera and ~172 species, many of which are still undescribed. About 18 species known or likely to occur in our area. The generic classification of the Anthiinae is not satisfactory. The genus *Anthias* is currently restricted to several Atlantic species. The Indo-Pacific species formerly included in the genera *Anthias* and *Mirolabrichthys* are provisionally placed in the genus *Pseudanthias*.

KOESTER
Acanthistius sebastoides
(Castelnau 1861)

3 cm juvenile
27 cm adult

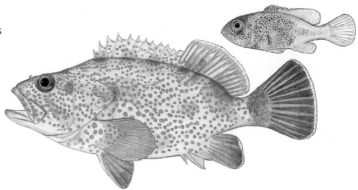

Dorsal fin 11–13 spines, 15–17 rays; pectoral fin rays 19–21; anal fin rays 7–8; **front nostrils with broad, usually fringed, flap**; preopercle lower edge with 2–3 large antrorse spines; **maxilla with minute embedded scales**. Head and body buff, **covered with small orange spots** and a few scattered dark brown blotches; tail and anal fins dark grey; pelvic fins yellowish. Attains 35 cm.

Endemic, False Bay to Durban.

Rocky bottom in depths of 1–25 m. Feeds on benthic crustaceans and fish. Adults sedentary and solitary. The pelagic larvae metamor-

phose to the benthic juvenile stage at 9 mm SL.

Flesh excellent, but not popular as foodfish because of its small size. Hardy aquarium fish.

SIMILAR SPECIES

The whiteblotch koester, *Acanthistius* sp., has body white, with irregular brown blotches overlain by orange or russet markings; series of 5 white blotches along base of dorsal fin; vertical white streak at base of tail fin; distinct ctenoid scales on maxilla; 18 pectoral fin rays. Endemic to KZN and the Eastern Cape.

THREADFIN GOLDIE
Nemanthias carberryi
Smith 1954

3 cm SL juvenile
8 cm SL male
4 cm SL female

Dorsal fin 11 spines (12 in small juveniles, but 1st spine minute and disappears with growth), 16–17 rays; anal fin rays 7; pectoral fin rays 20–21. **Adults with first 2 dorsal fin spines elongate** and flexible; pelvic fins and tail fin lobes filamentous; front of upper lip thickened, with **nipple-like papilla at midline**; maxilla scaly. Males have purple-edged yellow band from eye to pectoral fin base, upper half of head reddish, dorsal fin red with lower rear part yellow, lower tail fin lobe elongate and pelvic fins reaching past anal fin origin. Females mostly yellow-orange, with equal-sized tail fin lobes. Attains 8 cm SL.

Western Indian Ocean, Gulf of Aden to Aliwal Shoal, Chagos, Madagascar, Comoros, Seychelles and Maldives; juveniles drift to Port Alfred.

Schooling fish, common over coral reefs in 10–30 m. Colour pattern varies with locality. Males in the Maldives lack the elongate lower tail fin lobe of males from southern Africa and may represent a different species.

JLB Smith mistook the juvenile as a distinct species because of its extra dorsal fin spine and distinctive colour pattern. Can be kept in large aquaria with other threadfin goldies.

SEA GOLDIE
Pseudanthias squamipinnis
(Peters 1855)

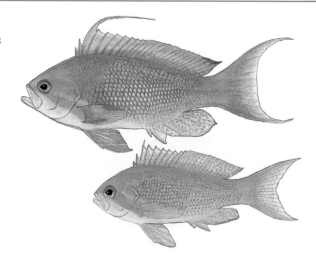

9 cm SL male
7 cm SL female

Dorsal fin 10 spines, 15–17 rays; anal fin rays 6–7; pectoral fin rays 16–18; maxilla scaly; **tail fin lunate; slender filament on rear edge of front nostrils. Adult male with elongated 3rd dorsal fin spine and 2 red spots on pectoral fins**. Attains 10 cm SL.

Tropical and subtropical waters of Indo-West Pacific, Red Sea to Aliwal Shoal; juveniles drift to Knysna in summer.

Coral reefs in 10–25 m. Schooling species, feeds on zooplankton (copepods, amphipods, fish and crustacean larvae, gastropod veligers and mysids) above reef, and dives into reef at approach of danger. Females mature at ~70 mm SL (2 years). The social units of this harem type of reproduction include a large, distinctively coloured adult male and numerous smaller, more uniformly orange females and small juveniles. The male spawns with several females of his harem. If the male is taken by a predator, the largest (dominant) female changes sex and colour pattern to take the place of the missing male. Transformation of an ovary to a testis, and simultaneous colour pattern change occur within two weeks in the sea goldie.

Usually the most common and abundant species of *Pseudanthias* on shallow coral reefs of the Indo-West Pacific region. Colour and size of sexual transition vary with locality and may indicate distinct species differences. Colourful aquarium fish; needs a large tank, other goldies for company, and excellent water quality.

SIMILAR SPECIES

The silver-streak goldie, *Pseudanthias cooperi* (Regan 1902), has no elongated dorsal fin spine, pectoral fin rays 18–20, LL scales 48–52, no nostril tentacle, male reddish dorsally, silvery grey below, tail fin red with blue edges. Males in nuptial colours have a silver streak running just above the lateral line. Indo-West Pacific, south to Aliwal Shoal.

Subfamily Epinephelinae ▫ Rockcods (Groupers)

Dorsal fin continuous with **7–11 spines, 10–21 rays; anal fin rays 7–10; branched tail fin rays 15; supramaxilla present; upper jaw reaching below or beyond eye; inner teeth on jaws and palate depressible; scales small, more than 8 rows between LL and middle dorsal fin spines; LL scales inconspicuous**, usually smaller than contiguous body scales and mostly covered by them; soft dorsal, tail and anal fins scaly; upper part of pectoral fin base joined to body by scaly flap of skin. Size range 20 cm to 2.7 m.

Demersal fish, generally associated with coral or rocky reefs; although juveniles are often found in seagrass beds, and adults of a few species prefer sandy or silty areas. Some species occur in 100–370 m (rarely to 500 m); however most inhabit depths less than 100 m, and juveniles are often found in tide pools.

As major predators of the coral reef ecosystem, rockcods feed on a variety of fish, crustaceans and cephalopods. Most rockcods (*Epinephelus and Cephalopholis* spp) are sedentary ambush predators, hiding amongst the coral and rocks until an unwary fish or crustacean goes by, then catching their prey with a quick lunge and snap of their jaws. The large head and mouth of the typical rockcod enable it to suck in a large volume of water (and the prey) in less than a second. The numerous inwardly depressible teeth are well adapted

for seizing prey and preventing its escape from the mouth. Adult coralgroupers (*Plectropomus* spp) and lyretails (*Variola* spp) are primarily piscivorous, and they are usually seen patrolling the reef or shallows in search of prey.

Most rockcods appear to be protogynous hermaphrodites, but this protogynous mode of reproduction is complicated in certain species by large females that do not change sex, and by small males that are mature at the same size as the smallest females.

Rockcods (a.k.a. 'groupers') are excellent eating and bring the highest prices in fish markets, especially in the coastal fisheries of tropical and subtropical areas. As top predators, rockcods are often the cause of ciguatera poisoning (fortunately ciguatera is not known from southern Africa); the liver may also be toxic from high levels of vitamin A.

It has been estimated that 90% of the world harvest of marine food is derived from artisanal fisheries, and rockcods are a major component of the artisanal fisheries resource. Worldwide and in southern Africa, rockcod populations are threatened by overfishing. Most species reside for many years in one small area, and these areas can be 'fished out' when too many people harvest this resource. Many groupers gather in large aggregations at particular sites for spawning, and some fishermen target these aggregations as they provide lucrative catches. The removal of many fish in spawning condition is likely to diminish the reproductive capacity of these species.

The subfamily occurs worldwide in tropical and warm temperate waters. Fifteen genera and ~160 species; 57 species known or likely to occur in our area.

PEACOCK ROCKCOD
Cephalopholis argus
Bloch & Schneider 1801

28 cm

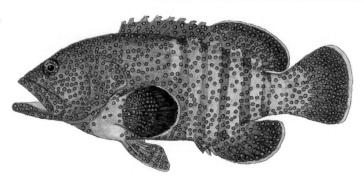

Dorsal fin 9 spines, 15–17 rays; anal fin rays 9; pectoral fin rays 16–18; body depth less than head length, 2.7–3.2 times in SL. **Head and body brown, covered with black-edged blue spots**; often with 5–6 pale bars on rear of body and pale area over chest; rear margin of median fins usually with narrow white edge; distal part of pectoral fins sometimes maroon-brown. Attains 65 cm.

Indo-central Pacific, Red Sea, Oman to Aliwal Shoal, juveniles drift to the Eastern Cape.

Usually associated with exposed coral reefs in 1–10 m, also in tide pools and to depths of 40 m. Ambush predator, feeds by day or night, mainly on fish and crustaceans; sometimes follows a moray eel as it forages over the reef in

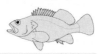

order to catch fleeing small fish and crustaceans frightened from their hiding places by the eel. Females mature at ~30 cm. Spawns in groups; probably protogynous. In the Red Sea it occurs in groups of up to 12 fish, but in Hawaii it is described as a 'solitary fish'.

Common and important to artisanal fisheries throughout Indo-West Pacific, but often implicated in cases of ciguatera poisoning.

― SIMILAR SPECIES ――――――――――――

The brownbarred rockcod, *Cephalopholis boenak* (Bloch 1790), is dark brown, usually with 7–8 dark bars on body, but it lacks the blue ocelli of the peacock rockcod and has 8 anal fin rays. Usually found on dead reefs in protected waters. Indo-West Pacific, Kenya to Maputo.

CORAL ROCKCOD
Cephalopholis miniata
(Forsskål 1775)

19 cm

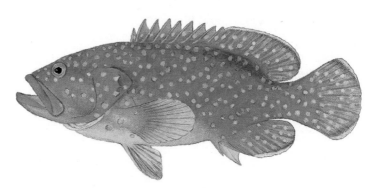

Dorsal fin 9 spines, 14–16 rays; anal fin rays 9; pectoral fin rays 17–18; **body depth usually less than head length, 2.6–3.0 times in SL. Head, body and median fins reddish orange, covered with blue spots** extending onto maxillae and lips, but not on underside of lower jaw; juveniles with fewer spots; sometimes shows dark bars on body. Attains 40 cm.

Tropical and subtropical Indo-West Pacific, Red Sea, Oman to Aliwal Shoal.

Usually on exposed coral reefs in 2–150 m. Sedentary territorial species that catches most of its prey with a quick rush from the bottom; feeds during day on fish schooling above the reef (mainly sea goldies) and crustaceans. Females mature at 25 cm SL; males produced by sexual transition of older females. A dominant male and his harem of 2–12 females can occupy a territory of up to 475 m^2.

Although juveniles are attractive aquarium fish, they soon grow too large for most home aquaria. Small but excellent food-fish.

― SIMILAR SPECIES ――――――――――――

The sixblotch rockcod, *Cephalopholis sexmaculata* (Rüppell 1830), has 4–5 squarish dark blotches at the base of the dorsal fin, another faint blotch on the nape and 2 smaller ones on the peduncle (blotches sometimes merging with dark red vertical bars), and most specimens with dark-edged blue lines around the eye. Indo-central Pacific, Red Sea, Oman to Aliwal Shoal.

WHITE-EDGED ROCKCOD
Epinephelus albomarginatus
Boulenger 1903

23 cm

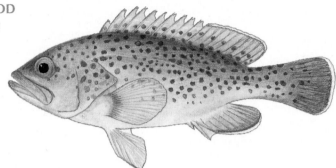

Dorsal fin 11 spines, 14 rays; anal fin rays 8; pectoral fin rays 17–18; tail fin truncate with rounded corners; **spinous dorsal fin membranes distinctly incised; body depth less than head length, 2.6–3.0 times in SL**; midlateral body scales distinctly ctenoid. **Head, body and dorsal fin with brown spots; paired fins and margin of spinous dorsal fin yellow; soft dorsal, anal and tail fins with white edge**. Attains 82 cm, 13 kg (± 16 years).

Endemic, southern Mozambique to East London.

Coral reefs, rocky bottom in 10–120 m. Feeds on benthic invertebrates, fish and squid. Females mature at 60 cm (7 years) in KZN, 38 cm (3 years) in Mozambique; changes sex at 73 cm (12 years). Spawns off northern KZN and Mozambique from October to February. Grows slowly and is non-migratory; hence vulnerable to overfishing.

Good eating; usually caught by ski-boat fishermen. Known as 'Captain Fine' to anglers in KZN. Catch restricted. SADSAA all-tackle record: 12.3 kg.

SIMILAR SPECIES

The speckled rockcod, *Epinephelus magniscuttis* Postel, Fourmanoir & Guézé 1964, occurs in 50–300 m; lacks white edges on median fins, has yellow margin on dorsal fin, but pectoral and pelvic fins are not yellow. Attains 70 cm. Known only from Sodwana Bay, Mozambique, Mauritius and Réunion.

The streakyspot rockcod, *Epinephelus longispinis* (Kner 1864), has dark reddish brown spots that become crowded and elongated to form short oblique streaks on rear part of body and peduncle, and the longest dorsal fin spine is longer than any of the dorsal fin rays. Attains 55 cm. Indo-West Pacific, Kenya to the Eastern Cape.

CATFACE ROCKCOD
Epinephelus andersoni
Boulenger 1903

50 cm adult
5 cm juvenile

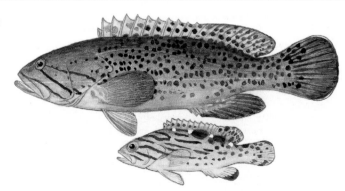

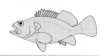

Dorsal fin 11 spines, 13–15 rays; anal fin rays 8; pectoral fin rays 17–19; spinous dorsal fin membranes incised; body depth less than head length, 3.2–3.7 times in SL; mid-lateral body scales slightly rough (most embedded). **Head and body with brown spots; head with 3 dark stripes, 2 posteriorly from eye, 1 continued backwards from maxillary groove** (head stripes barely discernible on dark fish); dark spots also present on dorsal fin and upper part of tail fin; some fish show 3 or 4 white spots along dorsal fin base. Juveniles with dark stripes which break into spots on rear of body and dark blotch at base of posterior dorsal fin spines. Attains 87 cm, 9 kg (±11 years).

Endemic, Mozambique to Knysna, but most common between Richards Bay and Durban. Reports from Madagascar are dubious.

Reefs and rocky bottom from shore to 70 m; juveniles in tide pools and on inshore reefs. Feeds on fish, crabs and spiny lobsters. A sedentary species, usually found in caves and crevices. Females mature at 50–60 cm (~3 years); some males are produced by transition of mature females, others do not go through a female stage. Spawns in summer off KZN. A pair in the Durban oceanarium was observed to exhibit striking colour changes before swimming in tight spirals to the surface where spawning occurred.

Vulnerable to spearfishermen and anglers, hence its restricted catch status. SADSAA all-tackle record: 7.5 kg.

ORANGESPOTTED ROCKCOD
Epinephelus coioides
(Hamilton 1822)

40 cm (Persian Gulf)

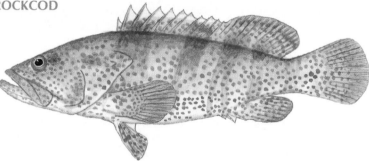

Dorsal fin 11 spines, 14–16 rays; anal fin rays 8; pectoral fin rays 18–20; tail fin rounded; LL scales 58–65; gill rakers 8–10 / 14–17; spinous dorsal fin membranes incised, longest spine shorter than longest ray; **body depth distinctly less than head length, 3.2–3.8 times in SL; inter-orbital width 5.0–6.2 times in head length; upper jaw length 17–20% SL.** Mid-lateral body scales rough. Head, body and usually median fins with **numerous orange to reddish brown spots** (diameter of largest spots ~4 or 5 times that of rear nostrils); **no pale spots on head or body;** **orange spots become poorly defined and darker with growth** and turn brown after death; spots on head often coalesce and become elongate, arranged in irregular rows radiating from eye; fins brown, with proximal parts spotted. Attains ~100 cm.

Mainly continental shores and large islands of tropical Indo-West Pacific, Red Sea, Persian Gulf to Durban. Recent immigrant to the Mediterranean Sea via the Suez Canal.

Often found in estuaries and also offshore to 100 m. Feeds mainly on fish, variety of

crustaceans, and occasionally cephalopods. In the Persian Gulf, females mature at 25–30 cm (2–3 years); sexual transition occurs at 55–75 cm. Probably spawns in groups.

Widely used in aquaculture; in Taiwanese markets and restaurants, it is more expensive than Malabar rockcod. *Epinephelus suillus* (Valenciennes 1828) was incorrectly used as the valid name in *Smiths' Sea Fishes* (Smith & Heemstra 1986).

SIMILAR SPECIES

Often mistaken for the Malabar rockcod (see p. 168) (which has black and white spots rather than orange spots) or the greasy rockcod (see p. 171) which has smooth scales on side of body, narrow inter-orbital width (6.8–8.1 times in head length) and longer upper jaw (21–24% SL).

BLUE AND YELLOW ROCKCOD
Epinephelus flavocaeruleus
(Lacepède 1802)

25 cm

Dorsal fin 11 spines, 15–17 rays; anal fin rays 8; pectoral fin rays 18–19; **tail fin truncate; spinous dorsal fin membranes not incised; body depth subequal to head length, 2.4–2.8 times in SL**; rear nostrils of adults much bigger than front nostrils; mid-lateral body scales rough. **Head and body dark blue**, sometimes with pale blue flecks; **fins and jaws bright yellow**; some fish with corners of tail fin and margins of soft dorsal, anal and pelvic fin tips blackish. **Yellow colour reduced with growth** (see p. 10); **large adults greyish, dark blue, violet, chestnut brown or almost black**. Attains 90 cm and at least 17 kg.

Indian Ocean, Oman to Algoa Bay; not known from Red Sea or Persian Gulf.

Reefs and rocky bottom from shore to 150 m; juveniles common in shallow water; adults usually caught in deep water. Solitary predator, feeds on a variety of fish, crabs, shrimp, spiny lobsters, squid and octopus. Females mature at ~50 cm SL; spawns off Kenya in November and December.

Excellent eating; caught with hook and line and spear. SADSAA all-tackle record: 16.3 kg.

SIMILAR SPECIES

White-blotched rockcod, *Epinephelus multinotatus* (Peters 1876), usually show irregular white spots on body and numerous dark reddish brown spots on ventral head and body. Indian Ocean, Persian Gulf to East London.

BRINDLEBASS
Epinephelus lanceolatus
(Bloch 1790)

29 cm subadult
8 cm juvenile
1.8 m adult (Pitcairn)

Dorsal fin 11 spines, 14–16 rays; anal fin rays 8; pectoral fin rays 18–20; tail fin rounded; **spinous dorsal fin membranes incised, fin spines distinctly shorter than fin rays; head very broad, inter-orbital width much greater than eye diameter, contained 3.3–6.2 times in head length, body robust, depth 2.4–3.4 times in SL, body width 1.5–1.8 times in body depth; lateral body scales smooth**. Small juveniles (8–14 cm) yellow, with irregular broad black bars on body; juveniles 20–50 cm SL with irregular white or yellow spots on black areas, fins with irregular black spots; adults (80–150 cm SL) dark brown with faint mottling, fins with numerous black spots; large adults (1.6–2.3 m SL) brown, the fins darker. Attains 2.7 m, ~400+ kg.

Indo-central Pacific, Red Sea, Oman to Algoa Bay.

Adults and juveniles in estuaries and harbours; small juveniles cryptic; adults in caves, on coral reefs and around wrecks to 100 m. Feeds on crustaceans, mainly spiny lobsters, but also on a variety of fish, including small sharks and batoids, and on juvenile sea turtles; in South African estuaries the main prey item is the mud crab, *Scylla serrata*. Age and growth not studied. Probably protogynous, like most rockcods that have been studied; females mature at 1.3 m.

If large brindlebass are caught, they should be released unharmed by cutting the trace close to the hook. This giant rockcod is inquisitive and unafraid of divers; consequently, spearing brindlebass in South African waters is illegal. Large adults often seen with attached remoras or a retinue of pilot fish (like a big shark).

— SIMILAR SPECIES ————

Large greasy rockcod (see p. 171), Malabar rockcod and orangespotted rockcod (see p. 165) are often mistaken for brindlebass, but in these species the head is not so broad (inter-orbital width contained more than 4 times in head length) and the dorsal fin spines are almost as long as the dorsal fin rays.

MALABAR ROCKCOD
Epinephelus malabaricus
(Bloch & Schneider 1801)

41 cm juvenile
3 cm juvenile

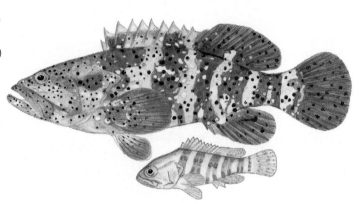

Dorsal fin 11 spines, 14–16 rays; anal fin rays 8; pectoral fin rays 18–20; gill rakers 8–11 / 15–18; spinous dorsal fin membranes incised; **body depth distinctly less than head length, 3.0–3.6 times in SL; inter-orbital width contained 4.5–6.5 times in head length; upper jaw length 17–22%, mid-lateral scales rough**. Grey to brown; body usually with 5 oblique dark bars that bifurcate ventrally; **head and body with numerous small, well spaced black spots (largest about twice size of rear nostrils) and (usually) irregular pale spots or blotches**; with growth, bars and white spots fade, black spots become more numerous. Attains 1.2+ m, 25+ kg.

Tropical Indo-West Pacific, Red Sea, Oman to East London.

Coral and rocky reefs, tide pools, estuaries, mangroves and sandy/mud bottom, shore to 150 m. Feeds on fish, crustaceans and occasionally octopus. Matures at 70–80 cm; spawning has been reported from August to October. Probably protogynous. No information on age and growth, but a 35 cm specimen put into the East London Aquarium in 1985 had attained a length of 1 m by 1996.

Common in markets of Indo-West Pacific; widely used in aquaculture. Caught with trawls, longline, traps, spear, and hook and line. Catch restricted. IGFA all-tackle record: 20 kg, Japan.

SIMILAR SPECIES

Often mistaken for orangespotted rockcod or greasy rockcod (see p. 165 and p. 171 respectively).

The adult blotchy rockcod, *Epinephelus fuscoguttatus* (Forsskål 1775), has body depth 2.6–2.9 times in SL; flank scales smooth; rear nostrils subtriangular, much larger than front nostrils; total gill rakers 29–31. Indo-central Pacific (but not known from Persian Gulf, Hawaii or French Polynesia), Red Sea, Kenya to Mozambique.

YELLOWBELLY ROCKCOD
Epinephelus marginatus
(Lowe 1834)

13 cm juvenile

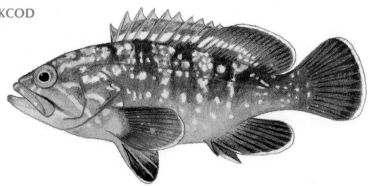

Dorsal fin 11 spines, 14–16 rays; anal fin rays 8; pectoral fin rays 17–19; body depth less than head length, 2.6–3.1 times in SL; mid-lateral body scales rough (small fish) or smooth (large adults). **Head and body brown or greyish dorsally, yellowish gold ventrally; irregular white, pale greenish yellow or silvery grey blotches usually visible on body and head** and mostly arranged in vertical series; black maxillary streak usually visible above upper jaw; median fins dark brown; **edges of anal and tail fins and often pectoral fins narrowly white; triangular outer part of spinous dorsal fin membrane and basal part of paired fins often yellow**. Attains 1.2 m, 35+ kg (Tunisia); age of a 118 cm Mediterranean yellowbelly was estimated at 35 years; maximum age for KZN fish is ~24 years.

Southern Brazil to Argentina, Azores, Portugal, Spain, France, Mediterranean, Madeira, Canary Islands, Cape Verde Islands and west coast of Africa to Angola; Knysna to Mozambique, also known from Oman.

Rocky bottom from shore to ~200 m; juveniles common in tide pools; large adults in the coelacanth habitat of the deep canyons off Sodwana Bay. Feeds on crabs, octopus and fish, with large adults taking more fish. Females mature at 44–53 cm (6–8 years) and change sex at 80–87 cm (15–17 years). Spawns in spring and summer off KZN and grows slowly (~6 cm/year for a 25–35 cm fish). Non-migratory; mean distance travelled for 30 tagged fish was 13 km.

Caught by ski-boat anglers off KZN and the Eastern Cape. The slow growth and site specificity of yellowbelly make them vulnerable to overfishing and may account for declines in catches of this fish. Catch now restricted.

Formerly identified as *Epinephelus guaza* (Linnaeus 1758), but that name was found to be based on a Caribbean rockcod of the genus *Mycteroperca*, so it cannot be used for the yellowbelly. SA angling record: 26.7 kg.

SIMILAR SPECIES

The moustache rockcod, *Epinephelus chabaudi* (Castelnau 1861), has 9 anal fin rays, no pale spots or blotches on body and no pale edge on fins. Western Indian Ocean, Kenya to Knysna, Seychelles and south-western coast of India.

HALFMOON ROCKCOD
Epinephelus rivulatus
(Valenciennes 1830)

27 cm adult

Dorsal fin 11 spines, 16–18 rays; anal fin rays 8; pectoral fin rays 17–19; upper edge of operculum straight, almost horizontal; body depth less than head length, 2.7–3.2 times in SL; mid-lateral body scales rough; upper rear part of head covered with minute scales and numerous pores. Colour variable; **body generally reddish to greenish brown with a small white or pale blue spot on each body scale**; 5 broad, irregular, oblique dark bars usually visible on body (3rd and 4th bars close together and may be partially joined); **head usually with 3–4 wavy blue lines radiating from eye; pectoral fins dusky, with dark red or reddish brown semicircular blotch on base of rays; 2 dark red or russet bands on chest and dark spot on front of isthmus**; median fins greenish yellow or greyish brown, **dorsal fin usually with dark brown to black line along base (may be restricted to base of spinous part)**. Attains ~50 cm, 4 kg (±13 years).

Tropical and warm temperate Indo-West Pacific, Oman, Kenya to Knysna, Madagascar and Mascarene Islands; no records from Red Sea or Persian Gulf.

Rocky or coral reefs in 1–150 m, algal flats, seagrass beds and mangroves. Sedentary and not afraid of divers. When a diver (or possibly a large predator) gets too close, the fish turns to face the intruder and opens its pectoral fins to make 2 enormous eye spots, one on each side of its head, the half-moon spot on the base of the pectoral fins forming the 'pupil' of the false eyes. The big ocelli make the fish look much larger and may deter predators.

Feeds on small fish and crustaceans. Females mature at 22 cm SL (18 months) and change sex at ~26 cm SL (5 years). Spawns from July to November.

Good eating, but generally too small to be a prized catch. Catch restricted. SADSAA all-tackle record: 1.6 kg.

GREASY ROCKCOD
Epinephelus tauvina
(Forsskål 1775)

14 cm juvenile
50 cm adult (Red Sea)

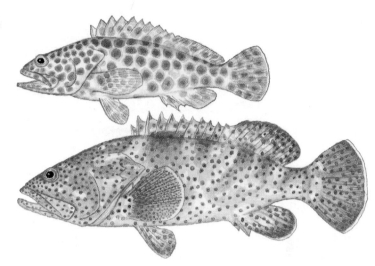

Dorsal fin 11 spines, 14–16 rays; anal fin rays 8; pectoral fin rays 18–20; **body depth 3.0–3.6 times, head length 2.1–2.4 times in SL; inter-orbital area narrow, flat to slightly concave, its width 6.8–8.1 times in head length and 3.1–4.0 times in upper jaw length; maxilla extends well past eye, the upper jaw length 21–24% SL; maxilla width 5.4–6.5% SL; lateral body scales smooth.** Head and body pale grey or brown, **covered with orange-red to brown spots, the centres darker than edges**; spots on head smaller anteriorly; large black blotch (or group of black spots) often visible on body at base of last 4 dorsal fin spines, extending onto lower part of dorsal fin; 5 faint dark bars may be present on the body, 4 below the dorsal fin and the 5th on the peduncle (these bars may be represented by dusky blotches at the base of the dorsal fin and the dark saddle blotch on the peduncle); fins also covered with dark spots, those on pectoral fins becoming smaller and less distinct on distal part of fin; rear margin of tail fin, and anal and pectoral fins often with white edge; dark spots on soft dorsal, tail and anal fins of juveniles are so close-set that pale interspaces form a white reticulum. Attains 75 cm; reports of larger *E. tauvina* are apparently based on misidentifications of orangespotted rockcod, Malabar rockcod or brindlebass.

Widely distributed in tropical and sub-tropical Indo-West Pacific, Red Sea to the Eastern Cape.

Clear water areas on coral reefs; juveniles on reef flats and in tide pools; adults down to 52 m. Unlike Malabar and orangespotted rockcod, the greasy rockcod is rarely found in estuaries. Feeds almost exclusively on fish. Little known about its biology.

Caught with hook and line, spear and traps.

POTATO BASS
Epinephelus tukula
Morgans 1959

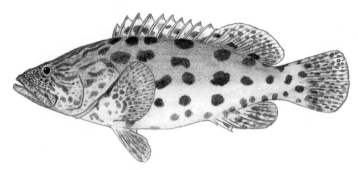

39 cm juvenile

Dorsal fin 11 spines, 14–15 rays; anal fin rays 8; pectoral fin rays 18–20; **body depth 2.9–3.5 times, head length 2.3–2.6 times in SL**; lateral body scales rough. **Head and body grey with several dark, widely spaced blotches, mostly larger than eye, round to oval or dumb-bell shaped**; head with brown spots and streaks (many radiating from eye, especially posteriorly); dark spots on fins, smaller towards margins. Attains 2.2 m, 300 kg.

Tropical and subtropical Indo-West Pacific, Red Sea, Oman to Aliwal Shoal.

Coral reefs; juveniles in tide pools, adults in 10–230 m. Feeds on variety of reef fish, skates, crabs and spiny lobsters. Females mature at 90 cm SL.

An aggressive territorial species, unafraid of divers. The large size and territorial behaviour of the potato bass make it especially vulnerable to spearfishing, hence spearing this species is illegal in South Africa. Considered inferior to other rockcods for eating.

MARBLED CORALGROUPER
Plectropomus punctatus
Quoy & Gaimard 1824

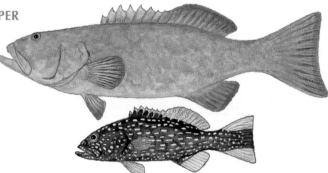

1.1 m adult
10 cm juvenile

Dorsal fin 7–8 spines, 10–12 rays; anal fin rays 8 (spines difficult to see in large fish); pectoral fin rays 16–18; body depth 2.9–3.9 times, head length 2.7–3.1 times in SL. **Adult brown to orange, greenish dorsally, with irregular pale marbling; fins dark with blue margins. Juvenile brown with numerous elongate white spots**; 7–12 cm SL juveniles with soft dorsal, anal and pelvic fins, and

upper and lower third of tail fin hyaline. Attains 1.1 m, 12.2 kg.

Western Indian Ocean, Oman, Kenya to Aliwal Shoal and islands of the south-western Indian Ocean.

Shallow water on coral reefs; adults to 62 m. Feeds on reef fish. Caught with hook and line, trolling, spear and on benthic longlines.

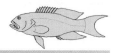

YELLOW-EDGE LYRETAIL
Variola louti
(Forsskål 1775)

37 cm adult
9 cm juvenile

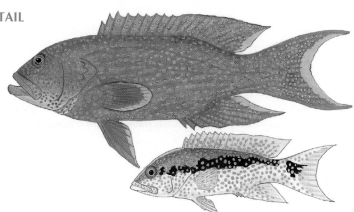

Dorsal fin 9 spines, 13–14 rays; anal fin rays 8; pectoral fin rays 16–19; tail fin lunate; body depth 2.8–3.3 times, head length 2.5–2.8 times in SL. Head, body and fins brown to orange-red (fish from deep water more reddish) with many round or elongate spots of blue to pink; **rear margin of fins broadly yellow**. Juveniles with irregular black band dorsally on body from eye to rear of dorsal fin; head and body below band white, black blotch at base of tail fin; blue spots on head, body and fins. Attains 81 cm, 12 kg.

Tropical Indo-central Pacific, Red Sea, Oman to Port St Johns.

Coral reefs in 3–50 m; usually in clear water below 15 m; also reported from 240 m. Prefers islands and offshore reefs. Active throughout the day, often seen cruising the reef. Feeds mainly on fish, also some crabs, shrimp and stomatopods. Females mature at 33 cm SL; spawns December to February.

Important food-fish of the Indo-Pacific region, but often causes ciguatera poisoning. Although apparently not toxic at Réunion, it is prohibited from sale at the nearby island of Mauritius. Caught with handlines, spear and traps.

Subfamily Serraninae   Seabasses (Comber)

Dorsal fin continuous with 10 spines, 13–15 rays; anal fin with 3 spines, 7–8 rays; tail fin truncate to emarginate, with 15 branched rays; no supramaxilla; upper jaw reaching below or beyond eye; small fixed teeth on jaws, vomer and palatines; scales ctenoid; **LL complete, scales distinct, subequal in size and number to scales of adjacent rows; soft dorsal and anal fins and most of tail fin naked**; maxilla naked; no scaly flap of skin at upper end of pectoral fin base. Size range 20–30 cm.

Demersal fish on sandy bottom and rocky reefs from shore to 200 m. Common but not abundant; most species too small to be of importance as food-fish.

Worldwide in tropical and temperate waters. About 10 genera, ~50 species, one in our area.

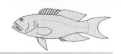

AFRICAN SEABASS
Serranus knysnaensis
Gilchrist 1904

9 cm juvenile
20 cm adult

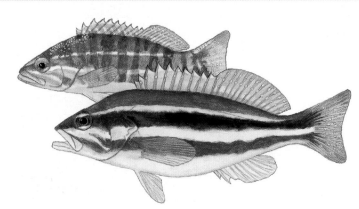

Dorsal fin 10 spines, 13–15 rays; anal fin rays 7–8; pectoral fin rays 15–17; LL scales 70–77; body elongate, not much compressed; **lower gill rakers 13–15** (including rudiments); tail fin emarginate. Head and body brownish dorsally, pale pinkish below; body usually with **2 irregular dark longitudinal bands from head to tail fin** and often with several short dark brown bars; tail and soft dorsal fin with pale blue spots. Attains 30 cm.

Endemic, False Bay to Durban.

Rocky bottom in depths of 1–200 m. Feeds on fish and crustaceans. Previously confused with the comber, *Serranus cabrilla* (Linnaeus 1758), of the Mediterranean and eastern North Atlantic. The comber was known to Aristotle, the ancient Greek philosopher, naturalist and anatomist, as a synchronous hermaphrodite with functional testes and ovary in a single individual. Like the comber, our African seabass also appears to be a synchronous hermaphrodite. A common sedentary species on reefs of the Eastern Cape.

Edible but not usually caught by anglers because of its small size.

SIMILAR SPECIES

The koester (see p. 159) is deeper bodied (depth 2.3–2.5 times in SL), has 11–13 dorsal fin spines, rounded tail fin and is covered with small orange spots.

Subfamily Grammistinae ▫ Soapfish

Dorsal fin divided, or continuous but deeply notched, with 7–9 spines and 10–14 soft-rays; anal fin with 2–3 spines, 8–9 soft-rays; pectoral fin rays 13–18; tail fin rounded to truncate, with 15 branched rays; pelvic fins with 1 spine, 5 branched rays, **inner ray broadly joined to belly by a membrane; upper edge of operculum joined to head;** scales small, ctenoid or cycloid; **skin with a thick coat of mucus containing the toxin grammistin, which gives the fish a bitter taste** and deters predators. Size range 10–35 cm.
Demersal fish of coral and rocky reefs from shore to 200 m.

Worldwide in tropical and subtropical waters. The Subfamily Grammistinae provisionally comprises 10 genera, including (in our area) the genera *Aporops*, *Aulacocephalus*, *Belonoperca*, *Grammistes*, *Grammistops*, *Pogonoperca* and *Pseudogramma*; ~29 species, 7 in our area.

ARROWHEAD SOAPFISH
Belonoperca chabanaudi
Fowler & Bean 1930

5 cm juvenile
18 cm adult

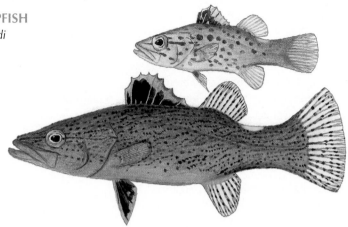

First dorsal fin with 8 spines, 2nd dorsal fin with 1 spine, 10 rays; anal fin 2 spines, 8 rays; pectoral fin rays 13–15; body depth 3.5–3.7 times in SL and much less than head length; scales rough; preopercle coarsely serrate; subopercle and interopercle also serrate. **Head, body and tail fin greenish blue to brown**, with numerous irregular small dark brown spots and a **bright yellow blotch on peduncle behind dorsal fin**; large blue-edged black spot on 1st dorsal fin. Attains 15 cm.

Indo-West Pacific, Kenya to Sodwana Bay; not known from Red Sea or Oman.

Reef species usually in caves and under ledges in depths of 4–50 m. Cryptic species, more active at dusk. Feeds mainly on small fish and crustaceans.

The noxious mucus of this soapfish is less apparent than that of the sixstripe soapfish.

SIMILAR SPECIES

Some cardinalfish (Family Apogonidae, see p. 182) resemble the arrowhead soapfish, but they have larger scales and only 6–7 dorsal fin spines.

The glowfish (see p. 242) has a bright gold spot below rear end of dorsal fin, but it also has a continuous dorsal fin and forked tail fin.

SIXSTRIPE SOAPFISH
Grammistes sexlineatus
(Thunberg 1792)

19 cm adult (Mauritius)
10 cm subadult
2 cm juvenile (Comoros)
2.5 cm juvenile

Body robust, depth about equal to head length, 2.3–2.8 times in SL; dorsal fin divided to base, with 7 spines, 13–14 rays; anal fin 2 spines, 9 rays; pectoral fin rays 16–18; LL scales 60–72; upper edge of opercle bound to body; scales rough, embedded. **Body dark brown; small juveniles with round yellow spots, larger juveniles with 2–6 yellow stripes; in large adults, stripes break into series of short dashes**. Attains 27 cm.

Indo-West Pacific, Red Sea, Oman to Algoa Bay and all western Indian Ocean islands.

Shallow coral or rocky reefs; juveniles found in tide pools. Not seen deeper than 50 m. Solitary species usually in caves or hiding under ledges. Feeds on crustaceans and fish. The skin produces a thick coat of toxic mucus. A good aquarium fish if kept by itself, but the toxin is increased when the fish is stressed, and other fish or invertebrates confined to a small aquarium with the soapfish will soon die.

The distinctive colour pattern makes it easy for predators to learn to avoid this bad-tasting fish and difficult to confuse this fish with other species.

FAMILY PSEUDOCHROMIDAE ■ Dottybacks & Snakelets

This family now comprises 4 subfamilies: the dottybacks, Pseudochrominae; the snakelets, Congrogadinae [previously recognised as a separate family]; the Anisochrominae (1 genus, ~4 species) and the Pseudoplesiopinae (5 genera, ~20 species).

Dutoiti

Snakelet

Subfamily Pseudochrominae ■ Dottybacks

Body rather elongate; dorsal fin 1–3 weak spines, 21–37 rays; anal fin 1–3 weak spines, 13–19 rays; pelvic fins 1 spine, 3–5 rays; branched tail fin rays 15; opercular bones smooth; scales small to moderate, mostly smooth; cheeks and opercle scaly; LL interrupted; maxilla exposed; small slender teeth on jaws, vomer and palatines; small canines usually present at front of jaws; no molars or incisors. Size range 3–12 cm.

Coral and rocky reefs from shore to 30 m.

Pseudochromis species produce a ball of eggs which is laid in an empty shell or under a ledge and guarded by the male.

Indo-central Pacific. At least 7 genera, ~80 species, 7 in our area.

DUTOITI
Pseudochromis dutoiti
Smith 1955

8 cm adult
2 cm juvenile

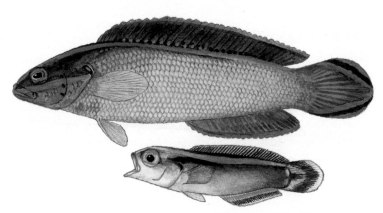

Dorsal fin 3 spines, 28–33 rays; anal fin 3 spines, 16–19 rays; pectoral fin rays 18–19. Bright blue band along dorsal fin base and along top of head to upper jaw; another blue band from tip of lower jaw, under eye to opercle edge; 2 blue-edged black bands on upper and lower margin of tail fin; dorsal and anal fins with blue edges. Attains 9 cm.

Known only from Kenya to Park Rynie.

Reefs and rocky bottom from shore to at least 25 m. Juveniles and occasionally adults found in tide pools. Feeds on benthic crustaceans, worms and fish. Although most *Pseudochromis* are cryptic species and not usually seen by divers, Dutoiti is often observed swimming actively (with a lot of tail-wagging) about the reef.

This dottyback does well in aquaria but, like most species of *Pseudochromis*, it is aggressive towards other fish.

SIMILAR SPECIES

The male lipstick dottyback, *Pseudochromis kristinae* Gill 2004, has reddish pink body, the colour continues posteriorly onto central part of tail fin; head and front part of body

yellow, snout and lips reddish; body scales above and behind pectoral fin with a large dark blue or black spot; proximal half of dorsal and anal fin membranes dusky, with numerous small red spots and streaks; females with head and body uniform dusky brownish; dorsal fin dusky basally, outer part clear; black ring with outer edge of pale blue around eye. Kenya to Sodwana Bay, Comoros and Madagascar.

The dark dottyback, *Pseudochromis melas* Lubbock 1977, has body dark bluish black with yellow-edged ocellus on upper edge of operculum. Kenya to Sodwana Bay.

The Natal dottyback, *Pseudochromis natalensis* Regan 1916, has a blue spot on each body scale and dark spot on upper margin of operculum. Northern Mozambique to Aliwal Shoal.

The Arabian bluestriped dottyback, *Pseudochromis aldabraensis* Bauchot-Boutin 1958, is very similar in colour, but the blue stripe under the eye extends to the dark spot on the operculum, and the tail fin has no black streak within blue margin of lower part of fin. Aldabra Islands, Pakistan, Kuwait, Oman to Sri Lanka.

Subfamily Congrogadinae ▫ Snakelets

Body elongate, with long dorsal and anal fins; pelvic fins rudimentary (1 spine, 2–3 tiny rays) or absent; branched tail fin rays 10; dorsal fin with 1–2 short spines, 32–77 rays; anal fin with 26–65 rays, no spine; pectoral fins short with 8–14 rays; scales small, cycloid and head scaly or naked; LL short and incomplete or developed as 3 or 4 separate LLs on each side of body; single spine on opercle; teeth short, conical; gill rakers rudimentary; branchiostegal membranes united, joined to or free from isthmus. Size range 5–50 cm.

Tide pools and sandy bottom near reefs.

Indo-central Pacific, with 8 genera, 22 species, 5 in our area.

SNAKELET
Halidesmus scapularis
Günther 1872

16 cm

Three lateral lines (dorsal, mid-lateral and ventral); dorsal fin 1 spine, 58–63 rays; anal fin rays 48–52; pectoral fin rays 8–10; pelvic fins 1 spine, 2–3 rays. Head and body brown, sometimes with numerous narrow dusky crossbars; **dark ocellus above opercle**; fins dark posteriorly; often dark spots on tail fin and rear of dorsal fin. Attains 20 cm.

Endemic, False Bay to Park Rynie.

Shallow water from intertidal region to 16 m; often in tide pools and near mouths of rivers. Little-known cryptic species. Agile little fish, difficult to catch; when pursued, leaves the water, wriggling over rocks like a snake in a hurry.

— SIMILAR SPECIES ————

The Zulu snakelet, *Halimuraena shakai* Winterbottom 1978, has no pelvic fins, 47–49 dorsal fin rays, and 36–38 anal fin rays; known from Sodwana Bay, Mauritius and Rodrigues.

The 3 subtidal endemic species of *Natalichthys, N. ori, N. sam* and *N. leptus*, have a single lateral line, and are found only off KZN.

FAMILY PLESIOPIDAE ▪ Longfins

Body oblong to elongate, slightly compressed; scales rough, extending onto cheeks and operculum; **dorsal fin with 10–13 spines, 6–10 rays; anal fin with 3 spines, 8–9 rays; pelvic fins long, with 1 spine and 4 rays; LL interrupted below rear of dorsal fin and continued along mid-lateral part of peduncle; preopercle smooth; no spines on opercle.** Size range 8–25 cm.

Frequents coral reefs and rocky shores.

Indo-Pacific, with ~11 genera, 50 species, 2 in our area.

BLUESPOTTED LONGFIN
Plesiops multisquamatus
Inger 1955

18 cm

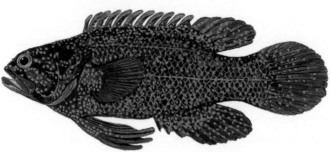

Dorsal fin 12–13 spines, 6–7 rays, interspinous membranes deeply incised; anal fin 3 spines, 8 rays; pectoral fin rays 21–23. LL scales 25–30 / 13–19. **Dark brown, covered with blue dots** (1–4 on each body scale); adults usually have **black blotch at upper end of gill opening**. Attains 25 cm.

Endemic, Kosi Bay to Port Edward.

Shallow coral and rocky reefs; not known below 3 m. This poorly known species is probably nocturnal. Apparently rare (more specimens wanted); like other cryptic fish, bluespotted longfins may not be rare, just difficult to see and collect. This species has more LL scales than other *Plesiops*, hence the name *multisquamatus*.

SIMILAR SPECIES

The redtip longfin, *Plesiops coeruleolineatus* Rüppell 1835, has 10–12 dorsal fin spines; upper LL scales 18–21; dorsal fin spines with red tips and blue stripe along dorsal fin base. Indo-West Pacific, south to Maputo.

FAMILY TERAPONIDAE ▪ Thornfish

Body oblong, slightly compressed; **dorsal fin with 11–13 spines, 9–11 rays; anal fin with 3 spines, 7–11 rays; tail fin truncate to shallowly forked; scales small and rough, extending onto cheeks and operculum; preopercle serrate, opercle with 2 strong spines.** Size range 15–33 cm. Shallow coastal waters, often found in estuaries.

Indo-Pacific, with ~16 genera and 45 species, 3 in our area.

Trumpeter

Thornfish

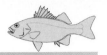

TRUMPETER
Pelates quadrilineatus
(Bloch 1790)

14 cm adult

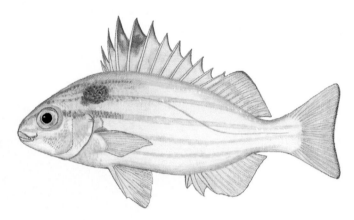

Dorsal fin spines 12–13, rays 9–11, fin margin slightly notched before soft-rayed part; anal fin spines 3, rays 9–11; LL scales 60–69. Silvery with **4–6 dark stripes**; dark blotches present or absent at front of dorsal fin and below dorsal fin origin; tail fin pale or dusky; mouth and gill cavity red. Juveniles with 6–7 dusky bars on body. Attains 30 cm.

Continental Indo-West Pacific, Red Sea, Oman to Bushmans River near Port Alfred. Immigrant to the Mediterranean Sea via the Suez Canal. Abundant in Maputo Bay.

Coastal species, frequents weedy areas, often found in estuaries. Juveniles feed on seagrass and small crustaceans; adults feed on plankton. Breeds in the sea. Swimbladder divided, the anterior chamber connected to skull by muscles that vibrate the swimbladder to produce a croaking sound.

SIMILAR SPECIES

See thornfish below and striped grunter (p. 193).

The lined piggy, *Pomadasys stridens* (Forsskål 1775), also lacks black blotches on dorsal fin and behind head, but it has a dark blotch on the opercle, 13–14 dorsal fin rays and 7–8 anal fin rays. Western Indian Ocean, Red Sea, Persian Gulf to KZN.

THORNFISH
Terapon jarbua
(Forsskål 1775)

13 cm

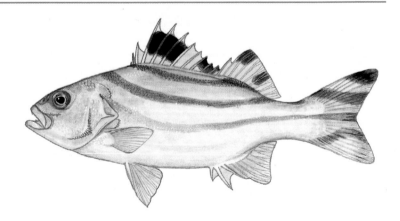

Dorsal fin spines 11–12, rays 9–11, fin margin deeply notched before last spine; anal fin spines 3, rays 7–10; pectoral fin rays 13–14; 2–5 large spines at angle of preopercle; LL scales 69–93. Body silvery, 3–4 curved dark stripes from head to soft dorsal and tail fin; black blotch on spinous dorsal fin. Attains 33 cm.

Indo-Pacific, uncommon south of the Kei River, but juveniles appear in Eastern Cape estuaries in summer, and are occasionally seen at Knysna.

Common in estuaries; juveniles and adults often in freshwater, but spawns in the sea. Small juveniles feed mainly on copepods and amphipods; large juveniles and adults eat benthic invertebrates and fish, and also scales and skin from larger fish. Scale feeding is done by groups of 2–7 thornfish attacking the rear part of the prey. Matures at 13 cm SL; spawning occurs in KZN in late spring and summer.

When captured, the thornfish assumes a U-shape by contracting muscles on one side of its body; simultaneously, the fin spines are erected and the large opercular spines are held at right angles to the head. This defensive posture may deter predators and allow the thornfish to feed on scales of larger fish with relative immunity from predation. The Xhosa name 'umnga' for *T. jarbua* means 'thorn-tree' and aptly describes the fish. Also known as 'pest of Saint Lucia' because it takes any bait and is a pain (literally) to remove from a hook. The dark curved stripes on the body provide camouflage over sand bottoms, resembling the ever-changing curved shadows cast by ripples at the surface.

SIMILAR SPECIES

The straight-lined thornfish, *Terapon theraps* Cuvier 1829, has 2–4 straight stripes on body, no enlarged spine at angle of preopercle, and 46–56 LL scales. Indo-West Pacific, Red Sea, Persian Gulf to Durban.

FAMILY PRIACANTHIDAE ▪ Bigeyes

Body oblong, somewhat compressed, depth 2–3 times in SL; **dorsal fin single, continuous, with 10 spines, 10–15 rays; anal fin with 3 spines, 11–16 rays; pectoral fins smaller than pelvic fins and much shorter than head**; tail fin truncate, convex or concave; scales small, rough and adherent, covering body, head and jaws. Size range 30–60 cm.

Demersal over coral and rocky reefs in 1–400 m. Mainly nocturnal, feed on zooplankton; the large eyes are provided with a *tapetum lucidum* (see glossary) which is responsible for the conspicuous eye shine of these fish.

Worldwide in tropical and warm temperate seas. Four genera and 18 species, ~4 in our area.

CRESCENT-TAIL BIGEYE
Priacanthus hamrur
(Forsskål 1775)

27 cm (colour variants;
Madagascar)

Dorsal fin spines 10, rays 13–15; anal fin spines 3, rays 13–16; **tail fin truncate in juveniles, concave in adults**; body depth 2.4–2.7 times in SL. This fish can change its colour from silvery to reddish in a few seconds; **median fins** dusky, **without distinct dark spots**; pelvic fins dusky, usually with black spot at base of first 3 rays. Attains 45 cm.

Indo-central Pacific, Red Sea, Oman to Knysna.

Coral reefs and rocky bottoms in 5–250 m. Usually inactive by day, seen singly or in small aggregations schooling above the reef. Females mature at 16 cm SL.

Excellent food-fish. Commonly seen by divers, rarely caught by anglers.

SIMILAR SPECIES

The glass bigeye, *Heteropriacanthus cruentatus* (Lacepède 1801), has the tail fin truncate (adults) or convex (juveniles), dark spots on median fins, but no spots on pelvic fins. Atlantic and Indo-central Pacific, Kenya to Aliwal Shoal.

FAMILY APOGONIDAE   Cardinalfish

Body oblong, slightly compressed; **two separate dorsal fins, 1st with 6–8 spines, 2nd with 1 spine, 9–11 rays; anal fin 2 spines, 8 rays; mouth large, maxilla exposed**; small slender teeth on jaws, vomer and palatines; canines present in some species; no molars or incisiform teeth; **opercle ends in a blunt flat point**; scales moderate to large, ctenoid or cycloid (no scales in *Gymnapogon*); LL complete. Size range 4–25 cm.

Most species nocturnal, feeding on small benthic invertebrates and zooplankton. Cardinalfish are one of the few marine fish that practise 'oral incubation' of the eggs. Males usually carry the eggs in their mouth, but females have been reported as incubators in a few species. Most species are small and occur on coral reefs; a few occur in estuaries or are restricted to freshwater. Cardinalfish generally adjust well to life in aquaria.

Worldwide. About 22 genera, ~250 species, ~53 species likely to be found in our area.

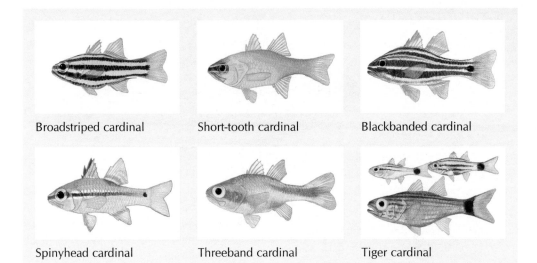

| Broadstriped cardinal | Short-tooth cardinal | Blackbanded cardinal |

| Spinyhead cardinal | Threeband cardinal | Tiger cardinal |

BROADSTRIPED CARDINAL
Apogon angustatus
(Smith & Radcliffe 1911)

8 cm

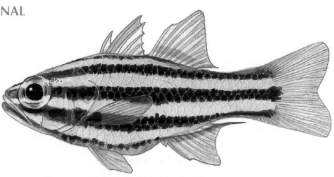

First dorsal fin with 7 spines, 2nd dorsal fin with 1 spine, 9 rays, last ray slightly elongate; last anal fin ray elongate, 1.3–1.6 times length of next-to-last ray; pectoral fin rays 14; LL scales 28; developed gill rakers 11–15. **Body with 5 dark stripes, black tail spot** (usually present) subequal to pupil; dark stripe along base of 2nd dorsal and anal fins. Attains 11 cm.

Indo-West Pacific, northern Mozambique to Aliwal Shoal; probably occurs as far north as Kenya.

Shallow coral reefs, common in 6–20 m.

SIMILAR SPECIES

The black-striped cardinal, *Apogon nigrofasciatus* Lachner 1953, has last anal fin ray not elongate, and 20–24 developed gill rakers. Indo-West Pacific, south to southern Mozambique.

The ninestripe cardinal, *Apogon taeniophorus* Regan 1908, has 4 dark stripes on each side of body plus a dark mid-dorsal stripe = 9 stripes; no elongate dorsal and anal rays, an extra short stripe on head above the mid-lateral stripe, tail spot often merged with mid-lateral stripe.

SHORT-TOOTH CARDINAL
Apogon apogonides
(Bleeker 1856)

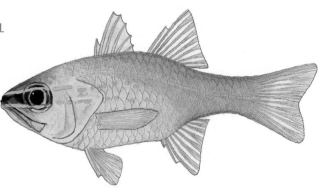

12 cm adult

First dorsal fin with 7 spines, 2nd dorsal fin with 1 spine, 9 rays; pectoral fin rays 14; developed gill rakers 15–17; canine teeth in lower jaw. **Adults yellow with dark stripe from tip of snout through eye.** Attains 12 cm.

Indo-West Pacific, Red Sea to Aliwal Shoal.

Coral reefs in 10–50 m. Usually seen by day in loose aggregations near coral reefs. A hardy aquarium fish.

SIMILAR SPECIES

The bandtail cardinal, *Apogon aureus* (Lacepède 1802), and the flower cardinal, *Apogon fleurieu* (Lacepède 1802), have similar blue lines across the eye, but *A. aureus* has a distinct hourglass-shaped black band encircling the tail fin base. *Apogon fleurieu* has a straight black bar with diffuse edges at tail fin base. Both species occur in the Indo-West Pacific area, Red Sea to Aliwal Shoal.

BLACKBANDED CARDINAL
Apogon cookii
Macleay 1881

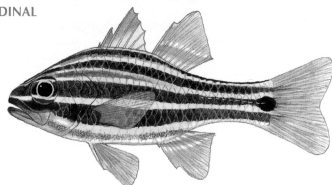

10 cm adult

First dorsal fin with 7 spines, 2nd dorsal fin with 1 spine, 9 rays; pectoral fin rays 15. Adults whitish with **6 dark stripes wider than pale interspaces, postocular stripe extends below 2nd dorsal fin; black tail spot pupil size or slightly larger; dark basal stripe on 2nd dorsal fin of males ~1/3 height of fin, narrower on females.** Attains 10 cm.

Indo-West Pacific, Red Sea, Oman to Aliwal Shoal.

Shallow coral reefs in caves and protected inshore waters. Probably feeds on bio-luminescent zooplankton, and this may be related to its having a black gut.

The ninestripe cardinal, *Apogon taeniophorus* Regan 1908, has more stripes, with postocular stripe confined to head, and tail spot smaller than pupil. Western Indian Ocean, Maldives to Sodwana Bay.

SPINYHEAD CARDINAL
Apogon kallopterus
Bleeker 1856

8 cm

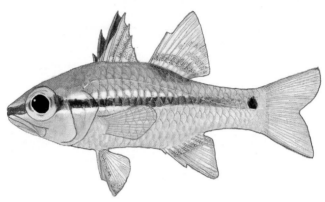

First dorsal fin with 7 spines, 2nd dorsal fin with 1 spine, 9 rays; pectoral fin rays 13; **preopercle ridge serrate; suborbital bones with spines**. Adults brownish; wide **dark stripe from tip of snout through eye to tail fin base** above LL; stripe sometimes fades, but never narrows posteriorly; **black tail spot above and touching LL**; membrane between first 3 dorsal fin spines may be black, brown or yellow; pelvic fins sometimes dark. Attains 15 cm.

Indo-West Pacific, Red Sea to Algoa Bay.

Coral reefs, usually near surge in 3–50 m. Diurnal species; forms small groups probably feeding on zooplankton.

The name *kallopterus* means beautiful fin.

SIMILAR SPECIES

The spurcheek cardinal, *Apogon fraenatus* Valenciennes 1832, has tail spot covering LL, dark mid-lateral stripe tapers posteriorly; some specimens with leading edge of 1st dorsal fin broadly black, followed by a white band. Indo-West Pacific, Red Sea to Aliwal Shoal.

THREEBAND CARDINAL
Apogon semiornatus
Peters 1876

7 cm adult

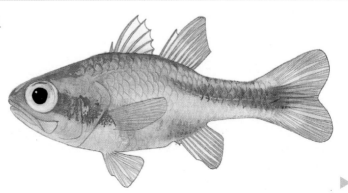

First dorsal fin with 6 spines, 2nd dorsal fin with 1 spine, 9 rays; pectoral fin rays 12. **Reddish with 3 dark bands on body: middle band from eye to tail fin, front of band usually fainter; lower band from eye to anal fin base; upper band mid-dorsally from head to peduncle**. Juveniles translucent posteriorly, with bands as in adult. Attains 7 cm.

Indo-West Pacific, Red Sea, Oman to the Eastern Cape.

Coral reefs in 3–50 m. Extremely common but usually hides in caves.

─ **SIMILAR SPECIES** ─

Apogon campbelli Smith 1949 is also translucent red but has no dark bands. Western Indian Ocean, Red Sea to at least Maputo. Previously confused with the ruby cardinal, *Apogon coccineus* Rüppell 1838, known from the Red Sea to the Persian Gulf.

TIGER CARDINAL
Cheilodipterus macrodon
(Lacepède 1802)

4 cm juvenile
5 cm juvenile
11 cm adult
(all Comoros)

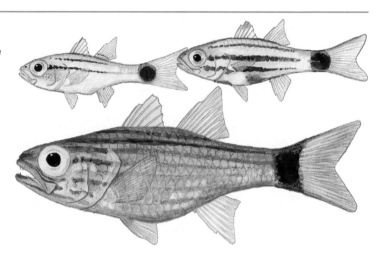

First dorsal fin with 6 spines, 2nd dorsal fin 1 spine, 9 rays; pectoral fin rays 12–13; predorsal scales 5; supramaxilla and **large canines** present. Adult with **7–10 dark stripes** (alternate dark stripes distinctly fainter on some fish) and upper and lower edges of tail fin also dark; 1st dorsal fin dark. Juveniles with 2–6 dark stripes on body; dark spot at tail fin base preceded by white area; the dark spot enlarges with growth to form **dark band on peduncle of adults**. Attains 25 cm.

Indo-West Pacific, Red Sea, Oman to Aliwal Shoal.

Coral reefs in 3–30 m. In late afternoon, when a female is ready to spawn, she approaches a male; if receptive, the male's dark stripes fade and a broad white bar appears on body. After swimming in circles and side-by-side for a few minutes, the male leads the female to a protected area and swims with his belly near the bottom; trembling rapidly, and moving slowly ahead, he presumably releases his sperm. The female follows closely, and pressing her swollen belly to the same area of the reef, she releases a group of eggs; the male then turns back and sucks the eggs into his mouth. The male carries the eggs in his mouth until they hatch.

The name *macrodon* (meaning 'large tooth') refers to the large canine teeth of this species. Identified as *Cheilodipterus lineatus* in *Smiths' Sea Fishes* (Smith & Heemstra 1986).

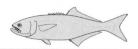

The adult dogtooth cardinal, *Cheilodipterus lineatus* (Forsskål 1775), has 13–16 dark lines (narrower than pale interspaces) on body. *Cheilodipterus arabicus* (Gmelin) and *Cheilodipterus caninus* Smith are synonyms of *C. lineatus*. Western Indian Ocean, Red Sea, Pakistan, Oman to Inhaca.

FAMILY POMATOMIDAE ▪ Elf

Body oblong, slightly compressed; **2 separate dorsal fins, 1st with 7–8 short spines, 2nd dorsal fin with 1 spine and 23–28 rays; anal fin with 2 minute spines, 23–27 rays**; pelvic fins with 1 spine, 5 rays; tail fin forked; maxilla exposed; lower jaw projecting slightly; jaws with a row of sharp compressed teeth; an inner series of small depressible teeth in upper jaw; villiform teeth on vomer and palatines; preopercle edge serrate; opercle ends in a flat blunt point; scales small, weakly ctenoid.

One genus with a single species.

ELF
Pomatomus saltatrix
(Linnaeus 1766)

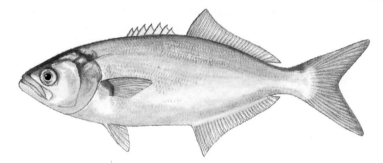

31 cm adult

Head and body bluish green dorsally, silvery below. Attains 1.2 m, 15 kg (10 years).

The distribution of elf is unique. It occurs in subtropical and temperate continental waters: both sides of Atlantic Ocean; along our coast from False Bay to Mozambique; possibly Madagascar, also Oman, Mediterranean, Australia, New Zealand and Malay Peninsula.

Coastal waters; juveniles and adults often found in estuaries. A swift and voracious predator, elf is renowned as one of our best sport fish. The Latin name *saltatrix* means 'dancing (or leaping) girl', and this species lives up to its name, often leaping out of the water in frenzied pursuit of prey or when fighting at the end of an angler's line. They will strike almost any moving lure or bait. When feeding on shoaling prey, they go berserk, attacking the dense shoals in packs, rushing through their prey, biting and ripping fish in a feeding frenzy similar to that of sharks or freshwater piranhas. Adults feed mainly (87%) on fish, but also take shrimp and squid; juveniles consume a variety of crustaceans, fish and cephalopods. In winter, elf undertake a seasonal migration from the south coast to KZN, where spawning occurs from September to December. Most of the pelagic larvae are carried south by the Agulhas Current, and the juveniles (<4 cm) spend their first year in estuaries and nearshore waters along the south coast. One-year-old fish are mature at 25 cm.

In KZN the elf is called 'shad' a name that Margaret Smith tried to discourage as a misnomer, because it is the name of a well known clupeid fish (related to pilchards and herrings) of North America, where the elf is known as 'bluefish'. In Australia it is called 'tailor' for its habit of cutting nets and fishing lines with its sharp teeth. The flesh is delicious fresh or smoked, but softens rapidly and does not keep well; elf should be bled and put on ice immediately after capture. One must be careful when removing the hook from a live elf; the razor-sharp teeth can cut a finger to the bone, and the serrated preopercle bone on the cheek can also deliver a nasty cut.

To protect the spawning stock, no fishing for elf is allowed from 1 September to 30 November in South Africa.

SIMILAR SPECIES

Yellowtail (*Seriola* spp) are superficially similar, but have a narrower peduncle, and the anal fin origin is well behind the origin of the 2nd dorsal fin.

FAMILY HAEMULIDAE ■ Rubberlips & Grunters

Body oblong, slightly compressed; dorsal fin with 9–14 spines, 13–25 rays; anal fin with 3 spines, 6–13 rays; pelvic fins with 1 spine, 5 rays; tail fin truncate to emarginate; **maxilla hidden when mouth is closed; jaws with a series of small teeth**, no molars or canines, no teeth on vomer or palatines; preopercle serrate; opercle ends in a blunt flat point; scales small to moderate, weakly ctenoid. Diurnal predators of shallow waters; adults feed mainly on benthic invertebrates by taking in mouthfuls of sand and expelling the sediment out their gill openings. Size range 20 cm to 1 m.

Worldwide in tropical and temperate waters. About 18 genera, ~ 120 species, 19 in our area.

Sailfin rubberlip

Whitebarred rubberlip

Spotted grunter

Javelin grunter

Piggy

Striped grunter

SAILFIN RUBBERLIP
Diagramma centurio
(Cuvier 1830)

~50 cm adult
(Seychelles)
13 cm juvenile

Dorsal fin with 9–10 spines, 21–25 rays, anterior spines elongated in small juveniles (2nd and 3rd spines longest in adults); anal fin rays 7; pectoral fins shorter than head, subequal to pelvic fins, rays 17–18; LL scales 56–66; gill rakers 3–9 / 14–15; lips of adults swollen. Adults and subadults (30–100 cm) uniform silvery grey or with numerous dark brown or black dots on head and dorsal part of body; subadults with slightly larger orange-brown spots scattered dorsally on the head, body and peduncle. Juveniles (~12 cm) grey or yellow, with broad black band from snout through eye to end of tail fin; another band from top of head to rear of dorsal fin; curving black band over front and basal two-thirds of dorsal fin, and black margins on pelvic and anal fins and corners of tail fin; additional stripes appear with growth, and at ~20 cm, stripes break up into spots. Attains ~1 m.

Western Indian Ocean, Kenya to Durban, Comoros, Madagascar and Seychelles.

Coral reefs in 3–50 m. Juveniles in seagrass beds. Large adults solitary or in small groups. Line-caught fish put up a respectable fight. Reputed to be an excellent eating fish.

SIMILAR SPECIES

Diagramma punctatum Cuvier 1830 is endemic to the Red Sea; juveniles are similar to *D. centurio*, but the subadults and adults have larger dark spots on the head and body.

Plectorhinchus species have 3rd, 4th or 5th dorsal fin spines longest.

WHITEBARRED RUBBERLIP
Plectorhinchus playfairi
(Pellegrin 1914)

48 cm adult

Dorsal fin 12 spines, 19–20 rays, 4th and 5th spines longest but shorter than longest rays; anal fin rays 7; pectoral fins shorter than head, subequal to pelvic fins, rays 16. **Head and body bronzy dorsally, with 4 white bars; lower half of body silvery white; fins blackish.** Lips of adults not much swollen. Attains 90 cm.

Western Indian Ocean, Red Sea, Oman to Port St Johns.

Coral reefs in 3–80 m. Usually solitary near coral; juveniles in estuaries. Excellent eating. Named for Lambert Playfair, of the British Colonial Service, who co-authored *The Fishes of Zanzibar* with Albert Günther in 1867.

SIMILAR SPECIES

The dusky rubberlip, *Plectorhinchus chubbi* (Regan 1919), is uniform dark grey or dusky. Western Indian Ocean, India, Kenya to the Eastern Cape.

SPOTTED GRUNTER
Pomadasys commersonnii
(Lacepède 1801)

79 cm adult
8 cm juvenile

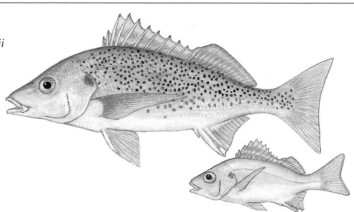

Dorsal fin 11 spines, 14–15 rays, 4th and 5th spines longest but shorter than longest rays; anal fin rays 7; pectoral fins equal head length, much longer than pelvic fins, rays 17–19. Body silver or brownish dorsally, with **numerous small black spots; single black spot on rear edge of opercle**; small juveniles (<8 cm) without black spots. Attains 90 cm, 10 kg (~15 years).

Tropical and warm temperate western Indian Ocean, India to Algoa Bay, and in summer to False Bay.

Shallow coastal waters; common in estuaries, often caught in surf, particularly near river mouths. Adults feed on crustaceans and bivalve molluscs. Matures at ~3 years, females 36 cm SL and males 30 cm SL.

Usually spawns at sea from August to December, but there are reports of spotted grunters spawning in Durban Harbour and in the St Lucia system. A 10-year-old fish is ~77 cm, 5.2 kg. Small juveniles (2–3 cm) enter estuaries in spring and summer, and may also be found in freshwater. After a year in the estuary, juveniles have attained 17–20 cm and usually return to the sea. In large adults, the supraoccipital bone at the back of the skull hyperossifies, causing visible swelling on the nape.

Margaret Smith wrote in *Smiths' Sea Fishes* (Smith & Heemstra 1986, p. 569): '... a fine game fish, but wary and easily frightened by noise, certainly in Cape estuaries; except in the Swartkops estuary it is apparently not disturbed by motorboats. It frequently blows

small creatures from holes in mud and sand, and in shallow water the tail may wave above the water. Hooked fishes blow the bait, especially bloodworms, with such force that it is shot far up the line. Takes prawn, crayfish, razorshell, sea-lice, marine worms, cheese and bacon, but rarely fish bait. Flesh delicate and tasty, improved by bleeding the fish and keeping cool, not frozen, for 12–18 hours. The strong spines and serrated preopercle can inflict deep cuts.

Easily killed by cold upwelling on our south Cape coast. This was probably responsible for many grunters being consumed by the strandlopers at the Cape. Numerous enlarged supraoccipital bones have been discovered in middens at False Bay, indicating that large numbers of these fishes were killed in that area, probably when upwelling occurred. Not rock haunting, they were not likely to be caught in primitive stone traps, and are too wary to have been caught or speared.'

SIMILAR SPECIES

The cock grunter, *Pomadasys multimaculatus* (Playfair 1867), has numerous dark spots on the head as well as on the body. Known only from Zanzibar to Algoa Bay.

JAVELIN GRUNTER
Pomadasys kaakan
(Cuvier 1830)

45 cm adult
24 cm juvenile

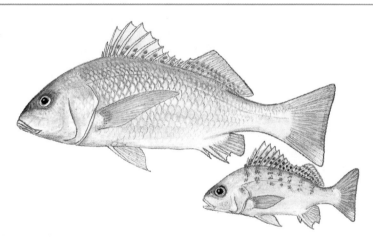

Dorsal fin with 12 strong spines,13–15 rays, 3rd and 4th spines twice length of 11th spine and longer than rays; anal fin rays 7–8; pectoral fins longer than pelvic fins. Head and body silvery, with **dark blotch on opercle; a series of dark spots on basal half of dorsal fin membrane; lower corner of tail fin pale**; juveniles with dark bars dorsally, breaking up into vertical series of dark spots with growth and disappearing in adults. Large adults with bony swelling on top of head. Attains 75 cm, 6 kg.

Tropical and subtropical Indo-West Pacific, Red Sea, Persian Gulf to the Eastern Cape.

Shallow coastal waters, also reported to 75 m; often in estuaries, juveniles common in turbid water. Burrowing prey are blasted from the sediment by a strong jet of water ejected through the mouth. Usually solitary, shoaling near river mouths during winter spawning season.

Excellent angling fish; often used for bait. When removed from the water, makes a loud grunting noise by grinding its pharyngeal teeth,

with the gas-filled swimbladder acting as an amplifier. *Kaakan* is the local name in India.

The saddle grunter, *Pomadasys maculatus* (Bloch 1793), has an oblique dark bar on the nape and a large black blotch on the spinous dorsal fin. Indo-West Pacific, Oman to the Eastern Cape.

PIGGY
Pomadasys olivaceus
(Day 1875)

7 cm juvenile
15 cm adult

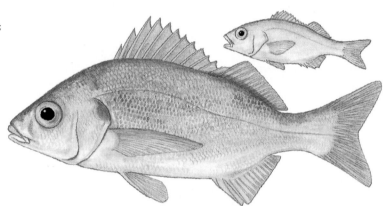

Dorsal fin with 12 strong spines, 15–17 rays, 3rd and 4th spines twice length of 11th spine and longer than rays; anal fin rays 11–13; pectoral fins longer than pelvic fins. **Head and body silvery to greenish, dark blotch on opercle; fins yellowish in juveniles, dusky in adults**. Attains 31 cm, 0.4 kg.

Tropical and temperate Indian Ocean, Oman, Somalia, Madagascar, Kosi Bay to False Bay. Reported from Swakopmund.

Shallow coastal waters; adults move to offshore reefs and soft substrate banks in 10–90 m; juveniles common in lower reaches of estuaries. Feeds on shrimp, stomatopods, crabs and fish. Matures at ~14 cm FL; spawns offshore throughout the year. Common shoaling species; prey for most larger predators. Piggies are sensitive to cold water, and cold upwelling along the south coast causes massive fish kills.

Used extensively for bait. The name 'piggy' refers to the grunting noise it makes.

── **SIMILAR SPECIES** ──────────

The saddle grunter, *Pomadasys maculatus* (Bloch 1793), has an oblique dark bar on the nape. Indo-West Pacific, Oman to the Eastern Cape.

STRIPED GRUNTER
Pomadasys striatus
(Gilchrist & Thompson 1908)

15 cm (dark form)
11 cm (pale form)

Dorsal fin 12 spines, 13–14 rays, 4th and 5th spines longer than longest rays; anal fin rays 6–7; pectoral fin rays 16–17, fins subequal to pelvic fins, less than head length; scale rows below LL rising posteriorly. Body brownish dorsally, with **3 longitudinal dark stripes**, lowest stripe from snout tip through eye, across upper part of operculum to tail fin; anal fin yellow on some fish. Attains 22 cm.

Known only from Knysna to Beira.

Rocky and coral reefs in 2–40 m. A schooling fish, common on Aliwal Shoal. Eaten by various piscivores; used for bait, but usually too small to be of interest as a food-fish.

SIMILAR SPECIES

The lined piggy, *Pomadasys stridens* (Forsskål 1775), has 4 dark stripes on the body; the lowest (mid-lateral) stripe is interrupted by a black blotch on the upper part of the oper-culum and is not continued on the head; scale rows below LL horizontal; 4th dorsal fin spine longer than longest dorsal soft-ray. Red Sea, Oman to Aliwal Shoal.

FAMILY DINOPERCIDAE ■ Cavebass

Body oblong, somewhat compressed; dorsal fin with 9–11 spines, 18–20 rays; anal fin with 3 spines, 12–14 rays; pelvic fins with 1 spine, 5 branched rays; no scaly axillary process at base of pelvic fins; tail fin truncate; maxilla exposed; small slender teeth on jaws, vomer and palatines; opercle ends in 2 blunt points; preopercle serrate; head, body and fins covered with small ctenoid scales. Maximum size 75 cm.
Shallow water fish of subtidal rocky reefs.

Western Indian Ocean and tropical eastern Atlantic. Two species, one in our area.

CAVEBASS
Dinoperca petersi
(Day 1875)

5 cm juvenile
19 cm subadult

Dorsal fin spines distinctly shorter than anterior rays which are much longer than posterior rays; 3rd anal fin spine longer than 2nd spine; body depth 2.3–2.5 times, head length 2.7–3.0 times in SL. **Head, body and fins dark brown; body with white specks**, fading in large adults; lower part of head pale, with a dark moustache streak across cheek. Small juveniles (<6 cm) resemble some cardinalfish, with silvery body and black markings; the markings on the dorsal fin make it appear to be two separate fins (as in cardinalfish). Attains 75 cm, 6 kg.

Pakistan to Gulf of Aden and south to Mossel Bay.

Rocky reefs in 5–75 m. Usually under ledges or at entrance to caves; juveniles rarely seen. Matures at ~30 cm; spawns off the KZN coast during winter. Feeds on shrimp, stomatopods, crabs and fish. Solitary territorial species, more active at night. Makes a loud drumming noise with its swimbladder when disturbed.

Caught by recreational and commercial ski-boat fishermen. Vulnerable to spearfishing. SADSAA all-tackle record: 5.1 kg.

SIMILAR SPECIES

Centrarchops atlanticus Reichenow 1877 [= *Centrarchops chapini* Fowler 1923], known only from Angola, is the other species in the family. It has 2nd anal fin spine longer than 3rd spine, body depth 1.9–2.0 times in SL, dark bars on body, and 4 large tubular pores on chin.

The redmouth rockcod, *Aethaloperca rogaa* (Forsskål 1775), has a smaller eye (diameter equals half snout length) and more rounded anal fin, with 8–9 rays. Indo-central Pacific, Red Sea, Persian Gulf to KZN.

FAMILY LUTJANIDAE ◾ Jobfish & Snappers

Body oblong or elongate; dorsal fin continuous with 10–12 strong spines, 10–16 rays; anal fin with 3 spines, 7–11 rays; **pelvic fins with 1 spine, 5 branched rays and scaly axillary process at base**; tail fin truncate to distinctly forked; **upper edge of maxilla partly covered by preorbital bone when mouth is closed**; jaws usually with more or less distinct canines at front; vomer and palatines generally with small conical teeth; opercle ends in 1 or 2 blunt points; **preopercle serrate; scales ctenoid; cheek and operculum scaly**; snout, preorbital and lower jaw naked. Size range 33 cm to 1.3 m.

Most species diurnal demersal fish of coral and rocky reefs in 3–550 m. Lutjanids are famous as excellent eating fish; important in sport and commercial fisheries.

Tropical and warm temperate waters of all oceans. Thirteen genera and ~105 species, 26 in our area.

Rusty jobfish	Green jobfish	River snapper
Twinspot snapper	Dory snapper	Humpback snapper
Bluebanded snapper	Speckled snapper	Russell's snapper
Blood snapper	Emperor snapper	Black and white snapper

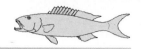

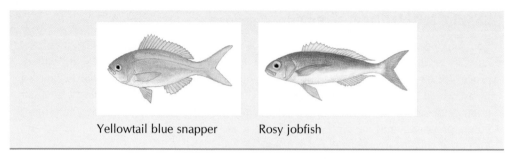

Yellowtail blue snapper   Rosy jobfish

RUSTY JOBFISH
Aphareus rutilans
Cuvier 1830

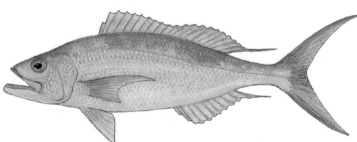

61 cm adult (Comoros)

Body elongate, depth subequal to head length, 3.7–3.9 times in SL; dorsal fin 10 spines, 10–11 rays; anal fin rays 8; **dorsal and anal fins naked, last rays distinctly elongate; tail fin deeply forked**, upper lobe longer than head; maxilla extends to below middle of eye; **upper jaw fixed (not protrusile); lower jaw protruding; teeth in jaws minute (no canines) and no teeth on roof of mouth**; gill rakers elongate, 16–10 / 32–35. Head and body silvery reddish to lavender dorsally; inside of mouth, gill chamber and gills shining silver; lower lip, edge of maxilla and edge of pre-orbital bone black. Attains 1.3 m, 11 kg.

Tropical and subtropical Indo-central Pacific, Oman to Port Alfred.

Coral and rocky reefs in depths of 50–330 m. Feeds on fish, squid and crustaceans. Solitary, usually caught near bottom, but sometimes by trolling.

Puts up a respectable fight on hook and line. Previously known (*Smiths' Sea Fishes* [Smith & Heemstra 1986]) as the 'red small-tooth job'.

SIMILAR SPECIES

The blue jobfish, *Aphareus furca* (Lacepède 1801), is steel blue dorsally, has deeper body (depth 2.9–3.5 times in SL) and gill rakers 6–10 / 16–18. Indo-Pacific from Africa to Cocos Island south of Costa Rica.

The ruby snapper, *Etelis coruscans* Valenciennes 1862, has dorsal fin margin deeply indented before soft-rayed part, and last dorsal and anal fin rays only slightly longer than penultimate rays. Indo-central Pacific, south to Algoa Bay.

GREEN JOBFISH
Aprion virescens
Valenciennes 1830

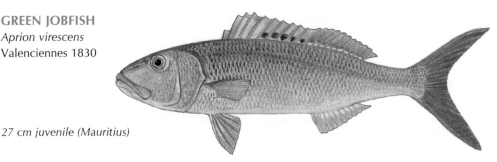

27 cm juvenile (Mauritius)

Body elongate, depth 3.7–4.5 times, head length 3.0–3.3 times in SL; dorsal fin 10 spines, 11 rays; anal fin rays 8; dorsal and anal fins naked, last rays slightly elongate; tail fin forked; pectoral fins short, about half head length and less than pelvic fins; eye diameter less than half snout length; **groove on snout below nostrils; inter-orbital area naked**, flat and broad, its width more than eye diameter; upper jaw slightly protrusile; distinct canines at front of jaws; minute teeth on vomer and palatines; gill rakers 7–8 / 14–16. Head and body dark green or blue dorsally, sides iridescent bluish purple; **basal half of rear spinous dorsal membranes dark**. Attains 1.1 m, 16 kg.

Tropical Indo-central Pacific, Gulf of Aden to East London; once found at Knysna.

Coral and rocky reefs in 20–180+ m. Feeds on fish, shrimp, crabs, cephalopods and zooplankton. Usually solitary, occasionally hunting over reefs in groups of 4–6 fish. Matures at 60–75 cm (3–4 years). Spawns in tropical African waters from January to May.

In KZN, this fish is better known by the Afrikaans name 'kaalkop' (bald head) in allusion to the absence of scales on the inter-orbital area. Favourite target of spear-fishermen. Caught near bottom and occasionally by trolling; strong fighter, but not known to leap from water. IGFA all-tackle record: 15.4 kg fish from Cape Vidal (north of St Lucia). Flesh excellent but has caused ciguatera poisoning.

RIVER SNAPPER
Lutjanus argentimaculatus
(Forsskål 1775)

55 cm adult
6 cm juvenile

Body robust, depth 2.5–2.9 times, head length 2.3–2.7 times in SL; dorsal fin 10 spines, 13–14 rays; anal fin rays 7–8; soft dorsal and anal fins mostly covered with small scales; tail fin truncate; preopercle notch shallow; **scale rows above LL horizontal. Greenish to russet dorsally**, reddish silvery below (specimens from freshwater or estuaries usually darker than fish in the sea); **scale edges silvery; juveniles and small adults with 2 blue lines under eye**; juveniles with 7–8 pale bars on body. Attains ~ 1.2 m and at least 16 kg.

Tropical Indo-central Pacific, Red Sea (and Mediterranean), Oman to Jeffreys Bay.

Coral and rocky reefs to 120 m; juveniles common in estuaries, among mangroves, and also in freshwater. Ambush predator, feeding on fish and decapod crustaceans. Matures at 45–60 cm (3–7 years). Spawns offshore in spring and summer.

Strong fighter when hooked. The powerful jaws are equipped with large canine teeth, and one should be careful when handling this fish. Adults look grey underwater. Flesh excellent.

TWINSPOT SNAPPER
Lutjanus bohar
(Forsskål 1775)

23 cm juvenile

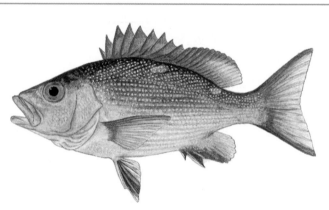

Body robust, depth 2.4–2.9 times, head length 2.4–2.9 times in SL; dorsal fin 10 spines, 13–14 rays; anal fin rays 8; tail fin emarginate to shallowly forked; **adults with nostrils in groove running forward from eye**; preopercle notch shallow; inter-orbital area flat; large canines at front of jaws; **scale rows above LL rising obliquely**. Dark brown dorsally, reddish on sides, the scales with a whitish spot forming white lines on sides; **juveniles and small adults with 2 whitish spots**, one below middle of dorsal fin, the other below rear dorsal fin rays; soft dorsal, anal and pelvic fins dusky with white leading edges; dorsal part of pectoral fins darker than rest of fin, pectoral axil black. Attains 90 cm and at least 13 kg (13 years).

Tropical Indo-central Pacific, Red Sea, Oman to Durban.

Coral reefs to 70 m. Feeds mainly on fish (hence commonly implicated in ciguatera poisonings) but also on crustaceans, echinoderms, pelagic tunicates and polychaetes. Matures at 45–55 cm (3–5 years). Spawns offshore in tropical areas. Usually solitary, occasionally in large schools over outer reef slopes.

Small juveniles have blackish submarginal stripes along upper and lower edges of tail fin and have been observed swimming with shoals of the similarly coloured golden chromis (*Chromis ternatensis*). Popular angling fish, strong fighter and fine eating.

DORY SNAPPER
Lutjanus fulviflamma
(Forsskål 1775)

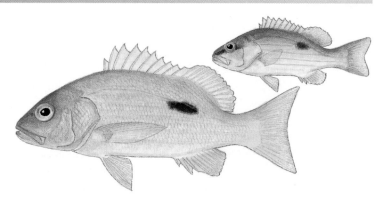

10 cm juvenile
28 cm adult

Body depth 2.6–2.9 times, head length 2.4–2.7 times in SL; dorsal fin 10 (rarely 11) spines, 12–14 rays; anal fin rays 8; preopercle notch shallow; preorbital width less than inter-orbital width; vomerine tooth patch diamond-shaped, with median posterior extension; gill rakers 6–7 / 7–11, including rudiments; **scale rows above LL rising obliquely**. Generally silvery white, greenish, pink or yellowish dorsally; oval **black spot on LL below front dorsal fin rays (most of spot below LL)**; ventral part of body pinkish with 6–7 yellow stripes; fins yellowish; juveniles with dark brown stripe from tip of snout through eye to mid body region. Attains ~35 cm (23 years).

Tropical Indo-central Pacific, Red Sea, Persian Gulf to East London, juveniles to Algoa Bay.

Coral and rocky reefs in 3–35 m; also over mud bottom; juveniles in mangroves, estuaries and in seagrass. Feeds on fish, crustaceans and polychaetes. Usually seen in shoals. Matures at 18–21 cm; spawns over reefs from August to December. The silvery pelagic post-larvae (13–20 mm SL) also have the characteristic black spot on LL.

Too small to be of much interest to anglers; good eating and may be important in subsistence fisheries.

SIMILAR SPECIES

Russell's snapper (see p. 202) has a dark spot mostly above the lateral line; juveniles have 4–8 blackish or golden brown lines on body.

HUMPBACK SNAPPER
Lutjanus gibbus
(Forsskål 1775)

12 cm juvenile (Comoros)
45 cm adult

Body robust, depth 2.2–2.5 times, head length 2.4–2.6 times in SL; **dorsal head profile of adult distinctly concave**; dorsal fin 10 spines, 13–14 rays; anal fin rays 8; **adult with broadly rounded tail fin lobes, upper one larger; preopercle notch deep, with prominent interopercle knob fitting into notch**. Adults dark reddish brown; head and body of juveniles pale red to bluish grey; soft dorsal, anal and tail fins dusky to black. Attains 50 cm (18 years).

Tropical Indo-central Pacific, Red Sea, Oman to Aliwal Shoal.

Coral reefs in 3–150 m, not common below 30 m; juveniles on seagrass beds and in mangroves. Feeds at night on fish, crabs, shrimp, molluscs and echinoids. Relatively inactive by day, and usually seen in large shoals. Matures at 26–31 cm; spawning occurs in tropical areas.

The dorsal head profile of large adults is a sinuous curve, with snout concave, forehead and nape strongly convex (hence the name 'humpback snapper'); adults also have the upper tail fin lobe enlarged, which accounts for the Australian name 'paddle-tail snapper'. Caught by boat anglers and spearfishermen.

BLUEBANDED SNAPPER
Lutjanus kasmira
(Forsskål 1775)

32 cm adult

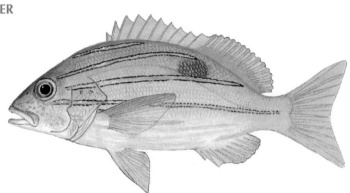

Body depth 2.4–2.8 times, head length 2.3–2.7 times in SL; dorsal fin 10 (rarely 11) spines, 14–15 rays; anal fin rays 7–8; preopercle notch deep, prominent interopercle knob fitting into notch; lower-limb gill rakers 13–15. **Body yellow dorsally, with 4 dark-edged blue stripes; 2 blue stripes below eye in fish >7 cm SL; body abruptly white or pale yellow ventrally, with bluish grey lines following scale rows**; black spot sometimes visible on LL below middle of dorsal fin. Attains 33 cm.

Tropical Indo-West Pacific, Red Sea, Oman to East London.

Coral and rocky reefs in 5–265 m, usually seen in 15–40 m. Feeds at night on fish, shrimp, crabs, stomatopods, cephalopods and planktonic crustaceans. Often seen in stationary shoals over reef during the day. Matures at 18–23 cm; spawns in small groups during early evening, in late winter and spring.

Although good eating, the species is too small to be of interest to anglers. A hardy aquarium fish (but needs a large tank).

SIMILAR SPECIES

The bluestriped snapper, *Lutjanus notatus* (Cuvier 1828), has 6–7 blue stripes on sides, the upper 3–4 inclined obliquely towards the

dorsal fin base, and 11–12 dorsal fin spines. Western Indian Ocean, Kenya to Durban, Madagascar and Mascarene Islands.

The Bengal snapper, *Lutjanus bengalensis* (Bloch 1790), has 4 blue stripes on body, 3rd stripe not running onto opercle, single stripe below eye, dorsal fin 11–12 spines, 12–14 rays, and 17–19 lower gill rakers. Indo-West Pacific, Oman to Sodwana Bay.

SPECKLED SNAPPER
Lutjanus rivulatus
(Cuvier 1828)

11 cm juvenile (India)
62 cm adult

Body deep, depth 2.1–2.4 times, head length 2.4–2.5 times in SL; dorsal fin 10 spines, 15–16 rays; anal fin rays 8–9; distinct preopercle notch; adults with thick lips; **scale rows above LL rising obliquely. Adults brown dorsally, silvery brown below, with 1–4 bluish spots on each scale**; head yellowish brown, covered with wavy blue lines; fins usually dusky with yellow margin. Juveniles with 3–8 faint dark bars on body and white spot on LL below 2nd to 4th dorsal rays. Attains 80 cm, 11 kg.

Tropical Indo-central Pacific, Red Sea, Oman to Kasouga near Port Alfred, rare south of Durban.

Coral and rocky reefs in 5–100 m. Feeds on fish, cephalopods, crustaceans, red bait, sea urchins and polychaete worms. Solitary, usually in caves or under ledges. Matures at 45–50 cm; spawns mainly in summer. A.k.a. 'blubberlip snapper'; in Australia, known as 'Maori sea-perch' as blue lines on head resemble tattooing on the face of Maori warriors. The white spot on flanks of juveniles can be turned on or off depending on the mood of the fish.

SIMILAR SPECIES

The adult lemonfish, *Plectorhinchus flavomaculatus* (Cuvier 1830), has thick lips and similar blue and gold lines on head; but is more elongate (body depth 2.6–2.8 times in SL), has 13–14 dorsal fin spines, pectoral fins subequal to pelvic fins, much shorter than head; the gold spots on the scales disappear in large adults. Indo-West Pacific, Red Sea to the Eastern Cape.

RUSSELL'S SNAPPER
Lutjanus russellii
(Bleeker 1849)

29 cm adult (Sri Lanka)
7 cm juvenile (Indonesia)

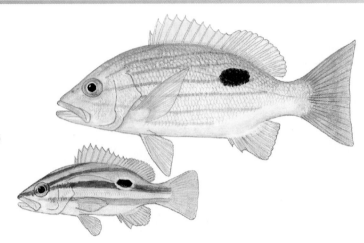

Body depth 2.6–2.8 times, head length 2.5–2.7 times in SL; dorsal fin 10 spines, 14 rays; anal fin rays 8; preopercle notch shallow; **scale rows above LL rising obliquely**; preorbital width subequal to interorbital width. Adults yellow-brown dorsally, yellow or pink below; oval **black spot, mainly above LL** and below front dorsal fin rays; usually **7–8 golden brown or yellow stripes** from head onto body, lower stripes horizontal, upper ones oblique; juveniles with fewer stripes. Attains 45 cm.

Tropical Indo-central Pacific, Red Sea, Persian Gulf to Durban.

Coral and rocky reefs in 3–80 m; juveniles in tide pools and mangrove areas. Feeds on crustaceans, mainly small crabs. Usually in small schools. Spawns in summer.

Caught near bottom, but will also rise to a trolled lure; puts up a respectable fight on light tackle. Does well in a large aquarium. Common in artisanal fisheries.

SIMILAR SPECIES

The onespot snapper, *Lutjanus monostigma* (Cuvier 1828), has black spot smaller than eye on LL (black spot of *L. russellii* is larger than eye) and has faint brown lines along scale rows. Tropical Indo-West Pacific, south to Sodwana Bay.

BLOOD SNAPPER
Lutjanus sanguineus
(Cuvier 1828)

75 cm adult (Kenya)
19 cm juvenile

Body depth 2.2–2.6 times, head length 2.3–2.8 times in SL; dorsal fin 11 spines, 12–14 rays; anal fin rays 8–9; preopercle notch shallow; **large adults with prominent hump on top of head and horizontal grooves behind eye**; preorbital width 2–3 times more than eye diameter; scale rows above LL rising obliquely. **Adults scarlet with silvery belly**; fins red to pink; roof of mouth and lips yellow. Juveniles with distinct brown band on forehead from dorsal fin origin to upper jaw and including eye; black saddle on peduncle preceded by pearly blotch; pelvic fins dusky to blackish. Attains 90 cm, 22 kg (13 years).

Western Indian Ocean, Red Sea, Persian Gulf to Algoa Bay.

Coral and rocky reefs in 10–100 m; also slightly turbid offshore banks. Feeds on reef fish, crabs, stomatopods, squid, cuttlefish and zooplankton. Nocturnal; rarely seen by day. Matures at 60–70 cm (6 years); spawns in tropical waters.

Caught from ski-boats off KZN and Mozambique; highly prized angling fish, strong fighter and excellent eating. Occasionally taken by spearfishermen.

SIMILAR SPECIES

The red steenbras (p. 230) is more silvery or bronze in colour, with only 10–11 dorsal fin rays.

EMPEROR SNAPPER
Lutjanus sebae
(Cuvier 1816)

10 cm juvenile
49 cm subadult (Kenya)

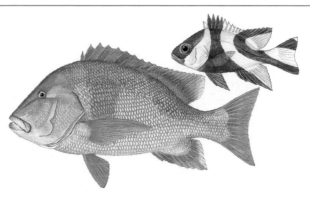

Body deep, depth 2.1–2.4 times, head length 2.3–2.5 times in SL; **dorsal fin** 11 spines, **15–16 rays**; anal fin rays 10; **soft dorsal and anal fins angular, middle rays elongate**; pectoral fin rays 17, fins reach past anal fin origin; preorbital width 2 or 3 times greater than eye diameter; dorsal snout profile slightly concave; preopercle notch moderate; adults with thick lips. Juveniles and subadults silvery white, with 3 broad brown to black bands as shown; with age, bands become fainter and disappear; **large adults dark red** with silver spot on each scale. Attains 1.1 m, 33 kg (35 years).

Tropical Indo-West Pacific, Red Sea, Oman to Durban.

Coral and rocky reefs in 5–180 m; caught over flat bottom by trawlers; juveniles in mangroves. Feeds during day and night on crabs, shrimp, crayfish, stomatopods, fish, squid and tunicates. Adults usually solitary and territorial. Juveniles occasionally seen hiding among long spines of *Diadema* sea urchins, where their bold stripes are effective camouflage. Matures at 60–70 cm (4 years); spawns over reefs.

Highly prized by anglers, fights gamely. May cause ciguatera.

203

BLACK AND WHITE SNAPPER
Macolor niger
(Forsskål 1775)

38 cm adult (western Indian Ocean)
20 cm intermediate juvenile (Japan)
5 cm small juvenile (Japan)

Body robust, depth 2.2–2.9 times, head length 2.6–2.8 times in SL; **dorsal fin 10 spines, 13–14 rays; anal fin rays 11 (rarely 10), middle dorsal and anal fin rays elongate**; pectoral fins reach vertical at anal fin origin; preopercle with deep notch, for elongate knob of interopercle; **dorsal head profile distinctly convex; gill rakers long and slender, 26–38 / 60–71. Large adults grey to black** (reticulate pale blue lines on head of fresh specimens); small juveniles (3–11 cm SL) mostly white with fins and adjacent parts of body black, head white, with large black area over eyes, cheeks and inter-orbital region; tip of snout and jaws black; larger juveniles (20–30 cm SL) black dorsally with 4–7 white spots, tips and middle part of tail fin white. Attains 75 cm.

Indo-central Pacific, Red Sea to Sodwana Bay, juveniles found at Durban.

Coral and rocky reefs in 5–90 m, usually seen in less than 30 m. Opportunistic carnivore, feeds on variety of fish, crustaceans and zooplankton. Large shoals of adults occur over steep slopes on outer reef. Juveniles and some adults solitary.

Superb eating fish.

SIMILAR SPECIES

The redmouth rockcod, *Aethaloperca rogaa* (Forsskål 1775), is superficially similar, but has shorter rounded pectoral fins (not much longer than pelvic fins), 17–19 dorsal fin rays, and preopercle has no notch. Indo-West Pacific, Persian Gulf, Red Sea to KZN.

YELLOWTAIL BLUE SNAPPER
Paracaesio xanthura
(Bleeker 1869)

19 cm

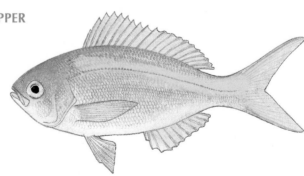

Body depth 2.6–3.1 times, head length 3.2–3.8 times in SL; dorsal fin 10 spines, 10 rays; anal fin rays 8; **last dorsal and anal fin rays shorter than penultimate ray**; no scales on soft dorsal and anal fins; tail fin lunate; upper jaw protrusile; gill rakers long and slender, 9–11 / 20–23; LL scales 68–72. Large adults have protruding teeth at front of lower jaw. Two colour patterns: cruising pattern uniform dark green-brown; the other pattern (perhaps an excitement or feeding pattern; see below) is **head and body bright blue**, paler ventrally, broad **yellow swath from dorsal fin origin along upper body to and including tail fin**. Attains 45 cm.

Tropical and subtropical Indo-West Pacific, south to Margate.

Coral reefs and banks in 20–150 m. Feeds mainly on zooplankton; usually in shoals well above bottom.

Allan Connell, a marine biologist at the CSIR, Durban, witnessed the change in colour pattern: 'Right on top of the reef, like a helicopter landing pad, was a flat area where two cleaner wrasse had a station. When I discovered the spot, three *Paracaesio* were virtually lying down on the rocks, and a big shoal was overhead, including blue-grey and green varieties. While I watched, a green fish came down to the station. As it became stationary, it suddenly changed colour to silvery, and then more slowly, went to the blue & yellow pattern we are accustomed to. I watched, spellbound, and saw two others go through a similar colour change.'

Excellent eating; caught with prawn bait on light tackle.

SIMILAR SPECIES

The ruby snapper, *Etelis coruscans* Valenciennes 1862, has more slender body (depth 3.4–3.8 times in SL), dorsal fin margin deeply notched before last spine, body reddish. Indo-Pacific, south to Algoa Bay.

The rusty fin snapper, *Paracaesio sordida* Abe & Shinohara 1962, has head and body dark grey to bluish grey or purplish brown, the scales pale blue to lavender with brown edges; dorsal and tail fins dusky red, russet or yellowish brown. Indo-central Pacific, Red Sea, Oman to Aliwal Shoal.

ROSY JOBFISH
Pristipomoides filamentosus
(Valenciennes 1830)

34 cm subadult

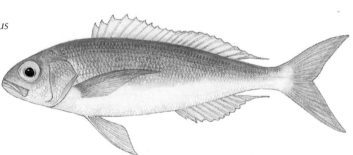

Body oblong-elongate, depth 3.2–3.8 times, head length 2.9–3.4 times in SL; dorsal fin 10 spines, 11 rays; anal fin rays 8; no scales on soft dorsal and anal fins; **last dorsal and anal fin rays elongate, much longer than other rays; pectoral fins subequal to head; tail fin forked, upper lobe longer than lower, subequal to head**; upper jaw protrusile; small canines at front of jaws; gill rakers 7–8 / 15–17; LL scales 57–62. Body silvery red to

lavender-brown; snout and inter-orbital area with yellow lines and blue spots; dorsal and tail fins pale blue to lavender with reddish orange margins; anal and pelvic fins of female usually hyaline, but male with dusky fins, orange-yellow between 1st and 2nd anal fin spines and between last 2 fin rays. Attains 1 m, 9 kg (18 years).

Indo-West Pacific, Red Sea, Oman to Algoa Bay.

Rocky reefs in 40–360 m. Feeds at night in the shallow end of its depth range on fish, stomatopods, amphipods and salps. Matures at 35 cm.

Fine eating fish; fights vigorously. Caught near bottom by ski-boat anglers. SADSAA all-tackle record: 3.1 kg.

SIMILAR SPECIES

The oblique banded snapper, *Pristipomoides zonatus* (Valenciennes 1830), is reddish with 3 or 4 oblique yellow bars on body, 1st on nape, last below rear end of dorsal fin often merging with yellow tail fin. Indo-Central Pacific, caught in 100–200 m off KZN.

The ruby snapper, *Etelis coruscans* Valenciennes 1862, has dorsal fin margin deeply notched before last spine, and colour more reddish. Indo-Pacific, south to Algoa Bay.

FAMILY CAESIONIDAE ■ Fusiliers

Body oblong or elongate, slightly compressed; dorsal fin 9–15 slender spines, 14–22 rays; anal fin 3 spines, 10–13 rays; pelvic fins with 1 spine and 5 rays; **tail fin forked; mouth small protrusile; maxilla partly covered by preorbital bone; jaws with minute conical teeth; palate usually toothless**; opercle ends in 1–2 blunt points; preopercle with minute serrations, usually hidden by skin; scales small to moderate, weakly ctenoid; cheek and operculum scaly; snout, preorbital and lower jaw naked. Size range 8–40 cm.

Small to moderate-sized diurnal shoaling fish, usually seen in midwater (where they feed on zooplankton) over or near coral and rocky reefs; at night, fusiliers take refuge in the reef.

Tropical and subtropical waters of Indo-central Pacific region. Closely related to Lutjanidae; 4 genera, ~20 species, 6 in our area.

Blue and gold fusilier

Yellowback fusilier

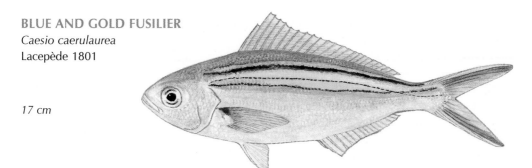

BLUE AND GOLD FUSILIER
Caesio caerulaurea
Lacepède 1801

17 cm

Body elongate, depth 3.1–3.9 times, head length 2.9–3.6 times in SL; dorsal fin 10 spines, 14–16 rays; anal fin rays 12–13; pectoral fin rays 19–22; dorsal and anal fins mostly covered with scales; rear edge of premaxilla with 1 bony process. **Head and body blue-green dorsally, silvery blue below; black-edged gold band mainly above LL from above eye to peduncle; dark band along middle of each tail fin lobe**; pectoral fin axil black, merging dorsally with small triangular dark mark on outer part of pectoral fin base. Night pattern mostly reddish. Attains 35 cm.

Indo-central Pacific, Gulf of Aden to Aliwal Shoal, juveniles occasionally to Port Alfred.

Coral reefs in 10–30 m; usually seen on outer reefs. Feeds on copepods and other zoo-plankton. Forms large shoals by day; hides in reef at night. In an aquarium, spawning occurs in pairs or with several males and a single female. Spawns from two hours before sunset until an hour after sunset, and the buoyant eggs are released near surface.

Common at Sodwana Bay; important to artisanal fisheries, but too small to be of interest to anglers (except as bait).

SIMILAR SPECIES

The bluestreak fusilier, *Pterocaesio tile* (Cuvier 1830), also has dark bands along each tail fin lobe, but it has a dark (rather than yellow) band along the lateral line and dark lines (or rows of dark spots) dorsally on body; *P. tile* also has 2 bony processes on the premaxilla. Indo-West Pacific, Somalia to Sodwana Bay.

YELLOWBACK FUSILIER
Caesio xanthonota
Bleeker 1853

*12 cm subadult
(Comoros)
7 cm juvenile*

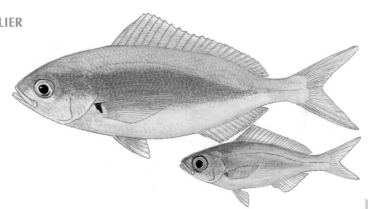

Body depth 2.9–3.3 times, head length 3.0–3.4 times in SL; dorsal fin 10 spines, 14–15 rays; anal fin rays 11–13; pectoral fin rays 20–22. **Head and body yellow dorsally, bright blue mid-laterally and silvery blue below; tail fin yellow**; pectoral fin axil black, merging dorsally with small triangular black mark on outer part of pectoral fin base. Juveniles with dark mid-lateral band. At night, the fish is mostly reddish. Attains ~40 cm.

Indo-West Pacific, Somalia to Sodwana Bay; not in Red Sea.

Coral reefs in 10–30 m.

SIMILAR SPECIES

Sometimes shoals with yellowtail fusilier, *Caesio teres* Seale 1906, which is mainly bright blue dorsally with upper rear part of body yellow; dorsal fin margin and tail fin yellow. Indo-West Pacific, Somalia to Sodwana Bay.

The yellowstriped fusilier, *Caesio varilineata* Carpenter 1987, has body bluish with 3–6 longitudinal yellow stripes; pectoral fin axil and tail fin tips black. Indian Ocean, Red Sea, Persian Gulf to Aliwal Shoal.

FAMILY SPARIDAE ■ Seabream

Body oblong, slightly compressed; **1 continuous dorsal fin with 10–13 spines and 8–16 rays; anal fin with 3 spines and 8–15 rays**; last dorsal and anal fin rays divided to their base but counted as a single ray; pelvic fins with 1 spine and 5 rays; tail fin emarginate to forked; **maxilla mostly hidden when mouth is closed; posterior tip of maxilla with a groove, into which the tip of the premaxilla fits forming a unique lateral joint of upper jaw bones; teeth conical or incisiform (compressed); most species with molar teeth; some species with enlarged canines or incisors at front of jaws; no teeth on vomer, palatines or tongue; preopercle edge smooth; opercle ends in a blunt flat point**; scales small to moderate, weakly ctenoid; opercles and cheeks scaly (cheeks naked in *Gymnocrotaphus*). Size range 30 cm to 2+ m.

Sparids occur in rocky and sandy areas near shore or on offshore reefs to 450 m; a few species are typically found in estuaries. Many sparids occur in large schools, others are usually seen singly or in small aggregations. Diurnal fish that feed on algae and/or a variety of prey. Eggs and larvae pelagic (except for steentjie which lay eggs in a depression on sandy bottom). Sparid fish occur in temperate and tropical waters, but most species are restricted to temperate continental areas. At oceanic islands, the 'sparid niche' seems to be occupied by the emperors (Family Lethrinidae) and wrasses. Most sparids are important food-fish, and they comprise the major component of line-caught fish in commercial and sport fisheries of South Africa.

The larger species grow slowly and the adults are territorial with small home ranges, making them vulnerable to overfishing.

Worldwide. About 29 genera, ~100 species, 41 species in our area.

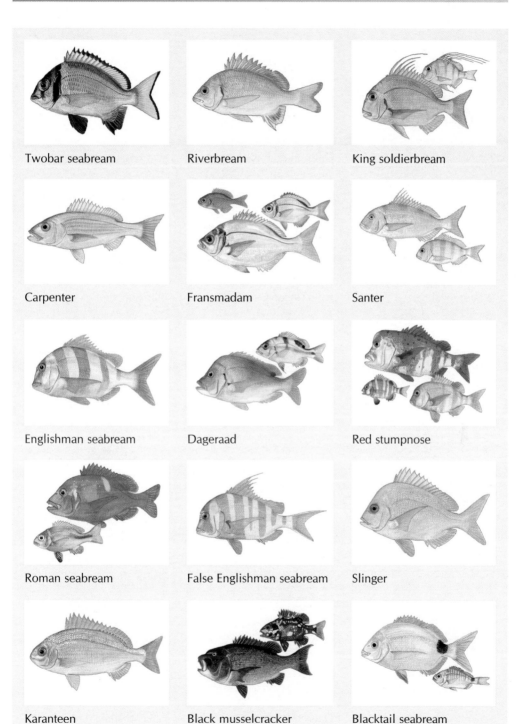

Twobar seabream

Riverbream

King soldierbream

Carpenter

Fransmadam

Santer

Englishman seabream

Dageraad

Red stumpnose

Roman seabream

False Englishman seabream

Slinger

Karanteen

Black musselcracker

Blacktail seabream

Zebra seabream

Janbruin seabream

Westcoast steenbras

White steenbras

Sand steenbras

Blue hottentot

Hottentot seabream

Bronze bream

Red steenbras

German seabream

Blueskin seabream

Scotsman seabream

Seventy-four seabream

Dane seabream

Panga seabream

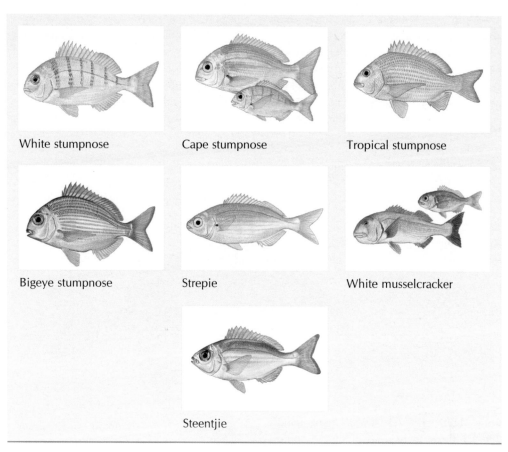

White stumpnose

Cape stumpnose

Tropical stumpnose

Bigeye stumpnose

Strepie

White musselcracker

Steentjie

TWOBAR SEABREAM
Acanthopagrus bifasciatus
(Forsskål 1775)

18 cm

Body depth 1.9–2.3 times, head length 3.1–3.3 times in SL; dorsal fin 11–12 spines, 12–15 rays; **anal fin rays 10–12, 2nd spine distinctly longer than 3rd; pectoral fin rays 15; jaws with 4–6 enlarged incisors at front, followed by 3–5 rows of molars;** LL scales

47–50; lower gill rakers 11–12; **inter-orbital area naked**, developing a bulge in large adults. Head and body silver; **2 black bars on head**; adults with blackish spot on each body scale; anal fin and pelvic fins blackish; pectoral fins yellow; dorsal and tail fins yellow with black margin. Attains 50 cm (19 years).

Western Indian Ocean, Red Sea, Oman to Durban, Madagascar and Mascarene Islands.

Inshore coral reefs, bays and estuaries in 15–30 m. Biology little known. Solitary or in small loose schools, which often include other sparids or grunters.

Not important as food-fish, but boldly marked juveniles are popular aquarium fish.

Red Sea specimens lack the black dorsal fin margin.

RIVERBREAM
Acanthopagrus vagus
Peters 1852

18 cm juvenile

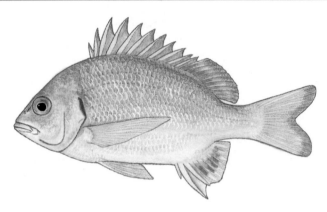

Body depth 1.9–2.5 times, head length 2.9–3.3 times in SL; dorsal fin 11 spines, 10–12 rays; anal fin rays 8, 2nd spine distinctly longer than 3rd; pectoral fin rays 15; jaws with 4–6 pointed incisors at front, followed by 3–5 rows of molars; dorsal head profile straight, inter-orbital area flat; lower edge of preorbital bone and front edge of snout straight; LL scales 43–45; lower gill rakers 9–11; inter-orbital area naked. Head, body and most fins silvery white; adults have yellow anal fin with membranes blackish basally, rear edge of operculum blackish; small black spot at upper end of pectoral fin base; fins of live juveniles bluish. Attains ~60 cm, 3 kg.

Distribution uncertain, as this species has been confused with *Acanthopagrus berda* (Forsskål 1775). Common in KZN and northwards to at least central Mozambique, southwards to Swartvlei.

Adults and juveniles in estuaries and in freshwater. Biological information for this species is problematic due to confusion with *A. berda*.

Although JLB Smith (1949) listed 7 different common names for the riverbream in *Sea Fishes of Southern Africa*, and 3 different species were described (named) based on fish from KZN, another from Mozambique and a fifth from Madagascar, both JLB Smith (1949) and Margaret Smith (Smith & Heemstra 1986) considered that there was only 1 species of riverbream in the western Indian Ocean. Recent analysis indicates that 3 distinct species of riverbream occur in southern Africa (Yukio Iwatsuki, pers. comm.). The fish illustrated here is the most common riverbream in our area, and this appears to be the species named *Acanthopagrus vagus* by Peters 1852.

Flesh excellent. JLB Smith (1949, p. 267) wrote in *Sea Fishes of Southern Africa*: 'A well known angling fish, cunning, furtive and wary, it rarely takes any bait in clear water in daylight, but often bites freely on most baits towards dusk, fights gamely.' In his description of the genus *Acanthopagrus*, Smith referred to the species as 'Rather rodent-like fishes of shallow water of the tropical Indo-Pacific.' When asked if he considered this fish 'rodent-like', AR Thorpe, a keen angler, replied: 'I certainly understand what JLB Smith meant when he said the riverbream was "rodent-like". I grew up catching riverbream and spent many hours as a youngster persuading them to take a bait. I often used to scatter putu (mielie pap) in shallow water and watch them warily approach; keep absolutely still, move a little closer, still again, until they would dart forward, grab the food and dash off, just like a mouse. Eventually, the only food left would be the piece with my hook in it' (Smith & Heemstra 1986, p. 581).

Important in the recreational shore fishery; also caught with fish traps and gill-nets in the artisanal fisheries of St Lucia and Kosi Bay.

SIMILAR SPECIES

The tropical stumpnose (see p. 237) has faint gold horizontal lines on body.

The picnic seabream, *Acanthopagrus berda* (Forsskål 1775), has dorsal head profile and inter-orbital area distinctly convex; jaws robust, maxilla curved; lower edge of pre-orbital bone indented above rear end of maxilla (more obvious in adults); front of snout slightly concave; anal fin with 9 rays. Head and body silvery, centres of scales dark; adults and fish from turbid water darker, almost black. Indo-West Pacific, Red Sea, Oman to at least East London; southern African distribution uncertain due to confusion with *A. vagus*.

Figure 38

Head of a riverbream (left) and a picnic seabream (right).

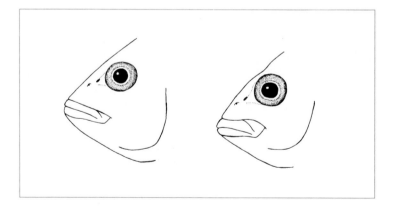

KING SOLDIERBREAM
Argyrops spinifer
(Forsskål 1775)

7 cm juvenile
22 cm subadult

Body depth 1.7–2.0 times, head length 3.5–3.7 times in SL; **dorsal fin 11–12 spines, 10–11 rays, first 2 spines short, 3rd to 7th elongate (longer than whole fish in small juveniles)**; anal fin rays 8, 2nd spine slightly longer than 3rd; pectoral fin rays 15; jaws with 4–6 enlarged canines at front, followed by a row of blunt conical teeth, then molars posteriorly; scaly inter-orbital area pointed anteriorly; large adults develop a bony bulge on nape. **Head and body silvery pink, with blue dots on body; upper part of opercular membrane red**. Juveniles silvery, with 5 faint pink bars on body; dorsal fin spines red distally. Attains 70 cm, 8 kg (17+ years).

Indo-West Pacific, Red Sea, Oman to Knysna, common off KZN.

Soft bottom (mud or sand) in 5–400 m; adults usually below 30 m. Feeds on stomatopods, crabs, fish, octopus, bivalve molluscs and shrimp.

Excellent food-fish, but nowhere abundant. Mainly caught by ski-boat anglers. Hyperostosis (bony growth) on the nape in large adults gives the fish a 'humpbacked' appearance and makes it look deformed. Hyperostosis is normal for *A. spinifer* and also occurs in some kingfish, spotted grunter, etc. In *A. spinifer*, it affects the supraoccipital skull bone at the nape, but in other species, hyperostosis may affect the ribs, various skull bones, or parts of the vertebrae. SADSAA all-tackle record: 6.2 kg.

SIMILAR SPECIES

The soldierbream, *Argyrops filamentosus* (Valenciennes 1830), is similar, but has 8–10 dorsal fin rays; juveniles have only 3rd and 4th dorsal fin spines elongate, and the inter-orbital scaly area is bluntly rounded anteriorly. Western Indian Ocean, Red Sea to the Eastern Cape in depths of 20–40 m.

CARPENTER
Argyrozona argyrozona
(Valenciennes 1830)

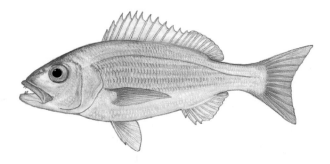

37 cm adult

Body depth about equal to head length, 2.9–3.1 times in SL; dorsal fin 12 spines, 10 rays; anal fin rays 8; pectoral fin rays 15–16, fins shorter than head; **jaws with 4 large canines at front, smaller conical teeth behind, no molars**; lower gill rakers 17–19; **inter-orbital area scaly**; rear nostrils circular. Head and body **silvery pink**; body **with ~7 horizontal series of blue spots**. Attains 80 cm, 5 kg (30+ years); fish over 50 cm are rare.

Endemic, Table Bay to northern Eastern Cape.

Adults usually on reefs and rocky bottom in 50–200 m; juveniles on inshore reefs in 10–40 m. Juveniles feed on mysids, crabs, crab larvae, amphipods and polychaete worms; adults eat primarily squid, anchovies and pilchards. Females mature at ~25–27 cm FL; males at ~26–28 cm. Spawns December to April throughout its range. Unlike most sparid species that have been studied, the carpenter is not hermaphroditic. Schooling migratory species, some migrations of over 300 km.

Good eating fish of considerable commercial importance; caught from ski-boats and in trawls. SADSAA all-tackle record: 3.98 kg.

SIMILAR SPECIES

Adult panga seabream (see p. 235) have canines at front of jaws curved outward, posterior teeth small molars; and the lips villose, looking almost furry.

FRANSMADAM
Boopsoidea inornata
Castelnau 1861

8 cm juvenile
11 cm juvenile
21 cm adult

Body depth greater than head length, 2.0–2.3 times in SL; dorsal fin 11 spines, 10–11 rays; anal fin rays 11; pectoral fin rays 15–16, fins longer than head; **outer teeth conical, inner teeth small molars**; LL with 59–65 conspicuous scales; **eye diameter greater than snout length; inter-orbital area, preopercle and soft dorsal and anal fins without scales. Body bronzy silver; rear edge of operculum black**; small juveniles reddish orange, larger juveniles silvery with yellow-orange fins. Attains 30 cm.

Endemic, Swartvlei to Aliwal Shoal.

Usually in rocky areas in 5–34 m; occasionally in subtidal gullies near shore; juveniles on shallow reefs and in tide pools. Feeds on tunicates, molluscs, planktonic crustaceans, worms and seaweeds; the latter are not digested, but taken for their epiphytic animal life. When plankton is abundant, fransmadam usually feed well above the reef, where they are vulnerable to large predators such as red steenbras and kob. Spawns in spring and summer.

Although good eating, fransmadam are regarded as a pest by anglers, because they easily strip bait intended for larger fish. They are good bait for large game fish.

SIMILAR SPECIES

Steentjie (see p. 241) look similar, but have eye diameter subequal to snout length and jaws with 4–6 rows of small incisors.

SANTER
Cheimerius nufar
(Ehrenberg 1830)

51 cm adult
10 cm juvenile

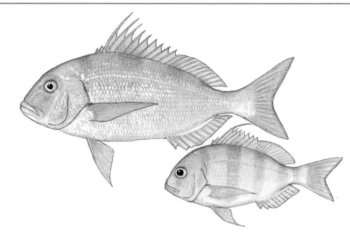

Body depth greater than head length, 2.2–2.5 times in SL; **dorsal fin** 11–12 spines, 10–11 rays, **first 2 spines short, the 3rd to 7th elongate**, especially in juveniles; anal fin rays 8; pectoral fin rays 16, fins longer than head; jaws with 4–6 slender canines at front, smaller conical teeth behind; no molars; LL scales 59–63; **lower gill rakers 13–16**; interorbital area partly scaly; preopercle margin with a few small scales; no scales on soft dorsal or anal fins; rear nostrils circular. Body **silvery pink with 4 or 5 faint red bars** (more obvious in juveniles); faint dark bar through eye. Attains 75 cm, 7 kg (22 years).

Continental shores of western Indian Ocean, Red Sea, Oman to False Bay.

Generally near reefs and rocky bottom in 7–130 m; juveniles on reefs and over sand near reefs in 7–60 m. Juveniles feed on mysids and other shrimp; adults eat fish, squid, stomatopods, shrimp, crabs and octopus. Matures at 34 cm (4 years). Juveniles hermaphroditic, but no evidence for sex change.

Spawns in spring off KZN and in summer off the Eastern Cape. Mating occurs at dawn, with males showing prominent white patch on their sides. Usually seen in loose schools.

Adults caught from shore in summer, or during stormy weather or cold water upwelling events; juveniles reported to shelter in estuaries when stormy weather approaches (*Cheimerius* means 'sign of storm'). Excellent food-fish, commercially important off KZN; caught by commercial and sport anglers, also taken in trawls.

SIMILAR SPECIES

Juvenile king soldierbream (see p. 214) also have 3rd to 7th dorsal fin spines elongate; but they lack the dark (red) bars seen on santer juveniles. Adults with bony bulge on nape and small molar teeth.

The soldierbream, *Argyrops filamentosus* (Valenciennes 1830), also has molar teeth; and the juveniles have only the 3rd and 4th dorsal fin spines elongate. Western Indian Ocean, Red Sea to the Eastern Cape.

ENGLISHMAN SEABREAM
Chrysoblephus anglicus
(Gilchrist & Thompson 1908)

44 cm adult

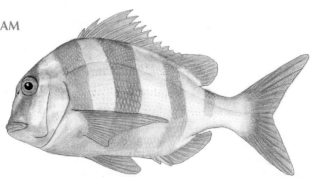

Body depth greater than head length, 2.0–2.3 times in SL; **dorsal head profile distinctly convex, snout profile steep**; dorsal fin 12 spines (3rd and 4th spines longest, but shorter than head) and 10 rays; anal fin rays 8; **pectoral fin rays 16–17, fins longer than head**; tail fin lobes of adults acute; jaws with 4–6 canines at front, 3–5 rows of molars behind; LL scales 65–68; inter-orbital area, preopercle margin and bases of soft dorsal and anal fins scaly. **Body silvery, with blue dot on dorsal scales and 4 red bars** (sometimes faint); front of head dark red; median fins dark. Attains 90 cm, 10 kg.

Endemic, Algoa Bay to southern Mozambique.

Coral and rocky reefs in 15–120 m. Feeds on crabs, shrimp, bivalves, squid and occasionally fish. Occurs singly or in small aggregations; often schools with slinger. Reproductive biology poorly known: matures at ~40 cm FL, and a few adults appear to change sex. Spawns in spring.

Good-eating fish, popular with ski-boat and commercial anglers and spearfishermen. SADSAA all-tackle record: 7 kg.

- SIMILAR SPECIES

Underwater, Englishman seabream might be confused with juvenile santer, but the latter have distinctly elongated dorsal fin spines.

See false Englishman seabream, p. 220.

DAGERAAD
Chrysoblephus cristiceps
(Valenciennes 1830)

8 cm juvenile
~48 cm adult male

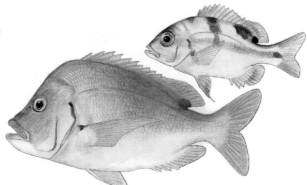

Body depth greater than head length, 2.0–2.3 times in SL; dorsal fin 12 spines (3rd spine shorter than head), 10 rays; anal fin rays 8;

pectoral fin rays 16, fins longer than head; tail fin forked, lobes rounded in adults; jaws with 4–6 slender canines at front and 3 or more

series of small molars behind; LL scales 59–61; lower gill rakers 10–13; inter-orbital area, preopercle margin and bases of soft dorsal and anal fins scaly. **Head and body orange, white below; front of head dark, rear margin black; adults with blue line below eye, median fins dark, with black spot at base of last 3 dorsal rays**. Juveniles pink, with horizontal mid-lateral band, 2 dark blotches below dorsal fin, black spot at rear end of dorsal fin base. Attains 75 cm, 9 kg (23 years).

Endemic, Cape Town to Durban; more common south of East London.

Rocky reefs of low relief in 25–100 m; juveniles common inshore, occasionally in tide pools. A schooling species; feeds mainly in early morning on crabs, polychaete worms, squid, fish, sea urchins and starfish. Females mature at 37–38 cm FL (9–10 years), change sex at ~42–46 cm FL; size at maturity and sex change are smaller (22 cm and 28 cm FL) in exploited populations. Spawns mostly in summer.

Caught on variety of baits; takes the hook gently. Dageraad are overfished, and urgent action is necessary to rebuild the stock. Large adults develop steep foreheads and are called 'wagon wheels'. According to Margaret Smith in *Smith's Sea Fishes* (Smith & Heemstra 1986, p. 584): 'Adult at death, one of the most beautiful of all creatures, as waves of different colours pass over the body, hence the early Dutch name dageraad (dawn).' The name may also refer to when the fish is feeding and easiest to catch.

SIMILAR SPECIES

The slinger (see p. 221) also has a blue line under eye, but it lacks the black spot at rear end of dorsal fin, and it has fewer LL scales (49–52).

RED STUMPNOSE
Chrysoblephus gibbiceps
(Valenciennes 1830)

56 cm adult male
2 cm juvenile
25 cm subadult

Body depth greater than head length, 2.0–2.4 times in SL; dorsal fin 11–12 spines (3rd spine shorter than head), 10–11 rays; anal fin rays 7–9; pectoral fin rays 17, fins longer than head; **large adults (males) develop a bulbous forehead; jaws with 4–6 slender canines at front, 3 or more series of small molar teeth behind**; LL scales 52–55; gill rakers 6–7 / 10–12; inter-orbital area, preopercle margin and bases of soft dorsal and anal fins scaly.

Head and body reddish orange dorsally and silvery white below, with **irregular black spots scattered over body; some fish display 5–7 red bars on body**; soft dorsal and anal fin membranes often blackish. Attains 75 cm, 9 kg.

Endemic, False Bay to Margate; more common south of East London.

Adults on rocky reefs in 30–150 m; juveniles on shallow reefs. Matures at ~30 cm FL; spawns in summer in the Eastern Cape. Sex change dubious. Solitary; feeds on gastro-pods, mussels, redbait, sea urchins, octopus, crabs, fish and polychaete worms.

Good eating; caught mainly by ski-boat anglers and commercial line fishermen on Agulhas Bank; a.k.a. 'Miss Lucy'; delicate feeder, difficult to hook. Currently (2004) over-exploited, and catch restrictions are necessary to rebuild the stock.

SIMILAR SPECIES

The Englishman seabream (see p. 217) lacks black spots on body.

ROMAN SEABREAM
Chrysoblephus laticeps
(Valenciennes 1830)

32 cm adult
4 cm juvenile

Body robust, depth greater than head length, 2.3–2.5 times in SL; dorsal fin 11–12 spines (3rd spine shorter than head), 10–11 rays; anal fin rays 8; pectoral fin rays 17–18, fins longer than head; jaws with 4–6 slender canines at front and 3 or more series of small molar teeth behind; inter-orbital area, pre-opercle margin and bases of soft dorsal and anal fins scaly. **Head and body reddish orange or scarlet, with white bar or triangular white blotch below middle of dorsal fin and another white blotch on rear of head; blue line joins the eyes**. Juvenile buff, with faint pale bluish blotches on head and body and dark mid-lateral band on peduncle; pelvic fin rays blackish, the membranes blue. Attains 50 cm FL, 5 kg.

Endemic, northern Namibia to Port St Johns; more common south of East London. Reported from Mauritius, but this record is dubious.

Rocky reefs in 5–100 m (juveniles usually inshore and adults offshore). Feeds on crustaceans, echinoderms (sea urchins and crinoids), molluscs and polychaete worms.

Juveniles move actively in groups of 3–6 fish over the reef, but they generally stay in one area. Adults are territorial ambush predators, and will defend their home cave or crevice against other fish, including roving juveniles if they approach too closely. One large male was observed to stay in or near his home cave for at least 2 years. Females mature at 17–20 cm FL, change sex at 30–33 cm (size at maturity and sex change smaller in exploited populations); spawns in summer. A 40 cm fish is 17 years old.

Popular angling fish; rarely caught from shore. Also taken by spearfishermen.

SIMILAR SPECIES

Adult unmistakable, but small juveniles might be mistaken for dageraad (see p. 217), which have 2 dark blotches below dorsal fin and black spot at rear end of dorsal fin base.

FALSE ENGLISHMAN SEABREAM
Chrysoblephus lophus
(Fowler 1925)

35 cm adult

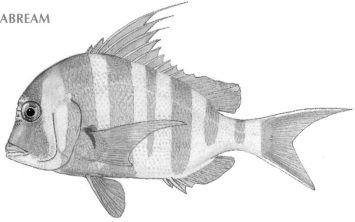

Body depth greater than head length, 2.0–2.3 times in SL; **dorsal fin 11 spines (3rd to 6th spines elongated in adults, 3rd spine longer than head)**, 10 rays; anal fin rays 9; pectoral fin rays 16–17, fins longer than head; tail fin lobes of adult acute, upper longer than lower lobe; jaws with 4–6 slender canines at front, 3 or more series of small molar teeth behind; LL scales 56–58; lower gill rakers 10–13; **inter-orbital area naked, becoming pitted with age**; preopercle margin and bases of soft dorsal and anal fins scaly. Head and body silvery white, with 5–8 reddish bars usually visible dorsally on body; small blue spots (1 per scale) on most body scales; **red, yellow or blue lines join eyes across inter-orbital area**; elongated dorsal fin spines blue or reddish. Attains 50 cm, 3 kg.

Endemic, Richards Bay to East London; reports from Mozambique unsubstantiated.

Coral and rocky reefs in 20–150 m. Biology little known. Spawns in spring. Feeds on gastropods, sea urchins, crabs and crayfish.

Flesh excellent. Caught sporadically from ski-boats and occasionally by spearfishermen. SADSAA all-tackle record: 3.1 kg.

SIMILAR SPECIES

The Englishman seabream (see p. 217) has 4 body bars and dorsal fin spines shorter than the head.

Juvenile red stumpnose (see p. 218) have no inter-orbital lines and no elongated dorsal fin spines.

SLINGER
Chrysoblephus puniceus
(Gilchrist & Thompson 1908)

23 cm subadult

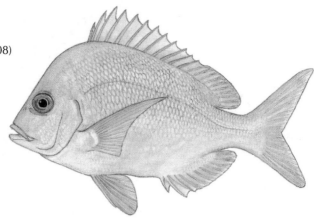

Body depth greater than head length, 2.0–2.3 times in SL; **adults with trenchant nape, the dorsal head profile steep**; dorsal fin 12 spines (3rd spine shorter than head), 10 rays; anal fin rays 8; pectoral fin rays 16, fins longer than head; tail fin forked; jaws with 4–6 slender canines at front, 3–5 series of small molar teeth behind; LL scales 49–52; lower gill rakers 14–16; inter-orbital area, preopercle margin and bases of soft dorsal and anal fins scaly. **Head and body bluish or pinkish silver, sometimes with small blue spots; blue line just below eye**. Attains 85 cm (65 cm FL) and 5 kg.

Adults occur from central Mozambique to Algoa Bay but are uncommon south of KZN, rarely caught in Algoa Bay; juveniles sometimes found at Knysna. Also reported from Madagascar.

Adults on coral and rocky reefs in 20–130 m and often seen with the coelacanths at 110–130 m off Sodwana Bay; juveniles common in 12–60 m. Feeds on crabs, shrimp, hermit crabs, bivalves, fish and zooplankton; often in large shoals. Matures at 24 cm (3 years), females change to male at 25–37 cm. Spawns off KZN in summer; during the spawning season, males defend temporary territories from other males.

Slinger are the most important commercial and recreational line-fish resource off KZN. As a result of heavier fishing pressure on the southern population, slinger caught off KZN are smaller than those taken off Mozambique.

SIMILAR SPECIES

Often caught with santer (see p. 216), but the elongated dorsal fin spines, absence of blue line under eye, and more pointed head of santer make them easy to separate.

Dageraad (see p. 217) also has a blue line under eye, but it has a black spot at end of dorsal fin base.

Blueskin seabream (see p. 232) has no blue line under eye and pectoral fins sub-equal to head.

KARANTEEN
Crenidens crenidens
(Forsskål 1775)

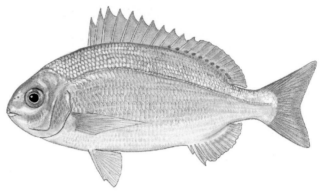

16 cm

Body depth greater than head length, 2.4–2.6 times in SL; dorsal fin 11 spines, 10 rays; anal fin rays 10; pectoral fin rays 13–14, fins longer than head; **jaws with 2–3 series of small incisors, outer series movable, with 5 brownish cusps, 3 middle cusps distinct**; several rows of small molars behind incisors; LL scales 49–60; lower gill rakers 9–11; no scales on inter-orbital area, preopercle margin or soft dorsal and anal fins, but these fins have a scaly basal sheath. **Head and body silvery, with faint series of dark spots (1 per scale) along body**; anal and paired fins often yellowish. Attains 30 cm.

Western Indian Ocean, Red Sea, Oman to Aliwal Shoal, juveniles to Algoa Bay.

Inshore, including estuaries and bays, but not found in areas of low salinity or high turbidity. Adults common along KZN coast, but spawning apparently occurs farther north. Karanteen feed heavily on seaweed, but they may be grazing these plants for the epiphytic animals that grow on them, rather than the plant material. Adults also forage on soft bottoms for crabs, worms and shrimp. Schooling species, easily caught on small hooks baited with shrimp or fish. Flesh excellent, but their small size precludes their being valued as an eating fish; often used as bait.

SIMILAR SPECIES

The strepie (see p. 239) has yellow stripes on body, black spot at upper end of pectoral fin base, and pectoral fins shorter than head.

BLACK MUSSELCRACKER
Cymatoceps nasutus
(Castelnau 1861)

10 cm juvenile
1.3 m adult male
(showing 'nose')

Body depth greater than head length, 2.3–2.5 times in SL; dorsal fin 12 spines, 10 rays; anal fin rays 8; pectoral fin rays 16–17, fins longer than head; **adults with 4–6 large stout conical teeth at front of jaws, 2 series of rounded molars behind**; juveniles with sharp conical inner teeth that are replaced by stout molars; LL scales 61–65, **scales above LL smaller than those below**; inter-orbital area and bases of soft dorsal and anal fins scaly. **Large adults develop thick lips and a large fleshy 'nose'. Adults dark grey to black; juveniles dark greenish brown with irregular white blotches**. Attains 1.3 m, 45 kg.

Endemic, Cape Town to Maputo.

Adults on rocky reefs in 2–100 m; juveniles over shallow reefs and algal beds. Adults feed on benthic organisms: starfish, sea urchins, crabs, cephalopods, chitons, gastropods and fish; juveniles feed mainly on crustaceans. Females mature at ~53 cm FL (10 years) and change sex at ~70 cm FL (~18 years). Grows slowly; a 1.1 m fish was estimated to be 45 years old. Territorial with small home range.

Premier sport fish, takes almost any bait and fights strongly. Caught from shore and ski-boats, also targeted by spearfishermen. In recent years, catches have declined markedly, and large adults are no longer common.

Flesh of large adults is coarse.

BLACKTAIL SEABREAM
Diplodus capensis
(Smith 1844)

38 cm adult
6 cm juvenile

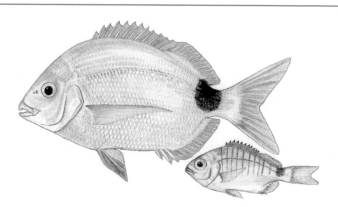

Body depth greater than head length, 1.9–2.3 times in SL; dorsal fin 12 spines, 14–15 rays; anal fin rays 13–14; pectoral fin rays 16–17, fins longer than head; tail fin forked; adult with 8 incisors at front of each jaw, 3–4 series of rounded molars behind; lips thin, not continued across front of mouth; inter-orbital area naked; scaly sheath at bases of soft dorsal and anal fins. **Head and body usually silvery, black blotch on top or side of peduncle below rear end of dorsal fin**; large adults almost uniformly black; juvenile with 8–10 faint dark bars dorsally on body; adults also show dark bars at night. Attains 45 cm FL, 3 kg (21+ years).

Angola to Mozambique.

Adults usually in rocky areas, from shore to 40 m; also occurs in surf off sandy beaches and in small groups in open water; juveniles in tide pools, estuaries and surf. Juveniles 2–3 cm SL consume copepods, polychaete worms, amphipods, insect larvae and ostracods; blacktail seabream more than 5 cm SL feed on algae, echinoids, anthozoans, sponges, bivalves and tunicates. Juveniles feed on vertical surfaces of gullies; in open water, they occur in large schools, often mixed with strepies. At night, blacktail hover in midwater or rest on

the bottom. Matures at 22 cm FL (3–4 years); some males change sex and thereafter spawn as females. Spawns July to September off KZN, October to December in Algoa Bay.

Flesh excellent. Probably the best fighter of our inshore angling fish; JLB Smith was of the opinion that the blacktail has twice the vigour of any trout of the same weight. This wary fish is caught on a variety of baits but is rarely hooked in clear water as it skilfully removes the bait. Because of their small size, blacktail are not much valued as food-fish, but they are popular as bait. Juveniles are the prey of many game fish, sharks and dolphins.

Blacktail seabream from north of Cape Vidal and Sodwana Bay are smaller (rarely over 30 cm FL) and the black tail blotch is mostly on the side of the peduncle, rather than dorsally as a 'saddle blotch'. Blacktail seabream from Namibia are larger than South African fish (some over 2 kg) and often have yellowish flecks on the body (Bruce Mann, ORI, pers. comm.). These different populations may represent separate species.

SIMILAR SPECIES

At a distance, juveniles might be confused with the false-eye damselfish, *Abudefduf sparoides* (Quoy & Gaimard 1825); but it has the black tail spot on the side of the peduncle, rather than a dorsal saddle blotch, as seen on blacktail seabream from south of Cape Vidal and St Lucia. Western Indian Ocean, Kenya to the Eastern Cape.

ZEBRA SEABREAM
Diplodus hottentotus
(Smith 1844)

44 cm large adult
29 cm adult
4 cm juvenile

Body depth greater than head length, 1.9–2.3 times in SL; dorsal fin 11 spines, 12–13 rays; anal fin rays 11; pectoral fin rays 15, fins longer than head; tail fin forked. Adults with 10–12 incisors at front of jaws, 2–3 series of rounded molars behind; lips thick, continued across front of mouth; inter-orbital area naked; scaly sheath at bases of soft dorsal and anal fins. **Head and body silvery or yellowish, with dark crossbars; adults show short dark bars in pale interspaces on belly**. At night the body bars are faint or absent. Attains 60 cm, 7 kg (33 years).

Endemic, False Bay to Kosi Bay.

Usually in rocky areas from shore to 120 m (seen in canyons with coelacanths off Sodwana Bay); juveniles on shallow reefs, in subtidal gullies, rock pools and often in estuaries. Juveniles diurnal carnivores, feeding mainly on

copepods, amphipods, polychaete worms, shrimp and insect larvae; adults eat worms and amphipods. Solitary or in small groups. Juveniles stay near cover; adults in open water or over reefs, and forage over intertidal zone at high tide. Long-time residents at specific sites. Matures at 29 cm FL (6 years). Spawns from September to January, does not change sex.

Good eating, but a freshly landed zebra seabream emits a strong, rather nauseating odour. Popular angling fish, caught from shore or ski-boats; fights strongly on light tackle. SADSAA record: 2.4 kg.

SIMILAR SPECIES

A novice fish watcher might confuse small zebra with a sergeant major damselfish (see p. 329) which also has dark bars on a silvery yellow body; but it has a small mouth with numerous tiny teeth and only 2 anal fin spines.

JANBRUIN SEABREAM
Gymnocrotaphus curvidens
Günther 1859

26 cm adult

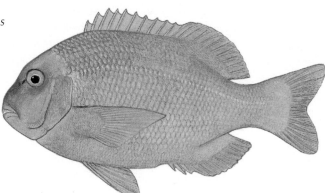

Body plump, depth greater than head length, 2.0–2.3 times in SL; dorsal fin 10 spines, 12 rays; anal fin rays 10; pectoral fins about equal to head; **tail fin slightly forked, rear edge of upper and lower lobes convex; adult with prominent, outwardly curved incisors at front of jaws**, band of small conical teeth behind, a few innermost teeth small molars; **head naked; soft dorsal and anal fin bases scaly. Body dark coppery brown; head bluish grey, eye a beautiful deep blue**; some fish with narrow dark bars on body. Attains 50 cm, 4 kg.

Endemic, False Bay to Port St Johns.

Rocky areas from shore to 80 m. Solitary; feeds on tunicates, algae, bryozoans, worms and crustaceans.

Flesh excellent. Usually caught from shore on redbait. Nowhere abundant. SA angling record: 2.8 kg; SA spearfishing record: 3.0 kg.

SIMILAR SPECIES

The blue hottentot and bronze bream (see p. 228 and p. 229 respectively) are similar, but they have jaws with 5 rows of incisors and no molars, some scales on cheek, and 10–18 lower gill rakers. The German seabream (see p. 231) and cristie, *Polyamblyodon gibbosum* (Pellegrin 1914), have scales on the cheek, 11 dorsal fin spines, and 14–18 lower gill rakers. The cristie occurs from KZN to Beira and Madagascar.

WESTCOAST STEENBRAS
Lithognathus aureti
Smith 1962

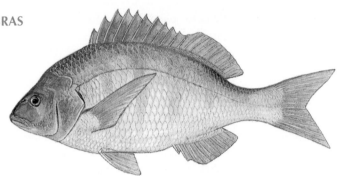

80 cm adult female

Body depth distinctly greater than head length, 2.4–2.6 times in SL; dorsal head profile slightly convex; dorsal fin 11 spines, 9–10 rays; anal fin rays 8–9; pectoral fin rays 15–16, fins longer than head in adults; peduncle depth 2.3–2.6 times in head; upper jaw protrusile; jaws with outer series of 10–12 conical teeth, 2 or more inner series of small molars; soft dorsal and anal fins naked; no scales on snout, inter-orbital area or preopercle flange. **Body mostly silver with 7 dark bars which fade with age**; head greyish silver; chest and belly white; dark spot at upper end of pectoral fin base. Attains ~1.2 m, 17+ kg (50+ years).

Endemic, Angola to Cape Town; rare south of Namibia.

Sandy bottom from shore to 10 m; juveniles occur in surf zone. Matures first as a male (for southern population) at about 35 cm FL (6 years), changes sex at about 41 cm (9–10 years); fish of the northern population grow faster, maturing at 41 cm (5 years) and changing sex at 50 cm (7 years). Spawns from October to February.

Highly valued as food-fish and important in recreational and commercial fisheries of Namibia. The use of set-nets was banned in 1992, and the stocks have recovered after the catch declined from a peak of 407 tonnes landed in 1980 to zero in 1993.

SIMILAR SPECIES

The sand steenbras has 12–13 dorsal fin rays, 10–11 anal fin rays and 10–14 dark bars on body. The white steenbras has longer head and more slender body.

WHITE STEENBRAS
Lithognathus lithognathus
(Cuvier 1829)

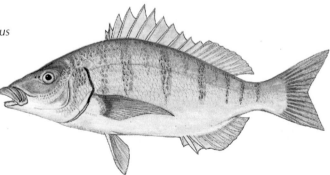

85 cm adult

Body depth subequal to head length, 2.7–3.2 times in SL; eye diameter about half snout length; **dorsal head profile straight or slightly concave**; dorsal fin 11 spines, 10 rays; anal fin rays 8–9; pectoral fin rays 16–17, fins shorter than head; peduncle depth 3.0–3.5 times in head length; mouth protrusile, teeth feeble, single outer series of conical teeth and 2 or more inner series of small molars; LL scales 44–51; inter-orbital area and soft dorsal and anal fins naked. **Head and body mostly silver, with 7 dark bars which fade with age.** Attains 1.5 m, 30+ kg (25–30 years).

Endemic, Angola to Thukela River.

Shallow water, over sand and close to reefs; adults in 1–25 m; small juveniles (<15 cm SL) in estuaries; larger juveniles (15–50 cm SL) in surf zone of sandy, silty sand or gravel areas. Matures at 54–65 cm SL (5–6 years); adults in the Western Cape undertake annual migrations to spawn off the northern Eastern Cape coast from June to August, returning to the Western Cape coast in summer. Does not change sex. Juveniles spend their first year in estuaries, where they grow 13 mm/month, feeding on amphipods, crabs, hermit crabs, polychaete worms, isopods and insect larvae. At 13–15 cm, juveniles move to surf zone. Adults feed on burrowing prey (cracker shrimp, small crabs, bloodworms, gastropods and bivalve molluscs) which are blasted from their burrows with a strong jet of water. In shallow water, white steenbras are often seen with their tails waving above the water as they root into the sand, blowing prey from their burrows.

Superb eating and premier angling fish; when hooked, they rush off and often break the line. Caught by anglers from beaches and in estuaries at dawn with shrimp or worm bait. Commercial seine fishermen also take many white steenbras, and the total catch has declined significantly in recent years. In 2002, as a result of estuarine degradation and heavy fishing pressure, the population collapsed. Stringent catch restrictions must be implemented to rebuild this resource.

SIMILAR SPECIES

The sand steenbras has more bars on body and more dorsal and anal fin rays.

SAND STEENBRAS
Lithognathus mormyrus
(Linnaeus 1758)

28 cm adult

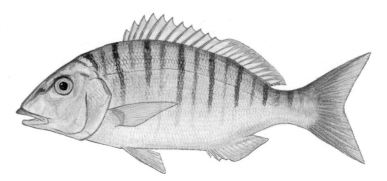

Body depth about equal to head length, **2.7–2.9 times in SL**; eye diameter less than snout length; **dorsal profile of snout convex**; dorsal fin 11 spines, 12–13 rays; anal fin rays 10–11; pectoral fin rays 15–17, fins shorter than head; peduncle depth 3.0–3.1 times in head length; mouth protrusile, teeth feeble, outer series of conical teeth and 2 or more

inner series of small molars; inter-orbital area and soft dorsal and anal fins naked. **Head and body mostly silver, with 13–14 narrow dark bars**. Attains 55 cm, 1 kg (10–12 years).

Mediterranean and west coast of Africa to Mozambique; common along west and south coasts of South Africa; also reported from Oman.

Adults over sandy bottom in 10–50 m; juveniles in bays and estuaries and school in surf zone or near mouth of permanently open estuaries. Feeds mainly on mole crabs, shrimp and bivalve molluscs. In the Mediterranean, males mature at 14 cm SL (2 years) and change sex at 21–28 cm (4–7 years). Spawns all along our coast.

Flesh excellent. Caught from shore on a variety of baits: shrimp, crabs, fish, worms, etc.

BLUE HOTTENTOT
Pachymetopon aeneum
(Gilchrist & Thompson 1908)

26 cm adult female

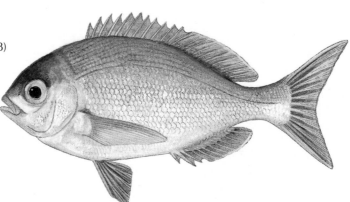

Body depth greater than head length, 2.2–2.5 times in SL; dorsal fin 10–11 spines, 11–13 rays; anal fin rays 10; **pectoral fins longer than head; jaws with ~5 rows of incisors; no molars; adult males with snout profile concave, inter-orbital area with distinct bulge**; LL scales 80–86; lower gill rakers 15–18; front of preopercle flange scaly; soft dorsal and anal fin bases scaly. **Body silvery bronze, streaked with blue; head cobalt blue**; colours fade to brownish grey after death. Attains 60 cm, 5 kg (12+ years).

Endemic, False Bay to Sodwana Bay.

Rocky reefs to 75 m; juveniles inshore in 10–20 m. Feeds on hydroids, tunicates, sponges, octocorals and gastropods. Females mature at 20–25 cm FL and change sex at 20–30 cm FL (4–9 years). Spawns from September to March.

Flesh excellent. Rarely caught from shore. SADSAA all-tackle record: 4.75 kg.

SIMILAR SPECIES

Anglers often confuse blue hottentot with bronze bream, which have the preopercle flange completely naked and 10–13 lower gill rakers.

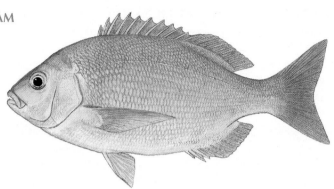

HOTTENTOT SEABREAM
Pachymetopon blochii
(Valenciennes 1830)

28 cm adult

Body depth greater than head length, 2.2–2.5 times in SL; dorsal fin with 10–11 spines, 11–12 rays; anal fin rays 10; **pectoral fins subequal to head**; jaws with ~5 rows of incisors, no molars; LL scales 60–67; lower gill rakers 13–14; snout profile straight; no bulge on inter-orbital area of adults; preopercle flange naked; soft dorsal and anal fin base scaly. **Body bluish grey or bronzy brown dorsally**, paler below; fins dusky; pectoral fin axil blackish. Attains 54 cm, 3 kg (12 years).

Endemic, Angola to Port Alfred; rare east of Cape Agulhas.

Rocky reefs and kelp beds from shore to at least 55 m. Omnivore, eats seaweed, amphipods, crabs, shrimp, worms, hydroids, molluscs, sea urchins, redbait and occasionally fish; adults feed mainly on algae. Matures at 22 cm FL (5 years); spawns throughout year, with peaks in summer and late autumn. Resident (non-migratory), hence especially vulnerable to overfishing.

Important catch of shore and boat anglers; also taken by spearfishermen. SADSAA all-tackle record: 2.4 kg.

SIMILAR SPECIES

Blue hottentot and bronze bream have pectoral fins distinctly longer than head and more numerous LL scales (80–86).

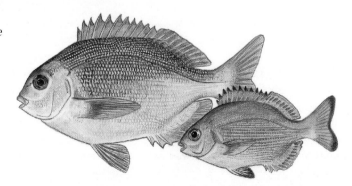

BRONZE BREAM
Pachymetopon grande
Günther 1859

30 cm FL adult
15 cm juvenile

Body depth distinctly greater than head length, 2.0–2.3 times in SL; dorsal fin 11 spines, 11 rays; anal fin rays 10–11; **pectoral fins longer than head; adults with snout profile concave, distinct bulge between eyes; jaws with ~5 rows of incisors**, no molars; LL

scales 80–85; lower gill rakers 10–13; pre-opercle flange naked; soft dorsal and anal fin bases scaly. **Head iridescent blue, body bronzy**; after death, colours fade to a uniform dull brown. Some yellow (xanthic) specimens are occasionally found. Attains 74 cm, 6 kg (40+ years).

Endemic, Western Cape to Maputo; reports from Madagascar unsubstantiated.

Rocky shores and reefs to 25 m; juveniles in seaweed. Feeds primarily on red and green algae. Matures at 30 cm FL (5 years); does not change sex. Spawns in groups from January to June. Adults in groups near caves, and reside in one area for many years.

Highly esteemed food and sport fish; difficult to hook, but fights strongly. Important catch of shore anglers and spearfishermen. Slow growth and late maturity make this species vulnerable to overfishing. SADSAA all-tackle record: 2.6 kg.

SIMILAR SPECIES

Blue hottentot (see p. 228) and the hottentot seabream have more teeth (30–36 in outer row of upper jaw) and lower gill rakers (13–18). German seabream have only the outer teeth as flattened incisors (~40 in upper jaw), inner teeth conical or molars. Chubs (Family Kyphosidae, see p. 250) might be confused with bronze bream, but the pectoral fins are distinctly shorter than head.

RED STEENBRAS
Petrus rupestris
(Valenciennes 1830)

1.5 m adult
29 cm juvenile

Body robust, depth subequal to head length, 2.5–3.0 times in SL; dorsal fin 11 spines, 10–11 rays; anal fin rays 8; **pectoral fins shorter than head; mouth large, jaws with 4–6 large canines at front and several rows of smaller conical teeth behind canines; no molars**; gill rakers short, 5–7 / 9–11; inter-orbital area and preopercle flange partly scaly; **soft dorsal and anal fins with fleshy scaly bases**. Red steenbras is **usually reddish or bronze**, but on soft bottoms from Mossel Bay to Durban it is a beautiful golden yellow; adult usually copper; males in breeding colour black dorsally, with black upper lip; juveniles reddish orange, with yellow belly and peduncle and dark red spot on peduncle behind dorsal fin base. Attains over 2 m and 70 kg; a 1.4 m fish was estimated to be 33 years old.

Endemic, False Bay to St Lucia.

Adults on rocky reefs in 20–160 m; juveniles on reefs in 10–30 m. Voracious carnivore, feeding mainly on fish and octopus. Large adults become semi-resident and territorial, but undertake migrations to spawning aggregations along the northern Eastern Cape coast and on the Agulhas Bank. Matures at 58–75 cm FL (7–9 years); spawns mainly July to October off the Eastern Cape.

Premier game fish, targeted by anglers and spearfishermen. Aggressive feeding behaviour of red steenbras, which take almost any fish baits, and anglers targeting their spawning aggregations make the species vulnerable to overfishing. Catches have declined markedly in recent years. In 1998, red steenbras was placed on the MCM Critical List of fish with bag limits of two per person per day. When the fish is pulled rapidly to the surface from reefs deeper than 20 m, the large gas-filled swimbladder over-expands and may rupture or cause internal bleeding. These injured fish may not survive when returned to the sea; consequently, when the daily bag limit is attained, one should stop fishing or move to another area to avoid injury to other red steenbras. Flesh excellent, but the liver of large fish contains a toxic level of Vitamin A. Red steenbras should be handled carefully, as the powerful jaws and large canines can inflict deep wounds that bleed profusely from an anticoagulant in the mucus of their mouth.

SIMILAR SPECIES

The river snapper (see p. 197) has a similar shape, but it has a dorsal fin with 10 spines, 13–14 rays and teeth on the roof of its mouth.

GERMAN SEABREAM
Polyamblyodon germanum
(Barnard 1934)

36 cm adult

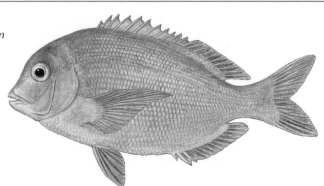

Body depth greater than head length, 2.2–2.5 times in SL; dorsal fin 11 spines, 11–12 rays; anal fin rays 10–11; **pectoral fin rays 17, fins longer than head; snout profile concave, inter-orbital area bulging in large adults; outer teeth strong, curved, chisel-like incisors**; rows of small molars or conical teeth behind incisors; LL scales 67–71; lower gill rakers 14–16; inter-orbital area and preopercle flange naked; soft dorsal and anal fin bases scaly. **Body grey-blue to bronzy**, paler below; forehead, cheeks and fins darker. Attains 50 cm.

Endemic, Algoa Bay to Maputo.

Coral and rocky reefs in 15–50 m. Biology little known. Feeds on crustaceans, gastropods, tunicates and fish. Flesh excellent. SADSAA all-tackle record: 2.5 kg.

SIMILAR SPECIES

Adult bronze bream (see p. 229) and blue hottentot (see p. 228) also have a bulging forehead, but these species have about 5 rows of incisors in each jaw, and bronze bream have only 10–13 lower gill rakers.

The cristie, *Polyamblyodon gibbosum* (Pellegrin 1914), has 13 dorsal fin rays, 15 pectoral fin rays, and pelvic fins fall well short of anus. Occurs from KZN to Beira, and Madagascar.

BLUESKIN SEABREAM
Polysteganus coeruleopunctatus
Klunzinger 1870

41 cm adult (Kenya)

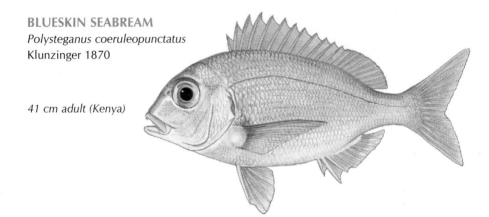

Body depth 2.3–2.5 times, head length 3.1–3.5 times in SL; **eye diameter subequal to pre-orbital depth**; rear nostrils oval; dorsal fin 12 spines, 10 rays; anal fin rays 8; pectoral fins subequal to head; jaws with 4–6 enlarged canines at front, smaller stout conical teeth behind, no molars; LL scales 52–56, **scales above LL smaller than those below**; lower gill rakers 11–13; inter-orbital area and pre-opercle flange scaly; low scaly sheath at dorsal and anal fin bases. **Head and body silvery red or pink, with blue spot on each scale**. Attains 60 cm, 5 kg.

Western Indian Ocean, Red Sea to the Eastern Cape.

Coral and rocky reefs in 50–450 m. Biology little known. Feeds primarily on crustaceans. A solitary species.

Caught by commercial and sport fishermen with squid or fish bait. SADSAA all-tackle record: 4.5 kg.

SIMILAR SPECIES

The slinger (see p. 221) has a blue line under eye, deeper body (adults with hump on nape) and small molars at back of the jaws. See also panga on p. 235.

SCOTSMAN SEABREAM
Polysteganus praeorbitalis
(Günther 1859)

31 cm juvenile

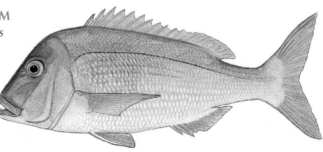

Body depth 2.5–2.8 times, head length 3.0–3.2 times in SL; preorbital depth 1.5–3.0 times eye diameter; **adults with prominent hump on nape**; dorsal fin 12 spines, 10 rays; anal fin rays 8; pectoral fins subequal to head; **jaws with 4–6 large canines at front, smaller conical teeth behind; no molars**; LL scales 59–63; lower gill rakers 15–16; scales above LL clearly smaller than those below; inter-orbital area and preopercle flange scaly; scaly sheath at base of soft dorsal and anal fins. Adults mostly **reddish pink, scales below LL pearly**; some silvery or blue stripes about eyes; juveniles sometimes more yellowish. Attains 90 cm, 11 kg.

Endemic, Algoa Bay to Beira.

Adults on rocky reefs in 50–120 m; juveniles in 10–30 m. Feeds on crabs, crayfish, fish and squid. Matures at ~40 cm FL; spawns off KZN in winter. Although normally solitary, Scotsman seabream aggregate for breeding and this makes them more vulnerable to overfishing.

Populations declined noticeably in recent years; catch restricted. Rarely caught from shore. Renowned as strong fighter (hence the name 'Scotsman'), often breaks free before it can be landed.

Resembles some emperors (*Lethrinus* spp, see family account p. 242), but they lack cheek scales and have 10 dorsal fin spines.

SEVENTY-FOUR SEABREAM
Polysteganus undulosus
(Regan 1908)

60 cm adult
9 cm juvenile

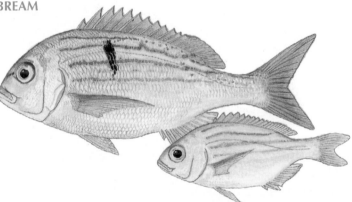

Body depth 2.5–2.8 times, head length 3.0–3.2 times in SL; dorsal fin 12 spines, 10 rays; anal fin rays 8–9; **pectoral fins longer than head; large adults have preorbital depth greater than eye diameter, some have prominent hump on nape; jaws with 4–6 enlarged canines at front, smaller conical teeth behind; no molars**; LL scales 58–62; lower gill rakers 14–16; scales above LL noticeably smaller than those below; inter-orbital area and preopercle flange scaly; scaly sheath at soft dorsal and anal fin bases. **Body silvery, with blue stripes and spots dorsally; adults with conspicuous black oval blotch across LL and below 5th and 6th dorsal fin spines**; males with dark blotch on chin. Attains ~1 m, 17 kg (20 years).

Endemic, Knysna to southern Mozambique.

Rocky reefs in depths of 20–200 m. Feeds on pelagic fish, cephalopods and crustaceans.

Both sexes mature at 65–75 cm SL (females 7 years, males 9 years). Apparently does not change sex. Large schools gather off KZN coast in late winter for spawning.

Flesh highly esteemed. Formerly abundant, but populations have declined drastically because of heavy fishing on spawning aggregations. Offshore line-boat catches in the 1920s were dominated by seventy-four seabream, but in 1989 only 0.8% of the total catch in KZN comprised seventy-four. The seventy-four seabream is now on the protected list, and the population seems to be slowly recovering, at least off the northern Eastern Cape. The name 'seventy-four' was said to be derived from the lines and spots on the body resembling rows of gun ports along the sides of the old man-of-war sailing ships.

DANE SEABREAM
Porcostoma dentata
(Gilchrist & Thompson 1908)

42 cm adult
6 cm juvenile

Body plump, depth distinctly greater than head length, 2.3–2.6 times in SL; dorsal fin 13 spines, 10–11 rays; anal fin rays 8–9; **pectoral fins longer than head; jaws with 4–6 enlarged protruding canines at front, smaller conical teeth and molars behind; preorbital bone covering maxilla when mouth is closed**; inter-orbital area, preopercle flange, soft dorsal and anal fins scaly. **Adults reddish orange dorsally, paler or yellow ventrally; mauve band joining eyes**; anterior LL scales either dark or silvery; fins yellow; dorsal and anal fin margins red. Juveniles yellow with 2 black blotches on LL. Attains 42 cm, 1 kg.

Endemic, Nature's Valley near Tsitsikamma to Beira; juveniles south to Knysna.

Coral and rocky reefs in 20–120 m; common on Aliwal Shoal and nearby Landers Reef, KZN. Feeds on crabs, stomatopods, polychaete worms and feather stars. Solitary inquisitive fish. Matures at 15 cm FL; spawns in spring.

Good eating, but too small to be of interest to anglers or spearfishermen.

SIMILAR SPECIES

The general physiognomy and canine teeth of Dane seabream resemble some wrasses (Family Labridae, see p. 335). Although wrasses may have molars on their pharyngeal bones, they never have molars on their jaw bones.

PANGA SEABREAM
Pterogymnus laniarius
(Valenciennes 1830)

23 cm adult

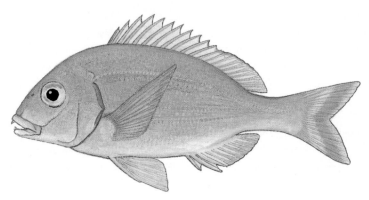

Body depth greater than head length, 2.3–2.6 times in SL; dorsal fin 12 spines, 10 rays; anal fin rays 8; pectoral fins subequal to head; **jaws with 4–6 enlarged canines at front, outer pair in each jaw curved outwards, smaller conical teeth and molars behind; lips of adults villose ('furry')**; LL scales 56–59; lower gill rakers 11–13; inter-orbital area and preopercle flange scaly; soft dorsal and anal fins naked, but with scaly basal sheath. Head and **body pinkish silver, with faint longitudinal yellow stripes and series of blue spots**; fins pale pink. Attains 45 cm FL, 1.5 kg (16 years).

Endemic, Namibia to Beira; one specimen known from Mauritius.

Adults on rocky reefs in 20–230 m. Unlike most sparids, the panga seabream does not change sex; matures at 20–28 cm FL (4–5 years), spawns all year round. Sometimes congregates in vast numbers. Probably the most abundant of our sparid fishes, and an important component of commercial trawl and handline fisheries.

SIMILAR SPECIES

The 'furry' lips, flaring canines and small molars of adults will separate panga seabream from blueskin seabream, carpenter or small seventy-four seabream (see pages 232, 214 and 233 respectively).

WHITE STUMPNOSE
Rhabdosargus globiceps
(Valenciennes 1830)

28 cm adult

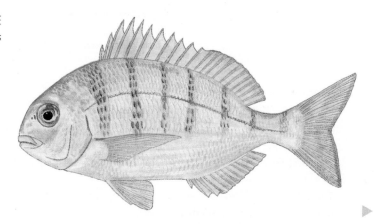

Body depth 2.3–2.6 times, head length 2.9–3.2 times in SL; dorsal fin 11 spines, 11–13 rays; **anal fin rays 10–11; pectoral fin rays 16–17**; jaws with 4–8 incisors at front, followed by 3–5 series of molars, inner rear molars much enlarged; LL scales 57–61; lower gill rakers 8–10; inter-orbital area, preopercle flange and soft dorsal and anal fins naked. **Body silvery with 5–7 faint bars**, first over nape, last on peduncle. Attains 50 cm FL, 3 kg (21 years).

Endemic from Angola to Qora River.

Adults in rocky areas and over sandy bottom from shore to 120 m; juveniles common in estuaries and in surf zone off sandy beaches. Juveniles omnivorous, those of 2 cm SL feed mainly on zooplankton; at 3 cm, they consume filamentous algae, amphipods and isopods; at 4 cm, their molars are beginning to develop and they can handle a variety of

shelled molluscs, crabs, shrimp and polychaete worms. Adults feed on bivalves, polychaetes, amphipods, barnacles and crabs. Matures at 17–23 cm FL (2–4 years). Spawns near shore in spring and summer; adults move offshore in winter. Does not change sex. Juveniles often shoal with Cape stumpnose.

Flesh excellent. Commonly caught by shore anglers in estuaries and along open coast; also of commercial importance in seine-net and line-boat fisheries. Catch restrictions. SADSAA all-tackle record: 2.1 kg.

— SIMILAR SPECIES —

Juvenile Cape stumpnose have faint dark bars, but they also have a mid-lateral yellow stripe along body and only 14–15 pectoral fin rays.

Sand steenbras (see p. 227) and juvenile white steenbras (see p. 226) have dark bars, but have longer head, more pointed snout, and small conical teeth at front of mouth.

CAPE STUMPNOSE
Rhabdosargus holubi
(Steindachner 1881)

13 cm juvenile
6 cm juvenile

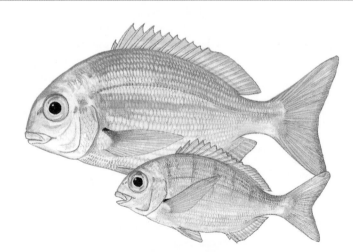

Body depth 2.2–2.4 times, head length 3.3–3.5 times in SL; dorsal fin 11 spines, 12–13 rays; **anal fin rays 10–11; pectoral fin rays 14–15**; jaws with 6–8 incisors at front, followed by 3–5 series of molars, innermost molars much enlarged; **front teeth of juve-**niles tricuspid; LL scales 55–57; lower gill rakers 8–9; inter-orbital area, and soft dorsal and anal fins naked; a few scales on preopercle flange. **Head and body silvery with golden mid-lateral band from head to peduncle**; juveniles with 5–6 faint bars,

which also appear on adults as a night colour pattern. Attains 45 cm, 3.5 kg.

Endemic, St Helena Bay to Maputo.

Rocky areas and over sandy bottom from shore to 50 m; juveniles common in seagrass beds of coastal lagoons and estuaries. Juveniles graze on algae and seagrass, but they digest only the epiphytic diatoms and encrusting organisms from this plant material. Adults feed on echinoderms, crustaceans, molluscs, barnacles, bryozoans and polychaete worms. Matures at 19–20 cm; spawns near shore in winter along KZN coast and from July to February in the Western and Eastern Cape Provinces. Adults migrate southwards in spring and are more common in Eastern Cape waters during summer. Juveniles use estuaries as nursery areas and grow from 1 cm to 10 cm in their first year; 2-year-old fish (14 cm SL) return to the sea.

Flesh excellent. Fights strongly on light tackle; takes almost any bait, but prefers worms or shrimp. Mostly caught by shore anglers. Too small to be of commercial importance. SA angling record: 3.5 kg.

SIMILAR SPECIES

Tropical stumpnose and bigeye stumpnose (see p. 238) lack the mid-lateral golden stripe, and their juveniles do not have tricuspid teeth.

TROPICAL STUMPNOSE
Rhabdosargus sarba
(Forsskål 1775)

37 cm adult

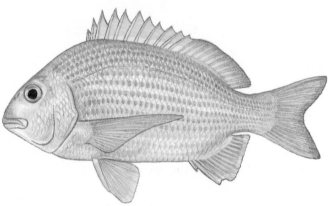

Body compressed, depth 1.9–2.2 times, head length 3.3–3.5 times in SL; dorsal fin 11 spines, 12–13 rays; **anal fin rays 11; pectoral fin rays 14–15**; jaws with 6–8 incisors at front, followed by 3–5 series of molars, innermost molars huge; front teeth of juveniles unicuspid; LL scales 56–59; **lower gill rakers 7–9**; inter-orbital area, preopercle flange, and soft dorsal and anal fins naked. **Head and body silvery, with dull gold spot at centre of each scale forming faint longitudinal lines along flanks**; usually a yellow streak from base of pelvic fins towards anal fin. Attains 80 cm, 12 kg.

Indo-West Pacific, Red Sea, Oman to the Eastern Cape (south to Wilderness near Swartvlei in summer).

Coastal waters, including estuaries; adults on reefs to 60 m; juveniles common in estuaries. Diurnal, schooling species; juveniles feed on algae, seagrass, amphipod crustaceans, crabs and bivalves. Adults feed on hard-shelled molluscs (gastropods, mussels, oysters, clams), sand dollars, sea urchins, sand-dwelling crabs and barnacles. Matures at 20 cm FL; most fish begin their reproductive activity as males, and when they are 2–3 years old (25–30 cm FL) they change to females. Spawns at night, inshore, from August to November. Juveniles 15–40 mm SL enter estuaries and remain there for at least a year, during which they grow ~14 mm per month. Adults >35 cm SL rarely found in estuaries.

Flesh excellent. Fights gamely, caught from shore or ski-boats with a variety of baits (prawns, mussels, mole crabs and redbait). Also taken by spearfishermen; caught by subsistence fishermen with traps and gill-nets in St Lucia and Kosi Bay.

BIGEYE STUMPNOSE
Rhabdosargus thorpei
Smith 1979

15 cm juvenile

Body depth 1.9–2.4 times, head length 3.0–3.4 times in SL; dorsal fin 11 spines, 13 rays; **anal fin rays 12; pectoral fin rays 14–16**, fins 1.1–1.4 times longer than head; jaws with 6 incisors at front, followed by 3–5 series of molars, innermost molars much enlarged; front teeth of juveniles unicuspid; LL scales 55–60; **lower gill rakers 10–12**; inter-orbital area, preopercle flange, and soft dorsal and anal fins naked. **Head and body silvery, ventral part of body, including anal and pelvic fins yellow**; dorso-lateral body scales with gold or bronzy centre, forming longitudinal series of spots; pectoral fin axil black. Attains 50 cm, 4 kg.

Endemic, Port Alfred to southern Mozambique; rare south of KZN.

Sandy shores and rocky reefs to 70 m; juveniles common in estuaries. Feeds mainly on shelled molluscs and crustaceans.

Flesh esteemed; caught by anglers from shore or from ski-boats.

STREPIE
Sarpa salpa
(Linnaeus 1758)

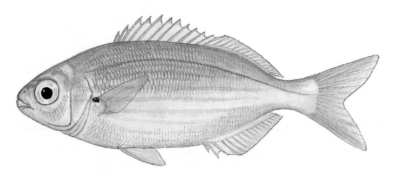

11 cm juvenile

Body depth 2.7–3.0 times, head length about 4.0 times in SL; dorsal fin 11 spines, 14–16 rays; anal fin rays 13–15; **pectoral fins shorter than head**; eye diameter subequal to snout length; **jaws with a row of incisors**, those in upper jaw notched, in lower jaw pointed; no molars; LL scales 71–79; lower gill rakers 12–14; inter-orbital area and pre-opercle flange naked; soft dorsal and anal fins naked, but with scaly basal sheath. **Body with 8–10 yellow stripes; pectoral fin axil black.** Attains 45 cm, 2 kg.

Mediterranean and eastern Atlantic, round South Africa to southern Mozambique.

Inshore over rocky areas; juveniles common in estuaries near seagrass beds, in surf zone along sandy beaches, in tide pools and over subtidal reefs. Juveniles <3 cm feed on small crustaceans (mainly copepods); larger juveniles and adults feed on eelgrass and red algae. Active little fish, with the shoals continuously moving over the reef grazing on algae. The black peritoneal lining of the abdominal cavity presumably inhibits photosynthetic activity of algae in the gut. Males mature at 14–15 cm FL (2 years); after one year of spawning as a male, most strepies change sex at about 18–22 cm FL, thereafter spawning as females. Some males do not change sex, and continue their reproductive life as males for another year or two. Also, some small (14–18 cm) adult females apparently skip the preliminary male stage. Spawns from April to September in KZN waters, with large shoals of spawning fish observed off Durban Bluff. Some adults appear to migrate from the west and south coasts to KZN for spawning, but spawning also occurs in Eastern Cape waters. Juveniles of 3–4 cm enter estuaries where they grow 12–14 mm/month for their first year. Fish 20–27 cm FL are estimated to be 6 years old.

This common shoaling species is eaten by a variety of fish predators; easily caught by shore anglers (especially during winter spawning season) and often used for bait. An excellent table fish.

WHITE MUSSELCRACKER
Sparodon durbanensis
(Castelnau 1861)

6 cm juvenile
90 cm adult

Body depth subequal to head length, 2.5–3.0 times in SL; inter-orbital area wide; snout and lower jaw robust, 4 incisors at front of each jaw, middle pair much enlarged and curved, upper jaw teeth overlapping those in lower jaw; molars large, in 3 or more series; dorsal fin 11 spines, 11 rays; anal rays 10; **pectoral fins shorter than head**; inter-orbital area and preopercle flange naked; soft dorsal and anal fin bases scaly. **Head and body silvery grey; belly white, fins darker, opercular margin blackish**; juveniles with longitudinal series of dark spots on body; median and pelvic fins orange or yellow. Attains 1.2 m, 30 kg (31 years).

Endemic, St Helena Bay to Thukela River.

Rocky bottom of inshore waters, rarely enters estuaries; juveniles in tide pools and on shallow reefs; adults more common on deeper reefs, to 30 m. Juveniles feed on crustaceans (copepods), algae, tube feet of sea urchins and polychaete worms; adults eat crabs, shelled molluscs, tunicates, crayfish, fish, sand dollars and worms. Matures at 35 cm FL; spawns from August to January. Usually solitary, but probably spawns in groups, as shoals of up to 30 large fish have been seen during spawning season. Except for spawning migrations, adults are restricted to one locality.

One of our best known angling fish, usually caught from shore; takes almost any bait, fights strongly and is difficult to land as the powerful jaws can straighten hooks. Good eating, but the flesh of large musselcrackers may be coarse; the head of large fish, baked whole, is considered a delicacy. SADSAA all-tackle record: 9.8 kg.

SIMILAR SPECIES

The black musselcracker (see p. 222) is usually darker, the front teeth conical, the body deeper (depth 2.3–2.5 times in SL), inter-orbital region scaly, and large adults develop a fleshy 'nose'.

STEENTJIE
Spondyliosoma emarginatum
(Valenciennes 1830)

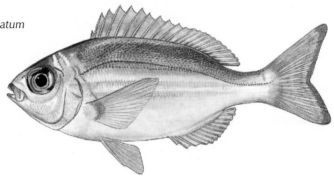

14 cm juvenile

Body depth 2.0–2.6 times, head length 3.3–3.5 times in SL; eye diameter subequal to snout length and 2.0–2.7 times preorbital depth; dorsal fin 11 spines, 11–13 rays; anal fin rays 10; pectoral fins equal to head; **jaws with 4–6 rows of slender lanceolate incisors, outer teeth movable, inner teeth of adults small blunt molars**; LL scales 80–92; lower gill rakers 15–18; inter-orbital area and preopercle flange naked; soft dorsal and anal fins with low scaly sheath. **Body brownish to silvery blue, with several faint golden stripes**, which fade soon after death. Attains 45 cm, 1 kg.

Endemic, St Helena Bay to Durban.

Rocky reefs in 2–60 m; also in estuaries of south coast. Feeds on tunicates (redbait), polychaete worms, crabs and amphipods. Matures at 20–22 cm; does not change sex; spawns off the Western Cape from September to January; eggs deposited on sandy bottom in a saucer-shaped depression about 50 cm in diameter and 20 cm deep. The eggs are protected in the nest by the male for a few days, but then he seems to lose interest.

Courting males dark bluish black anteriorly, rear part of body almost white with 3–5 dark bluish black, vertically elongate blotches; females ready to spawn are much paler, with white mark on flanks and pale spots near dorsal fin. Courting males territorial and defend their nest against certain types of intruders (male steentjies in nuptial dress and other similar-looking sparids), whereas other fish (dissimilar species) are ignored. Females in spawning colours appear to swim about at random and may deposit eggs in more than one nest.

Because of their small size, steentjie were mainly used for bait and anglers regarded them as a nuisance, adept at stealing bait intended for larger fish. But with the depletion of larger species, steentjie are now often considered suitable as a table fish.

SIMILAR SPECIES

The fransmadam (see p. 215) has a larger eye (diameter greater than snout length) and conical teeth.

FAMILY LETHRINIDAE ■ Emperors, Glowfish & Barenose

Body oblong, slightly compressed; **dorsal fin continuous with 10 spines, 9–11 rays; anal fin with 3 spines, 8–10 rays**; tail fin truncate to emarginate or shallowly forked; mouth moderate to large, **maxilla mostly hidden when mouth closed; teeth conical or molariform; no teeth on vomer, palatines or tongue; preopercle smooth; opercle ends in a blunt flat point**; scales distinct, weakly ctenoid; opercle scaly. Size range 20–80 cm.

Most lethrinids occur on or near coral reefs, where they feed at night on a variety of prey; juveniles of a few emperors are found in estuaries. Some species occur in large shoals, others are usually seen singly or in small aggregations. Protogynous hermaphroditism seems to be the normal reproductive mode.

Lethrinids are excellent food-fish and comprise an important component of Indo-Pacific commercial, sport and artisanal fisheries.

Tropical and subtropical Indo-Pacific region; 1 species of *Lethrinus* in the tropical eastern Atlantic Ocean. Five genera, ~40 species, 16 in our area.

Glowfish

Bluelined barenose

Yellowtail emperor

Blackspot emperor

Spangled emperor

Orangestriped emperor

GLOWFISH
Gnathodentex aureolineatus
(Lacepède 1802)

10 cm juveniles, light (Comoros) and dark colour forms

Body depth subequal to head length, 2.8–3.3 times in SL; eye diameter subequal to snout length; cheek with 3 rows of scales; dorsal fin rays 10; anal fin rays 8–9; pectoral fin rays 15; **maxilla with longitudinal denticulate ridge**; jaws with outer row of conical teeth, inner series of much smaller teeth; 4–6 canines at front of jaws; LL scales 68–74. Colour variable depending on habitat; pale over sand, darker in caves and on reefs; a distinctive **bright yellow blotch below soft dorsal fin**; dark phase reddish brown, with silver spot on each scale above LL, dark stripes below LL; pale phase mostly silver with yellowish stripes below LL; both phases have red dorsal and anal fin margins. Attains 30 cm, but fish larger than 20 cm are rare.

Indo-central Pacific, Somalia to St Lucia; no records from the Red Sea or Oman.

Usually on or near reefs in 3–100 m. Biology little known; occurs singly or in small groups in caves or under ledges, also in shoals of a hundred or more individuals over the reef. Feeds on benthic invertebrates.

Flesh edible. The distinctive bright yellow patch below dorsal fin rays is conspicuous, even in the dim light of caves.

— SIMILAR SPECIES —

The arrowhead soapfish (see p. 175) also has a bright yellow spot, but the spot is smaller, and mostly confined to upper surface of peduncle; the soapfish has 2 dorsal fins, and the body is longer (depth 3.5–3.7 times in SL).

BLUELINED BARENOSE
Gymnocranius grandoculis
(Valenciennes 1830)

~25 cm juvenile (Seychelles)
67 cm adult

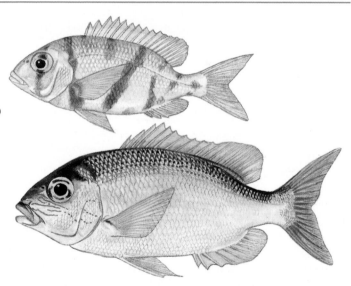

Body depth greater than head length, 1.9–2.6 times in SL; eye diameter less than snout length; cheek with 4–5 oblique rows of scales; dorsal and anal fin rays 9–10; pectoral fin rays 13–14; tail fin slightly forked, median rays longer than eye diameter; maxilla smooth; jaws with outer row of conical teeth, 4–6 canines at front and inner series of much smaller teeth; no molars; LL scales 46–51; $5\frac{1}{2}$ scales from middle dorsal fin spines to LL; gill rakers 1–4 / 5–6. Juveniles (<20 cm SL) with dark bar under eye and 5–6 more or less distinct irregular dark bars on body; adults with **wavy blue lines on snout and**

cheek, increasing in number with growth. Attains 80 cm.

Indo-central Pacific, Red Sea to Aliwal Shoal and Indian Ocean islands.

Adults on sandy and silty bottom in 50–100 m; juveniles in shallow water over seagrass beds and sandy, silty bottom. Biology little known; feeds mainly on benthic crustaceans and fish.

Previously identified as *Gymnocranius robinsoni* (a junior synonym) or *Gymno-cranius griseus*, which occurs in the eastern Indian and western Pacific oceans. IGFA all-tackle record: 5.5 kg.

SIMILAR SPECIES

The lemonfish, *Plectorhinchus flavomaculatus* (Cuvier 1830), has blue lines on head, yellow-orange stripes or spots on body, and longer dorsal fin with 12–14 spines and 19–22 rays. Indo-West Pacific, Red Sea to the Eastern Cape.

YELLOWTAIL EMPEROR
Lethrinus crocineus
Smith 1959

27 cm (Seychelles)

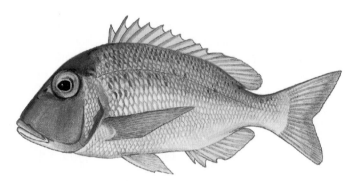

Body depth greater than head length, 2.3–2.4 times in SL; snout/head profile straight; snout (including upper jaw) 1.9–2.1 times in head length; $5^{1}/_{2}$ scale rows from middle dorsal fin spines to LL, topmost scales mostly covered by adjacent larger scales; preopercle, preorbital, cheek, inter-orbital area, and dorsal and anal fin bases naked; pectoral fins reach well past anal fin origin; inner pectoral fin base scaly; lateral teeth rounded. Body tan or yellowish; most scales with a dark spot; head brown; fins yellowish, dorsal fin edge reddish or yellowish; inside of mouth red; some fish with faint dark bars. Attains 60 cm, 9 kg.

Western Indian Ocean, Kenya to St Lucia; Sri Lanka, Seychelles, Comoros, Madagascar, Mauritius and Rodrigues.

Reefs and adjacent sandy areas to 150 m.

Caught with handlines and in traps. SADSAA all tackle record: 3.25 kg.

SIMILAR SPECIES

The sky emperor, *Lethrinus mahsena* (Forsskål 1775), has $4^{1}/_{2}$ scale rows from middle dorsal fin spines to LL; red bar at pectoral fin base sometimes extends above and below fin base, occasionally to operculum; tail fin reddish, especially the tips. Western Indian Ocean, south to Sodwana Bay.

BLACKSPOT EMPEROR
Lethrinus harak
(Forsskål 1775)

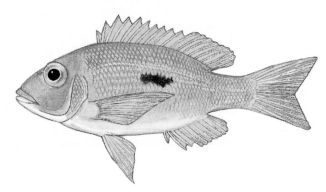

12 cm juvenile (Comoros)

Body depth greater than head length, 2.6–2.8 times in SL; snout/head profile slightly convex; snout (including upper jaw) 2.1–2.6 times in head length; preopercle, preorbital, cheek, inter-orbital area and dorsal and anal fin bases naked; 5¹/2 or 4¹/2 scale rows from middle dorsal fin spines to LL; inner pectoral fin base scaly; lateral teeth rounded. Body olive-brown or grey dorsally, with pale blue or white spot on scales and usually a **large oval black blotch just below LL and rear dorsal fin spines** (some fish lack black blotch and may be mistaken for other emperors, but the more slender body, short snout and other colour pattern features should signify the blackspot emperor); ~9 dark bars often visible on body. Attains 50 cm (15 years).

Indo-central Pacific, Red Sea, Oman to Sodwana Bay; also known from most islands.

Shallow sandy, coral rubble and seagrass areas near reefs; also found in mangrove areas. Feeds on crustaceans, molluscs, polychaete worms, echinoderms and fish. Solitary or in small groups; less wary than other emperors. Matures at ~25 cm. Spawns inshore in tropical areas throughout the year during the first 5 days of each lunar month.

Flesh excellent, but spoils rapidly. Caught with seines, gill-nets, traps and handlines. Fights gamely on light tackle.

SIMILAR SPECIES

Juveniles without a black blotch resemble the slender emperor, *Lethrinus variegatus* Valenciennes 1830; but this small species (maximum 20 cm) is more slender (body depth distinctly less than head length, 3.4–3.9 times in SL) and lacks scales on inner pectoral fin base. Indo-West Pacific, south to KZN.

SPANGLED EMPEROR
Lethrinus nebulosus
(Forsskål 1775)

22 cm juvenile
~5 cm juvenile (no locality)

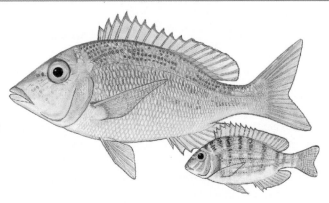

Body depth usually greater than head length, 2.5–2.8 times in SL; snout/head profile straight; snout (including upper jaw) 1.8–2.3 times in head length; preopercle, preorbital, cheek, inter-orbital area and dorsal and anal fin bases naked; 5^1/$_2$ scale rows from middle dorsal fin spines to LL; pectoral fin reaches vertical at anal fin origin; inner pectoral fin base scaly; lateral teeth rounded. Edges of scales dark; centre of dorsal body scales dark; **many scales above and below LL with pale blue or white spot; head brownish, with 3 blue lines and/or blue spots radiating forward from eyes.** Attains 80 cm, ~9 kg (20 years).

Indo-central Pacific, Red Sea, Oman to Algoa Bay.

Coral and rocky reefs, seagrass beds and mangrove areas from shore to 75 m. Feeds on echinoderms, crustaceans, molluscs and fish. Adults solitary or in small shoals; juveniles usually in large shoals in shallow, sheltered areas. Matures at 50–60 cm (4 years); spawns in tropical areas March to July.

Caught with handlines, spear, traps, trawls, seines and gill-nets. Fights strongly. The spangled emperor (a.k.a. 'blue emperor') is of major commercial importance as a food-fish in many countries of the Indo-Pacific region.

ORANGESTRIPED EMPEROR
Lethrinus obsoletus
(Forsskål 1775)

40 cm adult; above: usual pattern (Madagascar)
below: stress pattern (Seychelles)

Body depth subequal to head length, 2.5–2.8 times in SL; snout/head profile straight; snout (including upper jaw) 1.8–2.3 times in head length; preopercle, preorbital, cheek, inter-orbital area and dorsal and anal fin bases naked; 5^1/$_2$ scale rows from middle dorsal fin spines to LL; pectoral fin reaches vertical at anal fin origin; inner pectoral fin base scaly. Front teeth conical, rear teeth molars. **Edges of scales dark brown, shading to white ventrally; orange-yellow stripe through pectoral fin base to peduncle;** some fish with 2 faint orange-yellow stripes above and one below main stripe. Attains 60 cm (14 years).

Indo-West Pacific, Red Sea, Oman to Sodwana Bay.

Shallow weedy areas and coral reefs to 30 m. Although the orangestriped emperor is one of the most common emperors along the east coast of Africa, little is known of its biology. Occurs singly or in small groups. Feeds on molluscs, crustaceans and echinoderms.

Formerly known as *Lethrinus ramak* (Forsskål 1775); *ramak* is the Arabic name for this species.

FAMILY NEMIPTERIDAE ■ Spinecheeks & Threadfin Bream

Body oblong, slightly compressed; **dorsal fin continuous with 10 spines, 9–10 rays; anal fin with 3 spines, 6–7 rays**; tail fin shallowly forked, upper rays of some species elongated into a filament; **maxilla mostly hidden when mouth closed**; teeth villiform, with some enlarged canines anteriorly; no teeth on vomer, palatines or tongue; preopercle edge smooth; opercle ends in a blunt flat point; 2nd suborbital bone with free margin, which may be smooth, serrate or with a large posteriorly-directed spine (hence 'spinecheek'); scales distinct, weakly ctenoid; opercle and preopercle scaly; snout and suborbital area naked; dorsal and anal fins naked. Size range 10–28 cm.

Not important as food-fish, except in artisanal fisheries, where they comprise a significant component of the landings. Caught with trawls, gill-nets and handlines. Some species occur in large shoals, others are usually seen singly or in small aggregations.

Tropical and subtropical Indo-Pacific region. Five genera and ~65 species, 7 in our area.

SILVERFLASH SPINECHEEK
Scolopsis vosmeri
(Bloch 1792)

16 cm adult

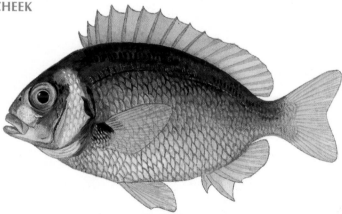

Body depth 2.0–2.6 times in SL; **rear edge of suborbital bone serrate, with distinct retrorse spine**; pectoral fin rays 17–19; LL scales 39–45; scales extend dorsally on head to nostrils; teeth small, slender; no canines; gill rakers rudimentary. Colour variable, usually reddish brown or yellowish, with dark spot at base of each scale; **head dark brown with white blotch over rear of head**; lower margin of operculum red, the upper edge black; lips and side of snout pale. Attains 20 cm.

Tropical Indo-West Pacific, Red Sea, Oman to Durban and western Indian Ocean islands.

Usually on mud or sand bottom near reefs, in 1–60 m. Feeds on benthic invertebrates. Does well in aquaria. The distinctive white flash on the operculum readily identifies this species.

FAMILY DICHISTIIDAE ■ Galjoen

Body compressed; head (except front of snout), body and fins covered with small firmly adherent ctenoid scales; **dorsal fin with 10 spines, 18–23 rays and deep notch before soft-rayed part; anal fin with 3 spines, 13–14 rays; soft dorsal and anal fins with high lobe anteriorly**; pectoral fins shorter than or subequal to head; pelvic fins with 1 spine, 5 rays; tail fin shallowly forked; maxilla reaching below front half of eye; lips thick; jaws with outer row of strong curved incisors, smaller teeth behind; molars on pharyngeal bones but no teeth on roof of mouth; inter-orbital width greater than eye diameter; preopercle serrate; branchiostegal membranes joined to isthmus. Size range 32–80 cm.

Important sport fish, caught by shore anglers in mixed rocky/sand areas.

The Family Dichistiidae [formerly Coracinidae] comprises 2 species restricted to southern Africa and Madagascar.

GALJOEN
Dichistius capensis
(Cuvier 1831)

3 cm juvenile
51 cm adult

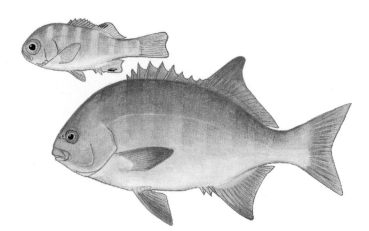

Body depth 2.2–2.4 times, head length 3.1–3.3 times in SL; dorsal fin rays 18 or 19; pectoral fins subequal to head. In rocky areas, galjoen are usually **dark grey, sometimes mottled or with 7–9 faint black bars**, but change to silvery in a few seconds when moving over white sand. Attains 80 cm, 6.5 kg (14+ years).

Endemic, Namibia to Durban.

Shallow rocks and sandy areas with strong wave action. Feeds on mussels, gastropods, barnacles, amphipods, isopods, redbait, poly-chaete worms and algae. Most galjoen remain in certain areas for long periods, but one fish tagged off Namibia was caught off East London. The number of migrants and reasons for such migrations are unknown. Females mature at 34 cm (6 years); males at 31 cm. Spawns from October to March.

Strong fighter; flesh much esteemed, almost transparent, becomes white with fine dark threads when cooked; flavour improved if fish is bled immediately after it is caught. SADSAA all-tackle record: 1.8 kg.

The banded galjoen, *Dichistius multifasciatus* (Pellegrin 1914), has body depth 1.6–1.8 times in SL, ~15–20 broad and narrow dark bars and 21–23 dorsal fin rays. Sodwana Bay to False Bay; also Madagascar.

FAMILY PARASCORPIDIDAE ▪ Jutjaw

Body oblong, compressed; **dorsal fin continuous with 11–12 spines, 15–17 rays; anal fin 3 spines, 13–15 rays; pectoral fins about half head length**; tail fin forked; pelvic fins with 1 spine, 5 rays; **mouth large, lower jaw projecting**; upper jaw not protrusile; maxilla exposed, scaly and reaches below rear edge of eye; no supramaxilla; minute teeth in narrow bands on jaws; roof of mouth with or without a few microscopic teeth; branchiostegal rays 7, membranes free from isthmus; gill rakers long, numerous and projecting into mouth; preopercle finely serrate; opercle with bluntly rounded, flat point; scales small, ctenoid; basal half of soft dorsal and anal fins scaly; head and lower jaw also scaly.

Single endemic species. Included in the Kyphosidae or Scorpididae by some authors, but it is not closely related to these families and deserves recognition as a separate family.

JUTJAW
Parascorpis typus
Bleeker 1875

46 cm adult
5 cm juvenile

Body depth much greater than head length, 2.0–2.2 times in SL; LL scales 60–70, obscured by overlying scales; gill rakers 18 / 36–40. **Dull grey-brown fish; inside of mouth and gill cavity white**; tongue dusky. Attains 60 cm.

Endemic, False Bay to Maputo.

On reefs in 15–200 m. As indicated by the feeble dentition and long numerous gill rakers, the jutjaw feeds on zooplankton (mainly krill and mysid crustaceans) which it strains from the water.

Usually not wary of divers. Rarely caught by anglers. SADSAA all-tackle record: 2.3 kg. Flesh good.

The pelagic armourhead, *Pseudopentaceros richardsoni* (Smith 1844), is superficially similar, but the soft dorsal and anal fins have many fewer rays, hence the bases of these fins are distinctly shorter than the fin bases of the jutjaw; and the mouth is smaller, with maxilla not reaching below eye.

FAMILY KYPHOSIDAE ■ Chubs & Stonebream

Body oblong, slightly compressed; **head length about half body depth**; dorsal fin continuous; tail fin emarginate; jaws with a series of long curved close-set incisors (*Kyphosus*) or a band of bristle-like teeth, with outer teeth enlarged and lanceolate (*Neoscorpis*); preopercle and opercle smooth; scales small, ctenoid, covering most of head, body and median fins; swimbladder bifurcate posteriorly, extending past anus. Size range 50–75 cm.

Generally in shallow water on reefs and rocky areas. Omnivorous; most species feed on algae and also consume a lot of microscopic invertebrates associated with the algae. The family has recently been expanded to include the Girellidae, Scorpididae and Microcanthidae families.

Worldwide in tropical and temperate waters. Seventeen genera, ~45 species, 4 in our area.

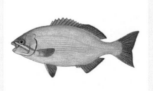

Grey chub

Stonebream

GREY CHUB
Kyphosus bigibbus
Lacepède 1801

60 cm adult (Oman)

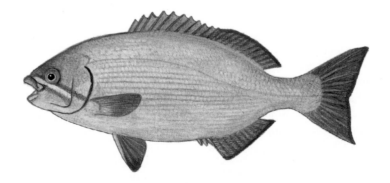

Dorsal fin with 10–11 spines, 11–13 rays; base of soft-rayed part shorter than spinous part; anal fin 3 spines, 10–12 rays; pectoral fins shorter than head; LL scales 51–55; gill rakers 5–7 / 15–17. Head and body generally silvery grey, scale edges brown, forming longitudinal lines on body; opercular edge dark brown; dark band from corner of mouth to angle of preopercle; some fish xanthic (entirely yellow), a yellow chub turned grey in 10 days when kept in an aquarium. Attains 75 cm and at least 10 kg.

Indo-central Pacific, Red Sea, Oman, Maputo to False Bay; may occur north of Maputo but seems to avoid equatorial waters.

Shallow coral and rocky reefs; juveniles often in open ocean with *Sargassum* weed or flotsam. Mainly herbivorous; often in large groups grazing on algae.

Chubs are also called 'rudderfish' from their habit of following ships and feeding on garbage discharged from them. The intestine is very long to allow effective digestion of the voluminous plant material. Good eating, but one must take care when cleaning the fish that the fillets are not contaminated by the foul-smelling gut contents. Provides excellent sport when caught on light tackle; takes a variety of animal bait and also pieces of seaweed.

SIMILAR SPECIES

The blue chub, *Kyphosus cinerascens* (Forsskål 1775), a more tropical Indo-Pacific species found north of East London, is silvery blue with silver stripe below eye; adults with anterior rays of dorsal and anal fins distinctly longer than posterior rays or dorsal fin spines.

The brassy chub, *Kyphosus vaigiensis* (Quoy & Gaimard 1825), has 13–15 dorsal fin rays, soft dorsal fin base longer than spinous fin base; brassy stripes along scale rows of body and 2 brassy stripes on side of head. Indo-West Pacific, south to Algoa Bay.

STONEBREAM
Neoscorpis lithophilus
(Gilchrist & Thompson 1908)

26 cm subadult
9 cm juvenile

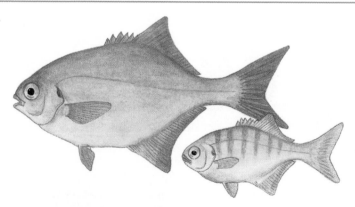

Body slightly compressed; head small, its length about half body depth; dorsal fin with 6–8 short stout spines folding into a deep groove and 20–23 rays; anal fin with 3 short spines covered by skin and scales and 23–26 rays; front dorsal and anal fin rays elongate, forming prominent lobe; pectoral fins pointed, subequal to head; maxilla expanded posteriorly, reaching below front edge of eye; LL scales 72–76; gill rakers 6–8 / 12–15. Head and body silvery grey; fins dark; rear edge of operculum black; juveniles with 7–8 faint bars on body. Attains 50 cm FL, 3 kg (~10 years).

Endemic, False Bay to southern Mozambique.

Usually caught in surf zone along rocky shores; juveniles common in tide pools. Feeds mainly on red algae, but will also take copepods and other small invertebrates. Adults usually solitary or in small groups; juveniles often in larger shoals. Matures at ~26–30 cm FL (~4 years). Spawns June to January mainly off northern KZN and southern Mozambique.

Despite its vegetarian diet, the stonebream is readily caught on shrimp or redbait and provides good sport on light tackle. Although the flesh is excellent, some folks are put off when they clean the fish by the unpleasant odour from the intestine. Important in shore fishery of KZN. Catch restricted.

FAMILY EPHIPPIDAE ▪ Batfish & Spadefish

Body oval, compressed; head short, forehead steep; head length less than half body depth; dorsal fin continuous with 5, 6 or 9 spines, 19–21 or 29–39 rays; anal fin with 3 spines and 15–17 or 21–30 rays; tail fin truncate or emarginate; pelvic fins longer than pectoral fins, which are shorter than head; mouth small, terminal, with flattened, incisor-like, tricuspid teeth; upper jaw not protrusile; eye well above a line from mouth to upper end of pectoral fin base; preopercle smooth; no spine on opercle; gill membranes broadly joined to isthmus. Size range 20–75 cm.

Found in a variety of shallow water habitats: estuaries, harbours and coral reefs.

A motley assemblage of fish represented in all oceans. Seven genera, ~13 species, 4 in our area.

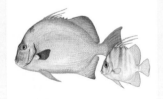

Longfin batfish   Spadefish

LONGFIN BATFISH
Platax teira
(Forsskål 1775)

42 cm adult
18 cm juvenile

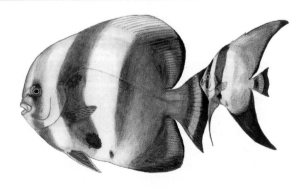

Body depth more than twice head length, 0.9–1.2 times in SL; **dorsal fin 5–6 spines, 29–34 rays**, spines much shorter than front rays; **anal fin with 3 hidden spines, 21–26 rays**; dorsal and anal fin spines hidden in front margin of fins, fins greatly elongated in juveniles; **adults with high, nearly vertical forehead and prominent hump on nape**; teeth tricuspid, lateral cusps nearly as large as middle cusp; 5 sensory pores on each side of lower jaw; body scales minute, rough. Adults with rear half of body grey-brown, front part with broad faint bar; front half of head dark grey, rear half white; **dark blotch usually present on side of belly and faint black streak on body at anal fin origin**; pelvic fins yellow or yellow-brown. Juveniles silvery grey, with dark bar on rear of body, extending into dorsal and anal fins; dark bar at front of body, narrow bar through eye. Attains 65 cm.

Indo-West Pacific, Red Sea, Oman to Knysna.

Juveniles and adults inshore on protected reefs and in mangrove areas; adults also on wrecks and deep reefs to 70 m. *Platax teira* may be solitary, in pairs or in large shoals. Adults often in groups well above the reef,

feeding on zooplankton; also eats algae and benthic invertebrates. Juveniles sometimes in mangrove areas floating on their side, resembling drifting yellow and brownish leaves; sometimes found drifting with *Sargassum* weed or flotsam in open ocean.

Adults on a reef frequented by divers can be easily approached. The flesh has been described as excellent, or rank with a weedy flavour. Long-finned juveniles are valuable in the aquarium trade, but adults need a large tank.

SIMILAR SPECIES

The orbicular batfish, *Platax orbicularis* (Forsskål 1775), has 34–39 dorsal fin rays, 25–30 anal fin rays; adults with more sloping head profile; juveniles (< 10 cm SL) are tan or reddish brown, with irregular black spots and blotches and small white ocelli on body, faint dark band behind head and dark eye band a vertical series of vermiculations. Indo-central Pacific, Oman to Durban.

The dusky batfish, *Platax pinnatus* (Linnaeus 1758), was wrongly included in *Smiths' Sea Fishes* (Smith & Heemstra 1986) as it is known only from the western Pacific Ocean.

SPADEFISH
Tripterodon orbis
Playfair 1867

~ 50 cm adult
12 cm juvenile

Body oval, depth more than twice head length, 1.2–1.4 times in SL; dorsal fin 9 spines, 19–21 rays, 1st spine very short, 3rd to 5th spines elongate (reaching well past last dorsal fin spine in juveniles), last 4 spines about half length of 5th spine and distinctly shorter than anterior soft-rays; anal fin 3 spines, 15–17 rays; anterior dorsal and anal fin rays much longer than posterior rays; 1st pelvic fin ray elongate, reaching past anal fin base in small juveniles; adults with high, nearly vertical forehead; mouth small with thick lips; jaws with ~4 rows of incisors, with 3 brown cusps; swimbladder bifurcate posteriorly; scales small. Adults silvery; juveniles silvery brown with dark bars; snout and lips dark. Attains 75 cm, 9 kg.

Apparently restricted to western Indian Ocean from Zanzibar to Algoa Bay.

Inshore waters, usually on reefs to 30 m. Juveniles taken in beach seines. Generally in loose aggregations over reefs, apparently feeding on zooplankton; also eats fish, bryozoans and other encrusting organisms. Spawns off KZN from March to May.

Adults provide good sport on light tackle. Commonly taken by spearfishermen; not wary of divers. Reasonably good eating.

SIMILAR SPECIES

The concertinafish (see p. 259) has a very protrusile mouth and falcate pectoral fins much longer than head, reaching anal fin base.

FAMILY MONODACTYLIDAE ■ Moonies

Body oval, compressed, covered with small scales extending onto median fins and head; dorsal and anal fin spines mostly covered by skin and scales; pectoral fin rays 16–18, fins shorter than head; small pelvic fins of juveniles become rudimentary or absent in adults; mouth small, oblique; upper jaw slightly protrusile, maxilla mostly exposed when mouth is closed; jaws with bands of tiny flattened or conical teeth; preopercle and opercle smooth; gill membranes separate, free from isthmus. Size range 20–25 cm.

Moonies are at home in freshwater or salt water; large shoals occur in estuaries and over shallow reefs. Feed mainly on zooplankton, which they pick individually from the water, hence their preference for clear water estuaries; also forage at the bottom for small epibenthic crustaceans (mysids, amphipods, isopods) and filamentous algae.

Indo-Pacific and also 1 species in the eastern Atlantic. Two or 3 genera and 5–6 species, 2 in our area.

Round moony

Oval moony

ROUND MOONY
Monodactylus argenteus
(Linnaeus 1758)

~ 15 cm adult
7 cm juvenile

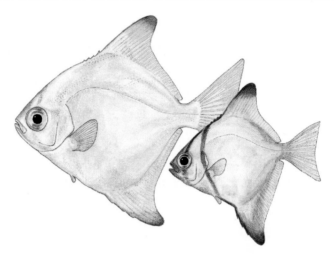

Body depth 1.2–1.6 times in SL; dorsal fin 8 spines, 27–30 rays; anal fin 3 spines, 27–30 rays; maxilla width subequal to preorbital depth (distance from edge of eye to maxilla) and 3.4–5.0 times in eye diameter; teeth flattened, tricuspid, middle cusp much longer than other cusps; gill rakers 8 / 18–22. **Adults silvery**; front lobes of dorsal and anal fins yellow, dusky yellow or blackish; **juveniles dusky silver with 2 dark stripes across head**. Attains 25 cm.

Widely distributed in Indo-West Pacific region, Red Sea to Breë River.

Rocky or sandy areas; adults in rivers, estuaries, harbours, as well as in the sea; juveniles common in freshwater or estuaries, usually over seagrass or algae beds. Matures at ~ 15 cm; spawns in the sea.

Readily taken on fly rod, but too small to be of interest to anglers; edible, but flesh softens quickly if left in the sun. Does well in an aquarium; eats almost anything and breeds in captivity.

OVAL MOONY
Monodactylus falciformis
Lacepède 1800

13 cm subadult
5 cm juvenile

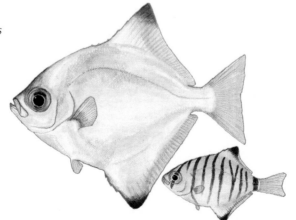

Body depth 1.5–2.0 times in SL; dorsal fin 8 spines, 25–30 rays; anal fin 3 spines, 25–29 rays; maxilla width distinctly greater than distance from edge of eye to maxilla and 2.7–3.7 times in eye diameter; gill rakers 9 / 22–24; teeth slender, slightly curved, needle-like. Adults silvery, with anterior lobes of dorsal and anal fins dusky yellow or blackish; **juveniles dusky silver with 11–12 narrow dark bars**. Attains 25 cm.

Tanzania to Breë River; also reported from Madagascar.

Rocky or sandy areas; adults in rivers, estuaries, harbours, as well as in the sea; juveniles common in freshwater or estuaries, usually over seagrass or algae beds. Matures at ~15 cm; spawns in the sea. More common than round moony along our south coast, and suitable for a cold water aquarium.

FAMILY GERREIDAE ■ Pursemouths

Body oblong-oval, compressed; head length less than body depth; dorsal fin continuous with 9–10 spines, 9–11 rays; anal fin with 3 spines, 7–8 rays; dorsal and anal fins fold into scaly sheath at fin bases; pelvic fins with 1 spine, 5 rays and well developed scaly axillary process; pectoral fins slightly longer than head; **mouth very protrusile, projecting downward when protruded**; teeth small, bristle-like, numerous; none on roof of mouth; scales large, thin, cycloid, more or less deciduous; cheek and opercle scaly; LL scale counts exclude scales on tail fin; preopercle smooth; no spines on opercle; branchiostegal membranes joined to isthmus. Size range 20–37 cm.

Pursemouths occur in clear water estuaries, coastal lagoons, sandy bays and on coral reefs.

Worldwide in tropical and warm temperate waters. Eight genera, ~40 species, 6 in our area.

Longspine pursemouth   Evenfin pursemouth

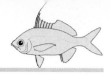

LONGSPINE PURSEMOUTH
Gerres macracanthus
Bleeker 1854

9 cm juvenile
12 cm subadult

Body depth 2.2–2.8 times in SL (for fish 6–17 cm SL); dorsal fin 9 spines, 10 rays; **2nd dorsal fin spine greatly elongate** (33–66% SL), much longer than head and reaching past base of last dorsal fin spine; anal fin rays 7–8; 2nd anal fin spine short, 9–14% SL; pectoral fin rays 15–17; tail fin lobes shorter than head; LL scales 41–44; **4–5 scales from 5th dorsal fin spine to LL. Body silvery, often with 6–10 indistinct dusky bars dorsally**. Attains 20 cm.

Indo-West Pacific, Red Sea to Algoa Bay.

Common in lower reaches of KZN estuaries; adults also in harbours and in the sea; juveniles usually over seagrass or algae beds. Small juveniles feed on estuarine copepods; larger juveniles (2–4 cm SL) eat polychaete worms, siphon tips from the sunset clam *Hiatula lunulata*, and chironomid (insect) larvae; fish larger than 4 cm SL feed mainly on bivalve siphon tips, polychaetes, amphipods and copepods. Feeds by day, and prefers clear water estuaries, as prey is found visually from movement on or just below the sand. Usually encountered in loose groups. Juveniles depend on estuaries as nursery areas.

Employs two different feeding tactics:
- for small benthic invertebrates (mainly worms or crustaceans), rapid protrusion of the mouth with simultaneous expansion of mouth and gill cavities produces a powerful suction that pulls the prey and some sand into the mouth. Most of the sand and other inedible items are separated in the mouth, then passed through the gill rakers and out the gill openings. Protrusion and retraction of the mouth is accomplished in 0.11–0.18 of a second;
- when the fish spots an exposed siphon tip of a buried bivalve, it cautiously approaches until it is within striking distance, the protrusile mouth shoots downwards, and the jaws clamp onto the siphon tip; as the siphon is rapidly contracted, the tip breaks off and provides the fish with a small but nutritious morsel of food. In their study of feeding in gerreid fish, Cyrus and Blaber (1982) found that in nearly all cases where stomachs contained only siphon tips (the most favoured food item in the Kosi system), no sand grains were present. This indicates that siphon nipping is accomplished without the strong suction used to capture small invertebrates. Presumably, the movement of water rushing into the mouth in suction feeding might alert the clam and cause it to retract the siphon before the fish can bite it.

Maturity is attained at ~11 cm SL; spawning occurs in the sea all year long.

Too small to be of much interest to anglers; flesh excellent, but softens quickly if left in sun.

SIMILAR SPECIES

Most recent authors (including Smith & Heemstra 1986) have confused *Gerres macracanthus* with the threadfin pursemouth (*Gerres filamentosus* Cuvier 1829), which is apparently rare in our area. The latter species also has an elongate 2nd dorsal fin spine, and small juveniles have faint dark bars on the body; on fish larger than 10 cm, the bars are replaced by ~10 vertical series of dark oval spots; *G. filamentosus* also has 43–46 LL scales, $4^{1}/_{2}$–$5^{1}/_{2}$ scales from 5th dorsal fin spine to LL, and a longer 2nd anal fin spine (12–20% SL).

In other South African gerreids, the 2nd dorsal fin spine is shorter, not reaching the last dorsal fin spine.

The smallscale pursemouth, *Gerres longirostris* (Lacepède 1801) [formerly identified as *Gerres acinaces* Bleeker 1854], has body depth 2.3–2.8 times in SL, 43–46 LL scales, 5–$6^{1}/_{2}$ scales between 5th dorsal fin spine and LL, tail fin lobes longer than head; tail with black inner margins. Indo-central Pacific, south to Algoa Bay.

The oblong pursemouth, *Gerres oblongus* Cuvier 1830, has slender body (depth 3.0–3.5 times in SL), 45–49 LL scales, pectoral fins subequal to head, not reaching past anus. Tropical Indo-West Pacific, south to Kosi Bay.

The slenderspine pursemouth, *Gerres oyena* (Forsskål 1775), has body depth 2.4–3.0 times in SL, 35–40 LL scales, 3–4 scales from 5th dorsal fin spine to LL, pectoral fins subequal to head, not reaching anus, and uniformly dusky tail fin. Indo-West Pacific, south to Kosi Bay.

EVENFIN PURSEMOUTH
Gerres methueni
Regan 1920

18 cm

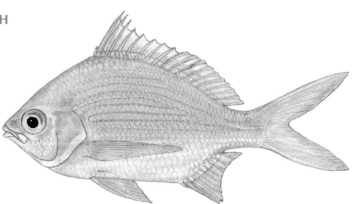

Body depth 2.1–2.3 times in SL; dorsal fin 9 spines, 10 rays, fin margin not notched before soft-rayed part, last 2 dorsal fin spines longer than eye diameter, last spine subequal to 1st soft-ray and more than half 2nd dorsal spine; anal fin falcate, rays 7, 2nd fin spine elongate, 14–18% SL, longer than eye diameter; tail fin lobes equal to pectoral fins and longer than head; pectoral fins reach past anal fin origin; LL scales 42–44; $4^{1}/_{2}$–$5^{1}/_{2}$ scales from 5th dorsal fin spine to LL; preopercle completely scaly. **Body silvery, with dark stripes following scale rows** above LL and on 4 or 5 scale rows below LL; spinous dorsal fin margin black; inner edge of tail fin dusky. Attains 30 cm.

Southwestern Indian Ocean, Algoa Bay to Mozambique and Madagascar.

Freshwater and estuaries. Feeding habits similar to the longspine pursemouth. Females mature at 14 cm SL, males at 11 cm SL. Euryhaline species, but prefers lower salinities (0.5–10‰); although spawning occurs in the sea, juveniles are known only from estuaries.

Gerres rappi (Barnard) is a synonym.

FAMILY DREPANEIDAE ■ Concertinafish (Sicklefish)

Body very deep (depth more than twice head length), rhomboid, strongly compressed and covered with small smooth (finely ctenoid) scales, which extend onto top of head and base of median fins; dorsal fin 8–10 spines (including small procumbent spine, visible only in juveniles), 19–22 rays, fin margin indented before soft-rayed part; anal fin 3 small spines,16–19 rays; **pectoral fins falcate, reaching peduncle and much longer than head**; tail fin rounded or bluntly cuneate in juveniles, almost truncate in adults; pelvic fins small with 1 spine, 5 branched rays and well developed scaly axillary process; **mouth protrusile, projecting downwards**; maxilla exposed when mouth is closed; jaws with bands of villiform teeth; no teeth on roof of mouth; ventral edge of preopercle with weak serrations; no spines on opercle; cheeks scaly, snout and inter-orbital region naked; gill membranes broadly joined to isthmus; swimbladder bifurcate posteriorly, the 2 horns extending posterior to abdominal cavity. Size range 45–50 cm.

Shallow coastal waters, in bays, harbours and estuaries; usually over sand or mud bottom.

Eastern Atlantic and Indo-West Pacific. One genus with 3 species, only one in our area.

CONCERTINAFISH
Drepane longimana
(Bloch & Schneider 1801)

12 cm

Body depth 1.0–1.3 times in SL; head short, forehead steep, head length less than half body depth; dorsal fin rays 19–22; anal fin rays 17–19; pectoral fin rays 16–18; posterior horns of swimbladder with 11 lateral appendages. **Head and body silvery, 4–8 dark bars usually visible** on dorsal part of body; soft dorsal fin with longitudinal series of black spots. Attains 50 cm.

Indo-West Pacific, Red Sea, Oman to East London.

Found in 2–94 m. Feeds on small benthic crustaceans and worms which are sucked off the bottom, along with a good bit of the sediment. Spawns inshore during spring.

Large adults have a bony swelling between the eyes from hyperostosis of frontal bones. Caught with hook and line, traps and in trawls. Flesh edible but not much esteemed. Outside South Africa the species is known as 'sicklefish', in allusion to the long falcate pectoral fins.

SIMILAR SPECIES

The spotted sicklefish, *Drepane punctata* (Linnaeus 1758), known from the Red Sea and Persian Gulf to the central Pacific, has 4–9 vertical series of black spots on the body.

The spadefish (see p. 253) has 3rd–5th dorsal fin spines elongated, mouth not protrusile, teeth small incisors with 3 brown cusps.

FAMILY MULLIDAE ▪ Goatfish

Goatfish are easily recognised by the **2 long barbels on chin and 2 distinctly separate dorsal fins**. Body oblong, slightly compressed, scales large, weakly ctenoid; 1st dorsal fin with 7–8 slender spines (1st spine tiny or hidden under skin), 2nd dorsal fin with 9 rays; anal fin with 1 minute hidden spine, 7–8 rays, 1st ray unbranched; pelvic fins with 1 spine, 5 rays and well developed scaly axillary process at fin base; preopercle smooth; opercle with small flat spine on rear edge. Jaws with band of villiform teeth or 1 row of conical teeth. *Upeneus* species with small teeth on vomer and palatines. Size range 18–53 cm.

Except for species of *Upeneus*, which usually occur on open sand or mud bottom, goatfish are generally found on or near rocky and coral reefs. They feed by day or night, mainly on benthic invertebrates (worms, crustaceans, brittlestars, heart urchins and small molluscs). The barbels are equipped with taste and touch receptors and used to probe the bottom in search of prey. When not in use the barbels are usually tucked away between the two halves of the lower jaw and the lower part of the gill covers. The goldsaddle goatfish, *Parupeneus cyclostomus* (Lacepède 1801), feeds mainly on fish, and this species inserts its long barbels into holes and crevices on the reef to flush out little fish from their refuges. Goatfish are highly prized food-fish in the Mediterranean and many other places where they are fished, but in our region they are of no commercial importance. Goatfish thrive in a large aquarium.

Tropical and warm temperate waters of all oceans. Five genera, ~35 species, 13 in our area.

Yellowstripe goatfish

Dash-dot goatfish

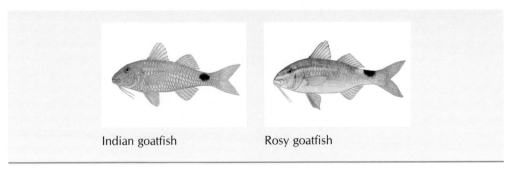

Indian goatfish   Rosy goatfish

YELLOWSTRIPE GOATFISH
Mulloidichthys flavolineatus
(Lacepède 1801)

18 cm

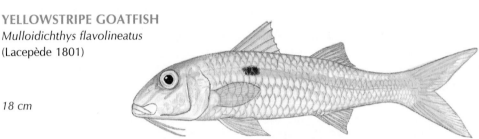

Body depth 3.9–4.6 times, head length 3.0–3.5 times in SL; LL scales 33–35; 4–5 scales between dorsal fins; soft dorsal and anal fins not scaly; jaws with villiform teeth, none on palate; barbel 1.5–1.8 times in head length, slightly shorter than snout plus eye diameter; lower gill rakers 18–22. **Body with 1–2 mid-lateral yellow stripes; usually a black spot on yellow stripe below 1st dorsal fin**; fins whitish, tail fin often yellow. Attains 40 cm (13 years).

Indo-Pacific, Red Sea, Oman to Knysna; rare south of KZN.

Coral reefs and adjacent sandy areas to 60 m. Feeds at night, mainly on polychaetes and small crustaceans on sand flats adjacent to the reef, with the same route from reef to foraging areas followed each evening. Often seen at Sodwana Bay in large shoals hovering above the reef. Tagging studies indicate that adults rarely leave their home range and may occupy a particular reef for several years. Grows to 32 cm FL in first 5 years; and for the next 7 years, the fish's length increases only 2–3 cm.

--- SIMILAR SPECIES ---

The yellowfin goatfish, *Mulloidichthys vanicolensis* (Valenciennes 1831), has yellow mid-lateral stripe, but never has a black spot below 1st dorsal fin; median and pelvic fins yellow; LL scales 35–37; lower gill rakers 20–25. Some yellowfin goatfish have 2–3 blue stripes along the sides and a row of blue spots along upper part of body; this blue-striped form is often seen in schools with the bluebanded snapper (see p. 200). Indo-central Pacific, south to southern KZN.

DASH-DOT GOATFISH
Parupeneus barberinus
(Lacepède 1801)

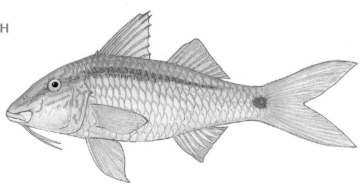

28 cm adult (Comoros)

Body depth 3.3–3.7 times, head length 2.9–3.2 times in SL; 2–3 scales between dorsal fins; soft dorsal and anal fins not scaly; jaws with 1 row of stout conical teeth, none on palate; barbel 1.2–1.5 times in head length, slightly less than snout plus eye diameter; gill rakers 6–7 / 19–25. **Black stripe from front of snout to eye and along LL to below rear end of soft dorsal fin base where it curves up to top of peduncle; oval black blotch on LL at base of tail fin**; fins whitish, anal and pelvic fins often yellowish. Night pattern mostly pale, with irregular reddish-brown spots and blotches. Attains 53 cm.

Indo-central Pacific, Oman to Mossel Bay, rare south of KZN.

Usually on seagrass beds, or sandy and coral rubble areas near reefs. Often in pairs or in small groups foraging along bottom. Diurnal, feeds mainly on crustaceans, especially amphipods, isopods and shrimp.

SIMILAR SPECIES

The longbarbel goatfish, *Parupeneus macronemus* (Lacepède 1801), has a black stripe from eye to peduncle followed by black blotch at base of tail fin, basal part of soft dorsal fin blackish, last ray of dorsal fin extending past tail blotch. Indo-West Pacific, Red Sea, Oman to Sodwana Bay.

The black-barred goatfish, *Parupeneus trifasciatus* (Lacepède 1801), has a black bar below each dorsal fin, sometimes a faint dark bar on the peduncle, and body depth greater than head length. *Parupeneus bifasciatus* (Lacepède) is a synonym. Indian Ocean, Oman to KZN and east to Christmas Island.

INDIAN GOATFISH
Parupeneus indicus
(Shaw 1803)

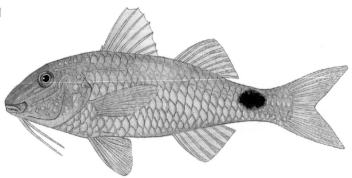

17 cm

Body depth 3.3–3.5 times, head length 3.1–3.3 times in SL; 2–3 scales between dorsal fins; soft dorsal and anal fins not scaly; 1 row of stout conical teeth on jaws, none on palate; barbels reach past preopercle, their length 1.3–1.5 times in head length; lower gill rakers 24–27. **Large oval black blotch on side of peduncle, larger golden blotch on LL above tip of pectoral fin**. Attains 35 cm.

Indo-West Pacific, Oman to Port Alfred.

Seagrass beds and silty sand bottom near reefs. Benthic species, common at Sodwana Bay, seen singly or in small groups. Feeds on crustaceans, octopus, worms and fish.

— SIMILAR SPECIES —

The redspot goatfish, *Parupeneus heptacanthus* (Lacepède 1802), is golden to pink dorsally, with faint longitudinal reddish stripes; dorsal body scales with pale blue spot; dark red spot usually visible below and behind 1st dorsal fin; body depth 3.0–3.4 times in SL; maxilla symmetrically convex; lower gill rakers 23–26. *Parupeneus cinnabarinus* (Cuvier) is a synonym. Indo-West Pacific, Red Sea, Persian Gulf to the Eastern Cape.

ROSY GOATFISH
Parupeneus rubescens
(Lacepède 1801)

27 cm adult

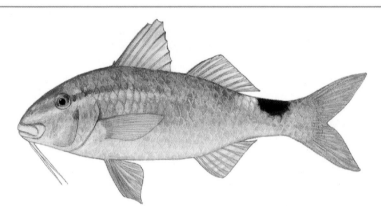

Body depth subequal to head length, 2.9–3.3 times in SL; 2–3 scales between dorsal fins; a row of stout conical teeth on jaws, none on palate; barbels extend past preopercle, their length 1.3–1.5 times in head length; gill rakers 29–32. Colour variable, usually reddish brown dorsally, scale edges darker; sides and ventral part of head and body reddish; a white or blue-edged **dark stripe from front of snout through eye to LL below 1st dorsal fin; black saddle blotch preceded by a white (or pale red) blotch on peduncle**. Attains 42 cm.

Western Indian Ocean, Red Sea, Oman to Cape Agulhas.

Seagrass and silty sand bottom near reefs to 200 m. Benthic species, usually solitary or in pairs, occasionally in small loose groups.

— SIMILAR SPECIES —

The reticulate goatfish, *Parupeneus ciliatus* (Lacepède 1802), known from Seychelles, Mauritius, Rodrigues and Zanzibar, may be found in our area. It has distinct dark edges on the scales (some fish with a red dendritic mark on dorsal body scales) and faint black and white saddle blotches on the peduncle.

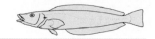

FAMILY MALACANTHIDAE ▪ Tilefish

Body oblong, somewhat compressed or elongate and subcylindrical; **single spine on rear edge of opercle**; tail fin truncate to lunate, with 15 branched rays; pelvic fins with 1 spine, 5 rays and no scaly axillary process at base; **mouth terminal, with villiform teeth and a few small canines; no teeth on palate or tongue**; preopercle serrate or smooth; branchiostegal membranes free from isthmus; branchiostegal rays 6; **scales minute, weakly ctenoid on most of body, cycloid on head**; opercle and cheek scaly.

The postlarvae have distinctive serrated ridges and spines on the head and are large (5–7 cm SL) before transforming to juveniles. JLB Smith (1956a) mistook a postlarval *Malacanthus brevirostris* for a distinct species and named it *Dikellorhynchus incredibilis*.

Subfamily Latilinae (= Branchiosteginae) ▪ Tilefish

Body oblong, somewhat compressed, body depth subequal to head length; **dorsal fin with 4–10 slender spines, 14–27 rays; mid-dorsal dermal ridge or flap of skin on top of head**; preopercle serrate. Size range 35–100 cm.

Generally found along edge of continental shelf or on upper slope region in 50–612 m. Some species are valuable food-fish and comprise an important component of line-caught fish in commercial and sport fisheries of some areas.

Worldwide in temperate and tropical seas. Three genera, ~28 species, 2 in our area.

The ribbed tilefish, *Branchiostegus doliatus* (Cuvier 1830), has dorsal fin with 7 spines, 16 rays; anal fin with 2 spines, 12 rays; body pink dorsally with 16–18 dark bars; dark blotch on operculum. Occurs in 9–600 m. Western Indian Ocean, Maputo to Durban and Mascarene Islands.

Subfamily Malacanthinae ▪ Sand Tilefish (Blanquillos)

Body elongate, cylindrical, slightly compressed near tail; body depth distinctly less than head length; **dorsal fin with 1–10 slender spines, 13–60 rays; no mid-dorsal dermal ridge on head**; preopercle edge smooth or serrate. Size range 30–45 cm.

Shallow water fish that build burrows in sand or rubble areas near reefs.

Tropical and temperate waters of all oceans. Two genera: *Malacanthus* (3 species) and *Hoplolatilus* (9 species); 2 species in our area.

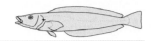

STRIPETAIL TILEFISH
Malacanthus brevirostris
Guichenot 1848

7 cm juvenile
23 cm adult

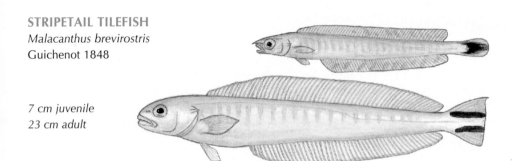

Body depth 6.2–8.3 times in SL; maxilla reaches below front of eye; cheek with 3 curving rows of scales; dorsal fin with 1–4 (usually 2) weak spines, 52–60 rays; anal fin with 1 weak spine, 46–53 rays; pectoral fin rays 15–17. Head and **body yellowish dorsally, pale grey-mauve below**; median fins transparent, but **adult tail fin with 2 black stripes**, one above and one below central bluish white area. Attains 30 cm.

Indo-Pacific, but not in Red Sea or Persian Gulf; Somalia to Aliwal Shoal, postlarvae drift to Mpekweni (near Port Alfred); also at most islands in the Indian Ocean and across the Pacific to Central America and Galapagos Islands.

On open sand or coral rubble bottom near reefs in 6–50 m. Feeds on benthic crustaceans, polychaete worms and small molluscs. Builds a burrow, usually under a rock; often seen in pairs, hovering near the burrow, into which they dive at the approach of danger. Swims with undulating shimmy of the flexible body; hence the name 'quakerfish'; also called 'flagtail blanquillo'.

SIMILAR SPECIES

The sand tilefish (or 'striped blanquillo'), *Malacanthus latovittatus* (Lacepède 1801), attains 40 cm; adult mostly greenish blue (body sometimes white ventrally), with prominent mid-lateral black band from head to tail fin, where it covers most of the fin except for a squarish white blotch on lower corner; juveniles, bicoloured, white dorsally and black below, or white with broad black band from tip of snout to tail. Sand tilefish also build burrows in shallow sand or rubble areas near reefs. Indo-West Pacific, Red Sea to St Lucia. *M. latovittatus* was originally described in the wrasse genus *Labrus*, and it does look more like the ringed wrasse, or the cigar wrasse, than any of the other tilefish. The black and white bicoloured juvenile of *M. latovittatus* is very similar to the bicoloured juvenile of the barred ringwrasse *Hologymnosus annulatus* (Lacepède 1801).

The spot-tail dart goby, *Ptereleotris heteroptera* (Bleeker 1855), is similar in size, shape and colour, but it has a single black spot on a yellow tail fin. Indo-central Pacific, Red Sea, Oman to Sodwana Bay.

FAMILY SILLAGINIDAE ▪ Sillagos (Whitings)

Body elongate, cylindrical, with small deciduous ctenoid scales; **2 dorsal fins, 1st with 11 spines, 2nd dorsal fin with 1 spine, 16–26 rays; anal fin with 2 weak spines, 14–26 rays**; tail fin emarginate; pelvic fins with 1 spine, 5 rays and no scaly axillary process; mouth terminal, **maxilla hidden by preorbital bone when mouth is closed**; small teeth on jaws and vomer, none on palatines or tongue; preopercle edge smooth; a **single sharp spine on rear edge of opercle**; scales present on opercle and cheek, snout naked; gill membranes free from isthmus; swimbladder simple or with elaborate appendages. Size range 15–36 cm.

Sillagos prefer shallow sandy areas in estuaries. Most species are important food-fish in artisanal fisheries. Caught from shore with beach seines, cast nets or hook and line.

Tropical and warm temperate Indo-West Pacific. Three genera, 31 species, 3 in our area.

SILVER SILLAGO
Sillago sihama
(Forsskål 1775)

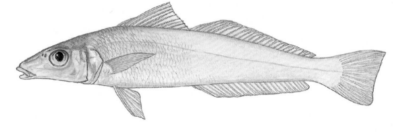

21 cm

Body depth 5.0–6.3 times in SL; **head length 3.3–4.1 times in SL**; soft dorsal fin 1 spine, 20–23 rays; anal fin 2 spines, 21–23 rays; 2–3 rows of cheek scales; swimbladder with anterior, antero-lateral and 2 posterior extensions. **Head and body silvery,** sometimes with a gold tint; **fins transparent**, corners of tail fin dusky. Attains 35 cm.

Indo-West Pacific, Red Sea, Persian Gulf to Knysna, Comoros and Madagascar.

Usually in protected inshore waters on sandy bottom. Adults feed on worms, benthic crustaceans (amphipods, copepods, small crabs and shrimp) and bivalve molluscs; small juveniles (<6 cm SL) feed on zooplankton (mainly copepods); larger juveniles eat benthic crustaceans, worms and bivalve siphon tips. Occurs in large shoals; dives into sand to escape predators or a seine.

Abundant in KZN estuaries. Caught with beach seines, cast nets and on small hooks with light tackle.

SIMILAR SPECIES

The clubfoot sillago, *Sillago chondropus* Bleeker 1849, has 1st ray of pelvic fins thick, bony and curved, and a minute pelvic fin spine joined to 1st ray. Indo-West Pacific, Oman to Durban.

The Indo-West Pacific oriental sillago, *Sillago aeolus* Jordan & Evermann 1902, with dark blotches on body and 17–19 anal fin rays, was previously confused with the trumpeter sillago, *Sillago maculata* Quoy & Gaimard 1824, which is confined to the east coast of Australia. Reported from Maputo.

FAMILY SCIAENIDAE ▪ Kob, Geelbek & Baardman

Body oblong to slightly elongate, somewhat compressed, with moderate cycloid or ctenoid scales; **2 contiguous dorsal fins, the 1st of 9–11 slender spines, 2nd dorsal fin with 1 spine, 22–31 rays; anal fin with 2 spines, 6–9 rays**; tail fin rounded, truncate or concave; pelvic fins with 1 spine, 5 rays and no scaly axillary process; mouth terminal or subterminal, maxilla more or less hidden by preorbital bone when mouth is closed; jaws with small conical teeth; canines present in some species; **no teeth on palate or tongue**; preopercle smooth; 1–2 flat blunt spines on rear edge of opercle; opercle and cheek scaly, snout naked; branchiostegal membranes free from isthmus; swimbladder well developed, carrot-shaped, hammer-shaped or anchor-shaped, and with various diverticula; peduncle length is measured from dorsal fin base to LL scale at tail fin base. Lateral line extends to end of tail fin. Size range 23 cm to 2 m.

Sciaenids generally prefer shallow sandy areas and are often found in estuaries. The larger species are of considerable economic importance as food-fish. Sciaenids are also called 'croakers' or 'drums' because they can produce a variety of sounds by means of muscles that vibrate the gas-filled swimbladder.

Tropical and temperate waters of all oceans. About 70 genera, 100+ species, 11 in our area.

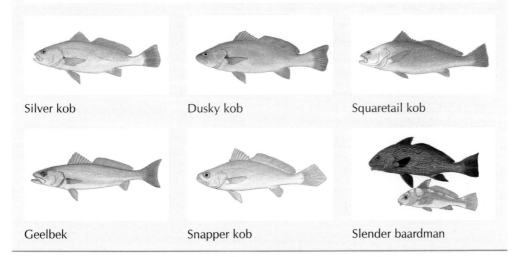

Silver kob   Dusky kob   Squaretail kob

Geelbek   Snapper kob   Slender baardman

SILVER KOB
Argyrosomus inodorus
Griffiths & Heemstra 1995

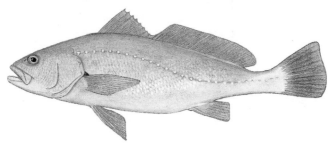

55 cm adult

▶

267

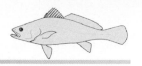

Body depth 3.6–4.2 times in SL; **peduncle length 12–15% SL; peduncle depth 58–74% peduncle length**; inter-orbital width 23–26% head length; pectoral fin 19–23% SL, reaching to or beyond vertical at tip of folded pelvic fin; 2nd dorsal fin 1 spine, 25–29 rays; anal fin rays 7; pectoral fin rays 16–17; gill rakers 4–6 / 10–12; pectoral fin axillary flap (fold of skin at upper end of pectoral fin base) naked; swimbladder appendages 31–42; drumming muscles (along inside of body cavity) only in males; urinary bladders rudimentary. **Head and body silvery**, becoming green/brown with bronze sheen dorsally, white below; inside of mouth pale yellow to yellowish grey; peritoneum white. Attains 1.5 m, 36.3 kg (25 years).

Namibia to Kei River.

Between Cape Agulhas and the Kei River, adults rarely in estuaries or in surf zone; but commonly caught by ski-boat anglers and trawlers in 10–120 m. West of Cape Agulhas, silver kob are more abundant in the surf zone. Juveniles common in soft-bottom bay areas in less than 50 m. Silver kob feed on pelagic fish, shrimp and squid. Females mature at 31–38 cm, males at 29–31 cm. Growth of silver kob from southern Namibia (maximum age 19 years) differed significantly from kob caught in northern Namibia (maximum age 28 years), although the maximum size (105 cm) is the same for kob from both areas. Spawns inshore from False Bay to Kei River during spring and summer.

Highly regarded as a food-fish (mostly sold fresh, sometimes frozen), and is an important commercial and recreational species wherever it occurs. In Namibia, where silver kob is the most important line fish caught by ski-boat and shore anglers, catches have declined markedly in recent years; also over-exploited along our south coast, and the catch is now restricted.

This species was named *inodorus* ('without odour'), as Marc Griffiths (who named the fish) first suspected that it differed from dusky kob when he noticed that it lacked the typical strong brassy/metallic smell of fresh dusky kob. Although the dusky kob differs in several internal characters (large urinary bladders, drumming muscles in both sexes, number and configuration of swimbladder appendages, configuration of the otolith, etc.), silver and dusky kob are difficult to separate on external characters.

SIMILAR SPECIES

The dusky kob has a shorter deeper peduncle, shorter pectoral fin (tip of fin not reaching vertical at tip of folded pelvic fin); it also attains a larger size than silver kob.

The squaretail kob (see p. 270) has the pectoral fin axillary flap scaly, 25–33 swimbladder appendages and large urinary bladders.

The west coast kob, *Argyrosomus coronus* Griffiths & Heemstra 1995 (known from Angola and Namibia, occasionally to St Helena Bay), has a longer, more pointed snout; shorter, deeper peduncle (peduncle length 10–12% SL; peduncle depth 76–94% peduncle length), 8–10 lower gill rakers, large urinary bladders, and drumming muscles in both sexes. Attains 70 cm.

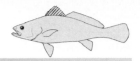

DUSKY KOB

Argyrosomus japonicus
(Temminck & Schlegel
1843)

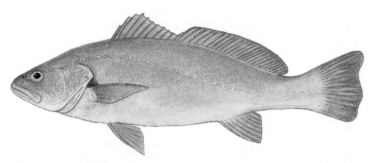

54 cm juvenile

Body depth 3.3–4.0 times in SL; **peduncle length 11–13% SL; peduncle depth 70–92% peduncle length**; inter-orbital width 21–24% head length; suborbital width 8.4–10.5% head length; pectoral fin 17–21% SL, usually not reaching vertical line at tip of pelvic fins; 2nd dorsal fin 1 spine, 25–30 rays; anal fin rays 7; pectoral fin rays 15–17; tail fin shape changes with growth; gill rakers 4–5 / 9–12; pectoral fin axillary flap naked; swimbladder appendages 21–31; drumming muscles (along inside of body cavity) present in both sexes; urinary bladders large. Head and body of juveniles silvery, becoming darker dorsally, paler below; live fish with a pearly sheen on head, flanks and dorsal part of body; adults golden brown, the dorsal and tail fins brownish, becoming darker with age; pectoral and anal fins white in 5–10 cm kob, becoming yellow and finally grey or grey-brown in kob >35 cm; inside of mouth white in juveniles, becoming yellow in large adults; peritoneum white; pectoral fin axillary flap grey to black. Underwater the fish usually shows a series of bright silver spots along the LL. Attains 1.8 m, 75 kg (42 years).

False Bay to southern Mozambique; also known from Oman, Pakistan, India, south coast of Australia, Hong Kong to Korea and Japan (the type locality).

Common in turbid estuaries and surf zone; also over rocky reefs and wrecks associated with sand to depths of 120 m. Small juveniles (3–15 cm) restricted to estuaries; larger juveniles (15–19 cm) occur in estuaries and the surf zone. Adults feed on fish, shrimp and squid; small juveniles (<5 cm) consume copepods and mysid shrimp. Juveniles larger than 25 cm and adults occur in estuaries, but most of the time they forage in the surf zone where they feed mainly on fish. Females mature at ~1.1 m (6 years), males at 92 cm to 1 m (5 years). Spawns on inshore reefs at night. Along the KZN coast, spawning occurs from August to November, and includes many migrants from the Eastern and Western Cape. Some reproductive activity also occurs from October to January along the Eastern and Western Cape coasts.

The dusky kob ('daga salmon' in KZN) is the most important angling resource of the inshore environment (estuaries and surf zone) from Cape Agulhas to Durban. Commercial boat anglers catch ~200 tonnes/year. Recreational anglers often target this species and are believed to catch at least as much and possibly more than commercial fishermen. Catches have declined markedly in recent years, and catch is now restricted.

In Australia, dusky kob (a.k.a. 'mulloway' or 'jewfish') is also an important commercial and recreational angling species. It is caught with hook and line, gill-nets, seines and trawls.

IGFA all-tackle record: 66.8 kg fish caught in the Sundays River estuary near Port Elizabeth. SA angling record: 73.5 kg.

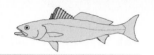

See above for distinction from silver kob.

The squaretail kob has a black pectoral fin axillary flap covered with scales, longer peduncle, longer pectoral fins, and wider distance from lower edge of eye to rear end of maxilla.

SQUARETAIL KOB
Argyrosomus thorpei
Smith 1977

~ 40 cm adult

Body depth 3.3–4.2 times in SL; **peduncle length 12–14% SL; peduncle depth 65–79% peduncle length**; inter-orbital width 19–24% head length; suborbital width 10–12% head length; pectoral fin length 20–23% SL, reaching past vertical at tip of pelvic fins; 2nd dorsal fin 1 spine, 26–28 rays; anal fin rays 7; pectoral fin rays 15–17; **tail fin S-shaped or occasionally truncate in adults**; pectoral axillary flap scaly; swimbladder appendages 25–33; drumming muscles (along inside of body cavity) in both sexes; urinary bladders large. **Head and body silvery, darker (blue with coppery sheen) dorsally, paler below; fins yellow-grey to orange-brown, occasionally reddish**; pectoral axillary flap black; inside of mouth pale yellow; inner side of operculum dusky yellow to black; peritoneum and ventral surface of swimbladder dusky. Attains 1.2 m (14 years).

Endemic from Algoa Bay to Xai-Xai; rare south of KZN.

Adults over rocky reefs and wrecks on sand to depths of 80 m. Juveniles on soft bottom in 15–50 m, common on Thukela Bank, and sometimes caught in estuaries. Non-migratory, shoaling species. Matures at ~33 cm (2 years). Spawns from June to September off KZN.

Squaretail kob was an important angling species in KZN, but catches declined drastically after 1990, and the stock has now collapsed. Catch restricted. SADSAA all-tackle record: 17 kg.

GEELBEK
Atractoscion aequidens
(Cuvier 1830)

1.1 m adult

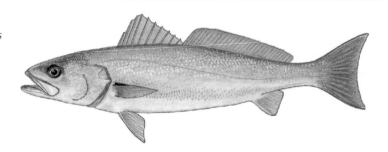

Body depth less than head length, 3.8–4.3 times in SL; **tail fin concave, upper and lower rays distinctly longer than middle rays**; mouth large, terminal, lower jaw projecting; no pores on chin; 2nd dorsal fin with 1 spine, 27–31 rays; anal fin rays 8–9; pectoral and pelvic fins shorter than head, 16–20% SL; pectoral axillary flap scaly; gill rakers short, becoming rudimentary with age. Body silvery with coppery sheen dorsally, white below; pectoral fin axillary flap black; **inside of mouth and gill cavity yellow**. Attains 1.3 m, 25 kg (9 years).

Gulf of Guinea to Angola; False Bay to southern Mozambique; also reported from northwestern Africa and Australia.

Adults over sandy bottom, rocky reefs and near wrecks or pinnacles in 15–150 m; juveniles occasionally in estuaries. Primarily piscivorous, feeding mainly on pilchards, maasbanker and mackerel, but will also take squid when it is abundant. Shoaling species, vulnerable to overfishing when spawning aggregations are targeted. Matures at 90 cm FL (5 years). Adults migrate from the Western and Eastern Cape coasts to KZN, where they spawn in the spring.

Highly-prized eating fish. IGFA all-tackle record: 14.9 kg geelbek caught in Algoa Bay. The dramatic decline in recent geelbek catches indicates that the stock has collapsed. Catch restricted. Sometimes referred to as 'Cape salmon'. Valuable commercial and sport fish in Australia, where it is called 'teraglin'.

SIMILAR SPECIES

The distinctive concave tail fin distinguishes geelbek from other sciaenid fish in our area.

SNAPPER KOB
Otolithes ruber
(Bloch & Schneider 1801)

19 cm juvenile

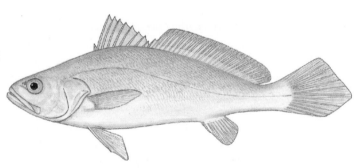

Body depth less than head length, 4.2–5.1 times in SL; **tail fin rounded or bluntly pointed, the middle rays longest**; mouth large, terminal, **lower jaw projecting, pair of large canines at front of both jaws**; no pores on chin; 2nd dorsal fin 1 spine, 27–30 rays; anal fin rays 7–8; pectoral and pelvic fins shorter than head, 16–20% SL; swimbladder with 30–37 paired appendages. Body silvery bronze with coppery or pearly sheen dorsally, white below; fins dusky yellow; pectoral fin axillary flap white. Attains 50 cm, 1.6 kg (7 years).

Indo-West Pacific, mainly continental; Oman to Algoa Bay.

Adults and juveniles over silty sand bottom from shore to 100 m; adults and juveniles common in large turbid estuaries. In estuaries, snapper kob feed mainly on clupeids and anchovies, but in the sea, they also eat squid and shrimp. Matures at ~24 cm (1–2 years). Spawns on Thukela Bank from August to January and in Algoa Bay from September to February; also on Sofala Bank south of Beira. Shoaling species of protected bays.

Excellent eating, caught by trawlers, beach seines and hook and line. Not much exploited because of their relatively small size, but off Durban, snapper kob are targeted by paddle-ski anglers. Also called 'long-tooth kob' or 'tiger-tooth croaker'.

─ **SIMILAR SPECIES** ─

The enlarged canines at front of jaws and the absence of pores on the chin will separate the snapper kob from other sciaenids in our area.

SLENDER BAARDMAN
Umbrina robinsoni
Gilchrist & Thompson
1908

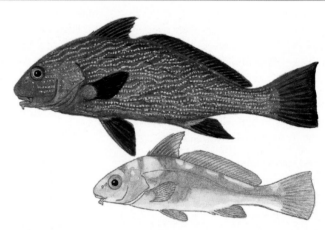

54 cm adult
~ 13 cm juvenile

Body depth subequal to head length, 2.8–3.9 times in SL; 2nd dorsal fin rays 22–27; **pectoral fin length 15–21% SL**; peduncle length (from rear end of anal fin base to middle of tail fin base) 26–34% SL; snout length 27–38% head length; eye diameter 1.3–2.5 times in snout length for fish >15 cm; swimbladder without appendages; chin barbel short, thick, tubular, with a pore at its tip. Adults can change from dark brown to silvery in a few seconds; **narrow wavy oblique white lines on body, less distinct with growth**; inside of gill cover pale. Attains at least 99 cm, 13 kg.

Western Indian Ocean, Oman to Cape Point and Madagascar.

Adults and juveniles on sand and reefs to 130 m (seen on videos in coelacanth habitat at Sodwana Bay); often in or near caves and ledges; juveniles 10–20 cm usually in mixed rock and sand surf zones; adults in groups along sandy beaches, in mixed sand and rock surf zones and over subtidal reefs; small juveniles occasionally in tide pools. Matures at ~35–40 cm, and spawns from November to January in the Western and Eastern Cape. In the warmer KZN waters, slender baardman mature at 45–50 cm and spawn all year round. Spawning occurs throughout the range, with no apparent spawning migrations or aggregations. Tagging studies indicate limited movement and small home ranges with a high degree of residency.

Excellent eating; caught by beach seines and hook and line. In *Smiths' Sea Fishes* (Smith & Heemstra 1986), the name *Umbrina ronchus* Valenciennes 1843 was used for the slender baardman. Recent research has shown that *Umbrina ronchus* is confined to the western Mediterranean, northeastern Atlantic, Canary Islands and west coast of Africa to Angola (Ken Hutchings and Marc Griffiths, pers. comm.).

The baardman, *Umbrina canariensis* Valenciennes 1843, has body depth greater than head length, 2.5–3.0 times in SL; 2nd dorsal fin rays 24–30, pectoral fin length 20–25% SL, equal to or longer than pelvic fin; peduncle short, 21–28% SL; snout short, 23–32% head length, subequal to eye diameter. Juveniles silvery, with 7–8 longitudinal wavy dark bands from head to soft dorsal fin; margins of median and pelvic fins blackish. Attains 42 cm; matures at 20–25 cm; spawns August to February. The baardman is an offshore species caught mainly with trawls in 40–300 m. Western Mediterranean and northeastern Atlantic to Canary Islands, southern Angola, and possibly northern Namibia. In our area baardman are most common from Cape Agulhas to East London; rarely caught off the KZN coast. Also reported from Oman and Pakistan.

The bellfish, *Johnius fuscolineatus* (von Bonde 1923), has a pore at the base of the chin barbel (pore is at tip of chin barbel in species of *Umbrina*) and 3–5 / 7–10 gill rakers. Southwestern Indian Ocean, Mozambique to KZN and Madagascar.

FAMILY MENIDAE ▪ Moonfish

Body disc-like, extremely compressed; scales tiny, barely visible, deciduous, none on head; 1 dorsal fin with 3–4 rudimentary spines (lost with age) and 40–45 rays; anal fin with 30–33 very short embedded rays, only their weakly branched tips visible; pectoral fins shorter than head; pelvic fins with 1 spine, 5 rays, the first 2 rays thickened, fused and greatly elongated; mouth oblique, protrusile; jaws with band of villiform teeth; no teeth on palate or tongue; preopercle smooth; no spine on opercle.

Inshore waters, usually over soft bottom in protected bays and estuaries. A single species.

MOONFISH
Mene maculata
(Bloch & Schneider 1801)

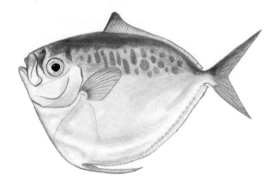

22 cm adult (Bali)

Head and body **silvery**, dorsal parts bluish green, **with 3–4 irregular rows of dark spots**. Attains 25 cm.

Continental Indo-West Pacific, Red Sea, Oman to Durban.

Juveniles feed on zooplankton (mainly copepods); adults eat small benthic crustaceans (mainly shrimp). A shoaling species. Readily dries in air without salt; used in India and other Asian countries for food.

Some ponyfish (Family Leiognathidae) are superficially similar, but the body is less deep and not as compressed, dorsal and anal fin spines are well developed, and the pelvic fin rays are not elongated.

FAMILY LEIOGNATHIDAE ▪ Ponyfish (Soapies)

Body oblong to elongate, compressed and slimy; scales small, thin, easily shed; dorsal fin single with 7–9 spines, 14–17 rays; anal fin with 3 spines, 13–15 rays; **anterior dorsal and anal fin spines can be locked in an erect position**; row of small retrorse spines and scaly sheath along base of dorsal and anal fins; pelvic fins small with 1 spine, 5 rays; **mouth small, very protrusile**, forming a tube when protruded; teeth villiform, except *Gazza* species which have a row of canines in jaws; no teeth on palate; lower preopercle edge serrate; opercle ends in a blunt flat point; 3 bony ridges on top of head, joining median bony ridge on nape. Branchiostegal rays 4–5, membranes united to isthmus; no pseudobranch. Size range 10–25 cm.

Ponyfish school over soft bottom in shallow water and are common in estuaries. As they are easily dried (without salt) in the hot tropical sun, ponyfish are an important source of protein for inland populations in the tropics. They also make excellent bait. Caught with seines, trawls, gill-nets, throw nets, fish traps and hook and line; marketed dried or fresh. Ponyfish (so-called for the horse-like snout) are also known as 'soapies' or 'slimies' for the copious mucus exuded when they are caught.

Another unusual feature of ponyfish is the internal light organ around the oesophagus. The light is restricted by an opaque membrane to two window-like areas. Light from the ventral window shines through translucent muscles of the chest and isthmus; light from the dorsal window is reflected through abdominal muscles via the swimbladder. The effect of this bioluminescence is a mottled illumination that obscures the fish's shape against the mottled background of their habitat. This disruptive illumination is most effective at twilight, when predation by piscivorous fish is most intense.

Tropical and subtropical Indo-West Pacific region; *Leiognathus klunzingeri* has entered the Mediterranean from the Red Sea. Three genera, ~25 species, 6 occur in our area.

Toothed ponyfish

Common ponyfish

TOOTHED PONYFISH
Gazza minuta
(Bloch 1795)

11 cm

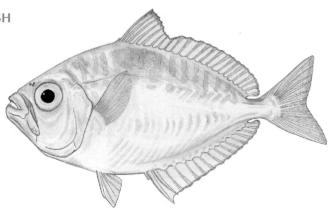

Body depth longer than head length, 2.1–3.3 times in SL; **mouth pointing forwards when protruded**, with a row of minute canines in jaws and a pair of **enlarged canines at front of upper jaw**; pectoral fin rays 16–18; gill rakers 4–6 / 16–18; no scales on head or lower part of body in front of line from pectoral fin base to base of pelvic fin spine; scales on body above LL extend anterior to 1st LL scale; bony ridge above eye serrate. **Head and body silvery, bluish grey dorsally, with dark orange-yellow to grey markings**; edge of dorsal fin blackish, anal and tail fins yellowish. Attains 18 cm.

Indo-central Pacific, Red Sea to Port Alfred.

Feeds on benthic crustaceans, polychaete worms and fish. Spawns in offshore waters.

Caught with beach seines and trawls to 40 m; mainly used as bait in South Africa.

SIMILAR SPECIES

Other ponyfish have minute teeth that are barely visible without a magnifying glass.

The scalybelly ponyfish, *Gazza squamiventralis* Yamashita & Kimura 2001 (known from Kenya and Maputo Bay), was confused with *G. minuta*, but differs in having scales extending anterior to a line from the pectoral fin base to the base of the pelvic fin spine, and a smooth bony ridge over the eye.

COMMON PONYFISH
Leiognathus equula
(Forsskål 1775)

15 cm

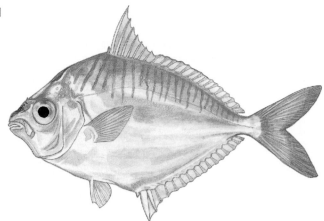

Body depth greater than head length, 1.6–2.1 times in SL; mouth horizontal when closed, projects downwards when protruded; jaws with band of slender villiform teeth. Head and body silvery; with several faint bars above LL; dorsal surface of peduncle brown; rear margin of tail fin dusky; anal and paired fins hyaline yellow. Attains 25 cm.

Indo-West Pacific, Red Sea to Great Fish River.

Adults over soft bottom from shore to 40 m. Juveniles use estuaries as nursery areas, where they feed on planktonic crustaceans. Adults feed on benthic crustaceans, polychaete worms and bivalve molluscs. Matures at ~15 cm; spawns in sea near river mouths along KZN coast from October to March.

This largest ponyfish is used mainly for bait in South Africa. Juveniles eaten by a variety of predators.

The species name is often incorrectly spelt *equulus*, but Forsskål chose the feminine Latin noun *equula* (meaning filly) for this ponyfish; hence it does not change its ending when shifted to another genus.

── **SIMILAR SPECIES** ────────

As implied by its name, the elongate ponyfish, *Leiognathus elongatus* (Günther 1874), is more elongate (body depth 3.3–4.6 times in SL); Indo-West Pacific, south to Maputo.

The slender ponyfish, *Secutor insidiator* (Bloch 1787), with no scales on cheeks, and the pugnose ponyfish, *Secutor ruconius* (Hamilton 1822), with scaly cheeks, have an upturned snout (dorsal head profile distinctly concave above eye) and an oblique mouth directed slightly upwards when protruded. These Indo-West Pacific species occur south to the Eastern Cape.

FAMILY LOBOTIDAE ▪ Tripletails

Body robust, slightly compressed, depth greater than head length; 1 continuous dorsal fin with 11–13 strong spines, 13–16 rays; anal fin with 3 spines, 9–12 rays; soft dorsal and anal fins large and broadly rounded, reaching past base of tail fin, so that (with the tail fin) the fish appears to have 3 tails; pectoral fins smaller than pelvic fins; scales ctenoid, covering head except preorbital region and jaws; upper jaw slightly protrusile; no supramaxilla; jaws with outer row of short, closely-set canines, and inner band of much smaller teeth; palate and tongue toothless; preopercle coarsely serrate in young, the serrations smaller but more numerous with growth; rear edge of opercle with 1–2 flat spines; nostrils round, close together; branchiostegal rays 6, membranes narrowly united, free from isthmus.

Juveniles and adults at home in estuaries or in the sea; sometimes far out in the open ocean, usually near the surface and associated with floating objects (logs, seaweed, etc.).

Tropical and warm temperate waters of all oceans. Two species, one in our area.

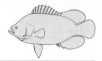

TRIPLETAIL
Lobotes surinamensis
(Bloch 1790)

63 cm adult (Japan)
4 cm juvenile
(Indonesia)

Body robust; eye small, its diameter equal to inter-orbital width in small juveniles, and less than half inter-orbital width in adults; snout short, its length about 5 times in head length and about half length of upper jaw; LL scales 42–46; gill rakers 6–7 / 13–15; soft dorsal, anal and tail fins covered with scales. **Adult dark brown or greenish yellow dorsally, grey below**; pectoral fins pale yellow; other fins darker than body; tail fin sometimes with yellow margin. Attains 1 m, 20 kg.

Atlantic, Indian and west-central Pacific Oceans, Plettenberg Bay to Mozambique.

Solitary species with broad spectrum of prey, including benthic crustaceans (mainly crabs and prawns) and a variety of fish. Spawns in summer. Small juveniles common in mangrove areas, where their black and yellow colouration and habit of floating on their sides makes them look like a floating mangrove leaf.

Highly-prized table fish, strong-fighting sport fish. IGFA all-tackle record: 19.2 kg from KZN.

SIMILAR SPECIES

Some rockcods are superficially similar (e.g. the redmouth rockcod, *Aethaloperca rogaa* [Forsskål 1775], the tomato rockcod, *Cephalopholis sonnerati* [Valenciennes 1828], or the brindlebass [see p. 167]) but they have much smaller scales, dorsal and anal fins do not reach past a vertical at tail fin base, and rear edge of opercle bears 3 flat points.

FAMILY POMACANTHIDAE ▪ Angelfish & Cherubfish

Body deep, oblong or disc-like, compressed; body depth distinctly greater than head length; 1 continuous dorsal fin with 11–15 strong spines, 15–25 rays; anal fin with 3 spines, 16–23 rays; soft dorsal and anal fins large, reaching to or beyond base of tail fin; pectoral fins with 16–21 rays, not longer than head; scales moderate to small, spinoid, the exposed portions with longitudinal ridges ending in sharp points; scales covering head, body and median fins; LL inconspicuous; mouth small, with small slender teeth; **adults of most species with enlarged spine at lower corner of preopercle**; nostrils minute, round, close together. Size range 8–46 cm.

Angelfish are among the most beautiful of all coral reef fish; juveniles of some species look very different from the adults. Adults of the larger species (genera *Pomacanthus* and *Apolemichthys*) usually occur near the bottom, singly or in pairs; they feed mainly on sponges, tunicates, zooantharians, bryozoans, soft corals, fish and invertebrate eggs, hydroids, algae and seagrass. The diminutive *Centropyge* species feed on benthic algae and detritus; some species feed in midwater on zooplankton, but will also take sponges, bryozoans, worms and algae. Angelfish are active by day and retreat to hiding places in the reef at night. Some species of *Centropyge* and *Genicanthus* are protogynous hermaphrodites, with a harem reproductive mode in which the largest fish is a male that spawns daily (when the water is warm enough) with each of the smaller females. If the male is taken by a predator, the largest female changes sex to take his place. Unlike other angelfish, the species of *Genicanthus* show marked sexual dichromatism, with males being decidedly more colourful than the females.

Although hybrids are rare in marine fish, they occur more often in angelfish than in other families. Some hybrids were described as distinct species (e.g. *Apolemichthys armitagei* Smith 1955, which appears to be a hybrid of *Apolemichthys trimaculatus* and *Apolemichthys xanthurus*).

Tropical and subtropical waters of all oceans. Seven genera and ~83 species, 12 in our area.

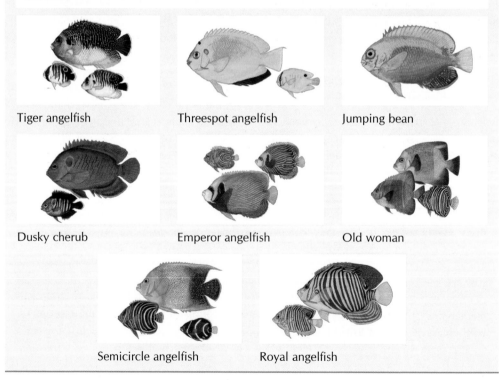

Tiger angelfish   Threespot angelfish   Jumping bean

Dusky cherub   Emperor angelfish   Old woman

Semicircle angelfish   Royal angelfish

TIGER ANGELFISH
Apolemichthys kingi
Heemstra 1984

21 cm adult
2 cm juvenile
5 cm juvenile

Rear end of dorsal and anal fins angular in adult; tail fin rounded; dorsal fin spines 15. Adult bicoloured, **upper part of body and tail fin brown to black, with wavy vertical yellow lines; head and lower part of body pale; large black spot at upper end of gill opening**; edge of dorsal fin and upper rear edge of tail fin white. Small juvenile (25 mm) resembles a butterflyfish, with curved black band from nape, through eye to pelvic fin origin; 5–6 black bars on body, gold ring at base of anterior dorsal fin rays. Attains 25 cm.

Endemic, adults known from southern Mozambique to Margate; a juvenile has been found at East London.

Coral reefs; usually in 20–40 m, occasionally shallower to 14 m. Solitary; juveniles cryptic and rarely seen.

The species was named for Dennis King, who first noticed this species and who (with the assistance of Peter van Niekerk) was instrumental in capturing the first specimens.

Unlikely to be confused with other species.

THREESPOT ANGELFISH
Apolemichthys trimaculatus
(Cuvier 1831)

16 cm adult
4 cm juvenile (Mauritius)

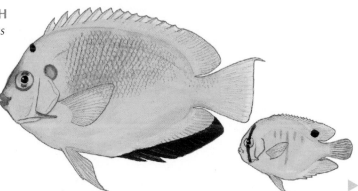

Tail fin rounded; dorsal fin spines 14. **Adult mainly yellow, with median black spot on nape and large dark spot on each side of head** behind upper end of gill opening; these latter 2 spots often faint or absent; basal part of anal fin white, the outer half black; lips dark blue; preopercle spine pale blue. Juveniles (2–4 cm) with small black spot at base of middle dorsal fin rays and black bar from nape through eye to lower edge of cheek. Attains 25 cm.

Indo-West Pacific, Kenya to Aliwal Shoal, rarely to Port St Johns.

Outer coral reefs in 8–60 m. Solitary, in pairs or in small groups. May live 24 years (in captivity), but are difficult to keep.

The name *trimaculatus* refers to the 3 spots on the head.

JUMPING BEAN
Centropyge acanthops
(Norman 1922)

5 cm (Comoros)

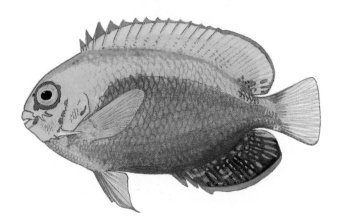

Tail fin rounded; dorsal fin with 14 spines, 16–17 rays; lower edge of head (subopercle, and interopercle and preorbital bones) spiny. **Anal fin and most of body dark blue; head, chest, dorsal fin and upper part of body yellow-orange**; tail fin yellow; blue ring around eye. Juvenile colours similar to adult. Attains 8 cm.

Western Indian Ocean, Oman to Algoa Bay and all islands.

In tide pools, on coral reefs and among coral rubble; usually in 8–40 m. Feeds mainly on algae; usually solitary; protandrous hermaphrodite (changes sex from male to female).

Popular aquarium fish that may live 8 years; a.k.a. 'African pygmy angelfish' or 'African cherubfish'.

DUSKY CHERUB
Centropyge multispinis
(Playfair 1867)

11 cm adult
3 cm juvenile

Tail fin rounded, fitting snugly between the rounded dorsal and anal fins; dorsal fin 14 spines, 15–17 rays; front of snout with U-shaped notch over upper jaw; lower edge of head (subopercle, interopercle and preorbital bones) spiny. **Body and fins dark brown, with black blotch behind upper end of gill opening and narrow dark bars on sides**; edges of median and pelvic fins blue; pectoral fins transparent with dark rays. Juveniles (2–3 cm) pale brown with 4 dark bars on body, some bars bifurcate. Attains 15 cm.

Indo-West Pacific, Red Sea, Oman to Aliwal Shoal; common at Sodwana Bay, juveniles occasionally to Port Alfred.

Tide pools, coral reefs and coral rubble in 1–40 m. Solitary or in small groups when feeding on algae; often hiding under ledges.

Does well in an aquarium. Named *multispinis* for the numerous spines on cheek, hence the alternate name 'many-spine cherubfish'.

--- SIMILAR SPECIES

The coral beauty, *Centropyge bispinosa* (Günther 1860), has head and median fins violet to dark brown or black, central part of body mostly orange to orange-brown, with irregular narrow dark bars; no black blotch behind upper gill opening. Indo-central Pacific, south to Sodwana Bay.

EMPEROR ANGELFISH
Pomacanthus imperator
(Bloch 1787)

6 cm juvenile (Mauritius)
12 cm subadult (Comoros)
32 cm adult

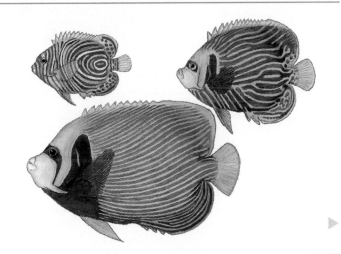

Dorsal, anal and tail fins rounded; dorsal fin 14 spines, 19–21 rays; anal fin rays 19–20; preopercle spine well developed. **Adult with alternating yellow and blue stripes on body; blue-edged dark mask over eyes**; chest and rear of head black; cheek, snout and mouth pale; tail fin yellow; anal fin dark brown with parallel curving blue lines. **Juveniles less than ~ 14 cm with blue and white stripes on head and body, forming concentric circles posteriorly**. Attains ~ 40 cm.

Indo-Pacific, Red Sea to Park Rynie, juveniles occasionally at East London in tide pools.

Adults solitary or in pairs on outer coral reefs near caves and ledges in 2–70 m. Territorial; adult emperor angelfish that enter their territory are attacked, but juveniles with a very different colour pattern are tolerated. Juveniles start changing to adult colouration at ~ 14 cm.

Juveniles can be kept in a large aquarium, but adults do not adapt well to captivity; a 29 cm SL aquarium fish was 16 years old.

─ SIMILAR SPECIES ────────────────

The goldtail angelfish, *Pomacanthus chrysurus* (Cuvier 1831), which is rare in our area, has head, body and fins dark brown, with 5–6 narrow curved white bars on body, blue lines on head, yellow circle behind upper end of gill opening and yellow tail fin; juveniles with curved white stripes on body, the tail fin yellow. Western Indian Ocean, Gulf of Aden to KZN.

OLD WOMAN
Pomacanthus rhomboides
(Gilchrist & Thompson 1908)

43 cm adult
14 cm subadult
7 cm juvenile

Adult with truncate tail and angular dorsal and anal fins; large adults develop a pronounced hump on the nape; spine at corner of preopercle small. **Adults drab**, brownish, with rear edges of scales black; **rear third of body pale bluish grey**. Head and body of juveniles dark, with pale yellow or bluish white slightly curved vertical stripes, alternating with pale blue lines; tail clear or dusky with pale spots. Attains 46 cm.

Southwestern Indian Ocean, Tanzania to South Africa; adults common from Maputo to Margate, juveniles found at Knysna during summer.

Coral and rocky reefs in 5–40 m. Adults usually in groups feeding on plankton well above reef, but they will also feed on sponges and algae on the bottom; juveniles solitary, often found in tide pools.

Previously known as *Pomacanthus striatus* (Rüppell 1836) but Rüppell's species is a synonym of *Pomacanthus maculosus* (Forsskål) of the Red Sea and northwestern Indian Ocean.

SEMICIRCLE ANGELFISH
Pomacanthus semicirculatus
(Cuvier 1831)

39 cm adult
9 cm juvenile
2 cm juvenile

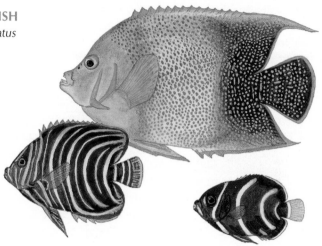

Tail fin rounded; **rear end of dorsal and anal fins pointed in adults**; dorsal fin 13 spines, 21–23 rays; anal fin rays 20–22; preopercle spine well developed. **Adults greyish yellow with numerous blue spots; median fins dark with pale spots, rear edge blue with submarginal black stripe. Juveniles dark, with semicircular alternating blue and white stripes on body, head and tail**. Attains ~40 cm.

Indo-Pacific, Red Sea, Oman to Margate; common at Sodwana Bay, juveniles occasionally reach Algoa Bay.

Adults and juveniles on wrecks or coral reefs near caves and ledges in 1–40 m. Juvenile pattern starts to change to that of adult at 8–16 cm.

Adults solitary. Popular aquarium fish, but not easy to keep.

ROYAL ANGELFISH
Pygoplites diacanthus
(Boddaert 1772)

25 cm adult
14 cm juvenile
(Comoros)

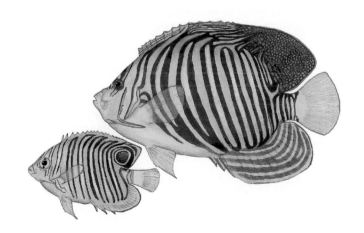

Tail fin rounded; rear end of dorsal and anal fins also rounded in adults; dorsal fin 14 spines, 18–19 rays; anal fin rays 18–19; preopercle spine well developed. Body of **adult yellow, with alternating yellow and white (or blue) bands**; anal fin with blue and yellow stripes parallel to margin; head yellow with blue lines; rear end of dorsal fin blue; tail fin yellow or greenish yellow. Juveniles with fewer bands, dark ocellus on soft dorsal fin. Attains 25 cm (17 years in captivity).

Indo-central Pacific, Red Sea to Aliwal Shoal.

Coral reefs in depths of 1–70 m. A wary fish, usually solitary or in pairs, rarely in small groups. Juveniles cryptic, rarely seen.

Difficult to keep in an aquarium. In the Pacific, royal angelfish have a grey chest; but the chest is yellow on fish from the Indian Ocean.

FAMILY CHAETODONTIDAE ▪ Butterflyfish & Coachmen (Bannerfish)

Body deep, oblong or disc-like, strongly compressed; body depth usually greater than head length; dorsal fin continuous with 11–18 strong spines and 14–28 rays; anal fin with 3–4 spines and 13–23 rays; soft dorsal and anal fins large, reaching to or beyond base of tail fin; pelvic fins with 1 spine, 5 rays; pectoral fins with 14–19 rays, not longer than head; scales moderate to small, ctenoid, covering head and body; LL inconspicuous; **no enlarged spine at corner of preopercle**; nostrils minute, close together; **mouth small with small slender teeth**; the Latin name *Chaetodon* (pronounced key-tow-don) means bristle tooth, and aptly describes the slender teeth of butterflyfish. Size range 10–47 cm.

Butterflyfish are common and conspicuous reef fish at depths of 1–250 m. Most species are associated with coral reefs, and coral polyps are common in the diet of many butterflyfish. They also feed on small benthic invertebrates (worms, crustaceans, molluscs) and algae or zooplankton. Butterflyfish usually occur in pairs, some are solitary but others form large groups. Their diurnal (active by day) habits and distinctive bright colours (featuring mainly yellow, white and black patterns) make them relatively easy for divers to identify. At night, most butterflyfish usually change colour and retreat into crevices or caves to sleep.

Worldwide in tropical and warm temperate seas. The family comprises 11 genera, at least 124 species. Twenty species known from our east coast, and another 4 may be seen in our area.

Threadfin butterflyfish

Blackburnie

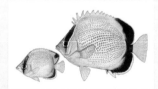

Blackedged butterflyfish

Gorgeous gussy

Teardrop butterflyfish

Whitespotted butterflyfish

Halfmoon butterflyfish

Pearly butterflyfish

Doublesash butterflyfish

Maypole butterflyfish

Right-angle butterflyfish

Vagabond butterflyfish

Longnose butterflyfish

Belted butterflyfish

Coachman

THREADFIN BUTTERFLYFISH
Chaetodon auriga
Forsskål 1775

13 cm adult
3 cm juvenile

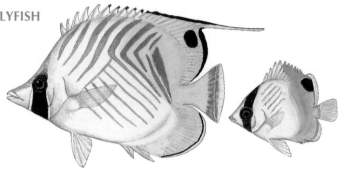

Dorsal fin 13 spines, 23–24 rays, the **anterior rays elongated into a filament** in large adults; usually a black spot at base of filament; anal fin rays 20–21. Body pale **grey or white with 2 opposing series of oblique dark lines**; black eye band wider below eye than above in adults. Attains 23 cm.

Indo-central Pacific, Red Sea, Oman to Aliwal Shoal, juveniles to Mossel Bay.

Usually on coral reefs, sand or coral rubble in 1–40 m. Feeds on coral polyps, crustaceans, worms, gastropods and algae. Adults usually in pairs.

Does well in aquaria. Red Sea specimens lack the black spot at rear end of dorsal fin.

— **SIMILAR SPECIES** —

The vagabond butterflyfish (see p. 292) has black stripes on median fins and lacks the dorsal fin filament.

BLACKBURNIE
Chaetodon blackburnii
Desjardins 1836

13 cm adult

Dorsal fin 16–17 spines, 21–23 rays; anal fin rays 16–18. **Body and dorsal and anal fins dark; head, chest and front part of body form yellow triangle**; 6–8 oblique stripes usually visible on front of body; eye band from dorsal fin origin to isthmus; tail fin base white, fin mostly transparent; pelvic fins yellow. Attains 14 cm.

Southwestern Indian Ocean, Kenya to KZN, juveniles to Algoa Bay. Also known from Mauritius.

Coral and rocky reefs in 1–70 m. Feeds on crustaceans, zooplankton and worms. Solitary or in pairs. Not easy to keep in aquaria.

BLACKEDGED BUTTERFLYFISH
Chaetodon dolosus
Ahl 1923

15 cm adult
6 cm juvenile (Kenya)

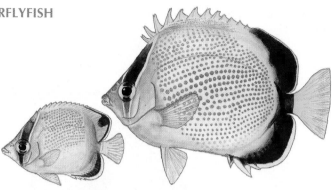

Dorsal fin 17–18 spines, 21–22 rays; anal fin rays 18–19. **Body and head whitish, with dark spot at centre of each body scale; eye band from dorsal fin origin to eye and fading below eye**; soft dorsal and anal fins with white edge and dark submarginal zone; tail fin yellow with black base; pelvic fins white; juveniles with black blotch on middle dorsal fin rays. Attains 15 cm.

Western Indian Ocean, Somalia to KZN, common at Aliwal Shoal, juveniles to Algoa Bay.

Coral and rocky reefs in 8–200 m; adults usually deeper than 20 m. Solitary or in pairs. Have been seen to turn grey when feeding.

─ **SIMILAR SPECIES** ──────────

The gorgeous gussy, which is also spotted, has black bar at mid tail fin, rear half hyaline, soft dorsal and anal fins covered with spots.

The citron butterflyfish, *Chaetodon citrinellus* Cuvier 1831, has dusky to reddish orange spots on body, but the anal fin has a narrow black margin. Indo-West Pacific, known from the Maldives.

GORGEOUS GUSSY
Chaetodon guttatissimus
Bennett 1833

10 cm adult (Comoros)

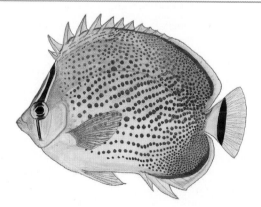

Dorsal fin 13 spines, 21–23 rays; anal fin rays 16–18. **Body pale, covered with spots extending onto dorsal and anal fins**; soft dorsal fin margin yellowish or orange; black bar at middle of tail fin, outer half of fin hyaline, proximal part white; eye band from nape to lower edge of preopercle. Attains 12 cm.

Indian Ocean from Kenya to Aliwal Shoal, juveniles to Algoa Bay.

Coral reefs in 1–70 m. Solitary, in pairs or in small groups. Feeds on worms, algae and coral polyps. Generally easy to keep in aquaria, but wild-caught adults are difficult to feed.

The Latin name *guttatissimus* means 'with many spots'.

See blackedged butterflyfish.

TEARDROP BUTTERFLYFISH
Chaetodon interruptus
Ahl 1923

18 cm adult
4 cm juvenile

Dorsal fin 13 spines, 21–23 rays; anal fin rays 17–20. **Head, body and fins yellow**, except tail fin which is hyaline; **teardrop spot below middle of dorsal fin in adult, white-edged black ocellus in juveniles**; stripe from rear edge of dorsal fin to rear edge of anal fin; dark eye band narrower than eye and extends from dorsal fin origin to edge of preopercle. Attains 20 cm.

Western Indian Ocean, Sri Lanka to Somalia, then south to Port Alfred; not known from Red Sea or northwestern Indian Ocean.

Coral and rocky reefs in 10–90 m; occasionally in tide pools. Solitary or in pairs, sometimes in small groups. Feeds on hard or soft coral polyps, sponges, worms and algae.

Also called 'limespot butterflyfish'. Previously identified as *Chaetodon unimaculatus*, which does not occur in our area. Not suitable for a home aquarium.

SIMILAR SPECIES

Chaetodon unimaculatus Bloch 1787 which occurs in the eastern Indian Ocean and West-central Pacific, has body mainly white and broader eye band (band width equals eye diameter) that extends onto chest.

The Indo-West Pacific archer butterflyfish, *Chaetodon bennetti* Cuvier 1831, is rare in our area but does occur at Sodwana Bay. It has a black ocellus below the rear dorsal fin spines, 2 oblique blue lines on lower body and a blue-edged eye band.

WHITESPOTTED BUTTERFLYFISH
Chaetodon kleinii
Bloch 1790

14 cm adult

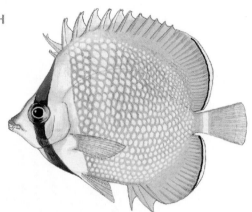

Dorsal fin 13 spines, 20–23 rays; anal fin rays 18–19. **Body yellowish with pale spot on each scale**; eye band from dorsal fin origin to chest; band above eye blue on some adults; some fish with faint white zone at mid body; median fins yellow; jaws dark. Attains 15 cm.

Indo-central Pacific, Somalia to KZN, juveniles to Algoa Bay.

Coral and rocky reefs in 1–70 m. Feeds mainly on soft corals, but also eats benthic invertebrates and zooplankton. Solitary or in pairs, rarely in small groups; usually in less than 10 m.

Thrives in aquaria; a.k.a. 'Kleinii'.

HALFMOON BUTTERFLYFISH
Chaetodon lunula
(Lacepède 1802)

5 cm juvenile
18 cm adult

Dorsal fin 12–13 spines, 23–25 rays; anal fin rays 17–19. Body yellow with oblique stripes; dorsal half dark; black mask over eyes adjoining white area on upper part of head; **black crescent from rear edge of head to middle of spinous dorsal fin**; black stripe along base of soft dorsal fin joining black blotch on peduncle; median fins yellow. Juveniles with black spot on soft dorsal fin and another on peduncle. Attains 25 cm.

Indo-central Pacific, Oman to Clayton Rocks near Port Alfred.

Coral and rocky reefs in 1–38 m. Feeds mainly at night on nudibranchs, tubeworm tentacles, coral polyps, benthic invertebrates, zooplankton and algae. Solitary or in pairs.

Does well in aquaria; a.k.a. 'raccoon butterflyfish'.

A similar Red Sea species, *Chaetodon fasciatus* Forsskål 1775, lacks black crescent behind head and black blotch on peduncle.

PEARLY BUTTERFLYFISH
Chaetodon madagaskariensis
Ahl 1923

10 cm adult

Dorsal fin 13–14 spines, 20–21 rays; anal fin rays 16–17. Body pearly white to grey, with **5–7 ragged dark chevrons; orange zone from soft dorsal fin to rear end of anal fin**; tail fin white with yellow-orange submarginal bar, rear margin hyaline; eye bands not joined to U-shaped black mark on nape. Attains 13 cm.

Western Indian Ocean, Somalia to Algoa Bay.

Coral and rocky reefs in 10–70 m. Feeds on benthic invertebrates and algae. Adults solitary or in pairs; juveniles in groups.

Does well in aquaria.

The western Pacific *Chaetodon mertensii* Cuvier 1831 is very similar, but it has the eye band continuous across forehead.

Chaetodon paucifasciatus Ahl 1923 of the Red Sea and Gulf of Aden, has a golden eye band, reddish zone over rear of dorsal and anal fins; tail fin yellow with red mark posteriorly.

DOUBLESASH BUTTERFLYFISH
Chaetodon marleyi
Regan 1921

10 cm subadult
2 cm juvenile
18 cm adult

Dorsal fin 11 spines, 22–25 rays; anal fin rays 18–19. Head and body pearly **white with 2 brown bands**; adult with brown or yellow spot at centre of scales; 1–2 black ocelli on middle of dorsal fin; brown eye band from nape to chest; pelvic, soft dorsal and anal fins yellowish; tail fin with orange or brown bar across middle of fin; dark bar on peduncle; black spot at tip of 2nd dorsal fin spine of juveniles. Attains 20 cm (4 years).

Endemic, Maputo to Lambert's Bay.

Subtropical coral and temperate rocky reefs in 1–120 m. Juveniles in tide pools and estuaries. Feeds mainly on tubeworm tentacles.

Males mature at ~11 cm (2 years). Spawns (probably in KZN) between May and November; females release multiple batches of pelagic eggs. Adults often in pairs.

Does well in cooler (<24° C) aquaria.

SIMILAR SPECIES

Chaetodon hoefleri Steindachner 1881 of the African west coast (Morocco to southern Angola), has 16–18 anal fin rays, 2nd body bar more vertical, juveniles without ocellus at front of soft dorsal fin, and shorter snout, 3.8–4.1 times in head length, versus 3.2–3.5 times in head length of *C. marleyi*.

MAYPOLE BUTTERFLYFISH
Chaetodon meyeri
Bloch & Schneider 1801

5 cm juvenile
8 cm juvenile (Comoros)
17 cm adult

Dorsal fin 12 spines, 23–24 rays; anal fin rays 18–20. Body, head and median fins **white or greyish, with curving black stripes**. Attains 17 cm.

Indo-central Pacific, Somalia to Sodwana Bay, juveniles to Durban.

Prefers well developed coral reefs in 2–25 m. Feeds only on coral polyps. Adults solitary or in pairs; juveniles usually in branching corals.

Difficult to keep in captivity and not recommended, because of its preference for eating coral polyps.

RIGHT-ANGLE BUTTERFLYFISH
Chaetodon trifascialis
Quoy & Gaimard 1825

13 cm; above: adult day pattern (Comoros) & below: night/stress pattern (western Pacific)
5 cm juvenile

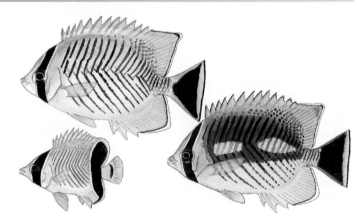

Body oblong, dorsal fin 13–15 spines, 14–16 rays; anal fin with 4 spines, 13–15 rays; soft dorsal and anal fins pointed in adults. Head and body white, with **~15 black chevrons from head to tail fin; dorsal and anal fins yellowish** with black-edged white margins; pelvic fins white; tail fin black with yellow margins; eye band from dorsal fin origin to isthmus. Juveniles similar to adults, but with yellow pelvic fins, broad black bar on rear of body, and tail fin yellow with black submarginal band. Night (stress) pattern dark with 2 pale blotches on body. Attains 17 cm.

Indo-central Pacific, Red Sea, Oman to Aliwal Shoal.

Coral reefs or limestone reefs with well developed soft corals in 2–30 m. Feeds on *Acropora* (plate or branching hard coral) polyps and mucus. Males defend their home corals from other males and other coral-eating butterflyfish, but a male's territory usually includes the territories of 2–3 females. Spawns in pairs at full or new moon. Adults solitary, occasionally in pairs; juveniles cryptic amongst coral branches.

Difficult (and not recommended) to keep in an aquarium.

VAGABOND BUTTERFLYFISH
Chaetodon vagabundus
Linnaeus 1758

14 cm adult
3 cm juvenile (Kenya)

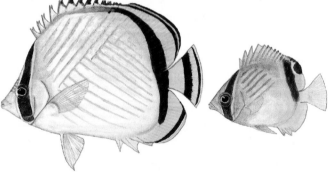

Dorsal fin 13 spines, 23–26 rays; anal fin rays 19–21. Head and body **white**, the body **with opposing series of grey stripes**; median fins yellow; black band from dorsal fin base to middle rays of anal fin; 1–2 black bars on tail fin; eye band wider below eye than above. Juveniles with black spot on soft dorsal fin. Attains 23 cm.

Indo-central Pacific, Oman to Aliwal Shoal, juveniles to Algoa Bay.

Coral reefs in 5–30 m, juveniles in tide pools and lagoons. Feeds on anemones, coral polyps, worms and algae, but will take other food in aquaria, and adapts well to captivity. Solitary, in pairs, or found in small groups.

— **SIMILAR SPECIES** ——————————————

The opposing dark stripes on body are similar to those on threadfin butterflyfish (see p. 286), which lacks black bands on rear of body and on tail fin.

The horseshoe butterflyfish, *Chaetodon pictus* Forsskål 1775, of the Red Sea, Oman and Gulf of Aden is very similar, but the black band running up the rear of the body merges with the black dorsal fin margin and eye band to form a horseshoe mark; the black tail fin bands are replaced by reddish brown bands; and the soft dorsal and anal fins of adults are more pointed.

LONGNOSE BUTTERFLYFISH
Forcipiger flavissimus
Jordan & McGregor 1898

15 cm

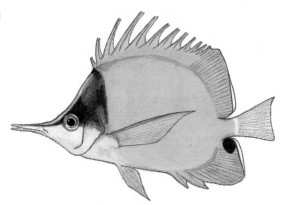

Snout elongate, its length contained 1.6–2.1 times in body depth and almost equal to distance from eye to pelvic fin origin; jaws protrusile; dorsal fin 12 spines, 22–24 rays; anal fin rays 17–18. Body, dorsal, anal and pelvic fins **bright yellow; upper half of head dark, lower half silvery grey**; black spot on rear end of anal fin; pectoral and tail fins hyaline. Attains 22 cm.

Indo-Pacific, Red Sea to Margate.

Coral reefs in 2–114 m. Feeds on tubeworm tentacles, hydroids, sea urchin pedicellaria, crustaceans and fish eggs. Usually in pairs.

Does well in captivity.

— **SIMILAR SPECIES** ——————————————

The Indo-central Pacific longsnout butterflyfish, *Forcipiger longirostris* (Broussonet 1782), which occurs at Sodwana Bay and Aliwal Shoal, has a longer snout (snout length contained 1.1–1.5 times in body depth), 11 dorsal fin spines, and horizontal rows of dark spots on chest.

BELTED BUTTERFLYFISH
Hemitaurichthys zoster
(Bennett 1831)

17 cm adult

Dorsal fin 11–12 spines, 24–25 rays; anal fin rays 20–21. **Centre of body white**, broader below; **rest of body and adjacent fins dark**; section of dorsal fin over white part of body yellowish; pectoral, pelvic and tail fins white. Attains 18 cm.

Indian Ocean, Oman to Aliwal Shoal.

Coral and rocky reefs in 1–120 m. At Sodwana Bay, belted butterflyfish are often seen in large schools feeding on zooplankton well above the reef to which they retreat at the approach of danger. At Aliwal Shoal, the species is solitary or in pairs and usually seen in caves or under ledges.

Also called 'pyramid butterflyfish' for the pyramid-shaped white area on the body.

COACHMAN
Heniochus acuminatus
(Linnaeus 1758)

19 cm adult
4 cm juvenile

Dorsal fin 11 (rarely 12) spines, the **anterior spines elongated to form a white banner** extending past tail fin; snout longer than eye diameter; large adults with short spine in front of each eye. Body white with 2 broad black bands; **black eye band restricted to inter-orbital** area. Attains 25 cm.

Indo-central Pacific, Oman to Aliwal Shoal, juveniles to Mossel Bay.

Coral and rocky reefs in 2–75 m. Feeds mainly on large zooplankton, but also takes benthic invertebrates. Juveniles pick parasites from other fish. Usually solitary, in pairs or in small groups swimming near bottom.

Also called 'bannerfish' for the elongate dorsal fin pennant. Does well in aquaria.

---SIMILAR SPECIES---

The similar schooling coachman, *Heniochus diphreutes* Jordan 1903, has shorter snout (about equal to eye diameter), more rounded chest, and eye band runs dorsally above inter-orbital area. Indo-West Pacific, Red Sea to Durban.

The coachman is often confused with the Moorish idol (see p. 408) which also has a long dorsal fin banner; but its tail fin is mainly black and the front black band runs over the eye.

Figure 39 *Head of a coachman (left) and a schooling coachman (right) showing differences in the inter-orbital eye band.*

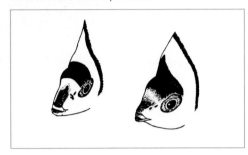

FAMILY OPLEGNATHIDAE ▪ Knifejaws

Body oblong, somewhat compressed, covered with minute, weakly ctenoid scales; dorsal fin continuous with 11–12 short spines, 11–24 rays; anal fin with 3 weak spines, 11–17 rays; anterior rays of soft dorsal and anal fins distinctly longer than spines or posterior rays; tail fin emarginate to forked, with 15 branched rays; mouth terminal, **teeth of adults fused to form a strong parrot-like beak** similar to that of parrotfish (Family Scaridae); small juveniles with separate incisors; no teeth on palate or tongue; preopercle and opercle smooth; branchiostegal membranes free from isthmus. Young brightly coloured; adult sombre. Size range 60–90 cm.

Common in rocky areas, from shore to 100 m; feed on algae and benthic invertebrates (tunicates, crustaceans, sponges, bryozoans, sea urchins, holothurians and barnacles).

Some species are valuable food-fish and comprise an important catch in trawl fisheries. Seldom caught by anglers; a.k.a. 'cuckoo bass' (because they ignore divers and are easy to spear) and 'beaked galjoen'. Flesh excellent.

Anti-tropical Indo-Pacific; subtropical and warm temperate waters of southern Africa, Japan, Australia and South America. One genus, ~7 species, 2 or 3 in our area.

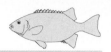

CAPE KNIFEJAW
Oplegnathus conwayi
Richardson 1840

50 cm adult
6 cm juvenile

Body more elongate with growth, the depth contained 1.8–2.8 times in SL; dorsal fin 12 spines, 11–14 rays; soft dorsal fin base less than base of spinous part and shorter than head; anal fin rays 11–13; top of head naked. **Juveniles (5–12 cm) yellow-orange, with black eye band from inter-orbital area to isthmus, black bar from soft dorsal fin to anal fin, and black blotch at base of pelvic fin. Adults grey with darker diffuse mask-like area around eyes**. Attains 90 cm and at least 7 kg (~14 years).

Endemic, False Bay to Aliwal Shoal.

Rocky reefs in 5–32 m. Feeds on sponges, tunicates, barnacles, bryozoans, sea urchins, holothurians and some algae. Matures at ~40 cm FL; grows slowly. Juveniles sometimes found under floating objects at sea.

SIMILAR SPECIES

The Natal knifejaw, *Oplegnathus robinsoni* Regan 1916, has dorsal fin with 11 spines, 20–24 rays, soft dorsal fin base longer than spinous fin base and subequal to head length (soft dorsal base much shorter than spinous part and much less than head in Cape knifejaw). Mozambique to KZN, juveniles to Tsitsikamma.

The Mozambique knifejaw, *Oplegnathus peaolopesi* Smith 1947, also has a long soft dorsal fin base. This rare species may be a large Natal knifejaw. Mozambique to Sodwana Bay.

FAMILY BRAMIDAE ■ Pomfrets & Fanfish

Body compressed, deep or elongate, covered with moderate thin scales; **dorsal fin continuous** with 31–57 rays (**no obvious spines**); anal fin with no spines, 22–50 rays; anterior or middle rays of dorsal and anal fins distinctly longer than posterior rays; tail fin emarginate to forked in adults, rounded in juveniles; pectoral fins much longer than pelvic fins. Mouth terminal, more or less oblique, with protruding lower jaw; maxilla scaly; teeth small, sharp,

slightly curved. Preopercle serrate in juveniles, smooth in adult; opercle smooth. Branchiostegal membranes free from isthmus. Size range 29 cm to ~1 m.

A difficult family, with much overlapping of fin spine and ray counts, and considerable changes in proportions and fin shapes with growth.

Most bramids are true pelagic fish, at home in the open ocean, and rarely venture near land. Some species are valuable food-fish and important components of trawl fisheries. Bramids are the major prey of large pelagic predators such as tunas, mackerels, marlin, etc.

Worldwide in tropical and temperate seas. Two disparate subfamilies are recognised; 6 genera, ~20 species, 8–9 in our area.

POMFRET
Brama brama
(Bonnaterre 1788)

50 cm adult

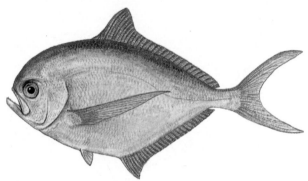

Body and head strongly compressed; dorsal head profile convex, eyes well below upper edge of head; left and right halves of lower jaw contiguous; body depth of adults (>40 cm SL) about 2.2 times in SL; tail fin lunate; anterior dorsal and anal fin rays forming short lobe at front of fin; **dorsal fin rays 35–38**, fin origin over pelvic fins; anal fin rays 29–32; pectoral fin rays 20–23, fins elongate, reaching well past anal fin origin; scales on peduncle not abruptly larger than those on middle of tail fin base; **LSS 70–80**; vertebrae 42–43. Head, body and median fins dark or mottled, silvery to black; pectoral fins black above, paler below; **inside of mouth black**. Attains at least 70 cm.

Worldwide in temperate seas: North Atlantic, Australia, New Zealand, Chile; Algoa Bay to Walvis Bay.

Usually near bottom in 50–1 000 m. Feeds on midwater and benthic fish, squid and zooplankton.

Highly prized food-fish, but some are heavily parasitised by cestode worms. Common in trawl catches from outer continental shelf; also caught on longlines off Portugal and the Atlantic coast of Spain.

SIMILAR SPECIES

The tropical pomfret, *Brama orcini* Cuvier 1831, has fewer (larger) scales (LSS 48–55) and fewer dorsal fin rays (32–36). Indo-Pacific, south to KZN.

The southern pomfret, *Brama australis* Valenciennes 1837, has fewer fin rays (dorsal 31–36, anal 26–29) and vertebrae (39–40). Temperate southern ocean.

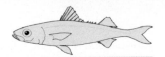

FAMILY EMMELICHTHYIDAE ■ Rovers

Body oblong to fusiform; dorsal fin continuous, notched, or divided into separate spinous and soft-rayed fins; soft dorsal and anal fins with scaly basal sheath; pelvic fins with well developed scaly axillary process; tail fin forked; **upper jaw very protrusile; maxilla scaly, not covered by preorbital bone when mouth is closed**; supramaxilla distinct, the proximal end free of maxilla; teeth rudimentary or absent; gill rakers long and numerous; scales weakly ctenoid, covering body and most of head. Size range 16–60 cm SL.

Adults usually near bottom in 100–500 m but nowhere abundant enough to be of significant commercial importance. Some species attain 40–60 cm and are excellent eating.

Occurring in all oceans, near islands, seamounts and continental shores. Three genera, ~12 species, 3 in our area.

SOUTHERN ROVER
Emmelichthys nitidus
Richardson 1845

34 cm adult

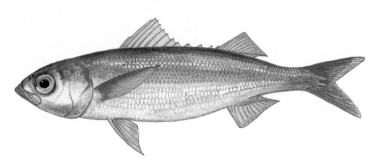

Body elongate, depth less than head length, 4.1–5.2 times in SL; spinous dorsal fin with 10 spines, separated from soft dorsal fin by a distinct gap containing 2–4 short, isolated or buried spines; spinous dorsal fin base longer than head; 2nd dorsal fin with 1 spine, 9–11 rays; anal fin 3 spines, 10 rays; LL scales 87–98; 2 fleshy protuberances on rear margin of gill cavity. **Generally reddish, blue dorsally and silvery white below**. Attains 50 cm.

Indo-West Pacific, Australia, New Zealand, Tristan da Cunha and St Paul and Amsterdam Islands; Western Cape to Algoa Bay.

Occasionally trawled in 100–500 m off the Western Cape. Feeds on planktonic crustaceans.

─ SIMILAR SPECIES ─

The Indo-West Pacific Japanese rubyfish, *Erythrocles schlegelii* (Richardson 1846), known from Kenya, Durban and Port Alfred, has the dorsal fin divided to the base before last spine, body depth less than head length and 66–71 LL scales.

The Indo-West Pacific rubyfish, *Plagiogeneion rubiginosum* (Hutton 1875), known from 500 m off Algoa Bay and from Vema Seamount west of Cape Town, has the dorsal fin undivided, and body depth greater than head length.

FAMILY CARANGIDAE ▪ Kingfish, Leervis, Queenfish, etc.

Body shape variable, deep and compressed to elongate and fusiform; scales small and cycloid; **some species with posterior LL scales modified as enlarged, spiny scutes** (thickened bony scales with a keel or spiny point). Jaws usually with small teeth in rows or bands (*Carangoides* spp) or a single row of moderate to large canines; species of *Caranx* have upper jaw with outer row of canines and inner band of villiform teeth; lower jaw with single row of teeth; teeth absent in adults of some species. Dorsal fin usually divided into separate spinous and soft-rayed fins or spinous fin is very low, with 4–8 spines (spines rudimentary or embedded in adults of some species, e.g. *Alectis*); **anal fin with 3 spines, first 2 spines set well in front of fin**; anal fin spines not visible (embedded) in adults of some species; tail fin forked. The usual length measurement for carangid fish is fork length (FL) measured from front of upper jaw to end of middle tail fin rays. In this book the length each species attains is TL unless otherwise stated. Gill raker counts are of total rakers and include rudiments. Juveniles are often difficult to match with adults, because of considerable changes in body shape and colour patterns with growth. Size range 25 cm to 1.9 m FL.

Carangids occur in a variety of habitats: coral and rocky reefs, in the surf along sandy beaches, and in estuaries. Some juveniles are typically found riding the bow wave in front of sharks or large bony fish, or are associated with jellyfish or flotsam in the open ocean. Many species occur in large schools and are of considerable economic importance in trawl or purse seine fisheries. Most carangids are swift predators, and the larger species are prized as sport fish and for their excellent eating qualities.

Carangids (a.k.a. 'jacks', 'trevallies' and 'scad' in other parts of the world) are found in tropical and temperate waters of all oceans. About 32 genera, ~143 species, 54 in our area.

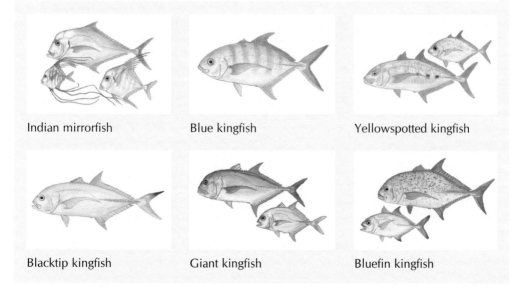

Indian mirrorfish

Blue kingfish

Yellowspotted kingfish

Blacktip kingfish

Giant kingfish

Bluefin kingfish

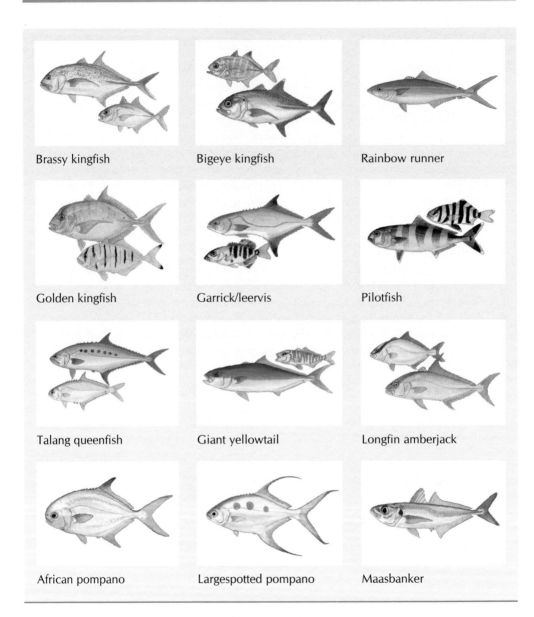

Brassy kingfish

Bigeye kingfish

Rainbow runner

Golden kingfish

Garrick/leervis

Pilotfish

Talang queenfish

Giant yellowtail

Longfin amberjack

African pompano

Largespotted pompano

Maasbanker

INDIAN MIRRORFISH
Alectis indicus
(Rüppell 1830)

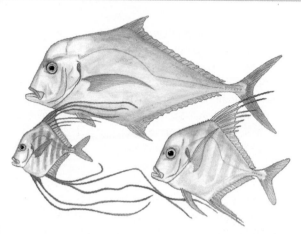

30 cm FL (Japan)
10 cm FL small juvenile
18 cm FL juvenile

Body angular, deep and much compressed, **depth 1.2–2.8 times in FL; forehead profile straight and very steep, profile of nape and head angular**; body apparently naked as the scales are minute and deeply embedded; dorsal and anal fin spines embedded in fish >17 cm FL; **anterior dorsal and anal fin rays greatly elongated in juveniles**; dorsal and anal fins with 1 spine and 18–20 rays; jaws with band of villiform teeth; gill rakers 8–11 / 21–26. **Head and body silvery**, greenish dorsally; diffuse spot on upper edge of operculum; juveniles with 5–7 broad dark bars, first from nape across eye to upper jaw. Attains 1.6 m, 25 kg.

Indo-West Pacific, Red Sea, Persian Gulf to Durban, juveniles to Algoa Bay.

Common near shore in sandy areas and occasionally over reefs; juveniles solitary, often on reefs; adults form large shoals. Biology poorly known. Adults feed on fish, squid and crustaceans.

Caught by shore anglers, spearfishermen and beach seines. Flesh excellent; a.k.a. 'Indian threadfish' or 'threadfin trevally'. SA angling record: 9.2 kg; SA spearfishing record: 21.4 kg.

SIMILAR SPECIES

The threadfin mirrorfish, *Alectis ciliaris* (Bloch 1787), has a broadly rounded dorsal head profile, upper jaw reaches to below middle of eye (not past vertical at front edge of eye in *A. indicus*); suborbital depth (from lower edge of eye to rear end of upper jaw) is 1.7–3.0 times in upper jaw length (0.8–1.0 times for *A. indicus*) and it has only 12–17 lower gill rakers. Circumtropical, Algoa Bay northwards.

BLUE KINGFISH
Carangoides ferdau
(Forsskål 1775)

30 cm FL

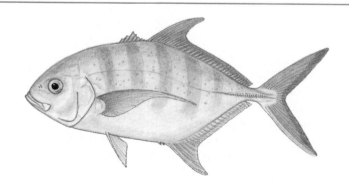

Body depth greater than head length and less than 3 times in FL; dorsal fin spines short, the longest subequal to eye diameter and $^1/_4$ length of dorsal fin lobe; naked area of chest not reaching past pelvic fin origin, separated from naked area at pectoral fin base by broad band of scales; dorsal fin rays 26–34; anal fin rays 21–26; first 2 anal fin spines not apparent in adults. Head and body blue-green above, silvery below, with 5–7 dusky bars on sides which may be faint or fade soon after death; numerous inconspicuous golden spots often present on upper half of body; no opercular spot; leading edge of anal fin and lower lobe of tail fin bluish white. Jaws with bands of villiform teeth. Attains 70 cm, 8 kg.

Indo-West Pacific, Red Sea, Oman to Algoa Bay; not common south of Durban.

Inshore along sandy beaches and coral and rocky reefs to 60 m. Feeds mainly on crustaceans (prawns and mole crabs) and fish. Often in small shoals.

Caught from shore or by ski-boat anglers. SA angling record: 5.9 kg; SA spearfishing record: 6.0 kg.

SIMILAR SPECIES

The yellowspotted kingfish is more elongate, 1st dorsal fin larger, and anterior anal fin spines are not completely embedded.

The longnose kingfish, *Carangoides chrysophrys* (Cuvier 1833), has 18–20 dorsal fin rays, longest dorsal fin spine distinctly greater than eye diameter, 14–17 anal fin rays, and a small black spot on upper edge of operculum. Indo-West Pacific, Algoa Bay northwards.

The coastal kingfish, *Carangoides caeruleopinnatus* (Rüppell 1830), often shows dark bars on body, but it has a higher spinous dorsal fin, 20–23 dorsal fin rays and a distinct black opercular spot. Indo-West Pacific, south to Durban.

YELLOWSPOTTED KINGFISH
Carangoides fulvoguttatus
(Forsskål 1775)

20 cm FL juvenile
70 cm FL adult

Body depth 3.0–3.7 times in FL; dorsal fin rays 25–30; 4th dorsal fin spine longer than eye diameter and about half length of dorsal fin lobe; naked area of chest extends past pelvic fin origin and may or may not be separated from pectoral fin base by band of scales; dorsal profile of snout straight; horizontal line from tip of snout runs distinctly below eye; jaws with bands of villiform teeth. Head and body silvery, blue-green above; numerous yellow spots often visible on upper part of body; large adults often with

2–5 black spots in mid-lateral row on rear part of body; tail fin yellowish. Attains 1 m and at least 18 kg.

Indo-West Pacific, Red Sea, Oman to Durban, juveniles to Algoa Bay.

Coral and rocky reefs to 100 m. Feeds on fish, swimming crabs, shrimp, stomatopods and squid.
    Caught from boats with live bait and lures; excellent sport fish. Good eating. SA angling record: 16 kg; SA spearfishing record: 18 kg.

SIMILAR SPECIES

The bludger, *Carangoides gymnostethus* (Cuvier 1833), has convex dorsal snout profile; straight line from tip of snout to fork of tail passes through lower edge of eye. Indo-West Pacific, Algoa Bay northwards.

BLACKTIP KINGFISH
Caranx heberi
(Bennett 1830)

55 cm FL adult

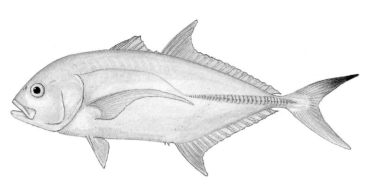

Body more elongate with growth, depth 2.5–3.8 times in FL; dorsal fin rays 18–21; longest dorsal fin spine longer than eye diameter, about half length of dorsal fin lobe; **chest naked ventrally except for small patch of prepelvic scales**; dorsal profile of head broadly rounded; dorsal fin lobe length 4.4–7.4 times in FL; LL scutes 30–40; gill rakers 24–26. **Tail fin yellow, distal half of upper lobe black**. Attains 1 m, 14 kg.

Indo-West Pacific, Persian Gulf to Knysna; rare south of KZN.

Coral and rocky reefs; juveniles common in estuaries and coastal waters; adults usually over rocky reefs in 5–20 m. Feeds on reef fish, anchovies, clupeids, squid, shrimp, stomatopods, crabs and small crayfish. More common during summer, but most spawning apparently occurs in tropical areas. Seems to have limited home range (about 3 km) compared to other carangid species. Matures at 50 cm FL.
    Blacktip kingfish readily take baits or lures and provide excellent sport on flyfishing tackle. SA angling record: 12.5 kg; SA spearfishing record: 11.2 kg. *Caranx sem* Cuvier and *Caranx williamsi* Smith are synonyms of *C. heberi*.

GIANT KINGFISH
Caranx ignobilis
(Forsskål 1775)

75 cm adult
22 cm juvenile

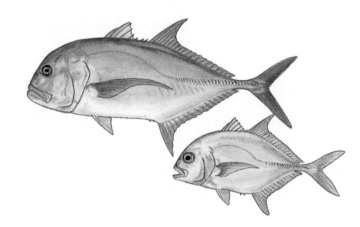

Body robust, depth 2.5–3.2 times in FL; dorsal fin rays 18–21; 4th dorsal fin spine longer than eye diameter, about half length of dorsal fin lobe; **chest naked ventrally, usually with small patch of prepelvic scales;** dorsal profile of head broadly rounded; dorsal fin lobe length 4.4–6.2 times in FL; LL scutes 26–38; lower gill rakers 15–17. Head and body silvery grey above, white below; body sometimes with numerous very small black spots; centres of scutes blackish; **no black spot on operculum;** fins usually dark grey, but fish from turbid coastal waters often have yellow fins; adult males may be almost completely black. Attains at least 1.6 m FL, 80 kg (~10 years).

Indo-central Pacific, Red Sea, Oman to Algoa Bay.

Coral and rocky reefs, surf areas along sandy shores; juveniles often in estuaries. Large adults solitary, but smaller fish are seen in groups. Adults feed primarily by day, mainly on fish, also on squid and crustaceans; juveniles in estuaries feed by day on fish and penaeid prawns. Matures at 65 cm FL (3 years); spawns in summer in KZN.

Famous strong-fighting game fish; caught from shore as well as from boats. IGFA all-tackle record: 66 kg fish from Hawaii. SA angling record: 55.3 kg; SA spearfishing record: 45.4 kg.

SIMILAR SPECIES

The circumtropical black jack, *Caranx lugubris* Poey 1860, is usually seen in clear offshore waters in 25–100 m. Body depth 2.4–2.8 times in FL; dorsal head profile steep and angular; chest completely scaly; dorsal fin lobe length 2.3–5.3 times in FL; lower gill rakers 17–22 (including rudiments); head, body and fins grey to black; dark spot at upper end of operculum; scutes black. Mozambique Channel and off KZN and East London.

The white kingfish, *Pseudocaranx dentex* (Bloch & Schneider 1801), has dorsal head profile less steep, no elevated lobes at front of dorsal and anal fins, longest dorsal fin spine longer than longest dorsal fin ray, dorsal fin rays 25–26, anal fin rays 21–22, breast completely scaly, and single row of blunt conical teeth in jaws. Anti-tropical, Mediterranean, Atlantic and Indo-West Pacific, Durban southwards.

BLUEFIN KINGFISH
Caranx melampygus
Cuvier 1833

49 cm FL adult
9 cm juvenile

Body slightly compressed, depth 2.8–3.2 times in FL; dorsal fin rays 21–24, fin lobe length 4.2–6.7 times in FL; longest dorsal fin spine longer than eye diameter, about half length of dorsal fin lobe; breast completely scaly; dorsal profile of front of head straight; snout long, 9–13 times in FL; LL scutes 27–42; gill rakers 25–29. **Adults with head and upper part of body greenish yellow with blue blotches and scattered dark spots (forming at about 20 cm FL and increasing in number with size); median fins bright blue.** Juveniles and young adults with median fins pale to dusky, pectoral fins yellow. Attains 1.2 m, 44 kg.

Indo-Pacific, Red Sea, Oman to Aliwal Shoal, adults rare south of Richards Bay.

Offshore coral reefs in 10–30 m. Feeds mainly during day and almost exclusively on reef fish. Often hunts in small groups that roam over the reef in search of prey. Matures at 40 cm FL; spawns during summer.

Highly esteemed as an eating fish. Readily takes a lure and provides excellent sport on light tackle; also targeted by spearfishermen. IGFA all-tackle world record: 12 kg fish from eastern Pacific. SA angling record: 8.8 kg; SA spearfishing record: 8 kg.

SIMILAR SPECIES

No other carangids have the brilliant blue dorsal and anal fins of adult bluefin kingfish.

BRASSY KINGFISH
Caranx papuensis
Alleyne & Macleay
1877

45 cm FL adult
9 cm FL juvenile

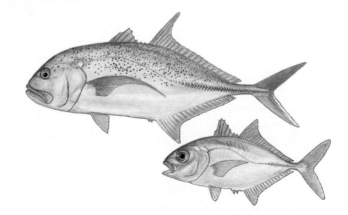

Body slightly compressed, depth 2.6–3.7 times in FL; dorsal fin rays 21–23, fin lobe length 5.2–6.1 times in FL; longest dorsal fin spine longer than eye diameter, about half length of dorsal fin lobe; chest naked ventrally, usually with patch of prepelvic scales; dorsal profile of head smoothly rounded; LL scutes 31–39; gill rakers 25–29. Adults yellow to blue-green above, silvery below; **bright white spot just behind upper edge of operculum**; scattered black spots appear on upper part of head and body at ～30 cm and become more numerous with growth; **upper tail fin lobe dark grey, lower lobe dusky to yellow with narrow white inner margin**; pelvic and anal fins yellow in juveniles, becoming dusky in adults. Attains 80 cm and at least 5 kg.

Indo-central Pacific, Kenya to Port Alfred.

Coral and rocky reefs, also along sandy beaches; juveniles in estuaries of northern KZN. Adults feed on reef fish, squid, prawns and crabs. Small juveniles (6–14 cm FL) shoal with juvenile bigeye kingfish and bluefin kingfish, and feed on mysids, small penaeid shrimp and fish. Adults solitary or in pairs.

Caught from shore or boats, using a variety of baits and lures. Flesh excellent. IGFA all-tackle record 4.4 kg. SA angling record: 4.0 kg; SA spearfishing record: 3.4 kg.

— **SIMILAR SPECIES** —

The bluefin kingfish has dorsal and anal fins electric blue, longer snout, breast completely scaly, and lacks white edge on tail fin lobes.

BIGEYE KINGFISH
Caranx sexfasciatus
Quoy & Gaimard 1825

14 cm juvenile
50 cm adult

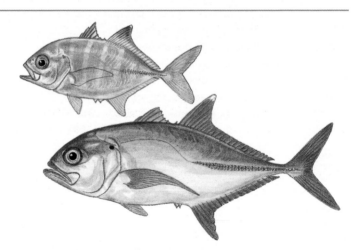

Body slightly compressed, depth 2.6–3.8 times in FL; dorsal fin rays 19–22, fin lobe length 5.2–6.6 times in FL; longest dorsal spine longer than eye diameter and about half length of dorsal fin lobe; **chest completely scaly**; dorsal profile of head smoothly rounded; LL scutes 27–36; gill rakers 6–8 / 15–19. Adults iridescent blue-green above, silvery below; **dark spot on upper edge of operculum of adults less than half size of** pupil; tip of dorsal and anal fin lobes white; scutes blackish. Juveniles brassy yellow with 5–6 dark bars. Males in courtship are black. Attains 1.2 m and at least 18 kg.

Indo-Pacific, Red Sea, Oman to Margate, juveniles to Knysna.

Common in clear water over coral and rocky reefs, also caught in surf along sandy beaches, occasionally in rivers. Adults lethargic, shoal-

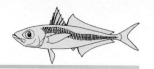

ing fish by day; but at dusk, these predators disperse and actively hunt their prey, primarily reef fish. In northern KZN, small juveniles (3–11 cm FL) shoal in estuaries where they feed on copepods during the day; larger juveniles are crepuscular predators and consume estuarine fish and penaeid shrimp. Matures at 45–50 cm FL. Spawns inshore in pairs during spring and summer; courtship begins at dusk, as the black male swims together with his pale partner. Juveniles less than a year old (3–7 cm FL) enter KZN estuaries from October to April. In this nursery environment, the young grow 12 cm/year for their first 2 years.

Caught at night by anglers fishing from boats or shore, using variety of baits and lures. Popular among anglers and spearfishermen. IGFA all-tackle record: 14.3 kg fish from the Seychelles; SA spearfishing record: 7 kg.

SIMILAR SPECIES

The Indo-West Pacific tille kingfish, *Caranx tille* Cuvier 1833, has a dark spot on upper edge of operculum at least half size of pupil; no white tip on dorsal and anal fin lobes, and longest dorsal fin spine more than half length of dorsal fin lobe. Indian Ocean, Zanzibar to Durban.

RAINBOW RUNNER
Elagatis bipinnulata
(Quoy & Gaimard 1825)

85 cm (Australia)

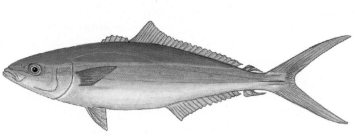

Body elongate, depth subequal to head length, 4.0–4.8 times in FL; no scutes in LL; pectoral fins small, about half head length; dorsal fin rays 25–28; anal fin rays 18–20; last 2 dorsal and anal fin rays are finlets separate from main fins; **mouth small, upper jaw ending well before eye in adult**; jaws with bands of minute teeth. Head and **body dark olive or blue dorsally, the sides with 2 parallel narrow blue stripes (brighter in juveniles) separated by greenish yellow stripe from eye to tail fin**; underside of body white; fins dusky olive. Attains 1.8 m, 46 kg.

Circumtropical, south to Durban; rare in eastern Atlantic, occasionally caught at St Helena Island.

Usually near surface in open ocean; juveniles associate with large sharks and floating objects at sea; occasionally found over deep coral and rocky reefs to depths of 150 m. Feeds on fish and planktonic crustaceans. Adults solitary or in small schools.

Rainbow runner are the preferred prey of marlin and other billfish, hence they are prized as bait by big game fishermen. Fine-eating sport fish; often used for sushi. Rainbow runner take a variety of lures and baits but they are difficult to land as the hook is easily torn from the soft mouth. IGFA all-tackle record: 17.1 kg.

SIMILAR SPECIES

Amberjacks (*Seriola* spp) also lack scutes on LL and have short pectoral fins, but they have no finlets behind the dorsal and anal fins, and a large mouth, the upper jaw ending below the eye.

GOLDEN KINGFISH
Gnathanodon speciosus
(Forsskål 1775)

50 cm FL adult
10 cm FL juvenile

Body oblong, more elongate with growth; body depth greater than head length in juveniles, less than head length in large adults, 2.3–3.5 times in FL; dorsal fin rays 18–20; longest dorsal fin spine longer than eye diameter, ~$^2/_3$ length of dorsal fin lobe; anal fin rays 15–17; soft dorsal and anal fin bases subequal; chest completely scaly; dorsal profile of head smoothly rounded; gill rakers 19–22 / 27–30; **mouth protrusile, lips thick; no teeth in adult; a few small teeth in lower jaw of juvenile. Juveniles golden, with black eye bar and 9 alternately faint and distinct dark bars on body; tips of tail fin black. Adults silvery, with a few scattered black blotches on body**. Attains 1.2 m, 15 kg.

Indo-Pacific, Red Sea, Oman to Sodwana Bay, juveniles to the Eastern Cape.

Sandy areas near coral reefs and off sandy beaches. The protrusile mouth is used to root in the sand, sucking up mouthfuls of sand and small animals living amongst the sand grains. The sand passes through the numerous gill rakers and out the gill openings, and the edible prey are swallowed. Juveniles often seen piloting sharks and other large fish; small juveniles commonly associate with pelagic jellyfish.

Caught from beaches and ski-boats with lures or prawn bait. Flesh excellent. Also known as 'golden jack'. SA angling record: 14 kg; SA spearfishing record: 14.8 kg.

GARRICK/LEERVIS
Lichia amia
(Linnaeus 1758)

1.4 m FL adult
5 cm juvenile

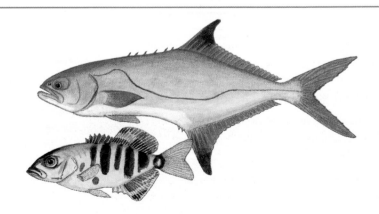

Body compressed, depth 2.7–3.5 times in SL; head pointed; pectoral fins shorter than head; 7 short isolated spines in front of soft dorsal fin; dorsal and anal fin lobes longer than pectoral fins; mouth large, extending past eye; upper lip separated from snout at midline by continuous groove; broad band of villiform teeth at front of jaws; lower jaw protruding; LL curving over pectoral fin then dipping behind fin, no scutes. Head and body blue-grey to greenish above, silvery below; fins dark. Small juveniles yellow, upper parts of head and body black, with 6 or 7 black finger-like bars running down onto flanks; tail fin orange to hyaline. Attains 2.0 m, 50 kg.

Mediterranean and eastern Atlantic to South Africa, and all along our coast to Maputo; not known from St Helena island.

Adults near shore in clear water; juveniles usually in estuaries. Adults exclusively piscivorous, feeding heavily on elf, piggies and strepies. Pack hunting is used to catch fish in the surf zone and also to herd bait fish into a rocky gully. Large juveniles (17–30 cm FL) feed primarily on estuarine fish such as sardines, anchovies and mullet. Small juveniles (6–15 cm FL) feed on mysids, penaeid shrimp and fish; they can swallow prey 70% of their own length.

Most garrick spawn along the KZN coast from September to November. Growth of juveniles is rapid, with 11 cm increase in 6 months; matures at 75–85 cm FL (3–4 years); garrick 90 cm to 1.5 m FL are 5–9 years old.

Winter migrations on the east coast are usually associated with the annual Sardine Run which moves northwards from the Eastern Cape to KZN. The abundance of these pilchards may provide the extra food garrick require for increased gonad development during this period. A garrick tagged in False Bay was recaptured at Umhlanga, north of Durban; another tagged in Richards Bay was caught at Port Elizabeth.

Popular sport fish for shore anglers; prefers live or moving bait, such as small mullet or sardines, but also readily takes a lure. Flesh palatable. SA angling record: 32.2 kg; SA spearfishing record: 31.2 kg.

─ SIMILAR SPECIES ──────────────

Queenfish (*Scomberoides* spp) (see p. 310) are similar in shape and also lack scutes, but their LL is less curvy, and the upper jaw is joined by a ligament to the midline of the snout.

PILOTFISH
Naucrates ductor
(Linnaeus 1758)

3 cm FL juvenile
27 cm FL subadult

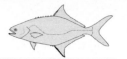

Body cylindrical; body depth subequal to head length, ~4.2 times in FL; dorsal and anal fins low, dorsal fin with 4–5 minute (embedded) anterior spines followed by soft-rayed fin with 1 spine, 25–29 rays; anal fin 1 spine, 15–17 rays; peduncle with no scutes, but a well developed fleshy keel on each side, and a transverse groove above and below at origin of dorsal and ventral tail fin lobes; pectoral fins shorter than head. Head and body blue above, silvery white below; body with 5 black bars, posterior bars extend onto dorsal and anal fins; pelvic fins black with white tip; tail fin dusky yellow with black blotch at base, distal half of fin lobes black with white tips. Attains 70 cm.

Worldwide in tropical and warm temperate seas.

Pelagic; usually seen riding the bow wave of sharks, manta rays, large bony fish, turtles and some ships; hence the name 'pilotfish'; juveniles associate with floating *Sargassum* weed and jellyfish. Depth range from surface to 200 m. Biology poorly known. The bow-wave-riding habit would presumably save energy for pilotfish. Said to feed on scraps left by sharks when they tear into their prey.

TALANG QUEENFISH
Scomberoides commersonnianus
Lacepède 1801

49 cm FL subadult
19 cm FL juvenile

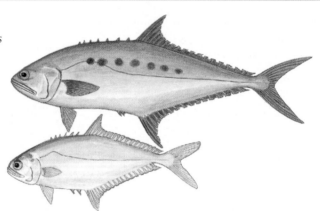

Body distinctly compressed; body depth greater than head length, ~3.2 times in FL; dorsal and anal fins with equally long bases, anterior rays forming high lobes, dorsal fin rays 19–21; dorsal fin preceded by 6–7 short separate sharp spines; anal fin rays 16–19; pectoral fins shorter than head or dorsal fin lobe; LL curved over pectoral fin, then straight to tail fin; no scutes or fleshy keel along rear of LL; mouth large, upper jaw extending well past eye; jaws with several rows of small teeth; gill rakers 8–15. Head and body blue-grey above LL, silvery white to brassy yellow below; 5–8 dark grey to silvery oval blotches above or touching LL; blackish spot on lower pectoral fin rays; dorsal fin lobe dark. Attains 1.2 m, 16 kg.

Indo-West Pacific, Red Sea, Persian Gulf to Algoa Bay.

Coral and rocky reefs; occasionally found in estuaries. Adults feed on variety of fish, squid and swimming crabs. Juveniles, 3–15 cm FL, have a specialised dentition that enables them to rip skin and scales from other fish. The outer teeth of the lower jaw have spatulate tips, are closely spaced and strongly curved outward; this arrangement produces a trough between the inner and outer rows of teeth, into which the upper jaw teeth fit as the

mouth is closed. When a juvenile queenfish strikes its prey, it pushes the side of its open mouth and tail against the side of the prey, while the middle half of the queenfish's body is held away from the prey. As the spatulate teeth are inserted under the scales, the mouth closes and the scales are clamped in the trough of the lower jaw by the upper jaw teeth; the flexure in the body is then used as leverage to lift and rip off the scales with adhering bits of skin. Although these small juveniles consume a variety of planktonic animals, fish scales are a major item of their diet; larger juveniles eat mysids, juvenile penaeid prawns and fish. Small juveniles often assume a leaf-like posture, floating on their side at the surface or in midwater. Apparently spawns in tropical waters, as juveniles are unknown in South African waters.

Dorsal and anal fin spines venomous, and these fish should be handled with care. A popular sport fish, but not highly rated as an eating fish. *Scomberoides* species are also known as 'leatherjackets'. SA angling record: 11.7 kg; SA spearfishing record: 14.4 kg.

SIMILAR SPECIES

The Indo-West Pacific doublespotted queenfish, *Scomberoides lysan* (Forsskål 1775), is common north of Durban, and large shoals of juveniles occur in clear water estuaries of northern KZN; *S. lysan* has a smaller mouth (upper jaw reaches only to or slightly past vertical at rear edge of eye), one row of dark spots above and one row below lateral line; distal half of dorsal and anal fin lobes black.

The needlescaled queenfish, *Scomberoides tol* (Cuvier 1832), has 5–8 oval black spots on or touching lateral line, upper jaw not reaching past eye, and distal half of dorsal fin lobe black. Indian Ocean, south to KZN.

Queenfish are often misidentified as king or queen mackerels (see p. 419 and p. 420 respectively). These scombrid fish have a distinct spinous dorsal fin with 15–18 spines connected by the fin membrane, no anal fin spines, pelvic fins smaller than pectoral fins, and a fleshy mid-lateral keel on each side of the peduncle.

GIANT YELLOWTAIL
Seriola lalandi
Valenciennes 1833

5 cm FL juvenile
80 cm FL adult

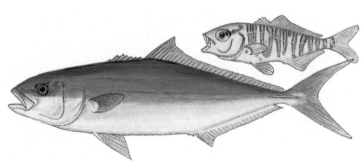

Body elongate, depth 4.2–5.2 times in FL; spinous dorsal fin with 7 short spines, 30–35 rays, dorsal fin lobe not longer than pectoral fins; anal fin rays 19–22; pectoral fins distinctly shorter than head; LL curved over pectoral fin, then straight to tail fin, no scutes; low fleshy keel along each side of peduncle and transverse groove at origin of dorsal and ventral tail fin lobes; upper jaw extends to below eye; supramaxilla not wider than upper lip; jaws with several rows of small teeth. **Head and body blue to olive above LL,**

silvery white to brassy yellow below; yellow or bronze stripe along midside of some fish; median and paired fins yellow; juveniles with ~11 dark bars on body. Attains 1.9 m FL, 97 kg (10+ years).

Circumglobal, several disjunct populations confined to subtropical and warm temperate waters; Namibia to northern KZN; also at seamounts and oceanic islands such as St Helena and Tristan da Cunha.

Pelagic coastal species, found offshore to 110 m. Occurs in large schools. Feeds on fish, squid and crustaceans. Matures at 61–72 cm FL (2–3 years). Spawns mainly from October to March on the Agulhas Bank and up the east coast to KZN. Yellowtail are among the predators that follow the annual Sardine Run of pilchards that move northwards along our east coast in May and June.

Prized as a strong-fighting game fish and excellent table fish. Most commercial and sport fishing for yellowtail occurs on the Agulhas Bank in summer. Usually caught from ski-boats, but during the Sardine Run, many yellowtail are also caught from shore by beach seines or anglers, as they readily take lures and sardine bait. Catches from commercial boats using purse seines declined from 1976 to 1981, and this fishing method was banned in 1982. After the ban, catches of commercial and recreational line-boats increased. *S. lalandi* is also known as the 'southern yellowtail' or 'yellowtail amberjack'. SA angling record: 58.5 kg; SA spearfishing record: 34.2 kg.

— SIMILAR SPECIES

The greater amberjack, *Seriola dumerili* (Risso 1810), has a very wide upper jaw, with supramaxilla bone distinctly wider than upper lip or suborbital width; no fleshy keel on peduncle; fins of juveniles yellow, olive or amber; adults with dusky fins, but pelvic fins are pale distally. Worldwide, Algoa Bay northwards.

LONGFIN AMBERJACK
Seriola rivoliana
Valenciennes 1833

29 cm FL juvenile
(Madeira)
67 cm FL subadult

Body robust, depth 2.9–3.8 times in FL, distinctly greater than head length; spinous dorsal fin with 7 short spines; soft-rayed dorsal fin with 27–33 rays, the anterior rays forming a long lobe, 1.3–1.6 times length of pectoral fins; anal fin rays 18–22; pectoral fins distinctly shorter than head or pelvic fins; LL curved over pectoral fin, then straight to tail fin, with no scutes; no fleshy keel along side of peduncle, but a transverse groove at origin of dorsal and ventral tail fin lobes; mouth large, upper jaw extending to below

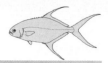

eye; jaws with several rows of small teeth; gill rakers of adults 22–26. **Adults blue-green above, paler below; faint amber stripe often visible along midside of body**; fins dark, except pelvic fins and anal fin whitish distally; juveniles (<18 cm FL) with 6 dark bars on body **and dark eye band from dorsal fin origin to upper jaw, usually visible** on adults. Attains 1.6 m FL, 60 kg.

Circumtropical, also in temperate waters in some areas; western Indian Ocean, Red Sea, Oman to Knysna.

Adults pelagic and usually well offshore on outer-reef slopes and banks; generally caught near bottom in 30–150 m. Juveniles (<20 cm) associate with seaweed and other floating objects in open ocean. Feeds mainly on fish. Biology little known.

Popular game fish, caught from ski-boats by trolling or fishing near bottom with lures and live bait. Also known as 'almaco amber-jack' or 'longfin yellowtail', an allusion to the high dorsal and anal fin lobes; the name 'yellowtail', applied to all species of *Seriola* in South Africa, is inappropriate and confusing for these fish. IGFA all tackle record: 59.9 kg from Mexico. SA angling record: 15.8 kg; SA spearfishing record: 7 kg.

SIMILAR SPECIES

The greater amberjack, *Seriola dumerili* (Risso 1810), has shorter dorsal and anal fin lobes, dorsal fin lobe subequal to pectoral fins. Indo-central Pacific, Persian Gulf to Algoa Bay; also in the Atlantic.

The blackbanded kingfish, *Seriolina nigro-fasciata* (Rüppell 1829), has dorsal fin lobe only slightly longer than pectoral fins; anal fin rays 15–18, the anal fin base less than half soft dorsal fin base; adult dark blue-grey above, silvery white below, tail fin and pelvic fins yellowish brown to black, spinous dorsal fin black; juveniles and small adults silvery, with 5–7 oblique dark bars or blotches on upper half of body, pelvic fins black, each tail fin lobe with a large dark blotch. Indo-West Pacific, Red Sea, Sri Lanka to Algoa Bay.

AFRICAN POMPANO
Trachinotus africanus
Smith 1967

28 cm FL

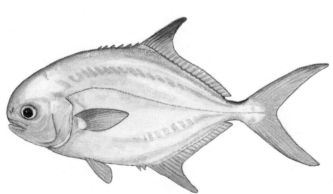

Body robust, depth distinctly longer than head, about 3 times in FL; dorsal fin with 6 short separate spines, followed by soft-rayed fin with 21–23 rays, the fin lobe subequal to length of pectoral fins and 4.0–5.3 times in FL; anal fin rays 19–21, anal fin base sub-equal to soft dorsal fin base; pectoral fins shorter than head, about twice length of pelvic fins; LL curved over pectoral fin, then straight to tail fin, with no scutes; no fleshy

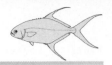

keel along side of peduncle, no grooves at origin of dorsal and ventral lobes of tail fin; **dorsal profile of head convex, snout bluntly rounded**, projecting slightly in front of upper jaw; jaws with band of villiform teeth; lower gill rakers 11–14. Adults **bluish above, silvery below; anal fin bright yellow** with fin lobe orange, tail and paired fins yellow, dorsal fin dusky. Attains 1 m, 25 kg.

Indian Ocean, Oman to False Bay.

Shallow coastal areas with reefs and rocky outcrops; juveniles occur in sheltered bays and estuaries. Feeds on rock mussels, sand mussels, sand dollars, crabs and mole crabs. Pharyngeal bones with large molars, forming a well developed grinding apparatus in gullet; this powerful mill can easily crush hard-shelled prey. Adults more abundant in

summer along KZN coast; spawning supposed to occur off northern KZN and Mozambique where adults congregate in large shoals. Growth of African pompano kept in the Durban oceanarium was extremely fast, with 2-year-old fish already mature.

Caught by shore anglers off KZN and Mozambique. SA angling record: 15 kg; SA spearfishing record: 13.6 kg. Superb eating fish, highly prized by anglers and spearfishermen.

SIMILAR SPECIES

The snubnose pompano, *Trachinotus blochii* (Lacepède 1801), has longer dorsal and anal fin lobes, dorsal lobe equal to fin base, 2.8–3.6 times in FL; dorsal fin rays 18–20; anal fin rays 16–18. Indo-West Pacific, Red Sea, Persian Gulf to Durban.

LARGESPOTTED POMPANO
Trachinotus botla
(Shaw 1803)

50 cm FL

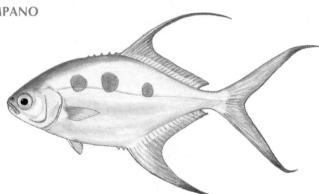

Body depth distinctly longer than head, 2.1–2.8 times in FL; dorsal fin with 6 short separate spines, followed by soft-rayed fin with 22–24 rays, anterior rays forming a long lobe more than twice length of pectoral fins and 2.3–3.0 times in FL; anal fin rays 19–21, anal fin base subequal to length of soft dorsal fin base, dorsal and anal fin lobes equal to or longer than fin bases; pectoral fins shorter than head, and less than twice length of

pelvic fins; tail deeply forked, the fin lobes elongate, about twice head length; LL curved over pectoral fin, then straight to tail fin, no scutes, no fleshy keel along side of peduncle, no grooves at origin of dorsal and ventral lobes of tail fin; head small, bluntly pointed with convex dorsal profile, mouth terminal; jaws with band of villiform teeth; lower gill rakers 11–15. **Head and body silvery; 1–5 dark oval spots on or slightly above LL, first**

2 spots larger than eye (spots absent on fish <15 cm); median fins dusky. Attains 75 cm FL, 3 kg.

Indian Ocean, Oman to Algoa Bay.

Shallow coastal waters; common in surf along sandy beaches. Occupies a limited home range of about 5 km. Feeds on mole crabs, small bivalves, sand mussels and worms. Almost all adults have a large parasitic isopod attached to the tongue. Despite restriction of the mouth cavity by this isopod, the fish seems to feed effectively. Biology poorly known. Spawns off KZN.

Important recreational and subsistence fish of northern KZN. SA angling record: 2.6 kg.

SIMILAR SPECIES

The Indo-West Pacific smallspotted pompano, *Trachinotus bailloni* (Lacepède 1801), has 1–5 black spots (smaller than eye) in a row on or near LL (spots absent in juveniles <15 cm); anal fin lobe subequal to head and longer than dorsal fin lobe, and 15–19 lower gill rakers. Red Sea, Persian Gulf to KZN.

MAASBANKER
Trachurus trachurus
(Linnaeus 1758)

25 cm FL

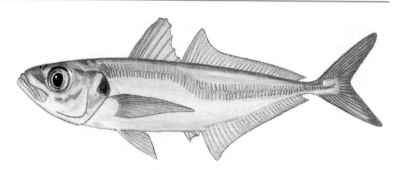

Body elongate, depth less than head length; spinous dorsal fin higher than soft dorsal fin lobe; dorsal fin rays 30–36; anal fin rays 24–32; pectoral fins reach vertical at anal fin origin; pectoral fin length equals head length; **LL with enlarged scute-like scales (may be overgrown by smaller body scales in large adults); dorsal branch of LL extends below rear half of soft dorsal fin; gill rakers long and numerous, total 64–74.** Head and body blue-green or dark grey above, silvery white below; black spot on rear edge of operculum. Attains 55 cm FL, 1.5 kg (16 years).

Mediterranean and eastern Atlantic from Norway to South Africa and round our coast to Maputo.

Epipelagic in open ocean from surface to 400 m. Occurs in large schools; feeds on plankton (krill, mysids and amphipods), which are strained from the water by the numerous long gill rakers. Caught with trawls near bottom during day. At night, maasbanker rise to the surface to feed on plankton. Matures at 30 cm FL (3 years). Juveniles are prey for tuna, marlin, yellowtail, dolphins and birds.

A single population in South African waters; spawns on the Agulhas Bank. Namibian stock separated from the South African population by upwelling off Lüderitz.

Maasbanker are important as food-fish and also for bait to catch large game fish and rock lobsters. In other countries, *Trachurus* are called 'scad', 'jack mackerel' or 'horse mackerel'.

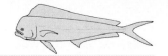

The African maasbanker, *Trachurus delagoa* Nekrasov 1970, has 53–59 gill rakers and the dorsal branch of the LL ends below the rear dorsal fin spines. Eastern Cape to Mozambique, southern Madagascar and Walters Shoals (south of Madagascar).

FAMILY CORYPHAENIDAE ■ Dorado (Dolphinfish)

Body compressed, elongate; adult males with bony crest on head, anterior head profile very steep, head depth greater than its length; body covered with minute thin cycloid scales; dorsal fin continuous, anterior rays twice length of posterior rays, fin origin on head; dorsal and anal fins elongate, reaching almost to tail fin; anal fin base less than half dorsal fin base; tail fin forked; pectoral fins shorter than head; pelvic fins, longer than pectoral fins, folding into groove on belly; lower jaw protruding; upper jaw reaches below eye; bands of villiform teeth on jaws, palate and tongue. No swimbladder.

Dorados are true pelagic fish, at home in the open ocean and sometimes caught near land. Valuable food-fish, much esteemed by anglers, spearfishermen and other human piscivores.

Worldwide in tropical and warm temperate seas. One genus with 2 species, one in our area.

DORADO
Coryphaena hippurus
Linnaeus 1758

1.8 m adult male
5 cm juvenile (Atlantic Ocean)
~ 1.3 m adult female

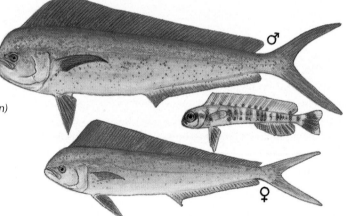

Body depth greatest behind head, tapering gradually towards tail, adult body depth 3.5–4.0 times in SL; dorsal fin rays 58–66; anal fin margin of adult concave on front half of fin; pectoral fins more than half head length; oval patch of villiform teeth on tongue. Head and body **iridescent blue-green dorsally, golden below with numerous spots**; dorsal fin dark with pale blue spots; small juveniles (<15 cm SL) dark, with about 15 dark bars extending into dorsal and anal fins. The live adult fish is incredibly beautiful, with waves of colour coursing over the head, body and fins; after death, the colours fade to a dull silvery blue-green and yellow. Attains 2 m (1.8 m FL), and 46 kg.

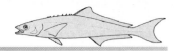

Recorded from continental localities and oceanic islands generally between 30° N & S latitudes; in our area known from Namibia and the Western Cape to the Red Sea and Oman.

Epipelagic in open ocean; often associated with drifting seaweed and other floating objects. Dorado feed on a variety of fish: flyingfish, black snake mackerel (Family Gempylidae), frigate mackerel (Family Scombridae), carangids, filefish, pufferfish, etc.; and also on squid. Much of their prey are small fish that congregate under floating patches of *Sargassum* weed and other drifting objects. Most feeding is done by day, but some dorado also feed on bright moonlit nights. Dorado occasionally visit reefs to prey on triggerfish, wrasses, damselfish and other reef fish. Growth is fast, females mature at 65–70 cm FL, 75–80 cm FL for males (4–5

months). Dorado spawn in pairs throughout year with a peak in summer. This fast-swimming predator lives only 4–5 years.

Highly prized as strong-fighting game fish and superb fish for the table. Dorado should be bled and put on ice immediately after capture to preserve its delicate flavour. IGFA all-tackle record: 39.9 kg fish from the Bahamas. SA angling record: 26.3 kg; SA spearfishing record: 10 kg.

SIMILAR SPECIES

The circumtropical bullet dorado, *Coryphaena equiselis* Linnaeus 1758, known from Angola, Namibia, Tanzania and northern Madagascar, may be found in our area. The body depth is greater (>25% FL), with greatest depth at anus; dorsal fin rays 52–59; anal fin margin straight or convex; pectoral fins about half head length; square patch of teeth on tongue.

FAMILY RACHYCENTRIDAE ▪ Prodigal Son (Cobia)

Body elongate, oval or circular in cross-section, greatest depth distinctly less than head length; head broad, depressed, inter-orbital width much greater than eye diameter; body covered with minute embedded scales; dorsal fin with 7–9 short isolated spines, followed by long-based soft fin with 33–36 rays; anal fin with 2–3 slender embedded spines, 22–28 rays; pectoral fins shorter than head but longer than pelvic fins; pectoral fin bases on lower half of body; protruding lower jaw; upper jaw reaches below front edge of eye; bands of villiform teeth on jaws, palate and tongue; no swimbladder.

Semi-pelagic, at home in open ocean and often near land.

A single worldwide species.

PRODIGAL SON
Rachycentron canadum
(Linnaeus 1766)

47 cm

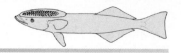

Body depth 5.4–8.0 times in SL; tail fin rounded or truncate in small juveniles, lunate in adults, with upper lobe longer; adults with anterior rays of dorsal and anal fins slightly elongated. Head and body **mostly dark brown, underside pale; dark band from snout across eye and head along mid-lateral part of body to tail fin; pale band just above dark mid-lateral band**; bands indistinct on large adults; fins dark, upper and lower edges of tail fin white. Attains 2 m, 68 kg.

Worldwide in tropical and temperate continental waters, but not in eastern Pacific; Indo-West Pacific, Red Sea, Oman to False Bay, also off Namibia.

Coral and rocky coastal reefs in 2–25 m; often attracted to floating buoys or wrecks; occasionally in estuaries. Feeds on portunid crabs, penaeid shrimp, stomatopods, fish and squid. Adults usually seen in small groups in shallow water. Juveniles often accompany whale sharks or large stingrays. A migratory species, visits South African waters during summer. Females grow faster and larger than males and mature at 85–110 cm FL (2 years); males at 52–60 cm FL (1 year). A large female can release 48 million eggs per spawning.

Powerful sport fish; caught from shore or ski-boats, trolling, drift fishing or bottom fishing with a variety of baits (swimming crabs, mole crabs, cut fish, squid and prawns); also caught with flyrod using streamer flies and large popping bugs. Flesh excellent, especially smoked. IGFA all-tackle record: 61.5 kg fish from Western Australia.

Also known as 'cobia' (USA) or 'black kingfish' (Australia).

— SIMILAR SPECIES —————

Body and fin shapes, and the broad depressed head resemble the shark remora.

FAMILY ECHENEIDAE ▪ Remoras (Suckerfish)

Body robust or slender and greatly elongate; head flattened on top, bearing a sucking disc by which remoras attach themselves to sharks, rays, bony fish, turtles, cetaceans, ships, etc. Dorsal and anal fins lack spines and are on rear half of body; scales minute, cycloid and embedded; lower jaw projecting; teeth short, slender and numerous, exposed on lower jaw; no spines on head bones; no swimbladder. Size range 30–90 cm.

The unique suction disc appears to be a modification of the dorsal fin spines. The two parallel series of ridges (laminae) on the disc are rough, with microscopic hooks (like Velcro). A live remora can be detached from its host by pushing it forwards as it is lifted away from the host; pulling the remora backwards only increases the suction. Some remoras prefer a certain host, but others will attach to a variety of animals, including divers.

Worldwide in tropical and temperate seas. Four genera, 8 species, 6 in our area.

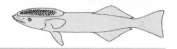

SHARK REMORA
Echeneis naucrates
Linnaeus 1758

~ *40 cm*
(no locality)

Body slender, depth 9–14 times in SL; sucking disc with 21–28 laminae, disc shorter than dorsal fin base and not reaching past pectoral fin tips; dorsal fin rays 34–42; anal fin rays 32–38; dorsal and anal fin margins concave; juveniles 4–12 cm SL with elongated central tail fin rays, which shrink with growth; in adults >60 cm SL upper and lower rays are elongated forming concave or forked tail fin. **Head white, body grey, with white-edged dark stripe from lower jaw, through eye to tail fin**; fins dark, tips of dorsal and anal fin lobes and corners of tail fin white. Attains 90 cm, 6 kg.

Worldwide in tropical and warm temperate waters; Namibia, False Bay to Beira, Red Sea, Oman and Persian Gulf.

Usually attached to sharks, but also found on barracuda (*Sphyraena* spp), other bony fish, large rays, turtles, dolphins and ships. Often seen swimming free near shore, occasionally observed resting on the bottom in shallow water.

Feeds on parasitic crustaceans attached to the host sharks, on scraps from feeding activities of their host, and on any small available prey.

Biology little known; matures at 58 cm.

Also called 'sharksucker'. The Latin word *remora* means delay or hindrance and was applied to these fish because remoras were thought to delay a ship's progress when they attached to the hull.

SIMILAR SPECIES

The rare slender remora, *Phtheirichthys lineatus* (Menzies 1791), has body depth 12–14 times in SL, a short disc which reaches only to or slightly past pectoral fin bases, 3 stripes along the sides: upper stripe pale blue, middle stripe black and lower stripe silvery. Attains 45 cm. Attaches to buoys, dead fish caught on longlines, turtles, porcupinefish and large rockcods; most often on barracuda (*Sphyraena* spp). Worldwide in tropical and subtropical waters.

The remora, *Remora remora* (Linnaeus 1758), has a more robust body, body depth 5–8 times in SL; sucking disc laminae 16–19, disc longer than dorsal fin base; tail fin emarginate; uniform dark brown. Attains 62 cm. Usually well offshore attached to several species of sharks; occasionally on billfish, mantas, yellowfin tuna and sea turtles. Juveniles often found in gill chambers of the host. Worldwide.

FAMILY CIRRHITIDAE ■ Hawkfish

Body oblong to elongate, slightly compressed; **dorsal fin continuous, but more or less notched before soft-rayed part, with 10 spines, 11–17 rays; 1 or more cirri on membrane behind tip of each dorsal fin spine**; anal fin with 3 spines and 6–7 rays; **pectoral fins with 14 rays, lower 5–7 rays unbranched, usually enlarged, with deeply incised membranes**; tail fin rounded, truncate or lunate; scales moderate, cycloid, 3–5 rows above LL; jaws with outer row of small canines, inner band of villiform teeth; a fringe of cirri on rear edge of front nostrils; 2 flattened indistinct spines on opercle; no swimbladder. Size range 8–28 cm.

Most species on shallow rocky or coral reefs, sitting on coral, sponges or rocks, using their thickened lower pectoral fin rays for support. Feed on benthic crustaceans, fish and plankton.

Worldwide in tropical and subtropical waters. Nine genera, ~35 species, 10 in our area.

Spotted hawkfish

Swallowtail hawkfish

SPOTTED HAWKFISH
Cirrhitichthys oxycephalus
(Bleeker 1855)

5 cm

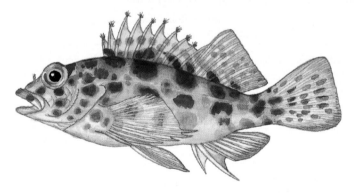

Dorsal fin rays 12–13, 1st ray elongate in fish >4 cm SL; spinous dorsal fin membranes distinctly incised, a tuft of cirri at tip of each spine; lower 6 pectoral rays unbranched; snout short, its length 3.5–3.7 times in head length; preopercle coarsely serrate; 4 rows of large scales on cheek; inter-orbital area naked; 3 scale rows between LL and last dorsal spine. Body with rectangular brown or red blotches in longitudinal rows and vertical series; smaller spots on head, ventral part of body, soft dorsal and centre of tail fin; dorsal fin spine tips dark with adjacent white spot and tuft of white cirri at tips. Attains 9 cm.

Indo-Pacific, Red Sea, Oman to East London.

Coral and rocky reefs in 2–40 m. Sits on, in or under corals. Probably protogynous, as males are territorial and maintain a harem of smaller females with which they spawn. If the water is warm enough, spawning occurs daily at dusk. The size of the harem depends on the size of the territory, with 6–7 females in the harem of a large territory. About 20 minutes before sunset, the male begins to show interest in the females and moves from one to another, nudging each on the abdomen to determine which may be ready to spawn. Ripe females move to the top of a prominent coral in their territory to await the male. The male nudges the swollen abdomen of a receptive female, and the two hop around the spawning area, with the male in close pursuit. The female perches on the highest part of a coral, with her head pointing upwards, the male close beside her. After 10–30 seconds, the pair streak towards the surface, releasing eggs and sperm about a metre above the coral. The female then departs, and the male picks another female to repeat the spawning sequence.

Does well in aquaria.

SIMILAR SPECIES

The humpback hawkfish, *Cirrhitichthys guichenoti* (Sauvage 1880), has distinct hump below front of dorsal fin, similar colour pattern but with dark lines radiating below eye, naked inter-orbital area, 7 anal fin rays, and long snout (snout length 2.7–2.8 times in head length). Southwestern Indian Ocean, previously only known from Madagascar, Réunion and Mauritius; recently found at Aliwal Shoal.

The Indo-West Pacific paletail hawkfish, *Cirrhitichthys aprinus* (Cuvier 1829), has similar colour pattern, but lacks spots on tail fin. Recently found at Aliwal Shoal, also spotted at the T-barge wreck off Umhlanga, near Durban.

SWALLOWTAIL HAWKFISH
Cyprinocirrhites polyactis
(Bleeker 1874)

19 cm

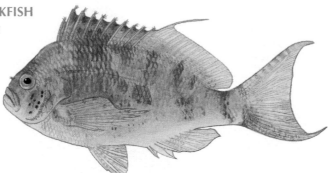

Tail fin of adults lunate, juveniles (<5 cm SL) with truncate tail fin; **dorsal fin rays 16–17, 1st ray elongate in fish >35 mm SL; lower 6 pectoral fin rays unbranched. Adult body and fins mottled yellow to golden orange-brown**; spinous dorsal fin margin dusky; juveniles (12–20 mm SL) with body brownish, head reddish, tiny white spots scattered over body, head and fins, black spot at front of dorsal fin. Attains 10 cm SL.

Indo-West Pacific, Kenya to Algoa Bay.

Feeds on zooplankton (mainly copepods and crustacean larvae); often schools with goldies

which also feed on plankton above the coral reef. Sits on sponges or coralline algae, but often seen swimming well above bottom in current-swept areas in 10–50 m.

only hawkfish that feeds mainly on plankton above the reef. A crescentic or deeply forked tail is characteristic of plankton-feeding fish (goldies, fusiliers, etc.) and other actively swimming species.

─ SIMILAR SPECIES ─────────────────

The swallowtail hawkfish is the only cirrhitid species with a lunate tail fin, and it is also the

FAMILY CHEILODACTYLIDAE ■ Fingerfins/Bank Steenbras (Bankies)

Dorsal fin continuous with 16–20 spines, 19–31 rays, soft-rayed part slightly higher than spinous part; tail fin forked; pectoral fin rays 13–14, lower 4–6 rays thick, unbranched and elongate; lips thick in adults; teeth villiform, in bands at front of jaws, but none on palate; scaly sheath along bases of dorsal and anal fins. Size range 18 cm to 1 m.

Most species are solitary and found on shallow rocky or coral reefs or in tide pools, sitting on the bottom using their thickened lower pectoral fin rays for support. Feeds on benthic crustaceans, worms and fish. The pelagic postlarval ('paperfish') stage (<8 cm) has an extremely compressed body, and is often found offshore, sheltering under floating objects. The larger species are important food-fish.

Worldwide in tropical and temperate North Pacific and Southern Hemisphere. Six genera, ~15 species, 5 endemic species in our area.

Redfingers

Twotone fingerfin

Bank steenbras

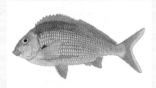

Natal fingerfin

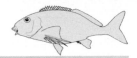

REDFINGERS
Cheilodactylus fasciatus
Lacepède 1803

19 cm

Body depth 3.2–3.7 times in SL; dorsal fin 17–19 spines, 23–25 rays, basal sheath of 6 scale rows; pectoral fin rays 14, lower 4–5 enlarged, unbranched. Body and head covered with irregular dark spots; **body with dark bars, upper part of bars offset from lower part; tail fin with stripes and spots**; pectoral fins with dark bands, lower rays reddish. Attains 30 cm.

Endemic, Cunene River to KZN.

Rocky shores and reefs to 25 m; juveniles common in tide pools of the Western and Eastern Cape. Feeds on benthic invertebrates (e.g. worms, crustaceans, gastropods).

Too small to be of interest to anglers. Suitable for cold water aquaria.

SIMILAR SPECIES

The barred fingerfin, *Cheilodactylus pixi* Smith 1980, has a pale body with 5 oblique dark bars, no dark marks on pectoral or tail fins. Attains 18 cm. Endemic, Knysna to Coffee Bay; photographed once at Aliwal Shoal. More common than redfingers in depths of 10–30 m, but *C. pixi* is usually smaller and rarely caught by anglers.

TWOTONE FINGERFIN
Chirodactylus brachydactylus
(Cuvier 1830)

5 cm juvenile
25 cm adult

Body depth 2.6–3.0 times in SL; dorsal fin 17–18 spines, 28–31 rays; pectoral fin rays 14, lower 6 enlarged, unbranched. Head and front of body brown dorsally, divided from pale ventral colour by silver line; 5 pale spots in row above LL. Juveniles silvery, anal and paired fins orange; black spot on rear dorsal fin spines. Attains 40 cm, 3 kg.

Endemic, Walvis Bay to Maputo.

Rocky shores, reefs and sandy areas near reefs to 240 m; juveniles common in rock pools. Feeds on benthic crabs, amphipods, bivalves and interstitial micro-fauna by ingesting mouthfuls of sand; the microscopic animals living amongst the sand grains are sifted out by the gill rakers, the sand is passed out through the gills. Matures at 25 cm; spawns during summer.

Flesh excellent. Rarely takes a hook, but its sedentary nature makes it an easy target for spearfishermen. SA angling record 0.9 kg; SA spearfishing record 2.6 kg. Adults need a large cold water aquarium.

On the south coast of KZN, the twotone fingerfin is called 'banky', as is the Natal fingerfin. Using the same name for different species often causes confusion.

SIMILAR SPECIES

The bank steenbras, not known from KZN, has 22–24 dorsal fin rays, and the head and body more uniform in colour.

BANK STEENBRAS
Chirodactylus grandis
(Günther 1860)

56 cm subadult

Body depth 2.7–2.9 times in SL; dorsal fin 17–18 spines, 22–24 rays; pectoral fins with 6 enlarged unbranched rays; LL scales 47–50. **Body pale grey, head and fins darker; red stripe usually in front of eye**. Attains 1 m.

Endemic, Walvis Bay to Port St Johns.

Rocky reefs in 20–150 m. Feeds mainly on polychaete worms, amphipods and other crustaceans.

Flesh highly esteemed. Caught by trawl and with hook and line from ski-boats; also popular with spearfishermen.

NATAL FINGERFIN
Chirodactylus jessicalenorum
Smith 1980

48 cm subadult

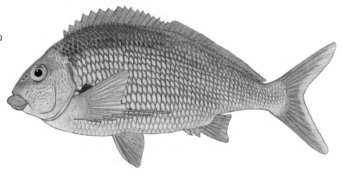

Body depth 2.6–2.8 times in SL; dorsal fin 17–18 spines, 26–27 rays; pectoral fin rays 14, lower 6 enlarged. Head and body **reddish dorsally, white below; dorsal scales at front of body with dark spot at centre of each scale; black (or dark red) blotch on flap of skin at upper end of pectoral fin base**. Attains 75 cm, 11 kg.

Endemic, Algoa Bay to Sodwana Bay.

Rocky reefs in depths of 3–38 m. Feeds on benthic invertebrates, mainly worms, crustaceans, molluscs and fish.

Flesh excellent. Rarely caught by anglers, but popular with spearfishermen. Known on KZN south coast as a 'banky' (as is the twotone fingerfin, see p. 323). SA spearfishing record: 10.2 kg.

FAMILY PEMPHERIDAE ■ Sweepers

Body compressed, especially ventrally, deep or oblong; dorsal fin with 8–10 soft rays and 5–6 inconspicuous graduated, slender spines closely applied to front edge of fin; dorsal fin base shorter than anal fin base, its origin in front of anal fin; anal fin with 3 minute spines, 17–47 rays; pectoral fins with 15–19 rays; pelvic fins with 1 spine, 5 rays, shorter than pectoral fins; tail fin emarginate or forked; **eyes huge, diameter much greater than snout length; mouth oblique, lower jaw projecting; maxilla broad and exposed when mouth is closed**; bands of minute teeth on jaws, vomer and palatines. Scales moderate, cycloid or ctenoid, deciduous or not; LL extends well onto tail fin. Size 8–17 cm.

Most species live on shallow rocky or coral reefs. During the day, they hover in schools in caves and under ledges; at night they disperse above the reef to feed on zooplankton. Not of commercial importance, except as aquarium fish. The identification of species of *Pempheris* is problematic; Dr Randall Mooi, who is revising the family, has provided information on the species in this book.

Tropical and subtropical waters of western Atlantic and Indo-central Pacific oceans. Two genera, ~27 species, 3–4 in our area.

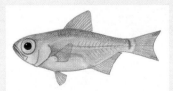

Slender sweeper

Blackstripe sweeper

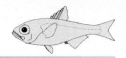

SLENDER SWEEPER
Parapriacanthus ransonneti
Steindachner 1870

8 cm

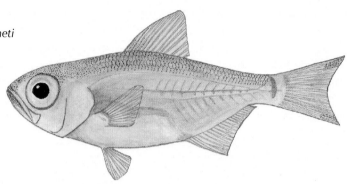

Body depth subequal to head length, 3 times in SL; dorsal fin 5 spines, 9 rays; **anal fin naked with 20–23 rays, fin base shorter than head**; scales minute, ctenoid; 67–75 LL scales on body + 8–10 on tail fin. **Body hyaline, pale pink or yellowish green; belly and sides of head silvery yellow**; dorsal scales of head and body with dark mark formed by a group of small chromatophores; narrow dark ring around peduncle at base of tail fin; tips of tail fin brownish. Attains 10 cm.

Indo-West Pacific, not in Red Sea, Oman to Coffee Bay.

Coral and rocky reefs in 4–50 m. Two luminescent organs inside abdominal cavity, one in front of pelvic fins, the other just in front of anus. Forms large dense schools in caves or against reef walls.

BLACKSTRIPE SWEEPER
Pempheris schwenkii
Bleeker 1855

13 cm

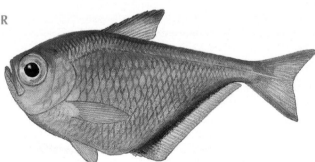

Body deep, distinctly compressed; body depth much longer than head length, 2.0–2.2 times in SL; dorsal fin 6 slender spines, 8–9 rays; anal fin scaly with 35–43 rays, fin base much longer than head; 3 scale rows between LL and dorsal fin; LL scales 46–55, mostly covered by overlying scales, and extending to tips of middle tail fin rays. **Body and head coppery brown** with silvery and brassy reflections; dorsal fin leading edge and tip blackish; **black stripe along base of anal fin**, tips of rays pale; no black blotch at pectoral fin base. Attains 17 cm.

Indo-West Pacific, Red Sea to the Eastern Cape.

Coral and rocky reefs in depths of 5–32 m; common in our area.

The Indo-West Pacific blackshoulder sweeper, *Pempheris nesogallica* Cuvier 1831, has 5–6 scale rows between LL and dorsal fin; 55–65 LL scales; 40–44 anal fin rays; distinct dark spot at pectoral fin base, and on anterior dorsal fin rays. Identified as '*Pempheris mangula*' in *Smiths' Sea Fishes* (Smith & Heemstra 1986).

FAMILY POMACENTRIDAE ■ Damselfish

Body deep, almost orbicular or oblong; body and most of head covered with moderate ctenoid scales, usually extending onto fins; dorsal fin single with 8–14 stout spines and 9–20 rays, spinous part longer but lower than soft-rayed part; anal fin with 2 spines, 9–18 rays; tail fin rounded (some juveniles), truncate, emarginate to deeply forked; mouth small, teeth conical or compressed incisors, uniserial or in 2 or more rows; no teeth on palate; 1 nostril (rarely 2) on each side of snout. Size range 7–30 cm.

Abundant on coral and rocky reefs; some species are common in tide pools, and a few are found in mangrove areas. According to how and what they eat, damselfish can be divided into three groups:

- schooling **planktivores** (e.g. *Chromis* spp, *Dascyllus* spp) that congregate in large groups above the reef to feed on zooplankton;
- roving **omnivores** (e.g. *Abudefduf* spp, *Pomacentrus* spp) that are solitary or occur in groups and feed on zooplankton, benthic invertebrates, algae and detritus;
- territorial **herbivores** (e.g. *Plectroglyphidodon* spp, *Stegastes* spp) that defend and feed on specific patches of benthic algae (these algae are usually enriched with an epilithic algal matrix that includes detritus and various invertebrates (small crustaceans, molluscs, worms, bacteria, fungi, diatoms and dinoflagellates) that live on the algae. Recent studies have shown that some territorial species that defend an algal patch may actually derive more nutrition from the detritus that settles on their algal crop than from the algae itself.

Damselfish lay demersal eggs, which are attached to a bare patch of reef by the female and then fertilised and guarded by the male.

Many damselfish are suited for life in an aquarium, and the more colourful species are valuable in the aquarium fish trade; however some species (e.g. *Stegastes*) are aggressive and tend to bully smaller fish.

Worldwide in tropical and temperate waters. Twenty-nine genera, ~350 species, ~50 in our area.

Spot sergeant

Sergeant major

Nosestripe anemonefish

Twobar anemonefish

Bluespotted chromis

Chocolate dip

Darkbar chromis

Domino

Sash damsel

SPOT SERGEANT
Abudefduf sordidus
(Forsskål 1775)

7 cm juvenile
18 cm adult

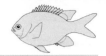

Body depth 1.5–1.8 times in SL; dorsal fin 13 spines, 14–16 rays; anal fin rays 14–15; tail fin lobes rounded; middle soft dorsal and anal fin rays elongated, fin margins bluntly rounded; preopercle smooth. **Body pale, usually with 6–7 dark bars, distinct black spot on upper surface of peduncle**, dark spot at upper end of pectoral fin base; small black spots above and behind eye and a series of black spots across nape. On some specimens, the bars are obscured by a dense overlay of small dark spots all over the body. Attains 23 cm.

Indo-central Pacific, Red Sea, Oman to Mossel Bay.

Adults usually along exposed rocky shores in 1–5 m; juveniles common in tide pools. Feeds mainly on algae, also eats benthic and planktonic crustaceans. Usually solitary.

SIMILAR SPECIES

The false-eye damsel, *Abudefduf sparoides* (Quoy & Gaimard 1829), has a black spot on the side of the peduncle. Western Indian Ocean, Kenya to the Eastern Cape.

SERGEANT MAJOR
Abudefduf vaigiensis
(Quoy & Gaimard 1825)

9 cm

Body depth 1.5–1.8 times in SL; dorsal fin 13 spines, 12–14 rays; anal fin rays 11–13; tail fin forked; adults with soft dorsal and anal fins pointed; preopercle smooth. **Body pale, dorsal surface yellow with 5 black bars**. Attains 20 cm.

Indo-central Pacific, Red Sea, Oman to Mossel Bay.

Usually in large schools over reefs in 2–20 m; juveniles in tide pools; small juveniles (2–6 cm) often associate with *Sargassum* weed and other floating objects in the open ocean. Feeds on zooplankton, benthic algae and benthic invertebrates. During the spawning season, a communal reproductive colony is established, with numerous males in breeding colours setting up adjacent territories that are used as nesting sites. Eggs are deposited on flat surfaces and guarded by the parents. Does well in aquaria but tends to bully smaller fish.

SIMILAR SPECIES

The barred sergeant, *Abudefduf septem-fasciatus* (Cuvier 1830), has 6 dark bars on body, 1st bar (just behind head) sometimes merges with dark colour of head; bars very faint on some fish. Indo-West Pacific, Kenya to Durban.

The spot sergeant has a distinct black spot on top of the peduncle; it also has more rays in dorsal and anal fins.

The fourbar damsel, *Abudefduf natalensis* Hensley & Randall 1983, has 4 dark bars on body, last bar merging with dark upper and lower margins of tail fin. Eastern Cape to at least Kosi Bay, northern limit uncertain.

NOSESTRIPE ANEMONEFISH
Amphiprion akallopisos
Bleeker 1853

9 cm (Comoros)

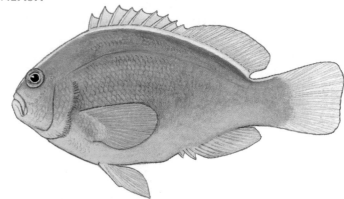

Body oblong, depth 2.1–2.5 times in SL; **dorsal fin 8–10 spines, 17–20 rays**; anal fin rays 12–14; pectoral fin rays 16–18; tail fin truncate or rounded; soft dorsal and anal fins pointed in adults; **inter-spinous dorsal fin membranes not indented; scales small; all opercular bones strongly serrate; teeth compressed. Head and body orange; a mid-dorsal white stripe from snout, along top of head and dorsal fin base**; dorsal and tail fins white; anal and paired fins yellowish. Attains 10 cm.

Indian Ocean, Kenya to Aliwal Shoal.

Usually found on outer edge of coral reefs in 3–25 m. Commensal with large anemones, *Heteractis magnifica* and *Stichodactyla mertensii*. Feeds on zooplankton and algae. Protandrous hermaphrodite (like most anemonefish), with each anemone host to a large dominant female, a slightly smaller adult male, and several smaller stunted juveniles. If the female is taken by a predator, the adult male changes sex and takes over the role of the dominant female who guards the anemone and her eggs. With the promotion of the male to his new exalted status as the 'Big Momma' of the family, the largest juvenile develops into a functional male that will spawn with the big female and help her defend their anemone.

Although the stinging tentacles of sea anemones are lethal to most small fish, the anemonefish has developed a commensal relationship with its host anemone. The juvenile *Amphiprion* and the anemone become acclimated to one another from gentle and very brief contacts between the fish and the tentacles of the anemone. This process of acclimation involves chemical changes in the mucus covering the fish, which the anemone then 'recognises' as a friend; and in future contacts, discharge of the anemone's stinging cells is inhibited by the anemonefish's mucus.

TWOBAR ANEMONEFISH
Amphiprion allardi
Klausewitz 1970

11 cm adult
2 cm juvenile

Body depth 1.8–2.2 times in SL; dorsal fin 10–11 spines, 15–17 rays, anterior inter-spinous membranes slightly incised; anal fin rays 13–15; pectoral fin rays 19–21; tail fin truncate or slightly emarginate; scales small; all opercular bones strongly serrate. **Head and body mostly dark brown to black; broad white bar from nape behind eye to interopercle; another narrower white bar at mid body; tail fin white**, other fins yellow; snout, lower jaw and chest yellow. Attains 14 cm.

Western Indian Ocean, Kenya to Aliwal Shoal.

Coral reefs in 2–32 m. Commensal with large anemones, *Heteractis aurora* and *Stichodactyla mertensii*. Feeds on algae, zooplankton (mainly copepods), worms, amphipods and isopods; biology similar to nosestripe anemonefish.

BLUESPOTTED CHROMIS
Chromis dasygenys
(Fowler 1935)

12 cm

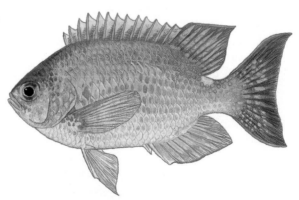

Body depth 2.1–2.3 times in SL; **dorsal fin 13 spines, 12–13 rays**; anal fin rays 12–13; pectoral fin rays 19–20; tail fin shallowly forked with acute lobes, upper and lower edges of tail fin base with 2–3 minute spiny procurrent rays; adults with middle soft dorsal and anal fin rays elongated, fin margins pointed; pre-opercle smooth; teeth more or less flattened, in a single row on jaws. Colour variable; generally **blue-grey with yellow suffusion dorsally on head and body, blue spot (more or less distinct) on each scale of sides and rear part of body**; lower part of head densely spotted with blue; dark spot at upper end of

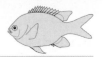

pectoral fin base; median and pelvic fins with pale blue edge; tail and soft dorsal fins dusky with blue spots; **white spot often visible on peduncle behind dorsal fin**. Attains 12 cm.

Endemic, adults from Inhaca to Park Rynie, juveniles occur south to Tsitsikamma.

Common on shallow reefs, weed beds and along rocky shores; also on wrecks to 25 m, often seen at mouth of Durban Harbour. Generally solitary, also in small groups near bottom. Nests on sand; biology little known.

SIMILAR SPECIES

Other species of *Chromis* have forked or lunate tail fins.

CHOCOLATE DIP
Chromis dimidiata
(Klunzinger 1871)

7 cm (Comoros)

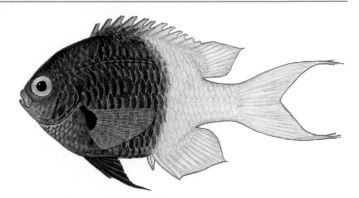

Body depth 2.0–2.2 times in SL; **dorsal fin 12 spines, 11–13 rays**; anal fin rays 12–13; pectoral fin rays 15–17; tail fin forked with filamentous lobes; adults with middle soft dorsal and anal fin rays elongated; preopercle smooth; teeth conical, in 2 or more rows on jaws. **Head, front half of body, paired fins and spinous dorsal fin dark brown; rear half of body, soft dorsal fin and anal fin abruptly white**; tail fin also white; large black spot at base of pectoral fins. Attains 9 cm.

Indian Ocean, Red Sea, Oman to Margate, juveniles occasionally found in Algoa Bay.

Tropical and subtropical coral and rocky reefs to 40 m. Feeds on zooplankton, often in large schools, also on small benthic invertebrates (worms and crustaceans).

Also known as 'half-and-half damsel'.

DARKBAR CHROMIS
Chromis weberi
Fowler & Bean 1928

13 cm

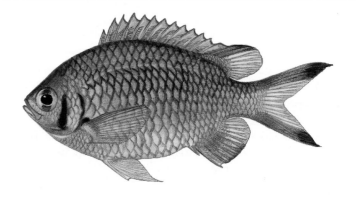

Body depth 2.1–2.4 times in SL; **dorsal fin 12–14 spines, 10–12 rays**; anal fin rays 10–12; pectoral fin rays 17–20; tail fin forked with acute lobes, adults with middle soft dorsal and anal fin rays longest; preopercle smooth. Teeth conical, in 2 or more rows on jaws. Generally brown or greenish grey; **rear margin of preopercle and operculum black**; pectoral fin axil dark brown; rear edge of body scales dark; fins coloured like body, but broad outer margin of tail fin lobes dark brown, the lobe tips black. Attains 14 cm.

Indo-central Pacific, Red Sea, Oman to Protea Bank.

Coral and rocky reefs in 3–30 m. Usually in schools feeding on zooplankton well above reef.

SIMILAR SPECIES

The doublebar chromis, *Chromis opercularis* (Günther 1867), is very similar; adults brownish silver or charcoal grey, the scale margins darker; thin black streak along rear edge of preopercle (sometimes absent) and another wider black band along rear margin of operculum, rear edge of gill cavity and over entire pectoral fin base; soft dorsal and anal fins of adult mostly black, the rear margin white; pelvic fins whitish with black spot at base. Juveniles (4 cm) of doublebar chromis have upper surface of peduncle and greatly elongated tail fin gold. Attains 16 cm. Indian Ocean, Kenya to Aliwal Shoal, Maldives, Andaman Sea and Christmas Island.

DOMINO
Dascyllus trimaculatus
(Rüppell 1829)

11 cm adult
4 cm juvenile
(Mauritius)

Body orbicular, compressed; depth 1.4–1.6 times in SL; dorsal head profile very steep; dorsal fin 12 spines, 14–16 rays; anal fin rays 14–15; pectoral fin rays 19–21; tail fin truncate with rounded corners; suborbital and rear edge of preopercle finely serrate; conical teeth in 1 row, with villiform teeth behind teeth at front of jaws. **Juveniles black, with median white spot on top of head and 1 larger white spot on each side below rear dorsal fin spines; adults dark with black scale edges, white spots reduced or absent.** Attains 13 cm.

Indo-central Pacific, Red Sea, Oman to Great Fish River.

Coral and rocky reefs in 1–55 m; juveniles often associate with sea anemones, or hide in branching corals, gorgonians and long-spined sea urchins. Feeds on zooplankton. Juveniles usually in groups of 10–50 fish; adults generally solitary. Like anemonefish, juvenile dominos that shelter in sea anemones are also not stung when they touch the tentacles.

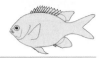

Superficially the adult sash damsel looks similar, but it has a more pointed head, no white spots, tip of upper fin lobe pale and tail fin shallowly forked.

SASH DAMSEL
Plectroglyphidodon leucozonus
(Bleeker 1859)

12 cm adult
4 cm juvenile (Mauritius)
10 cm intermediate colour

Body oblong, depth 1.7–2.0 times in SL; dorsal fin 12 spines, 15–16 rays; anal fin rays 12–13; pectoral fin rays 19–20; suborbital and preopercle smooth; teeth uniserial. **Head and body yellowish brown, scale edges darker; white vertical bar at mid body** (may be faint or absent in adult); dark spot at base of upper pectoral fin rays; upper tail fin lobe often pale. Juvenile with black ocellus on and below rear dorsal spines, black spot on peduncle behind dorsal fin. Attains 12 cm.

Indo-central Pacific, Red Sea, Oman to East London, occasional strays to Knysna.

Rocky shore and reef flats exposed to wave action in 0–4 m. Juveniles common in tide pools. Solitary territorial species, usually in surge zone where it feeds on patches of benthic algae.

The jewel damsel, *Plectroglyphidodon lacrymatus* (Quoy & Gaimard 1825), is brown with minute blue spots on body and head; body scales with dark margin; fins brown, except tail fin and rear of dorsal fin pale; blue spots more numerous and brighter on juveniles. Indo-West Pacific, south to Sodwana Bay.

The phoenix damsel, *Plectroglyphidodon phoenixensis* (Schultz 1943), is brown with dark scale margins and 4 pale bars, followed by a broad black band around the front half of the peduncle and a black ocellus in the soft dorsal fin. Indo-central Pacific, adults south to Sodwana Bay, juveniles occasionally to Algoa Bay.

FAMILY LABRIDAE ■ Wrasses, Tamarins, Hogfish, etc.

Body oblong to slender or distinctly elongate; covered with small to moderate cycloid scales, usually extending onto fins; **dorsal fin single with 7–14 spines, 6–21 rays; anal fin with 2–3 spines, 7–14 rays**; tail fin rounded or truncate in most species, emarginate to lunate in some; **mouth terminal, small to large, jaws more or less protrusile; maxilla covered by cheek bones when mouth is closed; lips thick in most species; teeth conical, or enlarged to form protruding canines, or a pair of chisel-like incisors at front of jaws; no teeth on palate**; preopercle serrate or smooth, the edge more or less exposed; no spines on opercle; 1 nostril on each side of snout. Wrasses are incredibly diverse in size and body shape, ranging from a 45 mm fairy wrasse, *Minilabrus striatus* Randall & Dor 1980, to the 2.3 m, 190 kg hump-head wrasse, *Cheilinus undulatus* Rüppell 1835. The latter has a robust ovate body, whereas the body of the aptly named cigar wrasse (see p. 341) is elongate and cylindrical.

Labrids are diurnal predators that feed on a variety of prey, usually crustaceans, molluscs, sea urchins, brittlestars and fish. The robust pharyngeal bones (between the gills) are fused into grinding plates with sturdy molar teeth to crush their hard prey.

Species of *Cirrhilabrus* and some species of *Thalassoma* feed on zooplankton just above the bottom. *Labroides* species and juveniles of *Bodianus* and *Labropsis* are 'cleaners', feeding on crustacean parasites of the fish they clean. Maori wrasses (*Cheilinus* spp) and ringwrasses (*Hologymnosus* spp) feed on fish and crustaceans. Adult *Labropsis*, *Labrichthys* and *Diproctacanthus* feed on coral polyps.

Species of the Tribe Pseudocheilini (genera *Pseudocheilinops*, *Cirrhilabrus*, *Paracheilinus*, *Pseudocheilinus* and *Pteragogus*) have eyes modified to function as bifocal lenses. The central part of the cornea and pupil are divided into two parts: the anterior part focuses on tiny prey in front of the snout, and the rear part scans the more distant field of vision.

Wrasses generally cruise over the reef using their pectoral fins, but they can also use their tail fin when a burst of speed is required. At night, most smaller species bury themselves in sand and sleep hidden from predators. Even during the day, some species will dive into the sand to escape a pursuing predator.

Labrids are broadcast spawners, with buoyant eggs and pelagic larvae. All wrasses so far studied are protogynous hermaphrodites, with a fish maturing first as a female (initial phase), and later in life, changing sex (and often colour) to become a male (terminal phase). Many labrid species have small 'primary' males, as well as the larger 'secondary' males that have transformed from the adult female state. Juveniles, females and primary males usually show a similar colour pattern associated with the initial phase, whereas secondary males (also referred to as terminal males) usually display a different, more colourful, terminal-phase pattern. Terminal males of some species are territorial and maintain a harem of females, with which they spawn in pairs sequentially. Primary males usually spawn in groups with several females.

Wrasses occur in tropical and temperate waters of all oceans. About 68 genera with ~460 valid species, plus ~30 undescribed species; at least 70 species occur in our area.

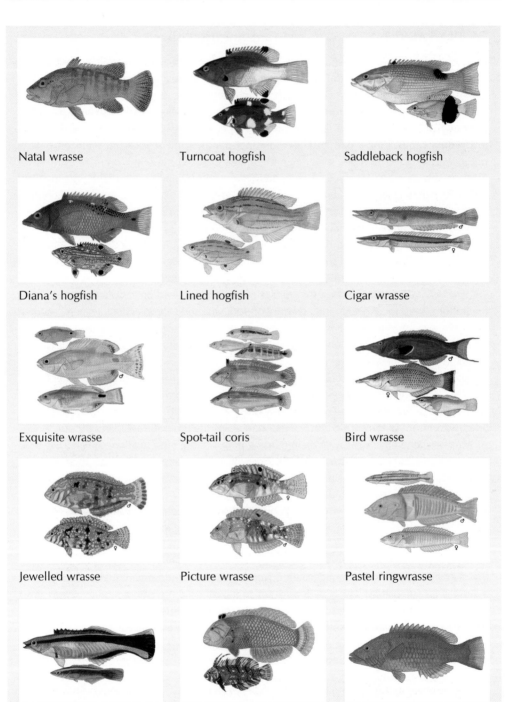

Natal wrasse

Turncoat hogfish

Saddleback hogfish

Diana's hogfish

Lined hogfish

Cigar wrasse

Exquisite wrasse

Spot-tail coris

Bird wrasse

Jewelled wrasse

Picture wrasse

Pastel ringwrasse

Bluestreak cleaner wrasse

Rockmover wrasse

Cheeklined wrasse

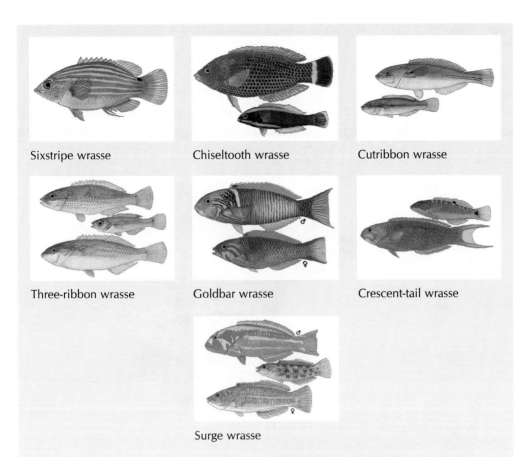

Sixstripe wrasse   Chiseltooth wrasse   Cutribbon wrasse

Three-ribbon wrasse   Goldbar wrasse   Crescent-tail wrasse

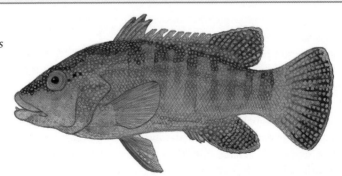

Surge wrasse

NATAL WRASSE
Anchichoerops natalensis
(Gilchrist & Thompson
1909)

58 cm

Body oblong, slightly compressed, depth 2.5–3.0 times in SL; **dorsal head profile distinctly convex; eye diameter less than cheek depth; adults with thick lips, upper jaw projecting slightly; 2 prominent canines on each side at front of jaws; dorsal fin 13** spines, 9 rays, the first 3 spines longer and nearly separate from rest of fin; anal fin rays 10–11; tail fin rounded; LL continuous; cheek and head behind eyes with small scales; **preopercle serrate. Colour reddish with yellow to orange spots or orange-yellow-**

brown with darker spots; **dark bars may be present on body**. Attains 75 cm, 16 kg.

Endemic, Tongaat to Kei River.

Rocky reefs in 10–55 m. Feeds on sponges, tunicates, crabs and crayfish. Lethargic inquisitive fish, rarely caught by anglers, unconcerned by divers, hence vulnerable to over-exploitation by spearfishermen. Protected species. Small juveniles unknown, probably cryptic.

SIMILAR SPECIES

Hogfish, (*Bodianus* spp), have 11–12 dorsal fin spines, but the first 3 spines are not enlarged or separate from the 4th spine.

TURNCOAT HOGFISH
Bodianus axillaris
(Bennett 1832)

18 cm male
16 cm female (starting the change to male)

Head pointed; dorsal fin 12 spines, 9–10 rays, spinous membranes deeply incised; anal fin rays 11–13; tail fin slightly convex, truncate or emarginate; pectoral fin rays 15–17; LL continuous; jaws equal, with a pair of canines at front of each jaw and a canine on each side at rear of upper jaw; scales dorsally on head reaching in front of nostrils. **Initial phase brown, juvenile black with 9 white blotches; terminal male reddish brown fading to white behind a line from abdomen to rear of dorsal fin; female and male also with 4 black spots**. Attains 20 cm.

Indo-West Pacific, Red Sea, Oman to Aliwal Shoal.

Coral and rocky reefs in 10–50 m; juveniles usually in branching corals or in caves and under ledges; adults solitary. Juveniles often act as cleaners removing parasites from other fish. Adults feed on small crustaceans, gastropods, bivalves and worms.

Does well in an aquarium.

SIMILAR SPECIES

The lyretail hogfish, *Bodianus anthioides* (Bennett 1832), also has head and front of body reddish brown and rear part white; but the tail fin is lunate, with upper and lower margins reddish brown to black and continued onto rear of body which also has several dark spots of various sizes; pelvic fins and leading margin of anal fin reddish orange; black spot at front of dorsal fin. Indo-West Pacific, Red Sea to Aliwal Shoal. Juveniles associate with black coral bushes and sponges in depths of 6–60 m.

SADDLEBACK HOGFISH
Bodianus bilunulatus
(Lacepède 1801)

20 cm female
7 cm juvenile

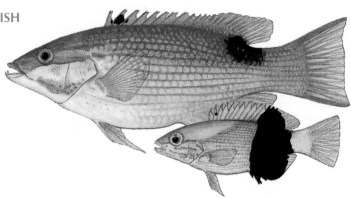

Head pointed, dorsal head profile slightly convex; dorsal fin 12 spines, 10 rays, spinous membranes deeply incised; anal fin rays 12–13; rear margin of tail fin slightly convex in juvenile, emarginate in adult; pectoral fin rays 16–17; pelvic fins reach to or beyond anus; LL continuous; jaws equal, with pair of canines at front of each jaw and a canine on each side at rear of upper jaw; scales dorsally on head to inter-orbital area. Adult reddish dorsally, pale ventrally; scales white, edge red, forming longitudinal red lines; **black blotch below soft dorsal fin**, fading with growth; black spot on 2nd dorsal fin spine; **curved white band from rear part of mouth across cheek to rear edge of head** (not present in large males). Juvenile pale, with reddish longitudinal lines, yellowish dorsally; black blotch from soft dorsal fin to anal fin. Attains 55 cm.

Indo-central Pacific, Kenya to Margate.

Offshore coral reefs in 8–108 m; juveniles often in coral rubble. Feeds on crustaceans, molluscs, sea urchins, brittlestars and fish. Adults need a large aquarium.

SIMILAR SPECIES

The goldsaddle hogfish, *Bodianus perditio* (Quoy & Gaimard 1834), is yellowish (juveniles) to reddish (adults) with numerous small yellow spots on head and front part of body; white to gold bar followed by black blotch over soft dorsal fin and adjacent part of body, adults have black blotch more diffuse, front half of dorsal fin black; tail fin yellow or reddish with yellow margins all round; tail fin of large adults double emarginate (middle part convex, upper and lower rays elongate). Anti-tropical Indo-West Pacific, Mozambique to Aliwal Shoal.

The blackbanded hogfish, *Bodianus macrourus* (Lacepède 1801), has body russet dorsally, with horizontal series of blue spots; head and lower sides yellowish, with longitudinal rows of blue spots and streaks; black zone across rear parts of dorsal and anal fins and body; rear part of peduncle pale blue, tail fin white. Mascarene Islands; may also occur at Madagascar and South Africa. *Bodianus hirsutus* (Lacepède) is a synonym.

DIANA'S HOGFISH
Bodianus diana
(Lacepède 1801)

18 cm adult
8 cm juvenile (Comoros)

Head pointed, dorsal head profile straight; **dorsal fin 12 spines, 10 rays, spinous membranes deeply incised; anal fin rays 12; tail fin convex in juvenile, truncate in adult**; pectoral fin rays 15–17; LL continuous; jaws equal, with pair of canines at front of each jaw and a canine on each side at rear of upper jaw; scales dorsally on head reaching above middle of eye. **Adult male and female similar, with head and dorsal part of body reddish purple to brown, yellowish on rest of body, scales rimmed with brown, except for those above LL on rear of body where each scale has a black spot**; 4–5 irregular pale spots in row above LL; **pale spots below dorsal fin conspicuous underwater**; pelvic fins mostly red or reddish brown, rear margin pale. Juveniles reddish brown, with rows of white blotches and spots; black spots at front and rear of dorsal fin, on front of anal fin, covering most of pelvic fins, and at base of pectoral fins; black spot at base of last 2 anal fin rays and base of middle tail fin rays. Attains 25 cm.

Indian Ocean to Java, Red Sea, Oman to Aliwal Shoal, juveniles to Kei River.

Coral reefs in 3–40 m. Juveniles and some adults act as cleaners and remove parasites from fish. Adults often associate with black corals and gorgonians. Does well in an aquarium.

— SIMILAR SPECIES —

Adult Diana wrasse in the Pacific have a large black spot on the pelvic fins and represent a different species.

LINED HOGFISH
Bodianus trilineatus
(Fowler 1934)

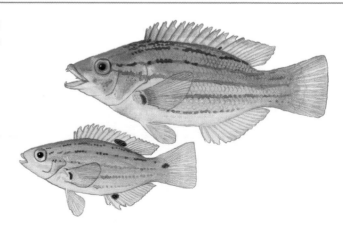

17 cm SL adult
7 cm SL juvenile

Head pointed, dorsal head profile straight; dorsal fin 12 spines, 10 rays, inter-spinous membranes distinctly incised; anal fin rays 12; margin of tail fin convex in young, truncate in adult; pectoral fin rays 15–17; pelvic fins of adult reach more than halfway to anus; LL continuous; pair of canines at front of each jaw and a canine on each side at rear of upper jaw; scales on head reach front nostrils. **Adult with head and body mostly reddish, yellow or white ventrally; 5 red stripes on flanks, upper 3 stripes with black spots; small black or dark red spot at base of lower pectoral fin rays; pelvic and anal fins white.** Juvenile with black spot at base of rear dorsal fin spines, another above LL at tail fin base, one at base of 3rd anal fin spine, and one at pectoral fin base. Attains 27 cm.

Western Indian Ocean, Red Sea to Park Rynie.

Coral reefs in 25–200 m.
    Does well in a large aquarium.

SIMILAR SPECIES

The rare allopatric *Bodianus leucostictus* (Bennett 1832) is very similar. It has body with 5 reddish horizontal stripes (and some black spots in juveniles) and rows of red spots between the stripes. Known from Comoros, Madagascar and Mascarene Islands.

CIGAR WRASSE
Cheilio inermis
(Forsskål 1775)

30 cm male (Kenya)
20 cm female

Body elongate and slightly compressed, depth less than half head length and 5.5–8.0 times in SL; snout elongate, 2–3 times eye diameter; low dorsal fin with 9 weak spines, 12–14 rays; low anal fin with 3 weak spines, 11–12 rays; pectoral fin rays 12; tail fin convex with acute corners; **pectoral fins shorter than snout; pelvic fins shorter than pectoral fins;** LL continuous, almost straight from gill opening to tail fin; branchiostegal membranes forming a free fold, not attached to isthmus. Generally greenish grey; occasionally brownish dorsally, abruptly pale below; some individuals yellow; juveniles and females usually with mid-lateral black stripe, which may be interrupted to form a series of spots and dashes; large males usually have an irregular yellow-orange to salmon pink area and white spots near tips of pectoral fins. Attains 50 cm.

Indo-Pacific, Red Sea, Oman to Kei River.

Seagrass beds and coral reefs to 30 m. Feeds on gastropods, bivalves, crabs, hermit crabs, shrimp and sea urchins.

SIMILAR SPECIES

The pastel ringwrasse (see p. 346) has body depth 3.7–5.4 times in SL, LL sharply bent downwards below rear of dorsal fin, gill membranes joined to isthmus; body with vertical bars.

EXQUISITE WRASSE
Cirrhilabrus exquisitus
Smith 1957

2 cm juvenile
10 cm male (Maldives)
8 cm female

Body oblong, slightly compressed; **dorsal fin 11 spines, 9 rays; anal fin rays 9**; pectoral fin rays 14–16; tail fin rounded, truncate or double emarginate with upper and lower rays longer (adults); **LL interrupted; preopercle finely serrate; eyes divided into 2 parts** (see family text). **Juvenile brown or reddish orange to purple, white spot on tip of snout, black spot at base of tail fin. Adult colour complex, always with peduncle spot above LL (spot faint on some adults).** Attains 11 cm.

Indo-Pacific, Kenya to Park Rynie.

Coral reefs in 6–32 m; often in coral rubble areas exposed to currents. Sometimes in groups above reef, where it feeds on zooplankton. Males defend a large harem of smaller females and display brilliant colours (blue spots and lines, pink on head, with orange or gold tail fin) during courtship.

SIMILAR SPECIES

The anti-social wrasse, *Cirrhilabrus* sp., is similar to the social wrasse, *Cirrhilabrus*

rubriventralis Springer & Randall 1974, of the Red Sea. The juvenile of the anti-social wrasse is reddish orange, with 2 longitudinal blue lines on body dorsally, 1 or 2 lines or rows of blue spots along mid-lateral part of body, and a small black spot between 1st and 2nd dorsal fin spines; the small black spot on the tail is on the upper half of the peduncle. Female (?) reddish orange dorsally, pale yellow below; numerous pale blue spots on mid-lateral body scales; dorsal fin reddish with central dark mauve band along middle of fin; anal fin reddish with blue margin and row of spots near base; tail fin red; pelvic fins dark mauve with red tip. Adult male orange to yellowish brown dorsally, with enlarged purplish black pelvic fins which reach middle of anal fin base, first 2 dorsal fin spines greatly elongated; anal fin pinkish purple with blue spots near base; dorsal fin bluish grey, a row of mauve spots on body at base of dorsal fin; horizontal line from mouth just below eye to rear edge of head. This species was photographed at Aliwal Shoal by Dennis King.

SPOT-TAIL CORIS
Coris caudimacula
(Quoy & Gaimard 1834)

4 cm juvenile
~ 3 cm juvenile
6 cm juvenile
18 cm male
10 cm female

Body compressed; **dorsal fin 9 spines, 12 rays, first 2 spines slightly elongated in adult male**; anal fin rays 12; pectoral fin rays 13; tail fin rounded; conical teeth at front of jaws; LL continuous; preopercle edge smooth. Colour variable, but always with **dark spot** (red or black, sometimes indistinct) **at tail fin base, at rear end of operculum and on 1st dorsal fin membrane**. Attains 20 cm.

Indian Ocean, Red Sea, Oman to East London, juveniles to Mossel Bay.

Coral and rocky reefs in 2–32 m. Feeds on crustaceans, molluscs, worms and brittlestars. Usually solitary; common in South African waters.

SIMILAR SPECIES

Other *Coris* are coloured differently, and males are larger with a deeper body.

BIRD WRASSE
Gomphosus caeruleus
Lacepède 1801

27 cm male (Madagascar)
16 cm female
4 cm juvenile

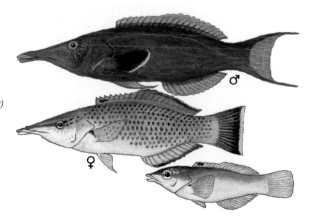

Body oblong, compressed; **snout and jaws greatly elongated in adult, forming a bird-like beak; snout relatively short in small juveniles; dorsal fin 8 spines, 13 rays, the inter-spinous membranes not incised; anal fin rays 11**; pectoral fin rays 15; tail fin slightly rounded in juvenile, truncate in females, truncate with longer upper and lower rays in males; small conical teeth at front of jaws; LL continuous; head naked; preopercle edge smooth. Female with upper part of head brown, body dark dorsally; lower part of head and body pale; each body scale (except those on chest and belly) with a dark spot. Male dark blue-green; dorsal and anal fins and central parabola of tail fin pale blue-green or yellow-green. Juvenile with dusky head, pale body, greenish dorsally; black spot at front of spinous dorsal fin. Attains 28 cm.

Indian Ocean, Red Sea, Oman to Aliwal Shoal, juveniles to the Eastern Cape.

Coral and rocky reefs in 10–32 m. Feeds on small invertebrates that are picked from cracks and crevices with the long slender beak. An active diurnal species that cruises the reef in an up and down motion powered by the pectoral fins.

SIMILAR SPECIES

The juvenile Pacific bird wrasse, *Gomphosus varius* Lacepède 1801, has 2 irregular black stripes: one from front of snout, through eye to base of upper tail fin rays; the 2nd from underside of head along ventral side of body to lower tail fin rays. Not known from Western Indian Ocean.

JEWELLED WRASSE
Halichoeres lapillus
Smith 1947

12 cm male
8 cm female

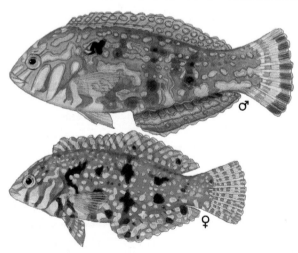

Body oblong and compressed, depth 2.8–3.3 times in SL; dorsal fin 9 spines, 11 rays, spinous membranes not incised; anal fin rays 11; pectoral fin rays 13; tail fin rounded; jaws with conical teeth; LL continuous; head, median dorsal region of nape and median part of chest naked; preopercle edge smooth.

Female red, with small white spots and black blotches; head with 3 oblique pale bands ventrally. **Male reddish orange, with irregular mauve or yellow or pale green markings** and streaks on head, body and median fins; black blotch behind upper end of gill opening. Attains 14 cm.

Western Indian Ocean, Oman to Aliwal Shoal.

Coral and rocky reefs with abundant algae in 5–18 m. Solitary or found in small groups, often with other wrasses.

The male divided wrasse, *Macropharyngodon bipartitus* Smith 1957, is green with irregular dark streaks and spots; dorsal and anal fins with rows of green spots and submarginal russet band. Female red with white spots; abdomen blackish with irregular pale markings. Western Indian Ocean, Oman to Aliwal Shoal.

PICTURE WRASSE
Halichoeres nebulosus
(Valenciennes 1839)

6 cm female
10 cm male (Mauritius)

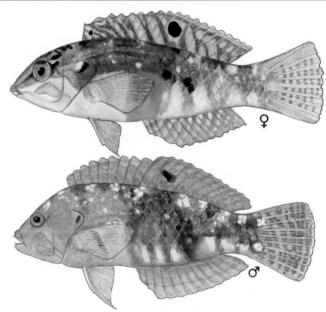

Body oblong and compressed, depth 2.9–3.5 times in SL; **dorsal fin 9 spines, 11–12 rays**, spinous membranes not incised; anal fin rays 11; pectoral fin rays 13–15; tail fin rounded; jaws with conical teeth; LL continuous; opercle naked; preopercle edge smooth. **Female with head and body brownish dorsally, large pale red area on side just in front of anal fin**, containing 2 or more white lines; black spot behind eye; black ocellus in middle of dorsal fin; small black spot on 1st spinous dorsal fin membrane; oblique reddish-brown stripes on dorsal and anal fins. **Male mainly greenish brown dorsally, paler below; red area on abdomen reduced or absent**; black blotches scattered over body; pink stripes on head; **black smudge at middle of dorsal fin**. Attains 12 cm.

Indo-West Pacific, Red Sea, Oman to Algoa Bay.

Surge zone of coral and rocky reefs; down to 40 m on some reefs; also in harbours on rubble.

The jewelled wrasse has a different pattern and it has no red patch on the rear of the abdomen.

PASTEL RINGWRASSE
Hologymnosus doliatus
(Lacepède 1801)

9 cm juvenile
44 cm male
28 cm female

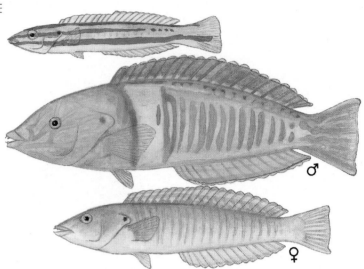

Body elongate and compressed, depth 3.7–5.4 times in SL; dorsal fin 9 spines, 12 rays, spinous membranes not incised; anal fin rays 12; pectoral fin rays 13, the fin short, half head length; tail fin truncate in juveniles and small females, double emarginate in males; teeth conical; **body covered with small scales; LL sharply bent downward below rear of dorsal fin**; head, median dorsal region of nape and median part of chest naked; gill membranes joined to isthmus; preopercle edge smooth. Small juveniles gold or silvery grey with 3 longitudinal red lines; with growth these lines break into spots, then expand into vertical orangish bars. **Initial phase pale green, blue, orange or pink with 20–23 bars on body. Terminal males pale blue-green to pale red or yellow, with lavender-blue bars and broad pale zone, bordered by purple bars, behind pectoral fins.** Dark spot on rear end of operculum of all stages. Attains 50 cm.

Indo-central Pacific, southern Red Sea, Oman to Margate.

Offshore coral reefs, deep sand flats and rubble areas below drop-offs to 30 m. Feeds mainly on fish and crustaceans. Juveniles in small groups near bottom; adults solitary or in pairs above the reef.

Pacific males have a narrower, more posterior white band behind pectoral fins.

SIMILAR SPECIES

The barred ringwrasse, *Hologymnosus annulatus* (Lacepède 1801), has pectoral fins more than half head length, tail fin lunate; juveniles bicoloured, upper half pale with longitudinal dark line dorsally, lower half of head, body and tail fin blackish; females brownish with ~18 faint dark bars; crescentic white mark on rear margin of tail fin; males greenish with dark bars on body. Indo-central Pacific, south to Sodwana Bay.

The cigar wrasse (see p. 341) has a more slender body (depth 5.5–8.0 times in SL), LL running straight from head to tail fin; colour pattern not barred.

BLUESTREAK CLEANER WRASSE
Labroides dimidiatus
(Valenciennes 1839)

9 cm
5 cm juvenile

Body elongate and compressed, depth equal to head length and 4.0–4.7 times in SL; dorsal fin 9 short slender spines, 11 rays, spinous membranes distinctly incised; anal fin rays 10; pectoral fin rays 13; pair of canines at front of each jaw, several rows of small teeth at sides of jaws; lower lip divided into 2 lobes by U-shaped notch at symphysis; preopercle edge smooth. Male and female colour the same. Adults bluish, becoming pale yellow or white anteriorly; **black stripe from snout through eye, broadening as it runs posteriorly to rear edge of tail fin**; narrow black stripe near base of dorsal and anal fins. Juveniles black, with electric blue stripe dorsally on head and body. Attains 12 cm.

Indo-central Pacific region, Red Sea, Oman to Algoa Bay, occasionally to Tsitsikamma.

Coral and rocky reefs from 2–40 m. Cleaner wrasse feed mainly on crustacean ectoparasites of fish, and are even allowed access inside the mouth and gill chambers of the larger client fish. A pair of adult cleaner wrasses will establish a 'cleaner station' at a prominent spot on the reef. Their conspicuous colour pattern and bobbing swimming motion advertise their services and attract various customers. Clients wait patiently with fins erect, mouths open and gill covers flared as the cleaners work over their bodies and pick off parasites. The cleaner station is regularly visited by local reef fish, and even passing pelagic fish (mantas, fusiliers, barracuda, kingfish, etc.) will stop in for the cleaning service.

SIMILAR SPECIES

Adult bicolour cleaner wrasse, *Labroides bicolor* Fowler & Bean 1928, are sexually dimorphic: male has dark blue head, body black anteriorly, pale posteriorly; tail fin with black submarginal crescent. Juvenile black, with yellow stripe dorsally from mouth to upper half of tail fin; female grey with black lateral stripe anteriorly. Indo-central Pacific, Oman to Aliwal Shoal. A solitary itinerant cleaner, roaming the reef, looking for fish in need of its services.

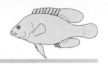

ROCKMOVER WRASSE
Novaculichthys taeniourus
(Lacepède 1801)

22 cm female (Mauritius)
9 cm juvenile

Body oblong and compressed, depth subequal to head length and 2.8–3.1 times in SL; **dorsal fin 9 slender spines, 12–13 rays, spinous membranes not incised, except in juveniles with first 2 dorsal fin spines greatly elongated and flexible; anal fin rays 12–13**; pectoral fin rays 13; tail fin rounded; pair of large canines at front of each jaw; LL interrupted; head naked except for short, near-vertical series of scales behind eye; branchiostegal membranes joined to isthmus; preopercle edge smooth. Adult **female brown, scales pale with dark margin, belly reddish**; head grey with dark streaks radiating from eye; iris red; **base of tail fin pale**; pectoral fin bases blackish; pelvic fins dark; first 2 dorsal fin membranes dark. **Male without dark streaks on head, belly like rest of body, and scales with a vertical yellowish line** instead of pale spot. Juvenile reddish, green or brown, with 4 rows of irregular white spots and narrow dark bars on body which extend into dorsal and anal fins; dorsal and anal fins with alternating coloured and transparent membranes, the fin rays mostly pigmented; tail fin transparent with dark rays; head with spots and white streaks radiating from eyes. Attains 30 cm.

Indo-Pacific, Red Sea, Oman to Aliwal Shoal.

Coral and rocky reefs, usually in rubble areas or sand flats to depths of 45 m. The adult rockmover wrasse often uses its mouth to lift bits of coral rubble to catch the small animals (crabs, brittlestars, molluscs, worms and sea urchins) hiding underneath. Adults usually in pairs, as they hunt their food co-operatively, and take turns, with one shifting the coral rubble and the other catching the fleeing prey. In a sandy area, adults will dive into the sand when threatened. Juveniles mimic drifting algae or seaweed as they float near the bottom, twisting and turning like a bit of weed pushed around by the current.

SIMILAR SPECIES

The seagrass wrasse, *Novaculoides macrolepidotus* (Bloch 1791), has body depth 3.4–3.9 times in SL; body green to brownish yellow, with dark blotches in a mid-lateral row. Indo-West Pacific, Red Sea to Durban. Juveniles often mimic seagrass blades or brown algae.

CHEEKLINED WRASSE
Oxycheilinus digramma
(Lacepède 1801)

~ 20 cm

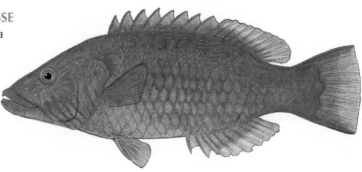

Body oblong, depth 2.8–3.3 times in SL; snout long, lower jaw slightly projecting, dorsal profile of snout straight or slightly concave; **dorsal fin 9 spines, 10 rays, spinous membranes incised; anal fin rays 8; pectoral fin rays 12**; pelvic fins short, not reaching anus; **tail fin rounded in juveniles and females, truncate or slightly emarginate in males**; LL interrupted; dorsal surface of head scaly to above middle of eyes; cheek and rear part of head also scaly; rear edge of pre-opercle free; snout naked. Colour variable, head and body greenish or grey, cheek and **lower part of operculum with 4–8 oblique red, maroon or pink lines**; dorsal part of head with similarly coloured streaks and spots; ventral part of body orange; proximal part of pelvic and anal fins reddish orange. Juvenile reddish brown, with 2 parallel white longitudinal stripes from front of head (one above and one below eye) to peduncle; dark oblique lines on lower part of head; red spots on pelvic and anal fins. Attains 35 cm.

Indo-central Pacific, Red Sea to Sodwana Bay.

Coral reefs to depths of 30 m. Feeds on crustaceans and fish. Solitary, swims high above reef; sometimes approaches divers.

SIMILAR SPECIES

Juvenile two-spot wrasse, *Oxycheilinus bimaculatus* (Valenciennes 1840), also have rounded tail fin, but their dorsal snout profile is convex; tail fin of adults wedge-shaped, with upper and middle rays elongate; small dark spot behind eye, larger diffuse spot usually present on body behind pectoral fins. This Indo-Pacific species extends south to Park Rynie.

SIXSTRIPE WRASSE
Pseudocheilinus hexataenia
(Bleeker 1857)

6 cm SL (Comoros)

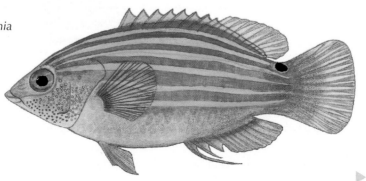

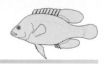

Body oblong and compressed, depth subequal to head length and 2.4–2.7 times in SL; dorsal fin 9 slender sharp spines, 11 rays, spinous membranes slightly incised; **anal fin 3 spines, 9 rays, first 1–2 spines with long filament at tip; pectoral fin rays 15–17**; tail fin rounded; eyes divided into 2 parts (see family text); 3 pairs of small canines at front of upper jaw, followed by a large recurved canine on each side; lower jaw with pair of canines at symphysis; **LL interrupted; cheek and opercle scaly; preopercle with membranous flap at angle, margin above serrate. Body purplish blue, with 6 yellow-orange stripes**, upper stripes extending onto head; **tail fin greenish, with black spot at base of upper fin rays**; yellow and red dots on lower part of head; 2 minute dots on front of lower lip. Attains 9 cm.

Indo-central Pacific, Red Sea, Oman to Aliwal Shoal.

Coral reefs in 2–35 m; usually in branches of live coral or rubble areas. Feeds on zooplankton and benthic crustaceans. A common active species, often seen in small groups.

SIMILAR SPECIES

The eightstripe wrasse, *Pseudocheilinus octotaenia* Jenkins 1901, has 8 lavender, magenta or purplish brown stripes on a yellow body; no dark spot on tail fin base. Similar habitat and habits to sixstripe wrasse. Attains 12 cm. Indo-central Pacific, south to Aliwal Shoal.

The pin-striped wrasse, *Pseudocheilinus evanidus* Jenkins 1901, is reddish with numerous pale longitudinal lines; conspicuous bluish white stripe from mouth along cheek. Cryptic species, in shallow areas and also to 40 m along drop-off walls with rubble patches. Attains 8 cm. Indo-central Pacific, Kenya to Margate.

CHISELTOOTH WRASSE
Pseudodax moluccanus
(Valenciennes 1840)

~ 17 cm adult
5 cm juvenile
(both Comoros)

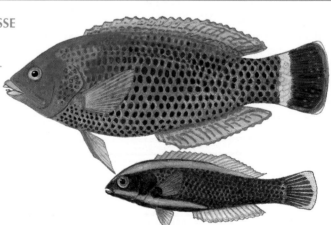

Body oblong, compressed, **depth distinctly more than head length and 2.4–2.9 times in SL**; dorsal fin 11 slender sharp spines, 12 rays, spinous membranes not incised; anal fin rays 14; pectoral fin rays 15; **pair of large, flattened, exposed incisor teeth at front of each jaw forming a beak-like mouth**; gill membranes united, forming free fold across isthmus; head scaly except for inter-orbital area, snout and chin; LL smoothly curved. Head and body greenish grey or brown, with dark spot on each body scale; nape and dorsal fin reddish orange; **lips yellow, with blue streak above upper lip and across cheek**; tail

fin blackish with pale base. Juvenile dark brown with 2 blue stripes, one dorsal and one ventral from front of head to rear ends of dorsal and anal fin bases; fins dark brown or reddish brown; tail fin base white. Attains 25 cm.

Indo-central Pacific, Red Sea to Sodwana Bay.

Coral reefs, usually in caves on seaward side of reefs to depths of 40 m. Adults feed on bryozoans, encrusting sponges and colonial ascidians. Juveniles in or near caves and act as 'cleaners'.

CUTRIBBON WRASSE
Stethojulis interrupta
(Bleeker 1851)

13 cm adult
8 cm juvenile

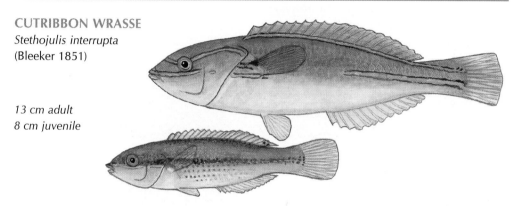

Body compressed; depth less than head length and 3.6–4.1 times in SL; **dorsal fin 9 slender sharp spines, 12 rays, spinous membranes not incised**; anal fin rays 11; pectoral fin rays 12–13; **jaws with single series of close-set incisors**; small canine at corner of mouth; LL sharply bent downwards below rear dorsal fin rays; gill membranes joined to isthmus; head naked; preopercle edge smooth. **Initial phase pinkish brown or green dorsally, whitish below**, with dark marks behind pectoral fins; white stripe from mouth to upper end of pectoral fin base. **Terminal male greenish brown dorsally, with blue line from nape along dorsal fin base to tail fin**; lower half of body pale blue to white, with blue line posteriorly between dorsal and ventral colours; **2 horizontal blue lines on head**, one through upper edge of eye and one below eye; **short blue line below pectoral fin base**; orange spot above pectoral fin base, black spot in axil of pectoral fin. Attains 13 cm.

Indo-West Pacific, Red Sea, Oman to Algoa Bay.

Coral and rocky reefs; usually in shallow water (2–15 m); juveniles in tide pools and seagrass beds. Feeds on benthic invertebrates (mainly crustaceans and molluscs). On rocky bottom, benthic prey are sucked into the mouth individually; on sandy substrate, a mouthful of sand is ingested; the tiny food organisms are then sorted out as the sand is passed through the gill rakers and out the gill openings. An active, fast-swimming little wrasse; usually seen in loose aggregations of initial phase fish with a single terminal male and other wrasses.

The terminal male of the bluelined wrasse, *Stethojulis albovittata* (Bonnaterre 1788), has a blue line from mouth along lower edge of eye, then curving over upper end of pectoral fin base, continuing posteriorly along mid-lateral part of body and onto middle tail fin rays; blue line along dorsal fin base curves down to top of eye; short blue line behind mid eye; pale line across lower part of head curving over pectoral fin base and above anal fin. Initial phase with upper half of body greenish to brown, covered with pale dots; lower half of body pale, with dark mark on each body scale; orange spot just above pectoral fin base; 2 tiny spots edged in pale blue at middle of tail fin base. Indo-Pacific, south to Sodwana Bay.

THREE-RIBBON WRASSE
Stethojulis strigiventer
(Bennett 1832)

11 cm female &
3 cm juvenile (Red Sea)
12 cm male (Comoros)

Body elongate and compressed, depth subequal to head, and 3.5–3.9 times in SL; **dorsal fin 9 slender sharp spines, 11 rays, spinous membranes not incised; anal fin rays 11; pectoral fin rays 14–15; jaws with single series of close-set incisors**; small canine at corner of mouth; LL bent sharply downwards below rear dorsal fin rays; gill membranes joined to isthmus; head naked; preopercle edge smooth. **Initial phase pale green or brown dorsally, upper half of head with dense maze-like darker pattern**; dorsal body scales with 2 small spots on each scale; lower half of body white with faint dark lines.

Terminal male with dorsal part of body green, **blue line along dorsal fin base not curving down to eye; upper blue line on head from front of snout to eye, to black spot on upper edge of operculum, continuing mid-laterally to tail fin**; pink zone from preopercle to pectoral fin base, lower body pale. All phases with tiny black spot just above LL on tail fin base. Attains 15 cm.

Indo-West Pacific, Oman to Algoa Bay.

Coral and rocky reefs, seagrass beds and tide pools; often in silty areas. Biology similar to cutribbon wrasse.

GOLDBAR WRASSE
Thalassoma hebraicum
(Lacepède 1801)

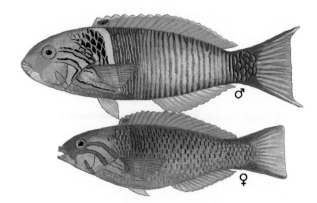

13 cm male
9 cm female

Body oblong and compressed, depth sub-equal to head length and 3.2–3.8 times in SL; **dorsal fin 8 slender sharp spines, 13 rays, spinous membranes not incised; anal fin rays 11; pectoral fin rays 15–16; tail fin truncate in female, lunate with elongate upper and lower rays in terminal male**; pair of canines at front of upper jaw, 1–2 pairs of canines at front of lower jaw; LL bent sharply downwards below rear dorsal fin rays; branchiostegal membranes joined to isthmus; head naked except for patch of small scales dorsally on opercle; preopercle edge smooth. Body of **initial phase blue-green with dark vertical lines; 2 oblique blue bands on chest and head**; tail fin yellow, upper and lower margins greenish; dorsal and anal fins yellow-green, black spot between 1st and 3rd dorsal fin spines. **Terminal male with bluntly rounded head; body with vertical blue streaks and lines, irregular gold bar from dorsal fin origin to belly**, preceded by dark blue scales with vertical black marks; head with green bands as on initial phase; pectoral fins hyaline; tail fin dark blue, upper and lower rays distinctly elongated. Attains 23 cm.

Indian Ocean, Kenya to Algoa Bay.

Coral and rocky reefs in 1–30 m, juveniles often in tide pools. Feeds on molluscs, crustaceans, sea urchins, brittlestars and worms.

SIMILAR SPECIES

The male twotone wrasse, *Thalassoma amblycephalum* (Bleeker 1856), is dark green with broad yellow blotch just behind head; head stripes salmon pink, pectoral fins yellow with blue blotch at tips; juvenile white, with broad dark brown band from front of snout over eye and along mid-lateral part of body to tail fin. Indo-central Pacific to the Eastern Cape.

CRESCENT-TAIL WRASSE
Thalassoma lunare
(Linnaeus 1758)

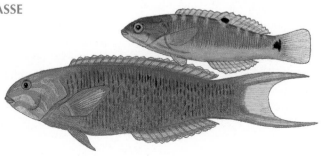

5 cm juvenile
~18 cm adult

Body oblong and compressed, depth subequal to head length and 3.1–3.7 times in SL; dorsal fin 8 slender sharp spines and 13 rays, spinous membranes not incised; anal fin rays 11; pectoral fin rays 15; **tail fin rounded in juvenile, emarginate in female, lunate with elongate upper and lower rays in terminal male**; pair of canines at front of each jaw; followed by row of progressively smaller conical teeth; no canines at corner of mouth; LL bent sharply downwards below rear dorsal fin rays; branchiostegal membranes joined to isthmus; head naked, except for small scales dorsally on opercle; preopercle edge smooth. **Initial phase olive with purplish vertical lines**; body blue ventrally; head pinkish with irregular blue stripes; black blotch above LL at tail fin base; black ocellus at front of soft dorsal rays; **tail fin of adults yellow with blue-edged purple upper and lower margins; pectoral fins pink with blue margins**; dorsal and anal fins mauve, with proximal and submarginal blue bands. Terminal male more bluish or green, especially the head. Attains 25 cm.

Indo-central Pacific, Red Sea, Oman to Algoa Bay.

Coral and rocky reefs in 1–32 m. Feeds on benthic invertebrates and fish. Usually in small groups on outer reef and in shallow lagoons. Bold inquisitive fish, not afraid of divers. Does well in aquaria.

SURGE WRASSE
Thalassoma purpureum
(Forsskål, 1775)

~ 20 cm male (western
Indian Ocean)
5 cm juvenile
15 cm female

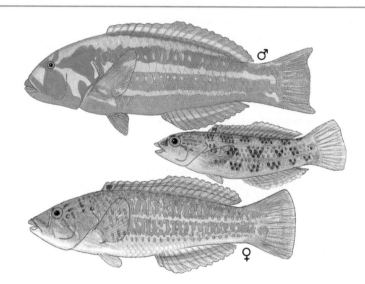

Body compressed, depth subequal to head length and 2.8–3.6 times in SL; dorsal fin 8 slender sharp spines, 13 rays, spinous membranes not incised; anal fin rays 11; pectoral fin rays 15–17; tail fin of juvenile rounded to truncate, emarginate or double emarginate in adult; pair of canines at front of each jaw; followed by row of progressively smaller conical teeth; no canines at corner of mouth; LL bent sharply downwards below rear dorsal fin rays; branchiostegal membranes joined to isthmus; head naked except for small scales dorsally on opercle; preopercle edge smooth. **Body of initial phase reddish orange (or white), with 2 horizontal rows of vertically elongate green spots**, the green spots of the upper row often contain vertically elongate red spots; head

and lower body greenish (or white), with orangish spots and streaks; V-shaped line in front of eye; dorsal fin red with green scaly sheath at base, green stripe along middle of fin and black spot over first 2 membranes; anal fin red, with blue stripe along middle of fin and pale scaly sheath; tail fin reddish orange with longitudinal streaks of blue/green, yellow posteriorly. Body of **terminal male blue/green with 3 longitudinal pink stripes**; head blue/green with pink stripes, including a large irregular bifurcate mark from eye to lower rear edge of operculum; dorsal and anal fins blue/green with pink stripe along middle of fins; tail fin blue/green with pink stripes; pectoral fins blue/green. Juvenile brownish with horizontal rows of W-shaped dark marks on body; dorsal and anal fins pale orange with green stripe along middle of fins; black spot on first 2 dorsal fin membranes. Attains 43 cm, 1.5 kg.

Indo-central Pacific, Red Sea to Coffee Bay, juveniles reach Algoa Bay.

Coral and rocky reefs, prefers areas exposed to surge and breaking waves; juveniles common in tide pools. Feeds on crustaceans, molluscs, sea urchins, brittlestars, worms and fish. The behaviour of the surge wrasse alternates between occasional (brief) periods of sedentary inactivity and frenetic swimming back and forth in the surge zone or over its territory. Terminal males are aggressive towards other males that encroach on their territory or attempt to associate with the females of their harem.

Often caught by shore anglers; but not usually eaten. An attractive and hardy aquarium fish, though larger fish tend to bully smaller fish in a community tank.

SIMILAR SPECIES

The ladder wrasse, *Thalassoma trilobatum* (Lacepède 1801), has similar colour pattern, but terminal male is orange to salmon pink, with 2 horizontal rows of yellow/blue/green rectangles on body; 4 narrow green bars joining upper row to irregular green band at base of dorsal fin; head and chest orange-brown without markings, head greenish dorsally; dorsal and anal fins greenish yellow, with broad blue/green margins on soft dorsal and anal fins; tail fin greenish with blue rear margin. Initial phase mostly greenish, with dark spots and streaks; 2 horizontal pink stripes (sometimes joined by vertical pink streaks) on lower half of body; dark marks arranged in staggered columns or interrupted rows; C-shaped dark line in front of eye. Like the surge wrasse, this species is an active fish of exposed rocky shores. Indo-central Pacific, south to East London.

FAMILY SCARIDAE ■ Parrotfish

Body oblong and robust (not slender or much compressed). Except for the few species of *Calotomus*, which have separate outer teeth, **the teeth of scarids are fused, forming beak-like jaws** that give the parrotfish their name. Mouth small, the jaws not protrusile; lips continuous with skin of the snout and lower jaw; maxilla covered by preorbital bone; no teeth on palate; **pharyngeal bones** (between the gills) **fused to form a unique grinding apparatus**; interlocking upper pharyngeal bones with 1–3 rows of molars arranged on a convex surface that rolls over the concave surface of the lower pharyngeal bones. Dorsal fin single

with 9 slender, often flexible spines and 10 rays; anal fin with 3 weak spines and 9 rays; tail fin rounded, truncate, lunate, emarginate or double emarginate. **Scales large, cycloid**, those of LL with numerous branching tubes; LL interrupted below rear dorsal fin rays, continued mid-laterally on peduncle. Head naked except for scales on cheek, operculum and (in some species) top of head. Preopercle and rear edge of opercle smooth. Size range 19 cm to 1.2 m.

Parrotfish are generally herbivorous, but some species may also feed on live coral. There are two types of feeding modes for parrotfish:

■ the excavators (*Chlorurus, Bolbometopon* and *Cetoscarus*) use their powerful jaws and strong tooth plates to gouge limestone and live coral tissue from the reef as they feed, leaving a distinctive double groove in the coral;

■ the scrapers (species of *Scarus*) with more delicate tooth plates, feed mainly on filamentous algae which they scrape from dead coral, rock and sand.

Scarids also feed on seagrass and detritus. The plant material and rock fragments are ground to a fine sediment in the pharyngeal mill and this mixture is swallowed by the parrotfish. The crushed plant cells are digested in the long intestine of the fish, and the crushed coral is voided as a white cloud of fine coral sand from the anus. The production of pulverised coral sand by parrotfish is the major source of calcium carbonate sediment on the reef. Scarids are common on coral or rocky reefs and in seagrass beds, the preferred habitat for some small parrotfish and the nursery area for the young of most species.

At night, most parrotfish sleep on the reef, usually well hidden in crevices and under ledges. Some species secrete a transparent mucous covering around themselves before they go to sleep; this mucous coat may contain their scent and help conceal the sleeping fish from nocturnal predators like moray eels.

Parrotfish are protogynous hermaphrodites, but some species have small mature males (primary males) that are coloured like juveniles or mature (initial phase) females as well as larger (terminal phase) males that represent transformed females. This reproductive mode, with two kinds of males, is called 'diandric protogyny'. Terminal males are more colourful than initial-phase fish, and juveniles and females of many species are similar and difficult to identify.

Scarids are good eating, but the soft flesh deteriorates rapidly in the tropics.

Tropical and warm temperate waters of all oceans. Ten genera and ~90 valid species, plus 2 additional undescribed species; 19 species in our area.

Star-eye parrotfish

Bluemoon parrotfish

Blue humphead parrotfish

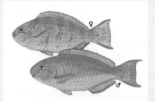

Bullethead parrotfish   Seagrass parrotfish   Bluebarred parrotfish

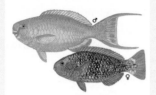

Ember parrotfish   Saddled parrotfish

STAR-EYE PARROTFISH
Calatomus viridescens
(Rüppell 1835)

*40 cm males (two colour
forms, top & bottom)
30 cm female (middle fish)*

Outer teeth at front of upper jaw separate, in 2–6 overlapping rows; upper jaw teeth overlapping lower jaw teeth when mouth is closed; **1 row of cheek scales**; pectoral fin rays 13; body depth 2.2–2.6 times in SL. Head, body and fins blue/green or brown, with irregular pink or white spots. **Head of terminal male green, with pink stripes radiating from eye** and 3 across top of snout. Sometimes with small purplish spots above pectoral fins. Attains 50 cm.

Indo-Pacific, Red Sea, Oman to Aliwal Shoal.

Coral reefs, seagrass beds, sandy and rubble areas with thick algal growth in 2–27 m. Feeds on encrusting and leafy algae and seagrass, and scapes algae from dead coral.

The Christmas parrotfish, *Calotomus carolinus* (Valenciennes), is a synonym.

SIMILAR SPECIES

The spinytooth parrotfish, *Calatomus spinidens* (Quoy & Gaimard 1824), has 1 row of narrowly flattened teeth on outer surface of upper jaw tooth plate; tail fin truncate or slightly emarginate in adults; body more slender, depth 2.7–3.1 times in SL. Initial phase mottled green to greyish brown, sometimes with faint broad stripes, often with 3 horizontal rows of whitish spots; upper and lower edges of tail fin with dusky spots. Terminal male with small faint orange spots on body and head, reddish orange stripes on head, including 2 stripes from lower jaw across rear of upper lip to eye; pectoral fin base black; black spot(s) on first 3 dorsal fin membranes. Indo-West Pacific, south to Maputo Bay.

BLUEMOON PARROTFISH
Chlorurus atrilunula
(Randall & Bruce 1983)

34 cm male
26 cm female

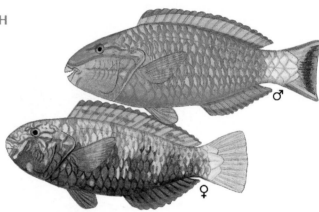

Body depth subequal to head length, 2.3–2.6 times in SL; **lips cover about half of tooth plates; 1–2 canines posteriorly on side of upper jaw**; cheek scales in 2 rows; **median predorsal scales 4**; tail fin truncate to emarginate in adults, rounded in juveniles; pectoral fin rays 15, fin 1.5–1.7 times in head length. **Initial phase brown on ventral half of head and body, the upper half white, with reddish mark on each scale**; 4 irregular whitish bars on body; head dorsally with reddish brown spots and wavy stripes; tail fin and rear of peduncle pale. **Terminal male head and body blue/green, front half of each body scale yellow or salmon pink**; peduncle and tail fin base white, the upper and lower margins blue with yellow submarginal stripes, central **rear part of fin a dark blue crescent**; dorsal and anal fins blue with broad pink band along middle of fins; broad green-edged salmon pink zone mid-laterally, from mouth to rear edge of head. Attains 36 cm.

Western Indian Ocean, Kenya to Sodwana Bay.

Coral reefs in 5–30 m. Originally described in the genus *Scarus*; recently shifted (along with 16 other Indo-Pacific species) to the genus *Chlorurus*.

BLUE HUMPHEAD PARROTFISH
Chlorurus cyanescens
(Valenciennes 1840)

47 cm male

Body depth subequal to head length, 2.3–2.6 times in SL; **lips cover about half of white tooth plates**; 1–2 canines posteriorly on side of upper jaw; cheek scales in 2 rows; median predorsal scales 3; terminal male with large fleshy protuberance above eye; tail fin rounded; pectoral fin rays 15. Terminal male with **head and front of body dark blue, rest of body yellowish green** with dark margins on scales; dorsal, anal and pelvic fins violet with pale blue edge; pectoral fins black; tooth plates bluish green with white edge. Initial phase unknown. Attains 50 cm.

Western Indian Ocean, Zanzibar to Aliwal Shoal, Madagascar and Mauritius; rare south of Sodwana Bay.

Coral reefs in 10–30 m. Solitary species; like other species of *Chlorurus*, this parrotfish uses its powerful jaws to gouge or bite off some of the coral's limestone skeleton as it feeds.

This species was originally described in the genus *Scarus*. The first South African record was based on a photograph by Dennis King taken at Sodwana Bay.

BULLETHEAD PARROTFISH
Chlorurus sordidus
(Forsskål 1775)

20 cm female
25 cm male (Bahrain)
7 cm juvenile (Japan)

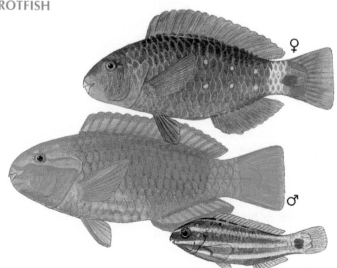

Body depth subequal to head length, 2.5–3.0 times in SL; lips cover about half of tooth plates; 1–2 conical teeth on side of upper tooth plate of males; cheek scales in 2 rows; median predorsal scales 4, the first 2 notably wider than last 2 scales; tail fin rounded in initial phase, truncate to slightly emarginate in males; pectoral fin rays 14–16. **Initial phase body and fins brown, often with 2 horizontal rows of 3–6 white spots on side of body;** peduncle white with dark blotch at base of tail fin (the white spots and peduncle pattern can be turned on or off by the fish). **Terminal male with body green, edges of scales purple or pale bluish grey; scales of peduncle blue with green edges; upper rear part of head green**; snout lavender, with green band along upper lip and curving up to eye; edge of lip pink; lower jaw with 2 broad transverse green or blue-green bands; cheek pale blue or greenish yellow; upper and lower margins of all fins dark blue, pectoral fins with lavender stripe. Juvenile uniform brown or brown with 4 pale stripes, pale peduncle, dark spot at tail fin base. Attains 40 cm.

Indo-central Pacific, Red Sea, Oman to Sodwana Bay.

Coral reefs, including rubble areas and reef flats; juveniles in seagrass beds.

Chlorurus sordidus was previously classified in the genus *Scarus*.

SEAGRASS PARROTFISH
Leptoscarus vaigiensis
(Quoy & Gaimard 1824)

23 cm male
20 cm female
(both Mauritius)

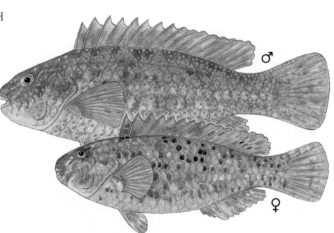

Body slender, depth 2.9–3.7 times in SL; teeth completely fused in each jaw, forming beak-like dental plates with a median suture; lips covering tooth plates; cheek scales in 1 row; median predorsal scales 4; dorsal fin spines flexible, spinous membranes distinctly incised; pectoral fin rays 13. **Head and body mottled olive-green to brown above, paler below; males with small blue spots on head,** body, anal and tail fins and irregular white stripe on body. Attains 35 cm.

Indo-Pacific, Oman to the Eastern Cape.

Seagrass beds and shallow areas with thick algal growth. Feeds in groups on seagrass. Females mature ~17 cm; fecundity was estimated at 670 000 eggs in one batch per season. Caught in artisanal fisheries in Kenya and probably elsewhere.

BLUEBARRED PARROTFISH
Scarus ghobban
Forsskål 1775

36 cm female
81 cm male (Mauritius)

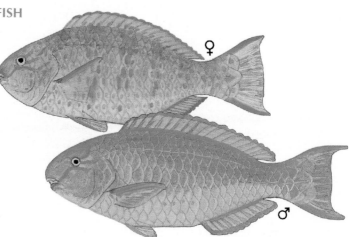

Body depth subequal to head length, 2.7–3.0 times in SL; **lips cover more than half of pale salmon to white tooth plates**; 1–3 conical teeth posteriorly on side of upper jaw of males; cheek scales usually in 3 rows, but only 1 scale in 3rd row; rear nostril oval, 2–5 times larger than front nostril; median predorsal scales 5–6; tail fin distinctly lunate in large males; pectoral fin rays 15–16. **Initial phase head and body dusky yellowish brown, body scales with a large blue spot**; 5 irregular bars (formed by intensification of the spots within the bars) often visible on body; blue stripes on head; margin of all fins blue-green. **Terminal male greenish, scales edged in salmon pink; dorsal and anal fins orange or bluish grey, with blue/green margin and band along base**; pectoral fins blue-green marginally, the centre salmon pink. Juveniles often with 2 white spots on sides. Attains 87 cm, 9.2 kg.

Indo-Pacific, Red Sea, Oman to Durban, juveniles to Algoa Bay.

Coral reefs and adjacent sandy areas of lagoons and bays; often in silty areas; juveniles on inshore reefs, adults usually in 15–40 m. Adults solitary, or sometimes in small groups.

The bluebarred parrotfish is the most widely distributed species of parrotfish; Pacific fish differ slightly in colour from those in the Indian Ocean. The species has been given 26 different scientific names.

SIMILAR SPECIES

The terminal male saddled parrotfish (see p. 362) is similar, but has upper part of head and front of body greyish; no conical teeth at rear of upper jaw; 13–14 pectoral fin rays, and broad green or blue zone from front of upper lip under eye to rear edge of operculum.

EMBER PARROTFISH
Scarus rubroviolaceus
Bleeker 1847

*60 cm male (includes
tail fin lobes)
32 cm female (Maldives)*

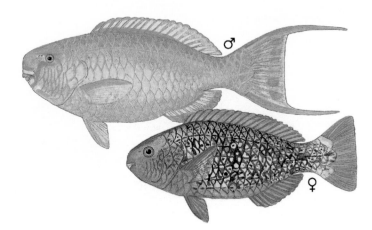

Body depth subequal to head length, 2.7–3.1 times in SL; **lips cover more than half of white tooth plates**; 1–3 conical teeth posteriorly on side of upper jaw in males; cheek scales in 3 rows, with 1–3 scales in 3rd row; snout blunt; median predorsal scales 5–7; tail fin lunate in adults; pectoral fin rays 14–16. **Initial phase body red, brown or greenish, covered with irregular pale spots**, most spots with 1–3 dark dots; front of head, ventral part of body, anal and paired fins reddish; tooth plates pale red to white. **Terminal male bluish green, mid-lateral part of body yellowish; top of head darker**, upper lip pink with submarginal dark blue band; iris orange; blue band below eye, onto lower jaw, where it encloses a pinkish band on lower lip; tooth plates blue-green. Juveniles white, with 3 brown bands from front of head to tail fin. Attains 66 cm.

Indo-Pacific, Oman to Protea Bank.

Coral reefs in 5–35 m. Most common parrotfish at Sodwana Bay; females often in schools or in groups with a terminal male. Feeds on benthic algae.

SADDLED PARROTFISH
Scarus scaber
Valenciennes 1840

*24 cm male (Djibouti)
19 cm female*

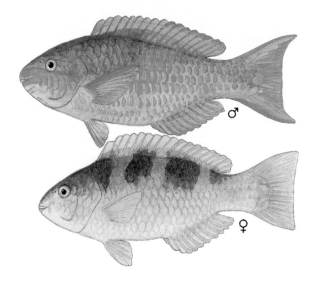

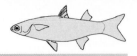

Body depth subequal to head length, 2.7–3.1 times in SL; lips cover most or all of white tooth plates; no conical teeth at rear of jaws; cheek scales in 3 rows, with 1–4 scales in 3rd row; snout blunt; nostrils small and close together; median predorsal scales 4–7; tail fin lunate in males, truncate or slightly emarginate in initial phase; pectoral fin rays 13–14. **Initial phase with head dusky greenish yellow or brown dorsally, pale below; dorsal part of body with 4 dark bars or saddle blotches. Terminal male blue/green, body scales with pink edges**; blue/green band on lips, joining behind mouth and running under eye to rear edge of operculum; edge of upper lip pink; dorsal part of head and front of body dark grey; blue/green stripe through upper part of eye. Attains 40 cm.

Western Indian Ocean, Oman to Sodwana Bay and various islands.

Inner coral reefs, often in silty areas in 5–25 m. Occurs in small groups of males and females.

FAMILY MUGILIDAE ▪ Mullet

Body cylindrical anteriorly, compressed posteriorly, body depth 3–4 times in SL; head small, depressed, its length less than body depth; inter-orbital area broad and scaly; **2 dorsal fins, the 1st with 4 slender stiff spines; 2nd dorsal fin with 1 slender spine and 6–9 rays**; anal fin with 3 spines and 8–10 rays; tail fin forked in most species; pectoral fin rays 12–18; pelvic fins with 1 slender spine, 5 soft-rays; body and most of head covered with thin, usually weakly ctenoid scales; no LL, but some species with 1 or more mucous grooves; axillary scale or scaly process present, rudimentary or absent at base of pectoral, pelvic and 1st dorsal fins. The **lateral scale series (LSS)** are the number of oblique scale series from upper end of gill opening to base of tail fin. Mouth small, terminal; jaw teeth minute, usually hidden by upper lip and in adults upper jaw teeth are mostly hidden in spongy tissue behind lip; lower jaw usually toothless; most species with microscopic teeth in mouth, variously present or absent on vomer, palatines, pterygoids and tongue; no spines on head; preopercle smooth and mostly hidden by scales; some species with well developed adipose eyelid; branchiostegal membranes separate, not attached to isthmus; gill rakers numerous, long and slender, forming an efficient filter. Size range 20 cm to 1.2 m.

Mullet feed mainly on detritus and are usually found over soft sediments (sand, silt and mud). They take in large quantities of sediment along with detritus; the fine particles and water pass through the gill rakers and out the gill openings; the coarse sediment, nutritious detritus and various minute living organisms (algae, crustaceans, molluscs, worms and various micro-organisms) are passed into the muscular stomach, which is similar to a chicken's gizzard. The organic material is physically broken down in the stomach and eventually passed into the long intestine where the nutrients are absorbed.

Mullet are common in estuaries, bays, coastal lagoons and along sandy shores. Two of our species are found in rivers, and the freshwater mullet, *Myxus capensis*, returns to the sea only to spawn. Mullet spawn in the sea, or in the lower reaches of estuaries, primarily during winter and spring. The young use estuaries as a nursery area, and mullet (both juveniles and

adults) comprise a major component of the estuarine fish fauna. Large catches of mullet are made with beach seines and floating gill-nets along the Western Cape coast. In summer, mullet are caught intertidally on the Agulhas coast in stone-walled traps when the fish are left stranded by the falling tide. Large mullet provide excellent sport on light tackle and are caught by anglers using flyrods or light tackle with bread, dough, stiff 'mielie' porridge, flying ants, prawn or even pilchard bait. Juveniles usually taken with a throw net and make excellent bait.

Because of their surface schooling habits, abundance and accessibility to coastal populations, mullet are commercially important, especially to artisanal fisheries. Widely used in aquaculture, due to their simple diet, hardiness in captivity, fast growth and tolerance for freshwater.

Worldwide in tropical and temperate waters. About 17 genera, ~70 species, 16 in our area. The taxonomy of this family is confused, and the composition and definition of the genera are obscure.

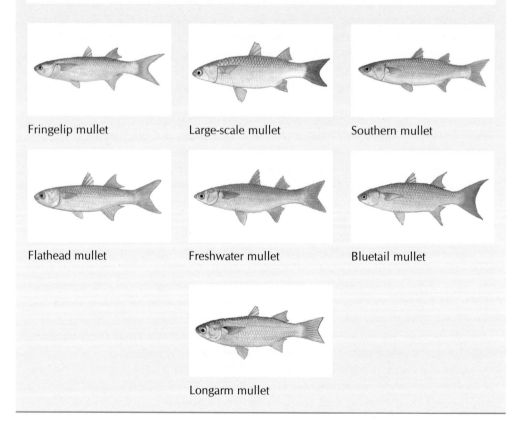

Fringelip mullet

Large-scale mullet

Southern mullet

Flathead mullet

Freshwater mullet

Bluetail mullet

Longarm mullet

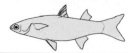

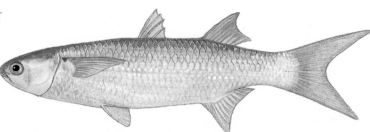

FRINGELIP MULLET
Crenimugil crenilabis
(Forsskål 1775)

60 cm adult

Body depth 3.5–4.0 times in SL; **no adipose eyelid; lips with distinct soft papillae but no teeth; minute teeth on tongue; scales with pliable membranous digitations on rear margin; LSS 38–41**; pectoral fins and 1st dorsal fin with enlarged axillary scale; anal fin rays 8; adults with anterior soft dorsal and anal fin rays 3–4 times length of posterior rays. Head and body olive-green dorsally, silvery below; pectoral fins pale yellow with black spot on upper end of base, purple spot in axil; tail fin bluish grey, rear margin blackish; other fins grey. Attains 60 cm.

Indo-central Pacific, Red Sea, Oman to Coffee Bay, juveniles to Algoa Bay.

Inshore over sandy bottom or coral reefs; juveniles in estuaries and tide pools. Spawns at night in large groups at surface.

SIMILAR SPECIES

Other mullet species lack papillae on upper lip.

LARGE-SCALE MULLET
Liza macrolepis
(Smith 1846)

31 cm adult

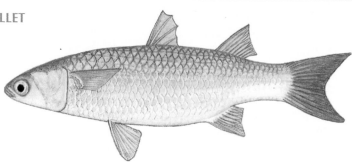

Body depth 3.6–4.2 times in SL; **no adipose eyelid; maxilla and premaxilla curved downwards, visible when mouth is shut; microscopic teeth on jaws, vomer, pterygoids and tongue; scales finely ctenoid; LSS 33–35**; pectoral fin axillary scale rudimentary; **anal fin rays 9, anterior rays ~3 times length of posterior rays**. Head and body greenish grey dorsally, silvery below; gold spot on opercle; rear edge of tail fin dusky. Attains 40 cm.

Indo-central Pacific, Red Sea, Oman to Knysna.

Common in estuaries of KZN; also in bays, along sandy shores and enters rivers. Post-larvae (10–20 mm) feed on copepods, cladocerans, insect larvae, fish eggs and diatoms; juveniles and adults feed by day on detritus, diatoms, dinoflagellates, filamentous algae, seagrass fragments, foraminiferans, benthic crustaceans and gastropods. Matures at 23 cm SL; spawns in lower reaches of estuaries during winter and spring.

Some authors assign this species to the genus *Chelon*.

The groovy mullet, *Liza dumerili* (Steindachner 1870), which also has a gold spot on the opercle, has scales on the nape with numerous wavy grooves and LSS 36–39. Senegal to Namibia and False Bay to Mozambique.

The diamond mullet, *Liza alata* (Steindachner 1892), is a larger fish (attains 75 cm) with dark scale margins that give the fish a distinctive reticulate ('diamond-shaped') pattern, and yellow pelvic fins about as long as pectoral fins in adults; the 2nd dorsal fin and the anal and tail fins of adults are distinctly falcate. The diamond mullet is a prodigious leaper and provides excellent sport on light tackle. Indo-West Pacific, south to Algoa Bay.

SOUTHERN MULLET
Liza richardsonii
(Smith 1846)

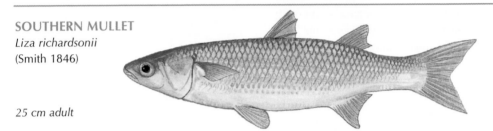

25 cm adult

Body depth 3.7–4.3 times in SL; **adipose eyelid rudimentary or absent**; maxilla and premaxilla curved downwards, **maxilla visible when mouth is shut**; microscopic, slightly flattened teeth on upper jaw; villiform teeth on vomer, palatines, pterygoids and tongue; scales finely ctenoid; **LSS 44–50**; pectoral fin axillary scale short or rudimentary; anal fin rays 9, anterior rays about twice length of posterior rays; pectoral fins folded forwards reach eyes. Head and body silvery, darker above, dorsal body scales with dark edges; median fins dusky; gold blotch on opercle. Attains 41 cm FL.

Endemic, Cunene River to St Lucia.

Common in estuaries, and abundant in the sea. Postlarvae (<20 mm SL) feed mainly on zooplankton (copepods and crab larvae); in estuaries, juveniles (>30 mm SL) and adults eat detritus, benthic diatoms, foraminiferans, unicellular and filamentous algae, seagrass and macro-algae; in the sea, more zooplankton is consumed. Feeds mainly by day. Matures at about 21 cm FL. Spawns close inshore between September and March in Eastern Cape waters; in the Western Cape, it apparently spawns throughout year. This mullet is truly euryhaline and has been found in salinities of 2–90‰. Juveniles common prey of many coastal predators (kob, garrick, elf and piscivorous birds); adults eaten by dusky, ragged-tooth and juvenile great white sharks.

Of great importance in commercial seine and gill-net fisheries of the Western Cape, with an annual catch of several million fish. Marketed fresh, or dried with salt and sold as 'bokkom'; smoked bokkom is considered a traditional Western Cape delicacy. Makes excellent bait.

The striped mullet, *Liza tricuspidens* (Smith 1935), has 7–8 dusky stripes along upper scale rows of body; pectoral fins longer than head minus snout; adipose eyelids small in adults; teeth in upper jaw relatively large, with 3 rounded cusps (lip must be pushed back to see 2 basal cusps); lower jaw and palatines toothless; LSS 43–48. Angola, False Bay to Kosi Bay,

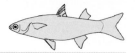

usually found in estuaries. According to JLB Smith (1949, p. 320), 'Large numbers are rarely taken by nets, as the species is characterised by the most extraordinary leaping powers; large fish [it attains 70 cm FL and 3 kg] are able to rise 2.4 m and clear 12 m with a single leap, which may be repeated several times.' Hence the alternate common name 'springer'. Smith also reported that striped mullet occasionally leap into boats that carry a light at night, and he knew of a man who was knocked from his seat when struck in the chest by a leaping mullet. Striped mullet are occasionally taken by anglers with prawn bait,

and they are incredible fighters on light tackle.

The squaretail mullet, *Liza vaigiensis* (Quoy & Gaimard 1825), has much larger scales (LSS 26–28), tail fin slightly emarginate (almost truncate), dusky streaks along upper scale rows of body; and pectoral fins black, with lower margin yellow in adults. Indo-central Pacific, Oman to Durban.

The St Lucia mullet, *Liza luciae* (Penrith & Penrith 1967), also has large scales (LSS 26–28), tail fin distinctly concave, pectoral fins shorter than head minus snout and with only 12–13 fin rays, dorsal fin rays 7. Port St Johns to Mozambique.

FLATHEAD MULLET
Mugil cephalus
Linnaeus 1758

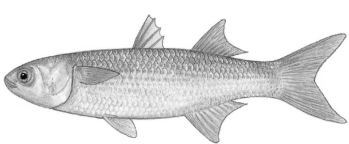

40 cm adult

Body depth 3.7–4.3 times in SL; **adipose eyelid well developed (except in juveniles < 3 cm SL)**, thick, with a narrow elliptical opening over pupil in adult, and adipose tissue also extends in front and behind eyeball; **maxilla straight, hidden by preorbital bone when mouth is shut;** jaws with curved compressed teeth in 1 or more rows; villiform teeth on pterygoids, vomer and palatines; tongue edentate; scales weakly ctenoid, rear edge membranous; **LSS 38–42; pectoral fin axillary scale long; anal fin rays 8 (rarely 9), anterior rays about twice length of posterior rays; soft dorsal and anal fins scaly only on front part of fin base;** pectoral fin rays 16–17, fin shorter than head minus snout; tail fin distinctly forked. Olive-green dorsally with ~7 dark stripes along dorsal body scales; fins dusky;

dark blue spot at base of pectoral fins disappears when fish are taken out of water. Attains 1.2 m FL, 8 kg (16 years). South African maximum size ~80 cm FL.

> Worldwide in tropical and temperate waters; all round the coast of southern Africa.

Juveniles and adults abundant in estuaries and rivers; also in the sea. Usually in large schools of like-sized fish; juveniles depend on estuaries for the first year of their life. Matures at 34–40 cm SL (~3 years). Spawns in groups; eggs are shed in batches in open water near the coast from May to September. Total fecundity for a 56 cm female was estimated at 4.2 million eggs. Renowned for its leaping abilities; adults often jump over float line of beach

seines. Flathead mullet, especially juveniles, fall prey to a variety of piscivores: sharks, elf, garrick, kob, barracuda, dolphins, seals, herons, cormorants, pelicans, sea eagles and man.

In April and May at St Lucia, there is a huge annual migration, the 'mullet run', of large mullet schools rushing out the mouth to spawn in the sea. This concentration of fish attracts sharks and crocodiles that make frenzied attacks on the milling fish. Sharks have been observed at low tide rolling over sand bars to get at the mullet.

This common species is of considerable commercial importance; caught from beaches and estuaries with seines, gill-nets, cast nets,

stake nets, lift nets and fish corrals. Sold fresh, live, frozen, smoked and salted; the roe is smoked or sold fresh. Juveniles used for bait. SADSAA all-tackle record: 4.5 kg. In the USA, a.k.a. 'striped' or 'grey mullet'.

SIMILAR SPECIES

The robust mullet, *Valamugil robustus* (Günther 1861), has well developed (but thin) adipose eyelid, 9 anal fin rays, no teeth on jaws or in mouth; LSS 36–39; soft dorsal and anal fins covered with scales; body silvery with traces of dark stripes along dorsal scale rows and distinct dark spot at upper end of pectoral fin bases. Eastern Cape estuaries to Inhambane and Madagascar.

FRESHWATER MULLET
Myxus capensis
(Valenciennes 1836)

30 cm adult

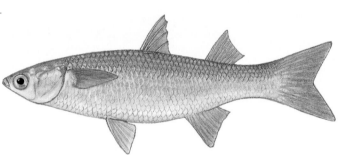

Body depth 3.9–4.6 times in SL; **adipose eyelid rudimentary; maxilla mostly hidden by preorbital bone when mouth is shut**; upper jaw with a row of close-set, flattened, recurved, spatulate teeth, with notch at each side of apex; lower jaw edentate; some fish with small cilia; villiform teeth on vomer, palatines, pterygoids and tongue; scales weakly ctenoid on flanks and belly; LSS 43–45; no pectoral fin axillary scale; 1st dorsal fin origin midway between tail fin and tip of snout; anal fin rays 9, anterior rays about twice length of posterior rays; soft dorsal and anal fins completely scaly; pectoral fin rays 17, fin shorter than head minus snout; tail fin distinctly forked. Fish from clear water

rivers or estuaries are silvery; in turbid water, the colour is almost black dorsally, silver below. Attains 45 cm FL.

Endemic, False Bay to Kosi Bay.

Spends most of its life in freshwater, ascending rivers as far as it can go, but returns to the sea to spawn. More abundant in estuaries than in rivers. Juveniles and adults feed on detritus, benthic diatoms, filamentous algae and insects. Females mature at 23 cm SL, males at ~19 cm SL; spawns in the sea from March to November. Tolerates a wide salinity range of 0–49‰, and survives prolonged exposure to low salinities and low temperatures that are fatal to most marine fish.

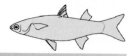

BLUETAIL MULLET
Valamugil buchanani
(Bleeker 1853)

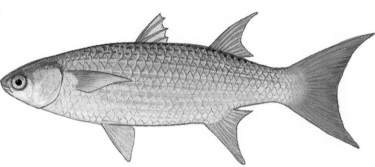

73 cm adult

Body depth 3.3–3.7 times in SL; adipose eyelid rudimentary; maxilla slightly curved downward at tip, hidden by preorbital bone when mouth is shut; microscopic teeth on jaws of small juveniles; no jaw teeth on larger fish; villiform teeth on pterygoids and front margin of tongue; vomer and palatines edentate; scales smooth with membranous edge; **LSS 33–36; pectoral fin axillary scale long; anal fin rays 9; fish >12 cm SL with distal margin of soft dorsal and anal fins falcate, the anterior lobe 3–4 times length of posterior rays and longer than pelvic fins**; pectoral fins longer than head minus snout. Body silvery, blue grey or greenish dorsally; dark spot at centre of each dorsal body scale; **tail fin electric blue**, upper and lower margins dark; soft dorsal fin dusky, leading edge dark; pectoral fins hyaline gold, with dark blue or black spot at upper end of fin base. Attains 1 m.

Indo-West Pacific, Oman to Breë estuary.

Juveniles prefer permanently open estuaries. Matures at ~40 cm FL; spawns inshore mainly between October and December.

Tail fin loses its bright blue colour soon after this mullet is taken out of water.

LONGARM MULLET
Valamugil cunnesius
(Valenciennes 1836)

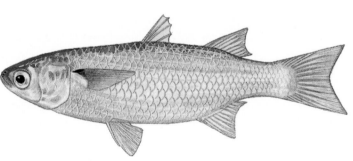

26 cm adult

Body depth 3.6–3.9 times in SL; **adipose eyelid well developed, posterior eyelid almost reaches pupil; snout bluntly rounded; maxilla tip curved downward, exposed in front of preorbital bone when mouth is shut**; microscopic pointed teeth in 1 row on upper jaw; villiform teeth on pterygoids and front margin of tongue; vomer and palatines edentate; scales smooth with membranous edge; LSS 37–43; pectoral fin axillary scale long; anal fin rays 9; pectoral fin rays 15–17, fin 23–25% SL, **longer than head minus**

snout and reaches past vertical at base of 3rd dorsal fin spine. Head and body silvery, dark spot at upper end of pectoral fin base connected to black streak in axil of fin; distal edge of dorsal fins and upper and rear edges dark. Attains 35 cm.

Indo-West Pacific, Oman to Algoa Bay; distribution uncertain because of confusion with other species.

Juveniles common in estuaries and lagoons. Usually feeds over mud bottom. Matures at 17 cm SL; spawns inshore near river mouths from October to May.

FAMILY POLYNEMIDAE ■ Threadfins

Body oblong-elongate, compressed posteriorly, body depth ~3–4 times in SL; head length subequal to body depth; inter-orbital area broad and scaly; **2 separate dorsal fins, 1st with 8 slender stiff spines, 2nd fin with 1 slender spine, 12–14 rays; anal fin with 2–3 spines, 11–13 rays; pectoral fins set low on body and divided into 2 parts: upper (rear) part with 13–18 rays joined by membrane, and lower (anterior) part with 3–6 separate elongate filamentous rays; tail fin deeply forked;** pelvic fins well behind pectoral fins, with 1 spine, 5 rays; **snout cartilaginous, translucent, bluntly pointed, projecting over upper jaw; maxilla extends behind eye**; villiform teeth in bands on jaws and palatines, also on vomer in some species; no upper lip; eyes covered with transparent adipose tissue; no spines on opercle; preopercle edge serrate or smooth; body and most of head covered with thin, usually weakly ctenoid scales; LL almost straight, continuing onto tail fin, usually with a branch on each lobe; branchiostegal membranes separate, not attached to isthmus; gill rakers well developed; swimbladder present in some species, absent in others. Polynemids range in size from 30 cm to ~1.8 m.

Threadfins occur in shallow coastal waters, in the sea or in estuaries, usually over soft sediments (sand, silt and mud). Feed mainly on benthic crustaceans (crabs, stomatopods, amphipods, mysids, penaeid prawns), worms and fish. The separate lower pectoral fin rays are used as 'feelers' to detect their prey, and this additional sensory ability is useful in the turbid areas that threadfins usually inhabit.

Generally good to eat, and of considerable economic importance in some areas. Caught with trawls, beach seines, gill-nets and by anglers. Some species used in aquaculture.

Worldwide in tropical and warm temperate seas. Eight genera, ~41 species, 4 in our area.

STRIPED THREADFIN
Polydactylus plebeius
(Broussonet 1782)

13 cm juvenile

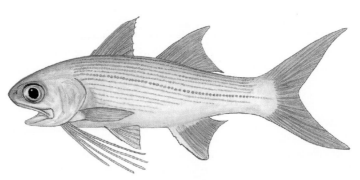

Body depth 3.1–4.0 times in SL; **2nd dorsal fin rays 12–13; anal fin with 3 spines, 11–12 rays; margin of dorsal and anal fins distinctly falcate; pectoral fins with 21–23 rays, lower (anterior) 5 rays unbranched and separate**; lower lip well developed; LL scales 60–68; LL continued to upper end of lower tail lobe. Head and body dusky silver above, paler below; **7 or 8 dark stripes along upper scale rows**; dorsal and tail fins pale with black rear margins; pectoral fin membranes blackish, the filaments white; pelvic and anal fins dusky yellow, leading edges white. Attains 55 cm.

Indo-central Pacific, Kenya to Knysna; not in Red Sea or Persian Gulf.

Estuaries and coastal waters over soft sediment to 122 m; avoids estuaries with low salinities. Males mature at 20 cm FL, change to females at about 30 cm FL. Spawns during last quarter of lunar cycle at high tide in shallow water.

Caught from shore by anglers using prawn or fish baits. SA angling record: 2.4 kg.

SIMILAR SPECIES

The African blackspot threadfin, *Polydactylus malagasyensis* Motomura & Iwatsuki 2001, was previously misidentified as *Polydactylus sextarius* (Bloch & Schneider 1801), which is known from India to New Guinea. *P. malagasyensis* occurs from Kenya to Algoa Bay, also at Madagascar; in estuaries and the sea in depths of 16–62 m. Black blotch at origin of LL; LL scales 46–51; pectoral fin rays 20, including 6 free rays at lower end of fin; no teeth on vomer; palatine tooth patch with sharp bend at anterior end.

The Indian threadfin, *Leptomelanosoma indicum* (Shaw 1804) [formerly known as *Polydactylus indicus*], is more slender, body depth 4.0–4.8 times in SL; dark brown to blackish, with pale LL; pectoral fin rays 17–19, including 5 free rays at lower end of pectoral fin base; swimbladder with numerous lateral appendages inserted into lateral body musculature. Indo-West Pacific, Mozambique to Durban.

FAMILY SPHYRAENIDAE ■ Barracuda

Body almost cylindrical, body depth 5–9 times in SL; head large, its length much greater than body depth, 2.5–4.0 times in SL; snout long and pointed; jaws elongate, lower jaw strongly projecting; large, sharp, flattened or conical teeth on jaws and on palatines; interorbital area broad, flat and scaly; **2 well separated dorsal fins, 1st with 5 slender stiff spines; 2nd dorsal fin with 1 slender spine and 8–9 rays; anal fin with 1–2 spines and 8–9 rays;**

pectoral fins set low on body, with 13–16 rays; tail fin forked in juveniles, forked or double emarginate in adults; pelvic fins with 1 slender spine and 5 soft-rays; body and most of head covered with small cycloid scales; LL straight, continues on tail fin; branchiostegal membranes separate, not attached to isthmus; preopercle smooth; no spines on head; gill rakers short or absent on 1st gill arch. Swimbladder present. Size range 30 cm to ~2 m.

Barracuda occur in estuaries and in shallow coastal waters over coral reefs, also on sand, silt or mud bottom. Feed mainly on fish, squid and cuttlefish. Generally good to eat, and of importance in artisanal and sport fisheries; caught with trawls, beach seines, gill-nets and by anglers. In some areas, large barracuda are notorious for causing ciguatera fish poisoning.

Tropical and warm temperate waters of all oceans. One genus and ~20 species; 8 species in our area. JLB Smith's (1949) record of *Sphyraena novaehollandiae* Günther 1860 from northern Mozambique was a mistake; this species is endemic to the coast of southern Australia.

Great barracuda   Pickhandle barracuda

GREAT BARRACUDA
Sphyraena barracuda
(Walbaum 1792)

*~50 cm subadult
(Mauritius)
14 cm juvenile (Japan)*

Body robust, slightly compressed, depth 6.4–8.3 times in SL; head length 2.5 (juvenile) to 3.6 (adult) times in SL; pelvic fin origins in front of dorsal fin origin; **tail fin forked in small juveniles, double emarginate in adults**; anal fin with 2 spines, 8–9 rays; preopercle without protruding membranous flap; **no gill rakers; LL scales 69–85. Adults dusky silver, bluish black dorsally, with ~20 inclined dark bars above LL and several fainter dark bars below LL; irregular black spots on rear part of body; 2nd dorsal fin and anal and tail fins of adults blackish, with white tips.** Colour of juveniles depends on habitat; over sandy bottom, small juveniles are uniformly pale; in seagrass beds or dark mangrove habitats, small juveniles have irregular greenish bars and resemble twigs. Attains 2 m, 50 kg.

Worldwide in tropical and subtropical waters, but not in eastern Pacific; Red Sea, Oman to Port Alfred.

Juveniles (< 30 cm) common inshore, in mangrove areas, estuaries, seagrass beds, in the surf along sandy beaches and often in tide pools. Adults occur on coral reefs, and at high tide they may venture over nearby seagrass beds.

Diurnal and crepuscular predator; feeds on a variety of fish. Even the smallest barracuda (20–79 mm SL) are piscivores, eating postlarval mullet, clupeids, pursemouths, silversides, etc. The prey of small juveniles (8–30 cm SL) comprises mainly gobies, silversides, clupeids, anchovies and needlefish; the latter were (including the beak) sometimes as long as the barracuda, and usually folded over several times in the stomach of the predator. Larger juveniles (30–50 cm SL) include small pursemouths and juvenile sparids in their diet. Juveniles usually hunt in groups, especially when in pursuit of schooling prey. Adults generally solitary and feed heavily on needlefish, halfbeaks, puffers, kingfish and mullet; large adults can swim very fast when chasing prey, but they are usually observed cruising slowly over the reef. Males mature at 55 cm FL (2 years), females at ~70 cm FL (3 years). Spawns in tropical waters during summer.

Large barracuda are formidable predators, and swimmers and scuba divers should be wary of them. Speared fish and flashing objects such as a ring, bracelet or wristwatch are attractive to barracuda, and attacks in turbid water may be due to the barracuda mistaking the flashing object for an erratically swimming bait fish. Spearing a large barracuda may provoke an attack, and splashing at the surface, swimming in turbid water or swimming at dusk all increase the risk of attack by barracuda; fortunately, attacks on humans are very rare.

Another danger from barracuda is that they are often responsible for ciguatera. Some specimens are safe to eat, while others are poisonous, depending on when and where the fish was caught and the size of the barracuda. Large fish are more likely to be poisonous because the toxin is concentrated as it is passed up the food chain from herbivorous fish to the top predators. Fish seem immune to ciguatera toxin, but humans and cats are especially sensitive to this poison. Fortunately, fish from southern African waters are apparently safe to eat, as there have been no cases of ciguatera caused by local fish. Several cases have been reported from Mauritius, and barracuda is among the notorious species banned from markets there.

The Latin word *Sphyraena* was used by the Romans for a pike-like fish. IGFA all-tackle record: 38.6 kg from Christmas Island (Republic of Kiribati).

SIMILAR SPECIES

The sharpfin barracuda, *Sphyraena acutipinnis* Day 1876, has 1 gill raker at angle of 1st gill arch; pelvic fin origins below or behind 1st dorsal fin origin; preopercle obliquely rounded, with small membranous flap on lower rear corner of large fish; opercle with 1 flexible flat spine; lower jaw with pointed cartilaginous tip; LL scales 122–128; body silvery grey, greenish dorsally, fins dusky. Attains 80 cm FL. Distribution uncertain, may be confined to Indian Ocean. India, Pakistan, Oman to Mossel Bay.

The yellowstripe barracuda, *Sphyraena obtusata* Cuvier 1829, is silvery, with dusky yellow band from snout through eye, above pectoral fin base to peduncle; tail fin yellow, rear margin and upper edge usually black; gill rakers 2, one at angle and one on lower limb of gill arch; pelvic fin origins in front of dorsal fin origin; preopercle angle with protruding

membranous flap; opercle with 1 flexible flat spine; no cartilaginous tip on lower jaw; pectoral fin tip reaches past vertical at dorsal fin origin; LL scales 80–91. Attains 30 cm FL. Indo-West Pacific, Red Sea, Oman to East London. *Sphyraena chrysotaenia* Klunzinger is a synonym.

The yellowtail barracuda, *Sphyraena flavicauda* Rüppell 1838, is silvery, with yellow (or brown) mid-lateral stripe from front of snout to pectoral fin base and tail fin; fins yellowish, edges of tail fin blackish; black blotch at pectoral fin base; 2 gill rakers near angle of 1st gill arch; pelvic fin origins in front of dorsal fin origin; preopercle corner with prominent membranous flap; 1 flexible flat spine on rear edge of opercle; lower jaw without cartilaginous tip; LL scales 72–90. Attains 45 cm FL. Indo-West Pacific, Red Sea, Oman to Durban.

PICKHANDLE BARRACUDA
Sphyraena jello
Cuvier 1829

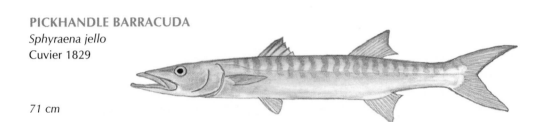

71 cm

Body depth 8–9 times in SL; head length 3.2–3.6 times in SL; no gill rakers; pelvic fin origins under or slightly in front of dorsal fin origin; pectoral fin tip reaches past vertical at dorsal fin origin; tail fin deeply forked in adults; anal fin with 2 spines, 9 rays; leading edge of soft dorsal fin distinctly longer than leading edge of spinous dorsal fin; no protruding membranous flap on preopercle corner; rear edge of opercle with 2 flat flexible spines; no cartilaginous tip on lower jaw; **LL scales 130–140. Body silvery, dusky yellowish green dorsally, adult with ~20 dark crossbars reaching only slightly below LL; dorsal fins dusky green; anal fin pale, tail fin dusky yellow**; juveniles with fewer, more irregular crossbars. Attains 1.4 m.

Indo-West Pacific, Red Sea, Oman to Knysna.

Coral and rocky reefs in 1–33 m. Biology little known; probably similar to great barracuda.

IGFA all-tackle record: 11.5 kg from Aliwal Shoal.

SIMILAR SPECIES

The blackspot barracuda, *Sphyraena forsteri* Cuvier 1829, has no gill rakers; pelvic fin origins ahead of dorsal fin origin; no protruding membranous flap on preopercle corner; 2 flexible flat spines on rear edge of opercle; lower jaw teeth compressed, contiguous, small to moderate at sides of jaw, increasing in size posteriorly, where they are slanted backwards, resembling coarse teeth on a saw; no cartilaginous tip on lower jaw; LL scales 112–123. Head and body silvery without dark crossbars; black axillary blotch at base of pectoral fins. Attains 80 cm FL. Indo-central Pacific, Oman to Algoa Bay.

The sawtooth barracuda, *Sphyraena putnamae* Jordan & Seale 1905, has no gill rakers, pelvic fin origins under or slightly ahead of dorsal fin origin; no protruding

membranous flap on preopercle corner, 2 flexible flat spines on rear edge of opercle, lower jaw with pointed cartilaginous tip; teeth compressed, contiguous and slanted backwards, resembling coarse teeth on a saw; LL scales 120–130; posterior ray of 2nd dorsal fin and anal fin of adult equal to or longer than anterior rays. Body bluish grey dorsally, silvery white below; about 15 dark bars on body, those along middle of body chevron-shaped, extending above and below LL; dorsal and tail fins and upper rays of pectoral fins dusky; pelvic and anal fins white. Attains 87 cm FL. Indo-central Pacific, south to Cape Vidal (north of St Lucia).

The blackfin barracuda, *Sphyraena qenie*

Klunzinger 1870, has no gill rakers, no protruding membranous flap on preopercle corner, 2 flexible flat spines on rear edge of opercle, lower jaw without pointed cartilaginous tip, teeth at side of lower jaw compressed, contiguous and erect, resembling coarse teeth on a saw; LL scales 123–136; pelvic fin origins ahead of dorsal fin origin. Body bluish black above, silvery white below, with 18–22 vertical or slightly curved dark crossbars, reaching well below LL (lower part of many bars may be offset from upper part); dorsal, anal and tail fins dark grey, except last 2 anal fin rays pale, contrasting with rest of fin. Attains 1.4 m FL. Indo-Pacific, Red Sea, Oman to Algoa Bay.

FAMILY OPISTOGNATHIDAE ● Jawfish

Small to moderate-sized fish; body elongate, the depth 4–5 times in SL; **head large, 3.2–3.8 times in SL; eyes large and set far forward, hence the snout is quite short; mouth enormous, maxilla half or more of head length and extending well past eye**; teeth moderate, slender, conical, in several rows at front of jaws, narrowing to 1 row at sides of jaws; no teeth on palatines, a few or none on vomer; dorsal fin long and continuous with 11 weak spines, 13–16 rays, the fin origin over gill opening; anal fin with 3 small spines, 13–15 rays; pelvic fins with 1 spine, 5 rays, outer 2 rays unbranched, fin origins anterior to pectoral fin bases; tail fin rounded with 12–14 branched rays; scales small, cycloid, usually none on head; LL close to dorsal fin, ending below middle of fin. Size range 9–47 cm.

Jawfish occur on sand or rubble bottoms in 1–200 m; they live in burrows which they excavate by using their capacious mouths to carry sand and pebbles. The vertical shaft of the burrow is lined and reinforced with small pebbles and shell fragments, and connects to a lower chamber into which the fish can retreat when threatened by a predator. Jawfish are usually seen sitting in the mouth of their burrow or hovering just above it. They feed on zooplankton and small benthic invertebrates.

Spawn in pairs. After fertilising the eggs, the male picks them up in his mouth; the eggs are kept in the mouth until the larvae hatch several days later.

Jawfish have been bred in captivity, but they are highly territorial, and two males should not be placed in the same aquarium. The large species need a deep aquarium, with lots of coarse sand to make their burrow.

Jawfish are found in tropical and subtropical waters of all oceans, but not in the eastern Atlantic. Three genera and ~90 species, half of which are presently undescribed; at least 4 species in our area. The family characters above apply only to the species in our area.

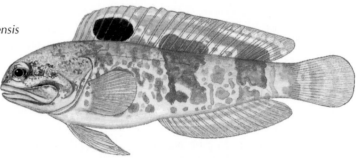

ROBUST JAWFISH
Opistognathus muscatensis
Boulenger 1888

28 cm adult

Body depth slightly less than head length, 3.4–4.0 times in SL; **maxilla rounded, widest at end; upper jaw length ~²/₃ head length, not reaching rear edge of operculum**; dorsal fin with 11 slender spines, 15 rays; length of 5th spine greater than peduncle depth. Head and body with irregular brown spots and blotches; **blue-edged ocellus between 3rd and 8th dorsal fin spines, dark blotch in middle of dorsal fin and 2nd dark blotch at rear of fin extending onto body**; black streak on head above upper edge of maxilla. Attains 47 cm.

Western Indian Ocean, Persian Gulf to Durban.

Sand or gravel bottom in 30–50 m. Juveniles feed on zooplankton; adults also include benthic invertebrates and fish in their diet. Matures at 27 cm.

SIMILAR SPECIES

The halfscaled jawfish, *Opistognathus margaretae* Smith-Vaniz 1983, is pinkish brown with black spot in dorsal fin at spines 3–5; body with 2 longitudinal series of pale spots; front nostril with a long cirrus; jaw 1.9–2.1 times in head length, rear end of maxilla truncate. Attains 92 mm. Known from Shimoni, Kenya, Sodwana Bay and Aliwal Shoal to depths of 31 m.

The bridled jawfish, *Opistognathus nigromarginatus* Rüppell 1830, has an enormous upper jaw, with maxilla tip reaching rear edge of head; body whitish with irregular brown markings; fins brownish grey with pale bluish spots; black ocellus between 4th and 8th dorsal fin spines. Attains 20 cm. Indo-West Pacific, Red Sea, Oman to Sodwana Bay.

FAMILY PINGUIPEDIDAE ■ Sandperch

Small to moderate-sized fish. **Body elongate, cylindrical anteriorly, slightly compressed posteriorly; body depth less than head length; eyes set high on the head and close together; dorsal fin with short spinous part of 5 small sharp spines, connected to soft-rayed part of 21–23 rays**; anal fin with 1 weak spine, 16–19 branched rays, fin origin well behind origin of soft dorsal fin; rear edge of tail fin convex, truncate or emarginate, the upper rays slightly longer in most adults; pectoral fins with 15–21 rays; pelvic fins with 1 hidden spine, 5 branched soft-rays, fin origins slightly ahead of pectoral fin bases. **Mouth terminal, maxilla mostly covered by preorbital bone; lips well developed; jaws with band of villiform teeth, outer row of larger slender teeth and a few curved canines at front of jaws; teeth present on vomer**, present or absent on palatines; branchiostegal rays 6, membranes united, attached

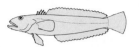

to front end of isthmus, forming free fold of skin across isthmus; opercle with 1 stout spine; preopercle edge smooth, broadly rounded; scales small to moderate, ctenoid, those on cheeks usually cycloid; LL complete, slightly curved above pectoral fin; swimbladder absent. *Parapercis* size range 13–30 cm.

Parapercis species are usually solitary fish, found sitting, propped up on their pelvic fins, on sandy or sand and rubble bottoms, generally near coral or rocky reefs. Most species feed on benthic invertebrates, but the rosy sandperch, *Parapercis schauinslandi*, is often seen in groups of 10–50 fish well above the bottom feeding on zooplankton. Several species are known to be protogynous hermaphrodites, and this type of sequential sex change is probably normal for this family. When an individual changes sex, it also usually shows significant alterations in its colour pattern.

Widely distributed in Indo-Pacific region. The family includes 4 or 5 genera, with ~70 species. The family diagnosis given above is based on *Parapercis*, the only genus represented in our area; 44 species in the genus, 8 in our area.

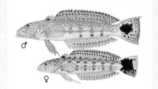

Blacktail sandperch   Spotted sandperch   Smallscale sandperch

BLACKTAIL SANDPERCH
Parapercis hexophtalma
(Cuvier 1829)

20 cm male (Red Sea)
7 cm juvenile (Comoros)

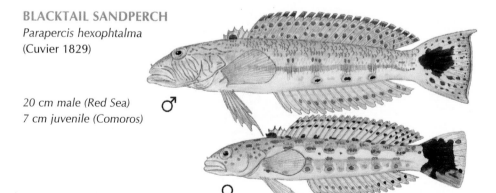

Dorsal fin rays 21, **membrane from last spine joins 1st ray opposite or above tip of spine**; anal fin rays 16–17; pectoral fin rays 16–18; LL scales 59–61; 6–8 scales from 1st dorsal fin ray to LL; 8 canines at front of lower jaw. **Squarish black blotch on middle of tail fin and small black spot on spinous dorsal fin**. Females (12–19 cm) white, with small dark

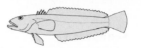

spots on head and dorso-lateral part of body. Males (>20 cm) pale dorsally, with numerous brown spots and short streaks; mid-lateral chain of white blotches from pectoral fin base to tail fin, with 1–2 dark spots at centre of each blotch; row of 3–4 small yellow-edged black spots along body near anal fin; cheek and lower rear part of head with oblique lines; 3–4 rows of small black spots along soft dorsal fin, 1 row on anal fin. Juveniles have rear third of tail fin white, proximal part black. Attains 28 cm.

Indo-West Pacific, Red Sea, Oman to Algoa Bay.

Shallow water over sand and rubble near coral and rocky reefs. Feeds on portunid crabs, alpheid shrimp, gastropods and fish. Females change sex at ~20 cm. Males defend a territory that includes the 2 or 3 females of their harem; the females have their own smaller sub-territories, which they defend from other females of the harem. At sunset,

the male makes a circuit of his territory to locate a female that is ready to spawn. After a series of courtship manoeuvres, the pair swim rapidly upwards less than a metre, release eggs and sperm at the peak of their vertical swim, and then rush back to the bottom. The mating sequence takes only 4 seconds. After spawning, the fish separate, and the male may go on to other females in his territory. If the other females are also receptive, the male may spawn with a second or third female.

Sandperch feed at dawn, dusk and during the day, but the evening 'rush hour' seems to be their busiest time of day, because they are either spawning, or foraging, or looking for their night-time shelter. At night, sandperch hide in a shallow depression or burrow under a large rock or part of the reef. Sometimes 2 or 3 fish (males and/or females) from adjacent territories will (peacefully) share the same shelter during the night; but during the day, these same fish will oppose any trespassers of their species.

SPOTTED SANDPERCH
Parapercis punctulata
(Cuvier 1829)

14 cm adult male
9 cm adult female

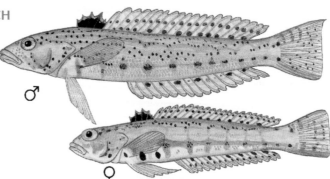

Dorsal fin rays 21, membrane from last spine joins 1st ray slightly below tip of spine; anal fin rays 17; pectoral fin rays 17–18; LL scales 55–57; 5 scales from 1st dorsal fin ray to LL; 6 canines at front of lower jaw. **Female (8–10 cm) with 3 black spots on each side of belly. Male (>10 cm SL) with 2 blackish brown** **lines across belly, 1st from lower end of pectoral fin base, with a short break at ventral midline; 2nd fainter but complete; indications of 3rd dark line across belly at anus are** visible on some large males; gold spots on snout and inter-orbital area. Both sexes: **upper and lower margins of tail fin reddish; spinous**

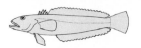

dorsal fin black, with yellow and red margin; row of ~8 reddish brown spots with black centre along lower part of body, last spot at base of lower tail fin rays; dorsal fin with row of black spots (1 behind each ray) along middle of fin, series of black spots (in groups of 2–3) along base of fin; anal fin white with 5–6 black spots near base of fin; small irregular dark spots on rear part of head. Attains 15 cm.

Southwestern Indian Ocean, Mozambique to Park Rynie, Seychelles, Madagascar and Mauritius.

Common singly or in pairs in sandy areas near coral reefs in 10–30 m. *Parapercis bivittata* Schultz from the Seychelles is a synonym.

SIMILAR SPECIES

The rosy sandperch, *Parapercis schauinslandi* (Steindachner 1900), has 2 longitudinal rows of ~9 pale reddish blotches or bars on body, one above and one below LL; small red or dark spot on base of upper and lower tail fin rays; spinous dorsal fin black with red margin; lower reddish blotches joined by reddish band on some fish; adult male with lunate tail fin; dorsal fin membrane from last spine joins 1st ray at or near its base. Attains 18 cm. Indo-central Pacific, Kosi Bay to Park Rynie in 20–50 m.

SMALLSCALE SANDPERCH
Parapercis robinsoni
Fowler 1929

23 cm

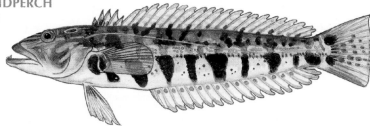

Dorsal fin rays 21–23, membrane from last spine joins 1st ray at base or slightly above base of 1st ray; anal fin rays 17–19; pectoral fin rays 16–18; **LL scales 77–86; 8 scales from 1st dorsal fin ray to LL**; 4–7 canines at front of lower jaw. **Body brown dorsally, including a pale mid-lateral band or chain of blotches; dorsal surface with dark Y- or V-shaped blotches** extending onto base of soft dorsal fin; body white ventrally, with 7–8 blackish blotches; pectoral fin base black with vertical white line; tail fin tawny with black spot at base of upper and lower rays, central part of fin with dark spots, the lower margin reddish brown; spinous dorsal fin white with black spot between 1st and 2nd spines; **blue lines between and below eyes; white lines on nape resemble a pair of spectacles**. Attains 30 cm.

Western Indian Ocean, Persian Gulf to Algoa Bay.

Sandy or silty sand bottoms in 6–55 m. Sexual dimorphism not apparent.

SIMILAR SPECIES

The gold-blotch sandperch, *Parapercis maritzi* Anderson 1992, has 5th dorsal fin spine longest, with membrane to 1st ray attached at level of spine tip; body rosy, pale ventrally, with 8 or 9 gold blotches; scarlet blotch behind pectoral fin base; spinous dorsal fin reddish. Attains 18 cm. Known only from trawls in 150–200 m off Mozambique and East London.

FAMILY BLENNIIDAE ■ Blennies

Small fish; body elongate, slightly compressed posteriorly and completely without scales; body depth subequal to head length; eyes set high in head and close together; **dorsal fin with 7–17 slender flexible spines, connected to a long soft-rayed part of 11–119 segmented rays**; rear edge of tail fin convex, truncate or emarginate (lunate in golden blenny); anal fin with 2 rudimentary weak spines and 14–119 segmented rays; pectoral fin rays 10–16; **pelvic fins rudimentary with 1 hidden spine, 1–4 segmented rays, origin anterior to pectoral fin base**; all fin rays unbranched except some tail fin rays bifid in some species; mouth terminal or snout slightly projecting; maxilla mostly covered by preorbital bone; lips well developed but upper lip without dorsal free margin across snout; jaws with short slender teeth; most species with a few canines; palatines without teeth, vomer with or without teeth; branchiostegal membranes united, attached to isthmus far forward, with a broad to narrow fold of skin across isthmus; LL complete, interrupted or absent. Size range 3–60 cm SL.

Blennies are generally solitary, sedentary fish, usually found sitting (propped up on their pelvic fins) on shallow sand or reef bottoms; some species occur in tide pools and are commonly seen hopping over rocks from one pool to another. Spawn in pairs, the female lays adhesive demersal eggs on rocks, which the male then guards.

Worldwide in tropical and temperate seas, a few species in fresh or brackish water. About 53 genera, ~350 species, ~45 in our area.

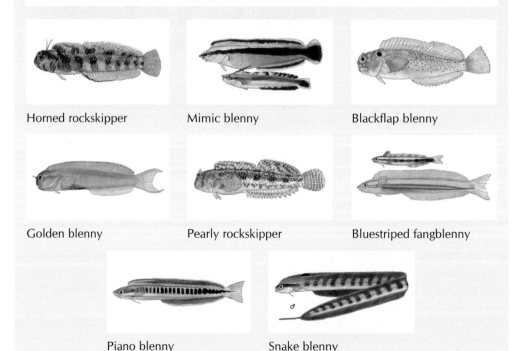

Horned rockskipper   Mimic blenny   Blackflap blenny

Golden blenny   Pearly rockskipper   Bluestriped fangblenny

Piano blenny   Snake blenny

HORNED ROCKSKIPPER
Antennablennius bifilum
(Günther 1861)

7 cm adult

Dorsal fin with shallow notch between spinous and segmented rays, 11–13 spines, 17–20 rays; anal fin rays 17–21; pectoral fin rays 14; pelvic fin rays 3; **2 long fleshy cirri, joined at base, on nape** in front of dorsal fin; no cirri on eye; short tentacle on nostril; gill opening extends below pectoral fin base. **Body pale with ~7 dark bars** extending into dorsal fin and numerous pale spots and streaks (females with fewer spots); **3 bands on underside of head**. Attains 8.5 cm.

Western Indian Ocean, Persian Gulf, northern Mozambique to Port Alfred, Madagascar, the Mascarenes and Comoros islands.

Tide pools and shallow reefs to 37 m.

SIMILAR SPECIES

The moustache rockskipper, *Antennablennius australis* Fraser-Brunner 1951, has a long nostril tentacle and two much shorter cirri on nape. Head and body brownish with numerous pale vertical lines becoming horizontal posteriorly. Western Indian Ocean, southern Red Sea, Oman to Algoa Bay.

The highbrow rockskipper, *Hirculops cornifer* (Rüppell 1830), has a long ribbon-like cirrus on eye, short simple cirrus on nape, dark spot on 1st dorsal fin membrane; anal fin spotted in female, dusky in male. Western Indian Ocean, Red Sea, Persian Gulf to Port St Johns.

MIMIC BLENNY
Aspidontus tractus
Fowler 1903

10 cm adult
7 cm juvenile

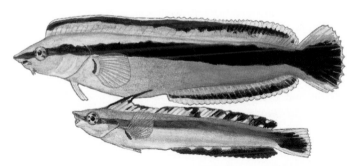

Head pointed, mouth below projecting snout; dorsal fin with 10–12 spines, 26–28 rays; postlarvae (4–6 cm SL) have high anterior dorsal fin spines; anal fin rays 25–28; pectoral fin rays 13–15; tail fin rays unbranched; gill opening extends below upper end of pectoral fin base; teeth close-set, slender, with **2 huge canines in lower** jaw. **Head and front of body pale, rear part of body dark blue, black stripe from front of snout to tail fin** and becoming wider on rear part of body; black stripe along margin of front part of dorsal fin, becoming submarginal along rear part of fin; pectoral fins transparent with black streak at base; tail fin mostly black. Attains 10 cm SL.

Indo-central Pacific, Red Sea, Oman to Aliwal Shoal.

Coral and rocky reefs in 2–30 m. A clever mimic of the bluestreak cleaner wrasse (see p. 347), the mimic blenny has even adopted the distinctive bobbing swimming motion of the wrasse. This blenny is a parasite, with huge curved canines that enable it to rip pieces from fins of unsuspecting victims that mistake it for a cleaner wrasse. Juveniles are full-time mimics, but adults also feed on demersal fish eggs, tubeworm tentacles and other invertebrates.

SIMILAR SPECIES

The floating blenny, *Aspidontus dussumieri* (Valenciennes 1836), has pale head and body without blue on rear part, dark stripe from inter-orbital area through eye, above pectoral fin base and along dorsal part of body to tail fin base. On juveniles the dark lateral stripe is broken into a series of blotches. Indo-central Pacific, Red Sea to Knysna.

BLACKFLAP BLENNY
Cirripectes auritus
Carlson 1981

6 cm

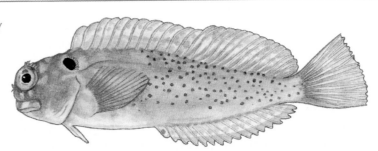

Head bluntly rounded; dorsal fin 12 spines, 15–17 rays; anal fin rays 16–18; pectoral fin rays 14–15; pelvic fin rays 4, innermost ray difficult to find; gill opening extends well below pectoral fin base; teeth numerous, freely movable; **large, weakly fringed black flap on each side of nape, with a row of up to 10 simple cirri between flaps; 3–4 simple cirri on nostrils and eyes**. Head, body and fins creamy, pink or brown, some fish with scattered dark dots on body. Attains 6 cm.

Indo-West Pacific, Kenya to Sodwana Bay.

Coral reefs in 6–25 m. Territorial, sits on shallow reefs; feeds on filamentous algae and detritus.

SIMILAR SPECIES

The muzzled rockskipper, *Cirripectes castaneus* (Valenciennes 1836), is dark grey with brown or reddish brown bars or spots on head and body; females often with reticulate pattern; bars become fainter and background colour darker on rear part of body; bars on head run from nape antero-ventrally to underside of head, forming 3 dark bands across lower jaw. Indo-central Pacific, Red Sea to Park Rynie.

Male redspotted blennies, *Cirripectes stigmaticus* Strasburg & Schultz 1953, have head and body dark, with bright red spots and wavy lines on rear part of body and some red marks on head; females greyish brown with russet reticulation enclosing pale olive spots on head and front half of body; dorsal fin rays 15; anal fin rays 16. Indo-West Pacific, Mozambique to Sodwana Bay.

The adult male brown blenny, *Cirripectes gilberti* Williams 1988, has uniformly brown body; female mottled brownish with red spots. Indian Ocean, Comoros, Seychelles to Sodwana Bay.

The quagga blenny, *Cirripectes quagga* (Fowler & Ball 1924), adult male has 1st dorsal fin spine elongate; dorsal fin membrane not attached to tail fin; lower lip crenulate medially; tips of anterior dorsal fin spines and tail fin rays yellow or red. Indo-central Pacific, south to Sodwana Bay.

GOLDEN BLENNY
Ecsenius midas
Starck 1969

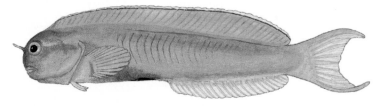

9 cm adult

Head bluntly rounded; tail fin lunate, with upper and lower rays greatly elongate and all rays unbranched; dorsal fin 13–14 spines, 19–21 rays, fin margin continuous (not notched); anal fin rays 20–23; pectoral fin rays 12–13; pelvic fin rays 3; teeth fixed, including 2 large canines in lower jaw; long simple cirrus on nostril, none on eye or nape. **Head, body and fins golden; black blotch around anus**; black edge along front half of dorsal fin. Attains 10 cm SL.

Indo-central Pacific, Red Sea to Aliwal Shoal.

Coral reefs where currents flow, 5–30 m. Unusual blenny, as it feeds on zoo-plankton and often schools with goldies above the reef; also resides in holes, like many reef blennies.

PEARLY ROCKSKIPPER
Entomacrodus striatus
(Valenciennes 1836)

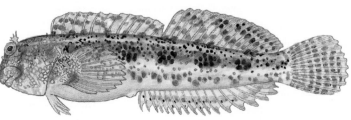

10 cm (Rodrigues)

Head bluntly rounded; **dorsal fin 12–14 spines, 14–16 rays, margin deeply notched behind spinous part**; anal fin rays 15–18; **single cirrus on each side of nape; eye tentacle with branches on each side**; teeth numerous, freely movable; upper lip margin crenulate; gill opening extends well below pectoral fin base. **Body pale with numerous dark spots**; dorsal and tail fins also spotted; **irregular blue/green mark behind eye and just above pectoral fin base**. Attains 9 cm SL.

Indo-central Pacific, Kenya to Durban.

Tide pools and shallow reefs. Feeds on filamentous algae and detritus. Most common and widespread species of the genus.

The leopard blenny, *Exallias brevis* (Kner 1868), has deep body; teeth freely movable; branching tentacle on eye and nostrils; dorsal fin high with 12 spines, 12–13 rays, fin margin deeply notched behind spinous part; transverse band of cirri on nape. Head, body and fins covered with small spots, some in clusters on body; spots brown on females, red on males; iris white with black spot at 12, 3, 6 and 9 o'clock. Feeds on polyps and mucus of corals. Attains 12 cm SL. Indo-central Pacific, Red Sea to Sodwana Bay.

BLUESTRIPED FANGBLENNY
Plagiotremus rhinorhynchos
(Bleeker 1852)

4 cm juvenile (Comoros)
8 cm adult

Head pointed, snout projecting over mouth; body slender, depth 6–8 times in SL; no LL; dorsal fin 10–12 spines, 31–37 rays; anal fin rays 29–33; tail fin with 11 unbranched rays; pectoral fin rays 11–13; pelvic fins with 1 minute spine and 3 rays; jaws with fixed incisors; **enormous curved canine on each side at rear of lower jaw. Colour variable, yellow to black; always with 2 bright blue stripes**, one along dorsal part of head and body to base of upper tail fin rays, the other stripe from snout across pectoral fin base and along lower part of body sometimes as far as tail fin. Juveniles, 3–4 cm SL, pale with 5–6 dark body bars extending into dorsal and anal fins. Attains 9 cm SL.

Indo-central Pacific, Red Sea, Oman to Knysna.

Coral reefs in 5–30 m. The huge canines at the back of the lower jaw enable this agile and quick little parasite to feed on the skin, scales and mucus of larger fish. Uses tube-worm burrows for shelter and nesting. Male courts female with a bobbing dance-like motion; after she deposits eggs in the worm tube, male guards them until they hatch.

The dark phase of this fish resembles the bluestreak cleaner wrasse (see p. 347), and this similarity may allow the blenny to approach closer to its unsuspecting victims before it is recognised.

PIANO BLENNY
Plagiotremus tapeinosoma
(Bleeker 1857)

7 cm

Head pointed, snout projecting over mouth; body slender, depth 6–8 times in SL; no LL; dorsal fin 7–9 spines, 34–39 segmented rays; anal fin rays 28–33; tail fin with 11 unbranched rays; pectoral fin rays 11–13; pelvic fins with 1 minute spine, 3 rays; **jaws with fixed incisors at front and huge curved canine on each side at rear of lower jaw. Body brownish dorsally, with row of 16–20 black blotches merging posteriorly to form wavy mid-lateral black band**, narrowing to black line along central tail fin ray; white stripe from tip of snout, under eye, across pectoral fin base and along lower part of body to tail fin. Attains 12 cm SL.

Indo-Pacific, Red Sea to False Bay.

Coral and rocky reefs in 5–32 m. Feeds on skin, scales and mucus of larger fish; also bites divers. Solitary or in small groups, often swims with similar planktivores to get close to its prey.

SNAKE BLENNY
Xiphasia setifer
Swainson 1839

30 cm male

♂

Body **compressed and extremely elongate, depth less than half head length and contained 30–40 times in SL**; dorsal fin also extremely elongate, with 13–14 slender flexible spines and 105–119 segmented rays, fin origin in adults between front edge of eyes; anal fin rays 107–119; **tail fin pointed, joined by membranes to dorsal and anal fins**; in males, the 2 central rays are greatly elongate; pectoral fin rays 12–14; pelvic fins 1 spine, 3 rays, inserted under pectoral fin bases; gill opening not extending below pectoral fin base; LL present; upper jaw with 12–30 fixed incisors, 10–34 in lower jaw; pair of enlarged canines in both jaws. Body **pale brown, with 20–28 broad dark bars extending into dorsal fin; small black ocellus at margin of dorsal fin** between 5th and 7th spines; margin of soft dorsal fin dusky with white edge. Attains 60 cm.

Indo-West Pacific, Red Sea, Oman to False Bay.

Occurs in burrows on mud or sandy substrate to 54 m. Eats crustaceans (mainly copepods), fish scales, polychaete worms, foraminifera and detritus; a few adults were caught apparently feeding in surface waters at night.

SIMILAR SPECIES

The white-edged snake blenny, *Xiphasia matsubarai* Okada & Suzuki 1952, has 10–11 pectoral fin rays; dorsal fin with 11 spines, 99–104 rays; anal fin rays 97–104; front part of anal fin white distally. Indo-West Pacific, south to False Bay.

FAMILY TRIPTERYGIIDAE ■ Triplefins

Small, cryptically coloured benthic fish. **Body elongate, subcylindrical anteriorly, slightly compressed posteriorly and mostly covered with ctenoid scales**; body depth about equal to head length; eyes set high in head and close together; **3 dorsal fins: 1st of 3–4 spines, 2nd of 8–16 spines, and 3rd fin of 8–12 segmented rays**; rear edge of tail fin truncate or rounded; anal fin with 1–2 short slender spines and 17–21 segmented rays, fin origin below middle of 2nd dorsal fin; pectoral fin rays 13–18; **pelvic fins with 1 hidden spine, 2–3 segmented rays**, fin origins on front of chest; dorsal and anal fin rays unbranched; tail fin with 13 rays, 9–11 branched; head pointed, mouth terminal, lips well developed; maxilla mostly covered by preorbital bone and upper lip; jaws with bands of small conical teeth; branchiostegal membranes united, attached to isthmus far forward, with broad to narrow fold of skin across isthmus; LL complete or interrupted. Size range 2–8 cm.

Triplefins are generally solitary, sedentary fish, usually found sitting (propped up on their pelvic fins) on coral or rocky reefs and sand bottoms; some species occur in tide pools and are easily overlooked because of their excellent camouflage colour patterns.

Feed on tiny invertebrates (crustaceans, molluscs, brittlestars and worms) that live amongst sand grains, algae and encrusting organisms. Males often have dark heads.

Worldwide in tropical and temperate seas. About 30 genera, ~140 species, 12 in our area.

Cape triplefin

Blackfin triplefin

Hotlips triplefin

CAPE TRIPLEFIN

Cremnochorites capensis
(Gilchrist & Thompson 1908)

4 cm female
7 cm male in breeding colours

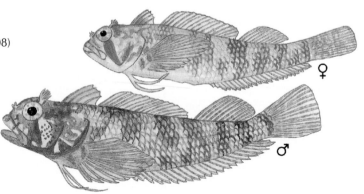

First dorsal fin 4 spines, 2nd fin 14–15 spines, 3rd fin 10–11 rays; anal fin 2 spines, 21–22 rays; pectoral fin rays 16; head covered with small denticle-like scales; ring of scales or scale-like spines around eye; orbital tentacle branched; LL scales 21–24 / 22–23. Body pale with irregular brown bars, brown bar below eye; breeding males with orange and/or yellow on head and 1st dorsal fin. Attains 8 cm.

Endemic, False Bay to Coffee Bay.

Rocky reefs in 5–20 m; taken by trawl in 30 m in False Bay.

SIMILAR SPECIES

The endemic Eastern Cape spiny triplefin, *Acanthanectes hystrix* Holleman & Buxton

1993, has 1st dorsal fin with 4 spines, 2nd dorsal fin spines 12–15 (dorsal fin spines with tiny lateral spinelets); top of head papillose, each papilla with a spine embedded in it; anal fin with 1 spine, 18–19 rays; body pale with 4–5 conspicuous irregular orange bars, the last dark-edged at tail fin base; anal and tail fins with numerous black spots.

The scaly head triplefin, *Norfolkia brachylepis* (Schultz 1960), also has 4 spines in 1st dorsal fin and irregular reddish brown and grey bars; but it differs in having an anal fin with 2 spines, 18–20 rays, front part of LL with 14–18 pored scales, orbital tentacle crenulate, and 2nd and 3rd dorsal fins of males mostly red. Indo-Pacific, Red Sea, Oman to Aliwal Shoal.

BLACKFIN TRIPLEFIN
Helcogramma fuscopinna
Holleman 1982

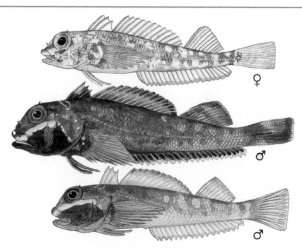

4 cm female (Rodrigues)
5 cm mature male
3 cm immature male

First dorsal fin with 3 spines, 2nd with 14 spines, 3rd with 10–11 rays; anal fin with 1 spine, 20–21 rays; pectoral fin rays 15–17; one LL row of 23–27 pored scales ending below 2nd and 3rd dorsal fin; head, nape and abdomen naked. Mature males with dorsal part of head and front part of body russet, sometimes with 5–6 pale blotches; lower half of head blackish, separated from upper half by blue-white line below eye and onto upper

lip; females and immature males nondescript with pinky-orange irregular bars to pale versions of mature males; pelvic and median fins dusky. Breeding males nearly black. Attains 6 cm SL.

Indian Ocean, not in Red Sea, Kenya to the Eastern Cape.

Coral and rocky reefs in 5–30 m.

HOTLIPS TRIPLEFIN
Helcogramma sp.

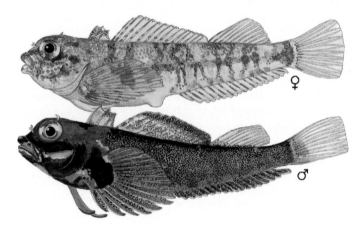

~4 cm female
4 cm male

First dorsal fin with 3 spines, 2nd with 12–14 spines, 3rd with 10–11 rays; 1st dorsal fin spines about half length of longest 2nd dorsal fin spines; **anal fin with 1 spine, 17–20 rays**; pectoral fin rays 15–16; LL a single row of 19–29 pored scales ending below 3rd dorsal fin; **head, nape and abdomen naked; small orbital cirrus above rear edge of pupil.** Body mottled, with broad dark greenish-grey or russet blotches interconnected dorsally (branching ventrally in female); **male dark, with red blotch on side of upper lip and electric blue streak bordered by black from mouth across cheek**; blue marks also at upper and lower ends of pectoral fin base; small black spot on membrane behind 3rd dorsal fin spine. Attains 4.5 cm.

Southwestern Indian Ocean, Bazaruto to East London.

Abundant in weedy tide pools and on shallow reefs. Unconfirmed reports from Kenya. Very dark males are probably in breeding colours, and may spawn with harem of females.

— SIMILAR SPECIES —

The hotlips triplefin was previously identified as *Helcogramma obtusirostre*, which is endemic to the Red Sea and does not have a red spot on upper lip of males.

FAMILY CLINIDAE ■ Clinids (Klipfish)

Clinids are small to moderate-sized, cryptically coloured benthic fish. **Body elongate, somewhat compressed or subcylindrical, generally covered with scales, but the scales are small, cycloid, embedded and usually inconspicuous (absent in *Clinoporus*)**; eyes usually high in the head and close together; dorsal fin long, origin on top of head (behind head in *Cancelloxus burrelli*) the fin **with 24–50 sharp spines and 0–14 soft-rays; anal fin with 2 spines, 19–43 soft-rays**; tail fin rounded or truncate, with 11–13 segmented rays; peduncle short or elongate; pectoral fins with 10–18 rays; pelvic fins on chest, with 1 hidden spine, 2–3 segmented rays; South African species with all fin rays unbranched; mouth terminal (lower jaw projecting in some species), rear end of maxilla visible with mouth closed; lips well developed; jaws with bands of small conical teeth; branchiostegal membranes united, forming a free fold over isthmus; LL usually curves down behind pectoral fin, forming a

straight mid-lateral line of disjointed horizontal tubes with a pore at each end. All South African species of clinids are viviparous, with males easily recognised by the presence of an intromittent organ near the anus. Size range (SA species) 5–30 cm.

Well camouflaged fish found in tide pools and estuaries under rocks and among algae, seaweed and kelp; subtidally, some species are found down to 50 m; especially common in tide pools along the south coast, as far as East London. Carnivorous, feeding on small crustaceans, bivalves, gastropods, worms, sea urchins and brittlestars.

Worldwide, mainly in temperate seas. About 20 genera, ~83 species; at least 41 species in our area, all are endemic to southern Africa.

Highfin clinid

Mouse clinid

Peacock clinid

HIGHFIN CLINID
Clinus superciliosus
(Linnaeus 1758)

9 cm female
13 cm male
8 cm male

Dorsal fin with 31–42 spines, 5–10 rays, first 3 spines forming a crest taller than rest of fin and much higher in males than in females; anal fin rays 21–30; pectoral fin rays 14–18; pelvic fins with 2 rays; tail fin with 13 rays; **tentacle above eye of females with short stalk, flattened tip and a few short simple branches; tentacle of adult male with long**

stalk and many fine filamentous branches towards tip. Colour extremely variable, from uniform green to black with 6 golden spots along mid-lateral part of body to greatly mottled with 6 dark bars on body; pale spot at base of tail fin. Attains 30 cm.

Northern Namibia all round our south coast to the Kei River.

Tide pools and rocky areas to depths of 10 m. Probably a complex of 2 or 3 similar species.

SIMILAR SPECIES

The old man clinid, *Clinus woodi* (Smith 1946), has deeper body, dorsal fin with 27–31 spines, 4–6 rays, dorsal crest completely separate from rest of fin, pectoral fin rays 12–14. Kei River to Inhambane.

The robust clinid, *Clinus robustus* Gilchrist & Thompson 1908, has 9–14 dorsal rays, 12 pectoral rays, 3 pelvic fin rays; dark bars on body extend into dorsal and anal fins. Subtidal amongst weed, False Bay to East London.

MOUSE CLINID
Fucomimus mus
(Gilchrist & Thompson 1908)

9 cm adult male

Body oblong, peduncle length about twice its depth); dorsal fin with 25–28 spines, 2–4 rays, first 3 spines joined only to base of 4th spine; anal fin rays 14–18; pectoral fin rays 10; pelvic fin rays 3, inner ray well developed; tail fin rays 11; no tentacle above eye. Colour reddish, green or brown depending on habitat; dorsal and anal fins with transparent windows, the last in each fin with rays bent to contain the window; tail fin mostly transparent; juveniles reddish with large silvery patches on flanks. Attains 10 cm.

False Bay to Coffee Bay.

Small lethargic species found in tide pools. Writhes like a snake when touched.

SIMILAR SPECIES

The slinky clinid, *Pavoclinus litorafontis* Penrith 1965, also has a long narrow peduncle, but it has 29–32 dorsal fin spines, 7–8 rays, no notch in membrane joining 3rd and 4th spines. Body mainly green, with darker green yellow and iridescent stripes; usually silver stripe across cheek and operculum; fins green, median fins with translucent patches. Attains 21 cm. Known only from False Bay.

Mya's clinid, *Pavoclinus myae* Christensen 1978, also has a long narrow peduncle; but it has 11–12 pectoral fin rays, 12 tail fin rays, 4th and 5th dorsal fin spines $\sim{}^2/_3$ length of 3rd and 6th spines. Body rusty red with dark maroon bars; large silver spot behind eye and at pectoral fin base; several smaller spots on preopercle and abdomen; 4 red bars radiating from eye. Attains 6 cm. Algoa Bay to north of East London.

PEACOCK CLINID
Pavoclinus pavo
(Gilchrist & Thompson
1908)

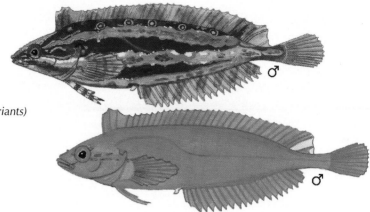

10 cm male (2 colour variants)

Body oblong, **peduncle length about twice its depth; head pointed; dorsal fin spines 30–36, rays 2–4; first 3 spines slightly elevated above 4th spine and set well forward of 4th spine**, membrane joining 3rd to 4th spine reaches tip of spine; anal fin rays 19–23; pectoral fin rays 11–12; pelvic fin rays 3, inner ray small; tail fin with 13 rays and no scales; no tentacle above eye. Colour variable depending on weed in which it lives. **Blue-green lines on head behind eye**. Attains 15 cm.

Lüderitz to Kei River.

Tide pools and shallow rocky areas among algae, rarely below 10 m.

— SIMILAR SPECIES ————————

The grass clinid, *Pavoclinus graminis* (Gilchrist & Thompson 1908), has similar fin ray counts and usually no notch between 3rd and 4th dorsal spines; first 3 dorsal spines slightly longer than other spines; peduncle depth more than half its length, and scales extend onto tail fin. Colour variable. Attains 16 cm. In tide pools from False Bay to Inhambane; also in 27 m at Aliwal Shoal.

The bluespot clinid, *Pavoclinus caeruleopunctatus* Zsilavecz 2001, has a more pronounced dorsal fin crest, with notch between 3rd and 4th spines and blue spots on head behind eye. Table Bay to Knysna, possibly to Tsitsikamma. On offshore reefs in 6–25 m.

FAMILY CALLIONYMIDAE ■ Dragonets

Small elongate benthic fish. Head broad and depressed; eyes on top of head and close together; preopercle with strong spine; no scales, but LL present; dorsal fin divided into separate spinous and soft-rayed portions, 1st dorsal fin origin on top or close behind head; with 1, 2 or 4 spines (first 1 or 2 spines separate in some species) and 8–11 soft-rays; anal fin with 6–12 soft-rays, no spines; tail fin rounded or elongate, with 11–13 segmented rays, middle 10 rays branched; peduncle elongate or short; pectoral fin rays 17–24; **pelvic fins large, widely separated, inserted anterior to pectoral fin bases, with 1 spine, 5 branched rays, inner rays longer and joined by membrane to pectoral fin bases**; head pointed, mouth terminal, upper jaw protrusile, rear end of maxilla visible when mouth is closed; lips well

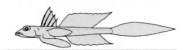

developed; jaws with bands of villiform teeth; gill opening restricted to a small dorsal pore. Size range 2.6–28 cm

Found on coral reefs, sandy and mud bottom to 400 m. Feed on small crustaceans, molluscs (bivalves and gastropods), worms, brittlestars and sea urchins. Spawn in pairs; eggs, larvae and postlarvae pelagic. Sexual dimorphism common; females noticeably smaller than males and males usually have a much larger 1st dorsal fin. Some colourful dragonets are important in the aquarium fish trade.

Worldwide in tropical and temperate seas. Taxonomy unsettled; genera poorly defined; ~140 species, 11 in our area.

STARRY DRAGONET
Neosynchiropus stellatus
(Smith 1963)

8 cm male
4 cm immature male
5 cm female

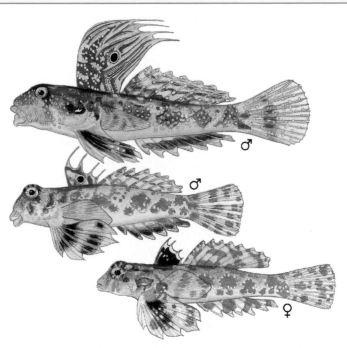

Head contained 3.0–4.4 times in SL; **snout length subequal to eye diameter**; LL without branches but connected across rear of head; **preopercle spine with a small accessory spine on inside edge of the main spine**; 1st dorsal fin with 4 spines, 2nd dorsal fin with 8 rays; anal fin with 7 branched rays; dorsal and anal fin rays branched, last ray double, but counted as one; 1st dorsal fin of male about twice soft dorsal fin height; pectoral fin rays 19–24; tail fin subequal to head. Body pale, mottled pink or straw-gold; immature males and females with **large, stellate, red to dark reddish brown blotches mid-laterally**; row of smaller red spots below; spinous dorsal fin brownish, with irregular white-edged black submarginal band; anal fin with dusky submarginal band; red blotches on tail fin; 2 faint dark blotches on pelvic fins. Adult male brownish with interconnected dark

blotches on body; lower half of head with blue spots; 1st dorsal fin with pale blue spots and flamboyant, blue-edged, dark brown stripes and white-edged black ocellus. Attains 7.5 cm.

Western Indian Ocean, Oman to Protea Bank.

Seagrass beds and sandy or coral rubble areas near coral and rocky reefs to 40 m. Occurs in loose groups of females and juveniles dominated by large male.

The genus *Neosynchiropus* comprises ~8 species that lack the interconnecting branch of the lateral-line canal that joins the left and right canals across the top of peduncle. The 3 species of *Synchiropus* (which do not occur in our area) have an interconnecting canal joining the lateral lines across the top of the peduncle.

SIMILAR SPECIES

The marbled dragonet, *Neosynchiropus marmoratus* (Peters 1855), has 2 small accessory spines on inside edge of the main preopercle spine, 7–8 dorsal fin rays; head and body dark greenish brown, covered with small blue or brown spots; spinous dorsal fin of male very tall and sail-like, the blue stripes on the spinous dorsal fin are so vivid that, despite the black in between, the fin looks bluish violet in males and females; pectoral fins and margin of pelvic fins reddish. Western Indian Ocean, south to Maputo.

FAMILY GOBIIDAE ■ Gobies, Mudskippers & Gliders

Gobies are mainly **small benthic fish of various shapes (oblong, elongate, or short and deep bodied) with various fin configurations. Head broad and depressed or pointed; mouth terminal or snout slightly projecting in front of mouth; lips well developed; jaws with conical teeth in 1 or more rows, some teeth enlarged as canines in some species; eyes on top of head and close together; body with or without scales; no LL. Lateral scale series (LSS)** are the number of oblique scale series from upper end of gill opening to tail fin base. **Dorsal fin generally divided into separate spinous and soft-rayed fins**, spinous dorsal fin origin close behind head, number of spines varies from 2–17, but is 6 in most species; 2nd dorsal and anal fins generally have 1 slender spine, 6–15 soft (segmented) rays; tail fin usually rounded (elongate and pointed or truncate in a few species) with 16–17 segmented rays; middle 15 rays branched; caudal peduncle elongate or short; pectoral fin rays 12–25; **pelvic fins close together, with short spine, 5 branched rays; in most gobies the pelvic fins are united to form a cup-like disc on which the goby rests when it is sitting on the bottom**; branchiostegal membranes usually broadly joined to isthmus, restricting gill opening to side of body. Size range 1–50 cm, most species <8 cm.

Small colourful or well camouflaged fish found in tide pools, seagrass beds, estuaries (including mangrove areas), on coral, coral rubble or rocky reefs, and sandy or mud bottom down to 200 m. Some gobies live in close association with other animals (sitting on sponges or gorgonians, or sharing a burrow with a shrimp). Gobies feed on small crustaceans, molluscs (bivalves and gastropods), worms and sea urchins. Spawn in pairs; eggs deposited in sheltered site or burrow on the bottom and guarded by male.

Worldwide, in tropical and temperate seas, some species occurring in freshwater. With about 230 genera and ~1 500 species, the Gobiidae comprises more species than any other family of marine fish; at least 111 species in our area.

Gorgeous shrimpgoby   Prison goby   Feather goby

GORGEOUS SHRIMPGOBY
Amblyeleotris wheeleri
(Polunin & Lubbock 1977)

7 cm

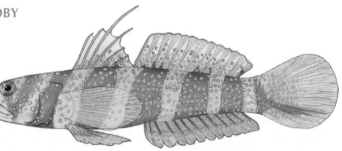

Body elongate, 4.5–5.2 times in SL; head rounded, mouth terminal; **1st dorsal fin with 6 spines, 3rd spine elongate; soft dorsal and anal fins with 1 spine, 12 rays; tail fin rounded, subequal to head;** pelvic fins joined for about half length of inner rays; scales small, LSS 50–58; midline of nape scaly to above operculum; body scales ctenoid behind soft dorsal fin origin; gill opening reaches to below preopercle. **Head and body whitish to pale yellow, with 6 slightly oblique, red to dark reddish brown bars**, last narrowest at base of tail fin; dark red bar from eye to rear end of mouth; numerous blue spots on head, body and fins; dorsal fins with small red spots; **tail fin with reddish oblique stripe ventrally.** Attains 8 cm SL.

Indo-West Pacific, Red Sea, Oman to Sodwana Bay.

Coral reefs; common in shallow water, but also to depths of 40 m. Often found sharing a burrow with a pair of snapping shrimp, *Alpheus ochrostriatus*. The shrimp dig the burrow and the goby sits at the entrance like a watch-dog, with one or both shrimp moving in and out the burrow carrying sand. One shrimp usually keeps its antennae touching the goby; when the goby sees a predator approaching, it turns round or reverses down the hole, with the shrimp hot on its tail.

— SIMILAR SPECIES

The pinkbar goby, *Amblyeleotris aurora* (Polunin & Lubbock 1977), has 4 broad pinkish bars, 1st on rear of head, last 2 continued onto base of soft dorsal and anal fins; pink blotch at centre of tail fin, red 'teardrop' from lower edge of eye to rear end of mouth; tail fin pointed, yellow with 3–9 orange-red spots. Western Indian Ocean, south to Sodwana Bay.

PRISON GOBY
Caffrogobius gilchristi
(Boulenger 1898)

12 cm

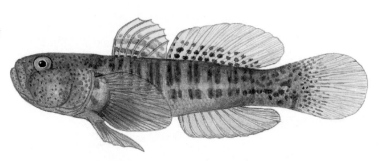

Body robust, depth subequal to head length; head rounded, its depth equal to its width, mouth terminal, cheek papillae pattern transverse; no flap on anterior nostrils; gill opening reaches below pectoral fin base; 1st dorsal fin 6 spines, 2nd dorsal fin 1 spine, 11–12 rays; anal fin 1 spine, 9–10 rays; pectoral fin rays 17–19, tips not free; tail fin shorter than head; LSS 43–52; predorsal scales to at least above opercle. Body of adult with **~ 16 irregular thin dark bars, usually in pairs** and broken along midside, forming 2 irregular broad longitudinal dark bands; head of adult with numerous small dark spots; 1st dorsal fin with 2–3 dark stripes; dark blotch at rear edge of head; specimens from the south coast may have pale bar at pectoral fin base; anal and pelvic fins dusky. Attains 15 cm SL.

Endemic, Cape Town to northern Mozambique.

Estuaries and rocky tide pools.

Formerly known as *Caffrogobius multifasciatus* (Smith), a synonym.

— SIMILAR SPECIES —

The endemic banded goby, *Caffrogobius caffer* (Günther 1874), has ~ 10 black bars on body; spinous dorsal fin with 2–3 pale stripes, anal fin rays 10–12, pectoral fin rays 19–21, dorsal fin rays 12–14; anterior nostrils with broad short flap. Common in tide pools and on shallow rocky reefs from False Bay to Maputo.

The barehead goby, *Caffrogobius nudiceps* (Valenciennes 1837), has 19–23 pectoral fin rays, 0–6 predorsal scales, LSS 43–50, and yellow band bordered in front by dark bar on pectoral fin base. Endemic, Walvis Bay to East London. Occurs on rocky reefs and in estuaries.

FEATHER GOBY
Callogobius plumatus
(Smith 1959)

6 cm

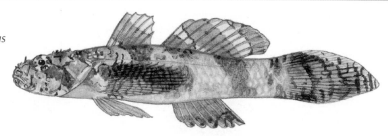

Body depth subequal to head length; **head depressed, bluntly rounded, with raised vertical skin ridges;** mouth terminal; nostrils tubular, front ones short; **gill opening reaches lower end of pectoral fin base; 1st dorsal fin 6 spines, 2nd dorsal fin 1 spine, 8–9 rays, the**

fin higher than the 1st dorsal fin; anal fin rays 6–7; pectoral fin rays 18–20, fin large, pointed, longer than head, reaching past anal fin origin; tail fin longer than head; pelvic fins fused; LSS 23–25; predorsal scales 6–12. Head and body pale, with dark markings as shown. Attains 6 cm.

Western Indian Ocean, Persian Gulf to Aliwal Shoal, also Mauritius and Seychelles.

Coral reefs in 5–25 m.

FAMILY MICRODESMIDAE ■ Hover Gobies (Dart Gobies) & Wormfish

Two subfamilies: the Ptereleotrinae and the Microdesminae.

The Microdesminae (wormfish), with 5 genera (including *Gunnelichthys*) and ~30 species, is represented in tropical and subtropical waters of all oceans.

The spot-tail wormfish, *Gunnelichthys curiosus* Dawson 1968, previously known from Maldives and Seychelles, was recently photographed at Aliwal Shoal. It has a long eel-like body; projecting lower jaw; body orange with neon blue stripe dorsally, black spot on tail fin; small black spot on rear edge of head. Found over sand and rubble in lagoons or on reef slopes from 4–38 m.

Subfamily Ptereleotrinae ■ Hover Gobies (Dart Gobies)

Elongate fish formerly included in Gobiidae; body depth contained 5–8 times in SL; head and body compressed; scales small, embedded; no LL; mouth oblique, lower jaw distinctly protruding; gill opening reaches below rear edge of preopercle; pelvic fins separate, below pectoral fin bases, 1 spine, 4–5 rays; 1st dorsal fin with 6 slender spines; 2nd dorsal and anal fins long, with 1 spine, 23–37 soft-rays. Size range 3–12 cm.

Hover gobies occur over sandy patches on or near coral reefs; usually seen hovering over their burrow, into which they retreat at the approach of a predator. Little is known of their biology, but they appear to feed on zooplankton near the bottom.

The Subfamily Ptereleotrinae, with 5 genera and ~44 species, is also represented worldwide in tropical and subtropical waters. Two genera and ~6 species occur in our area.

Fire goby

Scissortail dart goby

FIRE GOBY
Nemateleotris magnifica
Fowler 1938

5 cm

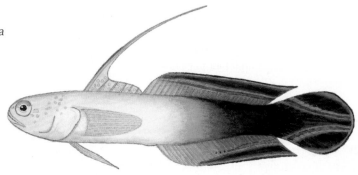

Head rounded, with low mid-dorsal ridge on nape; **1st dorsal fin spine greatly elongate, reaching well past soft dorsal fin origin, other 5 spines all short, the 1st dorsal fin margin L-shaped**; soft dorsal fin with 1 spine, 28–32 rays; anal fin rays 27–30; pelvic fins slender; pectoral fin rays 19–20; LSS 110–130. **Head and front half of body white; rear half of body and median fins orange-red**, sometimes dark posteriorly; rear ends of dorsal and anal fins with violet streak along middle of fin and continued as 2 oblique streaks converging posteriorly on tail fin. Attains 9 cm.

Indo-central Pacific, Kenya to Aliwal Shoal.

Near bottom on coral reefs in depths of 6–60 m. Adults in pairs, juveniles in small groups in caves and crevices. Feeds on zooplankton (mainly copepods and crustacean larvae). Usually seen hovering over its burrow, into which it dives at the approach of danger. Common at Sodwana Bay.

Popular aquarium fish, prefers a large tank and a mate.

SCISSORTAIL DART GOBY
Ptereleotris evides
(Jordan & Hubbs 1925)

13 cm adult
6 cm juvenile (Australia)

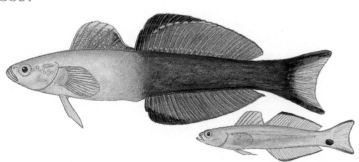

Body elongate, depth 5–6 times in SL; head compressed; lower jaw projecting; soft dorsal and anal fins higher anteriorly, with 23–25 rays; emarginate tail fin; pelvic fins short and separate; pectoral fin rays 22–23; scales minute, cycloid, LSS 135–148. Adult with head and front of body pale bluish; rear part of body, soft dorsal and anal fins, peduncle and upper and lower margins of tail fin dark blue to black; central part of tail fin pale; 1st dorsal fin pale yellowish grey; rear part of head and pectoral fin base with blue

streaks. Juvenile (5 cm SL) pale bluish grey, with dark blue oval spot at base of lower tail fin rays; margins of soft dorsal and anal fins and upper and lower margins of tail fin dark blue. Attains 13 cm SL.

Tropical Indo-West Pacific, Red Sea to Aliwal Shoal.

Coral and rocky reefs; usually in exposed outer-reef areas at depths of 2–30 m. Adults usually in pairs swimming above reef and near a burrow or crevice. Juveniles occur in groups in protected inshore areas. Feeds on zooplankton. Can be kept in a covered aquarium with other fish, but not with aggressive species.

— SIMILAR SPECIES —

The spot-tail dart goby, *Ptereleotris heteroptera* (Bleeker 1855), has head and body pale bluish grey, dorsal and anal fins hyaline; tail fin pale yellowish, with large oval black spot (faint or absent in juveniles) at centre or rear part of fin. Indo-Pacific, Kenya to Sodwana Bay.

The Indo-central Pacific zebra dart goby, *Ptereleotris zebra* (Fowler 1938), is bluish green with ~20 pink bars on body. Photographed at Sodwana Bay.

FAMILY ACANTHURIDAE ■ Surgeonfish & Unicornfish

Body deep and compressed; dorsal fin continuous with 4–9 spines, 19–33 rays; anal fin with 2–3 spines, 18–28 rays; pelvic fins with 1 spine, 3 or 5 rays; mouth small, jaws with single row of close-set teeth; no teeth on palate. Postlarvae large (25–30 mm SL) pelagic, orbicular, compressed, transparent, abdomen silvery, body with narrow vertical ridges; dorsal, anal and pelvic fin spines of postlarvae with many sharp (probably venomous) spinules.

This family is divided into 3 subfamilies, but only 2 subfamilies are represented in our area.

Pencilled surgeon

Powderblue surgeon

Brown surgeon

Convict surgeon

Lined bristletooth

Palette surgeon

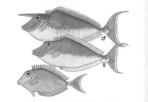

Sailfin tang   Humpback unicornfish   Spotted unicornfish

Subfamily Acanthurinae Surgeonfish

Body disc-shaped to oblong, compressed. **Tail with scalpel-like spine that folds into a groove on each side of peduncle**; although there are no specific muscles to erect this spine, when the tail is bent, the sharp anterior end of the spine is exposed and can deliver a deep cut to a predator or unwary person holding the fish. **Dorsal fin continuous, with 4–9 sharp spines, 19–33 rays; anal fin with 3 sharp spines, 18–28 rays; pelvic fins with 1 spine and 3 or 5 rays**; tail fin convex, truncate, emarginate or lunate; scales microscopic. Mouth small, terminal; 1 row of teeth in jaws; teeth close-set, either spatulate with denticulate tips, or slender and numerous with incurved tips; no teeth on palate. Size range 18–63 cm.

Most surgeonfish occur in shallow tropical and subtropical seas, but a few are found in deeper water (to 100 m). Surgeonfish feed mainly on algae, detritus or zooplankton. The detritus eaters (*Ctenochaetus*) also ingest a lot of sand with their food and have a thick-walled, gizzard-like stomach that helps break up the plant cells in their food; and, like most herbivores, they also have a very long intestine. Most surgeonfish spawn in large groups, and the eggs and larvae are pelagic. The distinctive pelagic pre-juvenile stage (called an 'acronurus') was originally described as a distinct genus and species. The long duration of the planktonic larvae and acronurus, which lasts 10 weeks in some species, accounts for the wide distribution of most surgeonfish. When the acronurus encounter shallow water over a suitable reef, they drop to the bottom; and within 4 or 5 days transform to the juvenile stage.

Figure 40
Postlarva of a convict surgeon from the Hawaiian Islands (drawn by Helen Randall).

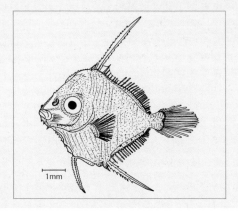

Worldwide in tropical and subtropical seas. Except for 5 species of *Acanthurus* in the Atlantic, all of the other species of this subfamily are Indo-Pacific in distribution. Four genera, with 51 species, 19 occur in our area.

PENCILLED SURGEON
Acanthurus dussumieri
Valenciennes 1835

34 cm adult
3 cm juvenile

Body oblong, depth 1.9–2.1 times in SL; dorsal fin 9 spines, 25–27 rays; anal fin rays 24–26; pelvic fins with 1 spine, 5 rays; tail fin concave in juveniles, lunate in adults; teeth fixed, spatulate. Large adults with distinctly convex forehead, snout projecting slightly in front of mouth. **Head and body tawny brown with numerous** irregular longitudinal **blue lines**; orange band across inter-orbital area joining yellow/orange area around eye; **socket of tail spine edged in black, spine white**; opercular membrane blackish; dorsal and anal fins yellowish, sometimes blue posteriorly; tail fin mainly blue with small black spots, yellow at base. Basal half of tail fin of juvenile white, rear hyaline. Attains 54 cm.

Indo-central Pacific, Oman to Algoa Bay.

Coral and rocky reefs in depths of 5–30 m; juveniles on shallow reefs with good algal growth; adults on outer reef slopes and shipwrecks.

Usually solitary, but spawns in aggregations. Does well in an aquarium but will outgrow a small tank.

SIMILAR SPECIES

The tailring surgeon, *Acanthurus blochii* Valenciennes 1835, has body dark olive to bluish brown, sometimes with pale dots; yellow spot behind eye; tail fin dark blue with whitish bar at base; tail spine dark. Attains 42 cm. Indo-Pacific, south to Durban.

The elongate surgeon, *Acanthurus mata* (Cuvier 1829), has snout 6.6–6.9 times in SL, and shorter than distance from eye to upper end of pectoral fin base; head and body dark brown with longitudinal blue lines, adult with yellow area behind eye and 2 yellow stripes in front of eye; black spot at upper end of gill opening; tail fin bluish, spine black; pale blue line along base and margin of soft dorsal and anal fins. Attains 50 cm; feeds on zooplankton; often in turbid water. Indo-central Pacific, south to the Eastern Cape.

POWDERBLUE SURGEON
Acanthurus leucosternon
Bennett 1832

15 cm

Body oblong, depth 1.7–1.9 times in SL; dorsal fin with 9 spines, 28–30 rays; anal fin rays 23–26; pelvic fins 1 spine, 5 rays; tail fin truncate to emarginate; teeth fixed, spatulate; snout profile straight or slightly concave. **Body blue, with white zone below and behind head; peduncle and spine yellow; head black** with white bar behind mouth; dorsal fin yellow with white edge and submarginal black line; anal and pelvic fins white; tail fin white, bordered with black or dark blue margins, rear edge white; pectoral fins hyaline yellow. Attains 23 cm (~11 years in an aquarium).

Indian Ocean, Oman to Sodwana Bay.

Coral reefs in 5–25 m. Usually seen in small to large groups when grazing on reef.

Can be difficult to keep in an aquarium; needs large amounts of algae.

BROWN SURGEON
Acanthurus nigrofuscus
(Forsskål 1775)

10 cm

Body oblong, depth 2.0–2.3 times in SL; dorsal fin 9 spines, 24–27 rays; anal fin rays 22–24; pelvic fins 1 spine, 5 rays; tail fin truncate to emarginate; **teeth fixed, spatulate;** snout longer than distance from eye to upper end of pectoral fin base, snout profile straight or slightly concave, mouth terminal. Head and body **brown, sometimes with bluish grey longitudinal lines on body; black spot at rear end of dorsal fin base and a smaller spot** (sometimes absent) **at rear end of anal fin base; head and chest with numerous small orange spots**; spine socket with black edge. Attains ~20 cm.

Indo-Pacific, Red Sea to Coffee Bay.

Coral and rocky reefs in 2–25 m; juveniles in tide pools. Often in groups; most common surgeonfish in South Africa.

SIMILAR SPECIES

The lined bristletooth is similar but only has orange spots on forehead and nape.

The chocolate surgeon, *Acanthurus thompsoni* (Fowler 1923), usually dark brown (sometimes grey), with dark spot at base of last 3–4 dorsal fin rays; tail fin white; interorbital area of adult swollen, forming small bump in front of eyes; snout shorter than distance from eye to upper end of pectoral fin base. Attains 27 cm; feeds primarily on zooplankton. Indo-central Pacific, south to Sodwana Bay.

The twospot bristletooth, *Ctenochaetus binotatus* Randall 1955, looks similar and also has a dark spot at rear end of dorsal and anal fins, but it has body orangish brown, with longitudinal blue lines and blue-grey dots on head and chest; teeth slender, flexible. Attains 22 cm. Indo-central Pacific, south to Durban.

CONVICT SURGEON
Acanthurus triostegus
(Linnaeus 1758)

24 cm male (in
spawning colouration,
no locality)
3 cm pre-juvenile
9 cm (typical pattern)

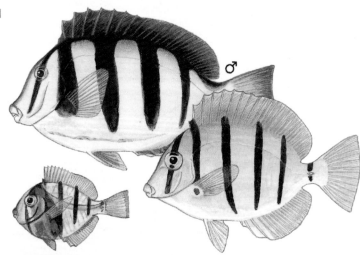

Body depth 1.8–1.9 times in SL; dorsal fin 9 spines, 22–24 rays; anal fin rays 19–22; very small spine on peduncle; teeth fixed, spatulate; snout longer than distance from eye to upper end of pectoral fin base, snout profile slightly concave, mouth terminal. **Head, body and fins pale greenish grey; 4 narrow dark bars on body,** 5th bar sometimes broken into 2 black spots at base of tail fin. Attains 27 cm.

Indo-Pacific (not in Red Sea or along coast of Arabian Peninsula), Kenya to Coffee Bay; postlarvae drifting to Algoa Bay.

Coral and rocky reefs from 2–45 m; juveniles often found in tide pools; adults common in shallow water. Usually occurs in large aggregations which roam the reef feeding on algae. Does well in an aquarium.

LINED BRISTLETOOTH
Ctenochaetus striatus
(Quoy & Gaimard 1825)

19 cm adult (Red Sea)
5 cm juvenile
(Mauritius)

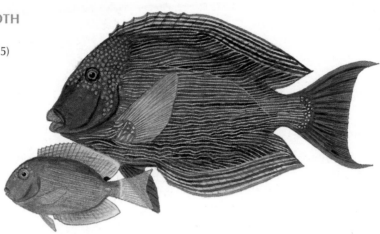

Body deep, depth 1.9–2.3 times in SL; **dorsal fin with 8 spines (1st spine small and easily overlooked), 27–31 rays; anal fin rays 24–28**; tail fin lunate in adult, emarginate in juvenile; **teeth slender and flexible**; snout profile convex, mouth terminal. **Head, body and fins dark brown with numerous longitudinal pale blue lines** on body and dorsal and anal fins; **nape and dorsal part of head covered with orange-yellow dots**; pectoral fins yellowish. Fish in breeding colours are pale, with black on margins of median fins and on mouth. Attains 26 cm (30+ years).

Indo-central Pacific, Red Sea, Oman to Aliwal Shoal.

Coral and rocky reefs in 2–25 m. Feeds on filamentous algae and detritus, often in large groups grazing over reef. Does well in an aquarium with a lot of algae.

SIMILAR SPECIES

The spotted bristletooth, *Ctenochaetus truncatus* Randall & Clements 2001 [formerly identified as *Ctenochaetus strigosus*, which is endemic to Hawaii], has head and body dark brown or tawny, covered with pale dots; edge of dorsal and anal fins pale blue; posterior edge of eye yellow, iris black with yellow ring around pupil; tail fin truncate to emarginate; juvenile bright yellow; dorsal fin rays 25–27; anal fin rays 22–25. Attains 18 cm. Indo-central Pacific, south to Sodwana Bay.

PALETTE SURGEON
Paracanthurus hepatus
(Linnaeus, 1766)

26 cm normal colouration
centre: male in breeding colours
(no locality or size)
5 cm juvenile

Body oblong, depth ~2.3 times in SL of adults; **dorsal fin 9 spines (1st spine much smaller than 2nd), 19–20 rays; anal fin rays 18–19; pelvic fins 1 spine, 3 rays**; tail fin truncate; snout profile convex, mouth terminal; **teeth fixed, spatulate.** Colour pattern distinctive; Pacific fish and juveniles from Indian Ocean have lower part of head and body blue. Attains 26 cm.

Indo-central Pacific, Kenya to Sodwana Bay.

Coral reefs or sandy areas with sponges; prefers reefs in clear water with some current. Juveniles hide amongst branching corals. Adults found in 10–30 m. Juveniles feed on zooplankton; adults also graze algae. Solitary or in loose groups; wary fish, difficult for divers to approach. Dorsal, anal and pelvic fin spines said to be venomous.

Does well in an aquarium on a balanced diet containing plant material.

SAILFIN TANG
Zebrasoma desjardinii
(Bennett 1836)

5 cm juvenile
9 cm (both
Mauritius)

Body disc-like, depth 1.8–2.0 times in SL; **dorsal fin distinctly elevated, with 4 spines, 27–31 rays, anterior rays elongate, the longest ray 2.1–2.5 times in SL; anal fin elevated less than dorsal fin, with 3 spines, 22–24 rays;** pelvic fins 1 spine, 5 rays; tail fin truncate or convex; snout profile slightly concave; teeth fixed, spatulate. **Body mostly dark, with alternating pale and dark bars** overlain with yellow and whitish vertical lines; lower part of body dark with yellow spots; head pale grey with close-set white spots, dark vertical band through eye; **dorsal and anal fins dark with curving yellow lines;** tail fin dark with or without pale spots. Small juvenile pale with dark vertical bars on body; 2 blackish bars on head; snout, pelvic fins and anal fin yellowish; dorsal fin dusky yellow. Large juveniles with yellow vertical lines on body. Attains 40 cm (13–14 years in an aquarium).

Indian Ocean, Red Sea to Sodwana Bay.

Coral reefs, usually in sheltered areas. Feeds on algae and detritus; adults solitary or in pairs. Spawns in groups.

— SIMILAR SPECIES —

Formerly identified as *Zebrasoma veliferum* or *velifer* (Bloch 1795), a Pacific species, usually has more dorsal and anal fin rays, yellow tail fin and no yellow spots on lower part of body.

The twotone tang, *Zebrasoma scopas* (Cuvier 1829), has head and front of body tawny, shading to dark brown posteriorly (including peduncle and tail fin); peduncle spine white; wavy pale blue longitudinal lines on body and pale blue dots on head and chest; 23–25 dorsal fin rays, 19–21 anal fin rays; an oval brush-like patch of bristles on body in front of tail spine of fish larger than 7 cm SL (patch larger and bristles longer in males). Attains 20 cm. Indo-Pacific, south to Sodwana Bay.

The spotted tang, *Zebrasoma gemmatum* (Valenciennes 1835), is dark brown with white spots or streaks on head and body, encroaching onto dorsal and anal fins; tail fin yellow or yellowish brown. Attains 23 cm. Sodwana Bay to Aliwal Shoal, Mauritius and Madagascar.

Subfamily Nasinae □ Unicornfish

Body ovate to oblong, compressed, more elongate with age; **peduncle narrow, with 1–2 bony plates bearing sharp lateral keels on each side of peduncle** (not apparent in juveniles <15 cm SL of some species); **dorsal fin continuous with 4–6 sharp spines, 24–31 rays; anal fin with 2 sharp spines, 23–31 rays; pelvic fins with 1 spine, 3 rays;** tail fin convex, truncate, emarginate or lunate, with adults of some species developing a long filament at upper and lower corners of fin; scales microscopic, close-set, non-overlapping, and with tiny bristles; mouth small, terminal; teeth close-set, mostly lanceolate with finely serrate edges; 1 row in jaws; no teeth on palate. A long bony 'horn' develops between the eyes of some species; the function of the unicornfish's horn is obscure. It occurs in both sexes of *Naso brevirostris*, but only in males of *Naso brachycentron*. Colour patterns variable and change quickly depending on habitat or mood of the fish. Fork length (FL), measured from front of upper jaw to end of middle tail fin rays, is the accepted length measurement for unicornfish. Size range 35 cm to 1 m FL.

Most unicornfish occur in shallow tropical and subtropical seas, but a few are found in deeper water (to 200+ m). Juveniles feed mainly on algae, detritus and micro-invertebrates; adults generally in schools feeding on zooplankton above coral reefs, but they also supplement their diet with algae and detritus. When feeding above the reef, the fish show typical pelagic fish counter-shading: head and body dark blue/green above and silvery below. Spawn in large aggregations; eggs and larvae pelagic. The 4 cm pre-juvenile (or keris) stage is similar to the acronurus pre-juvenile of surgeonfish, and was also originally described as a distinct genus and species (*Keris anguinosus*).

The bony keels on the peduncle can deliver a deep cut to a predator or a careless person trying to hold the fish. These wounds are not particularly painful, but should be cleaned and treated to prevent infection. The dorsal, anal and pelvic spines of some *Naso* are said to be venomous.

Indo-Pacific. One genus, ~18 species, 12 in our area.

HUMPBACK UNICORNFISH
Naso brachycentron
(Valenciennes 1835)

67 cm male
68 cm female
22 cm juvenile
(all Maldives; lengths
include tail filaments)

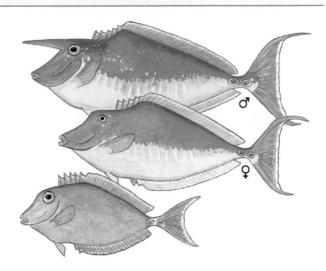

Body oblong, depth 2.6–2.9 times in FL; dorsal fin with 4 or 5 spines, 28–30 rays, **profile of nape below dorsal fin spines distinctly concave followed by hump below anterior rays** (juveniles <20 cm FL lack dorsal hump); anal fin rays 27–28; tail fin lunate, upper and lowermost rays elongate in adults; adults with 2 bony plates on side of peduncle, each plate with sharp keel ending in antrorse point; **long bony horn between eyes of adult males** projects well in front of mouth; females with small bump between eyes. **Head and body grey dorsally, pale ventrally**. Attains at least 60 cm FL.

Indo-central Pacific, Kenya to Sodwana Bay.

Shallow coral and rocky reefs to 30 m. Seen in large schools or small groups; difficult to approach underwater.

SIMILAR SPECIES

No other species of *Naso* has the distinctive humpback that develops in *Naso brachycentron*.

SPOTTED UNICORNFISH
Naso brevirostris
(Cuvier 1829)

42 cm male (Comoros)
38 cm (Red Sea)
3 cm (Marshall Islands)

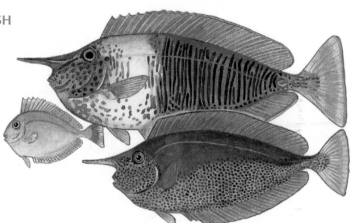

Body oblong, depth 2.0–3.0 times in FL; dorsal fin spines 6, dorsal and anal fin rays 27–29; tail fin truncate to slightly convex; **adult with long bony horn between eyes which projects well in front of mouth; profile of snout between upper lip and base of horn short and nearly vertical;** adult with 2 bony peduncular plates, each with a low keel. **Head and body bluish grey to greenish brown;** subadults with small dark spots on head and body; **adults with numerous irregular vertical blue lines on body, breaking into small spots on head; chest and belly white; tail fin with dark rear margin and broad, dull orange, submarginal band.** Temporary colour phases: pale blue-grey without dark markings or (males) broad white zone just behind head. Attains 60 cm (30+ years).

Indo-West Pacific, Kenya to Durban; postlarvae drift to Algoa Bay.

Coral and rocky reefs in 5–30 m. Juveniles feed mainly on algae; adults consume primarily zooplankton. Usually in schools.

— SIMILAR SPECIES ———————

The humpnose unicornfish, *Naso tuberosus* Lacepède 1801, is grey with 2 blue peduncular plates; adult with large bulbous protuberance on front of head. Southwestern Indian Ocean, Mozambique, Seychelles and Mauritius.

The bluespine unicornfish, *Naso unicornis* (Forsskål 1775), is grey with 2 blue peduncular plates; relatively short horn which does not project past mouth; adult tail fin with filaments. Indo-Pacific, south to KZN.

FAMILY ZANCLIDAE ▪ Moorish Idol

Head and body strongly compressed, disc-like, with minute rough scales; body depth 1.0–1.4 times in SL; no spine on peduncle; snout projecting, mouth small, teeth long, slender, bristle-like, mostly covered by wide lips; **dorsal fin with 6–7 spines, 39–42 rays, anterior dorsal fin spines elongated into a whip-like filament; anal fin with 3 spines, 31–37 rays, the anterior rays elongate, forming a pointed lobe at front of fin;** pelvic fins with 1 spine, 5 rays; short spine in front of each eye in adults, larger in males. Coral and rocky reefs in 5–182 m.

Indo-Pacific in tropical and subtropical waters. One species.

MOORISH IDOL
Zanclus cornutus
(Linnaeus 1758)

13cm adult
6 cm juvenile
12 cm adult (showing
night pattern)

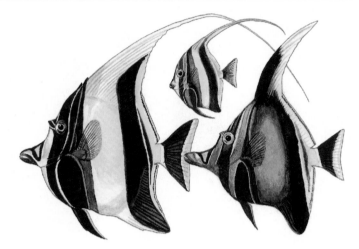

Third dorsal fin spine extremely elongate, usually longer than SL; adult with bony projection in front of each eye. Colour pattern and snout configuration distinctive. Attains 22 cm.

Indo-Pacific, Kenya to Aliwal Shoal, juveniles to Breë River.

Common on coral reefs, also in harbours near wharves and pilings. Pelagic postlarva transforms at ~8 cm to the juvenile stage and loses the stout curved preorbital spine below each eye. The name *Zanclus canescens* (Linnaeus) is a synonym based on the postlarva. The wide distribution (from Africa to Mexico) of this species is attributed to the long duration of the pelagic postlarval stage. Omnivorous, feeding on a variety of benthic invertebrates (sponges, tunicates, brittlestars, crustaceans, worms, bivalves, gastropods), algae and detritus. Occurs singly, in pairs, or in large schools.

Difficult to keep in an aquarium; juveniles adapt to captivity more easily.

SIMILAR SPECIES

Confusing the coachman butterflyfish (*Heniochus* spp) with the Moorish idol is common among novice fish watchers. The coachman has no black on the tail fin and lacks the protruding snout.

FAMILY SIGANIDAE ■ Rabbitfish

Moderate-sized fish; **body oblong, compressed, with minute embedded scales; head shorter than body depth, small terminal mouth; jaws with 1 row of bicuspid incisors; no teeth on vomer or palatines; upper jaw not protrusile; dorsal fin continuous with 13 sharp spines, 10 soft-rays; anal fin with 7 sharp spines, 9 rays; pelvic fins unique, with 2 sharp spines and 3 soft-rays in between spines, inner spine connected to abdomen by skin**; procumbent (pointing forward) spine in front of dorsal fin; tail fin truncate, emarginate or forked. Size range 30–50 cm.

Some species occur in small schools and are usually found in estuaries, on seagrass beds or over weedy bottom; other species are solitary or seen in pairs on coral reefs. Most rabbitfish are found in less than 15 m, but 2 species occur to depths of 50 m. All fin spines are venomous; although wounds can be very painful, they are not fatal. The pain is quickly

alleviated if the wound is immersed in hot (55° C) water. As indicated by their common name, rabbitfish are herbivores, feeding primarily on algae. They also ingest some detritus with their leafy food, and this detritus may be more nutritious than the algae. With their herbivorous diet, rapid growth and tasty flesh, rabbitfish are often used in aquaculture operations. Like many coral reef fish, rabbitfish display different colour patterns during the day and night, when resting, active or asleep, or when moving to a different habitat. When stressed, many species display a similar 'camouflage pattern' of irregular brown blotches.

This Indo-central Pacific family comprises 2 genera and ~30 species; 4 in our area.

BLUESPOTTED RABBITFISH
Siganus sutor
(Valenciennes 1835)

12 cm

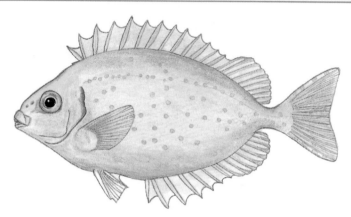

Body depth 2.2–2.6 times in SL; tail fin concave. Colour variable, depending on mood of fish and colour of its habitat; **head, body and fins usually silvery grey, covered with small, evenly spaced, pale blue spots**; top of head and dorsal fin yellowish; some specimens golden to dark brown. At night, spots white; dark blotch, slightly smaller than eye often visible at LL origin. Attains 50 cm.

Western Indian Ocean, Kenya to Sodwana Bay, strays to Knysna.

Coral and rocky reefs, estuaries and shallow coastal areas.

SIMILAR SPECIES

The forktail rabbitfish, *Siganus argenteus* (Quoy & Gaimard 1825), has more slender body (depth 2.4–3.0 times in SL), tail fin forked with pointed lobes; head and body pale bluish, bluish grey or brownish, with numerous small pale yellow spots which may join to form yellow stripes, especially ventrally on body; vertically elongate dark streak above pectoral fin base; dorsal fin and dorsal surface of head yellow. Attains 45 cm. Usually in schools in open water above reef, where it may be feeding on plankton. Indo-central Pacific, Red Sea to Ponta do Ouro.

The darkspotted rabbitfish, *Siganus laqueus* von Bonde 1934, has head, body and fins covered with small dark brown spots; eye-sized dark blotch (group of darker spots) at origin of LL, prominent in juveniles, diffuse in adults; inner margin of tail fin lobes convex. Attains 40 cm. Indian Ocean, Kenya to Kosi Bay, Maldives, Seychelles and Mauritius.

FAMILY GEMPYLIDAE ▫ Snoek, Snake Mackerel, Oilfish, etc.

Body elongate (depth 4–8 times in SL), or extremely elongate (depth 10–50 times in SL), compressed, or somewhat fusiform; head longer than body depth; mouth large, upper jaw ¹/₃ to ¹/₂ head length, not protrusile; teeth large, sharp, those at front of upper jaw often fang-like; 1 or 2 nostrils on each side of snout; dorsal fin(s) along entire length of body; anal fin shape resembles the soft-rayed dorsal fin; some species with separate finlets behind dorsal and anal fins; tail fin well developed or small, or absent; pectoral fins shorter than head; pelvic fins small, rudimentary or absent in adults.

Worldwide in tropical and temperate waters. Two subfamilies.

Snoek

Cutlassfish

Subfamily Gempylinae ▫ Snoek, Snake Mackerel & Oilfish

Body elongate (depth 4–17 times in SL), compressed or somewhat fusiform; 2 nostrils on each side of snout; dorsal fin divided into 2 contiguous fins; spinous dorsal base longer than soft-rayed base (excluding finlets); tail fin forked; no fleshy keels on peduncle (except in *Lepidocybium*); LL single or double; scales small and variously modified. Size range 30 cm to 2 m.

Large swift predators, usually in 200–500 m; often migrate to surface at night.

Worldwide. A disparate group comprising ~16 genera and ~23 species, including escolar, sackfish, gemfish and roudi; 9 species in our area.

SNOEK
Thyrsites atun
(Euphrasen 1791)

18 cm FL

Body elongate, compressed, depth 7–9 times in SL and about half head length; dorsal fin with 18–21 slender spines, 10–12 rays, fin **deeply divided between spinous and soft-rayed parts**; anal fin with 1 weak spine, 9–12 rays; dorsal and anal fins followed by row of

5–7 finlets; **pelvic fins small, with 1 weak spine and 5 rays**; LL single, bent down below rear dorsal fin spines; scales minute, thin, cycloid and deciduous; lower jaw projecting; no fleshy flap or cartilaginous projection at tip of jaws. **Head and body bluish grey dorsally, silvery below; spinous dorsal fin black**. Attains 1.8 m, 9 kg.

Restricted to temperate waters of Southern Hemisphere; southern Africa (Angola to Algoa Bay), Australia, New Zealand, South America, Tristan da Cunha Group and Gough Island (South Atlantic), and St Paul and Amsterdam Islands (southern Indian Ocean).

Mesopelagic and epipelagic near continents, islands and seamounts; near bottom during day, but often migrates to surface at night. Feeds on pelagic fish; small juveniles feed mainly on small lanternfish (Family Myctophidae); adults eat mainly pilchards, anchovies, redeye roundherring, crustaceans (mainly euphausiids) and cephalopods. Often in large schools. One-year-old fish are ~29 cm FL; matures at ~73 cm FL (3 years); 90 cm FL snoek is ~10 years old. Spawns in winter and spring in 150–400 m west of Cape Agulhas; eggs and larvae pelagic. Inshore/offshore migrations follow prey abundance.

Flesh excellent. Caught trolling or with handlines near bottom and in midwater; also taken in trawls. Snoek are of commercial importance in South Africa, Australia, New Zealand and southern South America.

SIMILAR SPECIES

The black snoek, *Thyrsitoides marleyi* Fowler 1929, has a cartilage protrusion at front of both jaws and bifurcate LL: anterior stem from upper end of gill opening to below 4th dorsal fin spine, where a ventral branch curves down to run along mid-lateral part of body to tail fin; upper branch of LL continues posteriorly near spinous dorsal fin base to below its rear end. Adults dark brown; juveniles silver with black blotch at front of spinous dorsal fin. Attains 1.5 m SL. Indo-West Pacific, south to Algoa Bay.

Subfamily Trichiurinae   Cutlassfish & Frostfish

Body extremely long (depth 10–50 times in SL) and laterally compressed like a ribbon; scales absent; mouth large, upper jaw not protrusile, lower jaw projecting; jaws with large compressed sharp teeth, those at front of upper jaw fang-like; single nostril on each side of snout; dorsal fin long and low, origin slightly behind eye, front part with slender flexible spines, rear part with unbranched segmented rays; tail fin small or absent; anal fin low or reduced to minute embedded spines; pelvic fins a small scale-like spine or absent; LL single. Body silver, dark bluish or greenish dorsally. Size range 90 cm to 2 m.

Voracious predators usually found near bottom or in midwater at 100–1 200 m; species of *Trichiurus* also occur in shallow coastal waters. Flesh excellent; *Trichiurus* and *Lepidopus* are of commercial importance in some areas.

Worldwide in tropical and temperate waters. Nine genera, with ~32 species, 5 in our area.

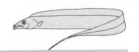

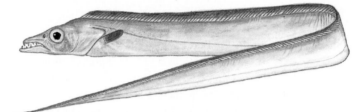

CUTLASSFISH
Trichiurus lepturus
Linnaeus 1758

51 cm

Body extremely elongate and strongly compressed, tapering posteriorly to a thin tubular tip; dorsal fin with 3 slender spines, 124–138 rays, longest rays more than half body depth; anal fin not apparent, the rays reduced to minute embedded or slightly exposed spinules; pectoral fins with smooth spine and 11–13 rays; **pelvic fins absent; tail fin absent**; LL curves behind pectoral fin to run along lower side of body; head with bony crest behind inter-orbital area; lower margin of operculum concave; small cartilaginous knob at tip of each jaw. **Head and body silvery.** Attains 1.2 m.

Worldwide in tropical and temperate waters along continental shores and nearby islands.

Bentho-pelagic from shore to 350 m; usually caught over sand or silty bottom. Juveniles eat primarily pelagic crustaceans in midwater by day; at night they form loose aggregations at the surface, where they feed on macro-zooplankton. During the day, adults eat a variety of fish, squid and crustaceans near the surface; and at night, they feed at the bottom.

Commonly taken by trawlers on Thukela Bank. SADSAA all-tackle record: 3.2 kg.

SIMILAR SPECIES

Some ribbonfish (Family Trachipteridae) are similar in their greatly elongate compressed body; but they have a very protrusile upper jaw with a broad maxilla (maxilla width greater than eye diameter), and teeth minute or absent.

The buttersnoek, *Lepidopus caudatus* (Euphrasen 1788), has an extremely elongate compressed body with a small forked tail fin and slender peduncle; the low dorsal fin runs from head to tail; anal fin with ~40 short isolated rays, in front of a low fin of ~20 short rays confined to rear half of body. Eastern Atlantic to South Africa, Australia and New Zealand.

FAMILY SCOMBRIDAE ■ Tuna, Mackerel & Bonito

Body robust, oblong or elongate and fusiform, moderately compressed in some genera; snout pointed, upper jaw not protrusile; maxilla slips under preorbital bone when mouth is closed; teeth large, moderate or small; **1st (spinous) dorsal fin usually short, separate from soft-rayed fin, and depressible into a groove; row of finlets behind dorsal and anal fins; tail fin lunate and stiff, with 2 short fleshy keels at base**, some species with additional longer keel along side of peduncle; pelvic fins with 6 soft-rays; body covered with small to moderate scales, or **with an area of embedded thick scales behind the head and around the pectoral fins called a corselet** and the rest of the body without scales or with minute thin scales. Swimbladder present or absent. Fork length (FL), from tip of snout to end of middle tail fin rays is the length measurement for scombrids. Size range 38 cm to 3 m.

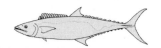

Fast-swimming voracious predators of the epipelagic zone of the open ocean; several species also occur in coastal waters. Most scombrids feed on a variety of pelagic fish, squid and crustaceans, but a few species eat primarily zooplankton.

Some tunas can maintain their body temperature several degrees above the ambient water temperature; this elevated body temperature increases the efficiency of the swimming muscles, especially during excursions into cold water below the thermocline. Scombrids do not change sex, and there are no obvious differences in the sexes. Batch spawning occurs in tropical and subtropical areas, often near shore; eggs and larvae are pelagic. Many species occur in large schools and are migratory; some tuna species make cross-ocean migrations, and *Scomberomorus* species make coastal migrations.

Scombrids are much esteemed as food-fish of great economic importance. They are often eaten raw ('sushi'), as they harbour few parasites. They are marketed fresh, frozen or canned. A freshly caught scombrid should be put on ice in the shade; if it is allowed to lie in the sun for several hours on a hot day, histamine develops in the flesh; and this may cause an allergic reaction when the fish is eaten. In the commercial fishery, scombrids are caught with purse seines, drift nets, longlines, hook and line (with live fish as bait) or by trolling a lure or bait. In the recreational fishery, most scombrids are caught by trolling a bait or lure at surface.

Worldwide in tropical and temperate seas. Fifteen genera, 51 species, 18 in our area.

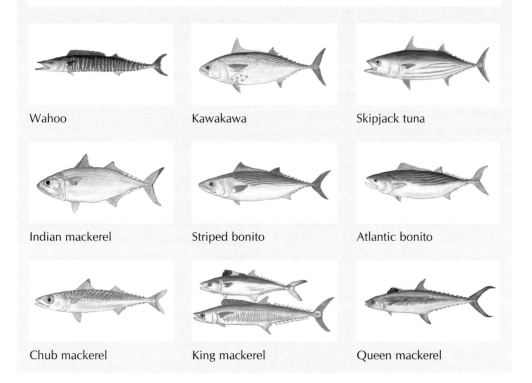

Wahoo

Kawakawa

Skipjack tuna

Indian mackerel

Striped bonito

Atlantic bonito

Chub mackerel

King mackerel

Queen mackerel

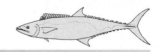

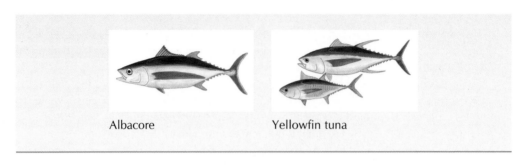

Albacore   Yellowfin tuna

WAHOO
Acanthocybium solandri
(Cuvier 1832)

60 cm FL juvenile

Body elongate, slightly compressed, depth **6.6–7.7 times in FL, snout and jaws elongate and beak-like, snout length about half of head length and 3–4 times longer than eye diameter**; jaws with compressed, triangular, finely serrate teeth; villiform teeth on vomer and palatines; **no gill rakers; 1st dorsal fin long and low, with 23–27 spines; soft dorsal rays 11–16 + 7–10 finlets; anal fin rays 11–14 + 7–10 finlets**; soft dorsal and anal fin lobes short, about half length of pectoral fins, which are less than half head length; pectoral fin rays 22–26; body covered with minute scales; large fleshy keel along midside of peduncle to tail fin base; swimbladder well developed. Head and body iridescent, blue-green dorsally, silvery below; live fish often show **24–30 dark blue bars on body**, the bars become dark grey after death. Attains 2.1 m FL, 83 kg.

Worldwide in tropical and subtropical waters. Taken by anglers from Algoa Bay to Sodwana Bay; also recorded from 50 km west of Cape Point.

Epipelagic in open ocean. Solitary predator, feeds on variety of fish (scombrids, porcupine-fish, flyingfish, sardines, etc.) and also squid. Sometimes in loose groups. Matures at 90 cm FL. The ovary of a 1.3 m FL female was estimated to contain 6 million eggs.

A premier angling fish; the speed and strength of the wahoo are awesome. Reputed to be among the fastest fish in the sea; it has been estimated at speeds of 77 km/h over short distances. Flesh excellent. IGFA all-tackle record: 72 kg fish from California.

KAWAKAWA
Euthynnus affinis
(Cantor 1849)

60 cm FL adult

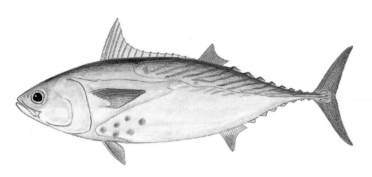

Body oblong, robust, depth subequal to head length, contained 3.8–4.3 times in FL; snout length subequal to eye diameter; 1st dorsal fin with 15–17 spines, fin height longer than snout; soft dorsal rays 12–13 + 8 finlets; narrow gap (about equal to eye diameter) between last dorsal fin spine and origin of soft dorsal fin; anal fin rays 13–14 + 7 finlets; pectoral fins more than half head length, 25–29 rays; mid-lateral keel on peduncle continued onto tail fin base; no swimbladder; 2 ridges on tongue; gill rakers 29–35; jaws with 1 row of small conical teeth; villiform teeth on vomer and palatines. Head and body bluish dorsally, silvery white below; wavy oblique dark bands on rear part of body above LL; dark spots appear between pectoral and pelvic fins when the fish is excited or stressed. Attains ~1 m FL and ~14 kg.

Warm waters of Indo-West Pacific, Red Sea, Oman to Cape St Francis.

Epipelagic, mainly coastal. Usually in small schools with other like-sized tuna. Feeds on fish, shrimp and squid. Matures at 48–65 cm FL (3 years); a 65 cm FL (4.6 kg) fish spawns ~2.5 million eggs per season. Spawns January to July off Kenya. Kawakawa are prey for marlin, large tuna and sharks.

Also known as 'eastern little tuna'. IGFA all-tackle world record: 11.8 kg fish from Australia.

SIMILAR SPECIES

The little tunny, *Euthynnus alletteratus* (Rafinesque 1810), known off Angola, has 37–40 gill rakers; no vomerine teeth.

The worldwide frigate tuna, *Auxis thazard* (Lacepède 1800), is more slender (body depth 4.0–4.6 times in FL), dorsal fin spines 11–12, wide gap (distinctly longer than pectoral fin) between spinous and soft dorsal fins. A small species, mature at 30 cm FL, attains 50 cm FL.

SKIPJACK TUNA
Katsuwonus pelamis
(Linnaeus 1758)

~50 cm FL adult

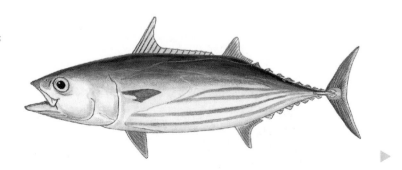

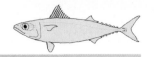

Body oblong, robust, depth subequal to head length, contained 3.7–4.1 times in FL; snout slightly longer than eye diameter; 1st dorsal fin spines 14–16, longest spine much longer than snout; 2nd dorsal fin with 14–15 rays + 7–9 finlets; anal rays 14–15 + 7–8 finlets; pectoral fins with 26–28 rays; fleshy process between pelvic fins forked, much shorter than pelvic fins; mid-lateral keel along peduncle continued onto tail fin base; no swimbladder; gill rakers 53–63; jaws with 1 row of small conical teeth; no teeth on vomer or palatines; tongue with 2 longitudinal ridges. Head and body dark **purplish blue dorsally, silvery white below, with 4–6 longitudinal dark stripes**. Attains 1.2 m FL and 35 kg (8–12 years).

Worldwide in tropical and warm temperate waters; all round our coast, most common from Algoa Bay to Maputo.

Epipelagic in open ocean from surface (at night) to ~260 m (during day). Feeds on variety of fish (including carangids, triggerfish and juvenile skipjack), crustaceans and squid, with feeding peaks at dawn and dusk.

Generally in large schools near surface in offshore waters; occasionally below 200 m, but usually above thermocline. Often associated with flotsam, sharks, whales or other tuna species. Predators are tuna, billfish and sharks. Matures at 41–45 cm FL; spawns in batches mainly May to September in subtropical waters.

The skipjack fishery is one of the most important scombrid fisheries; caught with purse seines, longlines, drift nets and pole-and-line gear; commonly taken at FADs (fish attracting devices); also caught by trolling a lure or bait. IGFA all-tackle record: 20.5 kg fish from Baja California, Mexico.

SIMILAR SPECIES

The cosmopolitan bullet tuna, *Auxis rochei* (Risso 1810), is more slender, body depth 4.1–4.7 times in FL; 10–11 dorsal fin spines, wide gap (distinctly longer than pectoral fin) between spinous and soft dorsal fins, and pectoral fin does not reach vertical at front end of scaleless area above scaly corselet. Matures at 30 cm FL, maximum 50 cm FL.

INDIAN MACKEREL
Rastrelliger kanagurta
(Cuvier 1816)

21 cm FL

Body oblong, robust, depth subequal to head length, 3.4–4.0 times in FL; snout length subequal to eye diameter; adipose eyelids cover front and rear of eye; 1st dorsal fin spines 8–11; height of fin much longer than snout; 2nd dorsal fin rays 11–13 + 5 finlets; anal fin rays 11–12 + 5 finlets; pectoral fins about half head length, with 19–20 rays; body covered with moderately large scales; 2 small fleshy keels on each side of tail fin base; no

mid-lateral keel on peduncle; swimbladder present; **gill rakers 48–59, visible through open mouth and longer than gill filaments**; rear edge of operculum straight; jaws with numerous minute conical teeth; no teeth on vomer or palatines. Head and body **blue-green, with longitudinal dark bands dorsally**, silvery below; black spot on body covered by lower margin of pectoral fin; dorsal fins yellowish with black tips. Attains 35 cm FL (~4 years).

Indo-West Pacific, Red Sea, Oman to Durban.

Epipelagic in coastal waters. Feeds by swimming through plankton concentrations with its mouth wide open, filtering out plankton with its long gill rakers. Occurs in schools of like-sized fish; restricted to temperatures above 17° C. Batch spawner.

STRIPED BONITO
Sarda orientalis
(Temminck &
Schlegel 1844)

45 cm FL adult

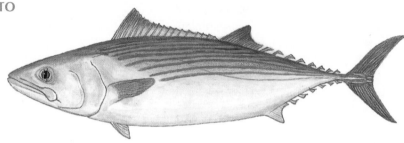

Body oblong, depth less than head length, 4.2–4.9 times in FL; snout length about twice eye diameter; 1st dorsal fin spines 17–19, longest spine slightly longer than snout; soft dorsal rays 14–17 + 7–9 finlets; anal fin rays 14–16 + 6–7 finlets; pectoral fins less than half head length, with 23–26 rays; body mostly covered with small scales but with corselet of thick scales at front of body; mid-lateral fleshy keel on peduncle continued onto tail fin base between 2 smaller keels; no swimbladder; gill rakers 9–13; jaws with a row of relatively large conical teeth, 12–20 on each side of upper jaw, 10–17 on each side of lower jaw; no teeth on vomer or palatines. **Head and body bluish grey, with 5–10 slightly oblique dark stripes dorsally**; faint bars sometimes visible on middle of body. Juveniles have dark vertical bars on body, but with growth, these are replaced by dark oblique stripes of adults. Attains 1 m FL, 12 kg.

Tropical and subtropical waters of Indo-Pacific, Red Sea, Oman, Mozambique to Cape St Francis.

Epipelagic in coastal waters; rarely caught from shore. Feeds on fish, squid, pelagic crustaceans (stomatopods, crab larvae, amphipods). Often schools with small tunas. Matures at 40 cm FL. IGFA all-tackle record: 10.7 kg fish from the Seychelles.

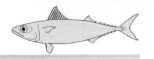

ATLANTIC BONITO
Sarda sarda
(Bloch 1793)

~ 40 cm FL

Body oblong, depth less than head length, contained 4.1–4.9 times in FL; snout length about twice eye diameter; 1st dorsal fin spines 20–23, longest spine about equal to snout; soft dorsal fin rays 15–18 + 7–9 finlets; anal rays 15–16 + 6–7 finlets; pectoral fins less than half head length, with 23–26 rays; body mostly covered with small scales but with corselet of thick scales at front of body; fleshy mid-lateral keel on peduncle, continued onto tail fin base between 2 smaller keels; no swimbladder; gill rakers 18–22; jaws with a row of small conical teeth. **Upper half of head and body blue, with 5–10 oblique dark stripes; lower half white.** Attains 92 cm FL, ~9 kg.

Tropical and temperate coasts of Atlantic Ocean, Mediterranean and Black Sea. Namibia to Port Alfred.

Epipelagic in coastal waters. Feeds mainly on schooling fish (including its own species), squid and shrimp. Migratory; large schools appear from Cape Point to Mossel Bay during summer.

IGFA all-tackle record: 8.3 kg fish from the Azores.

CHUB MACKEREL
Scomber japonicus
Houttuyn 1782

25 cm

Body slender, elongate, cylindrical, depth less than head length, 4.8–5.8 times in FL; snout slightly longer than eye diameter; 1st dorsal fin spines 9–10, longest spine longer than snout; soft dorsal fin rays 11–12 + 5 finlets; anal fin with 1 spine, 11–12 rays + 5 finlets; pectoral fins about half head length, with 19–21 rays; 2 small fleshy keels on base of tail fin; no keel on peduncle; body covered with small scales; swimbladder present; **gill rakers 39–46, shorter than gill filaments**; jaws with 1 row of minute conical teeth; adipose eyelids cover front and rear of eye. **Head and body greenish dorsally, with oblique wavy dark bands on body;** lower half of head and body white; mid-lateral part of body with small faint spots; tail fin yellowish. Attains 50 cm FL, 5 kg (8 years).

Anti-tropical distribution: northwestern, northeastern and southeastern Pacific; absent from Indian Ocean except for South

Africa, KZN to Western Cape; replaced in Atlantic Ocean by *Scomber colias* Gmelin 1789.

Epipelagic, coastal waters from surface to 300 m. Feeds on small fish, squid and zooplankton. Schools by size and often mixed in schools of other species (maasbanker, pilchards and other scombrids). Migrates southwards during winter, back northwards in summer. Matures at ~40 cm SL (3 years). Spawns along the Western and Eastern Cape coasts from June to September; spawns off KZN July to December.

Caught by commercial purse-seine and beach-seine fisheries mainly on west coast; also caught with handlines and by recreational ski-boat fishermen. IGFA all-tackle record: 2.17 kg fish from Mexico.

KING MACKEREL
Scomberomorus commerson
(Lacepède 1800)

21 cm FL juvenile
1 m FL adult

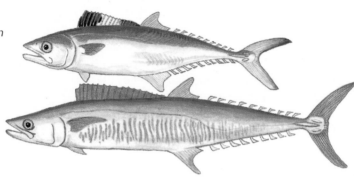

Body somewhat compressed, depth less than head length, contained 5.0–6.3 times in FL; snout length 3–4 times eye diameter; 1st dorsal fin with 15–18 spines, longest spine shorter than snout, fin margin straight; 2nd dorsal fin rays 15–20 + 8–11 finlets; anal fin rays 16–21 + 7–12 finlets; pectoral fins more than half head length, 21–24 rays; tail fin with 2 small fleshy keels on base of fin and larger mid-lateral keel on peduncle; body covered with small scales; LL sinuous, bending ventrally behind 2nd dorsal fin, then curving dorsally to mid-lateral keel; no swimbladder; gill rakers 0–2 / 1–8, shorter than gill filaments; jaws with row of large compressed triangular teeth. Head and body bluish grey dorsally, white ventrally, with numerous wavy dark bars on sides of body; 1st dorsal fin bright blue, rapidly fading to blackish blue at death; pectoral fins dusky; median fins pale grey to dusky. Juveniles (<30 cm FL) with few or no dark bars on body, 1st dorsal fin black anteriorly and posteriorly, middle third white. Attains 2.3 m FL, 70 kg (5 years).

Primarily subtropical and temperate waters of Indo-West Pacific, Red Sea, Oman to Mossel Bay, rarely to False Bay.

Epipelagic, coastal waters from surface to 300 m; juveniles inshore, in estuaries and over soft bottom. Schools by size. Feeds during day and night, mainly on fish (anchovies, pilchards and other clupeids, carangids, ponyfish, etc.); also eats squid and penaeid shrimp. Permanently resident in some areas, but also known to migrate from Mozambique to South Africa during summer. Females mature at ~1.1 m FL, males at ~71 cm FL; age at maturity 2 years. Spawns off Kenya to Mozambique from October to July.

Common in commercial and recreational ski-boat fisheries of KZN and also important

in spearfishery. Highly prized game fish, caught trolling or drift-fishing with live bait. Rarely taken by rock and surf anglers. Juveniles common in beach seine and trawl catches. Also known as 'narrowbarred Spanish mackerel', or (in KZN) as 'couta' or 'cuda'. Flesh excellent; large fish are usually cut into steaks. IGFA all-tackle record: 45 kg fish caught at Aliwal Shoal in 1982.

QUEEN MACKEREL
Scomberomorus plurilineatus
Fourmanoir 1966

74 cm FL adult male

Body somewhat compressed, depth greater than head length, 4.4–5.0 times in FL; snout length 2–3 times eye diameter; 1st dorsal fin low with 15–17 spines, longest spine subequal to snout, fin margin curved; 2nd dorsal fin rays 19–21 + 8–10 finlets; anal fin rays 19–22 + 7–10 finlets; pectoral fins more than half head length, 21–26 rays; 2 small fleshy keels on tail fin base and a larger mid-lateral keel on slender peduncle; body covered with small scales; **LL nearly straight from upper end of gill opening to mid-lateral keel; no swimbladder; gill rakers 12–15**; jaws with row of large compressed triangular teeth. Head and body dark bluish grey dorsally, white ventrally; **mid-lateral part of body with several horizontally elongate black streaks forming interrupted black lines and numerous irregular (round, oval or elongate) black spots**; peduncle and mid-lateral keel black dorsally; front part of spinous dorsal fin black, rear part white with black margin; soft dorsal and anal fins pale or silvery, the margins dusky; inner surface and axil of pectoral fin black, outer surface dusky with black margins. Juvenile with spots, developing interrupted lines at 40 cm. Attains 1.2 m FL, 14 kg (6 years).

Western Indian Ocean, Kenya to Storms River, Tsitsikamma, also west coast of Madagascar, Comoros and Seychelles.

Prefers clear water near coral reefs. Feeds mainly on fish (anchovies, clupeids, grunts, etc.); also squid and mantis shrimp (stomatopods). Forms large schools in the surf and backline over sand banks near shore. Spawns in Zanzibar Channel in August and September and off Mozambique in summer. Matures at age 2; females at 76–78 cm FL, males at 72–74 cm FL.

Known as 'kanadi kingfish' or 'kanadi seerfish' at Zanzibar and coast of Tanzania, where it is an important food-fish from March until August. Caught with gill-nets, also with hook and line using live bait or trolling.

In KZN, a popular game fish for recreational ski-boat anglers and spearfishermen; a.k.a. 'Natal snoek' or 'spotted mackerel'. Superb table fish but not easy to catch, as it is very finicky regarding when and which lure or bait it will accept. IGFA all-tackle record: (as 'kanadi seerfish') 12.5 kg fish from St Lucia.

ALBACORE
Thunnus alalunga
(Bonnaterre 1788)

~90 cm FL adult

Body robust, oblong, depth subequal to head length, 3.4–4.2 times in FL; snout length about twice eye diameter; 1st dorsal fin with 12–14 spines, 1st spine longer than snout or 2nd dorsal fin lobe; 2nd dorsal fin rays 13–16 + 7–9 finlets; anal fin rays 13–15 + 7–9 finlets; pectoral fin rays 31–36, fin greatly elongated; fish >50 cm FL have pectoral fins longer than head, reaching past anal fin lobe; 2 small fleshy keels on tail fin base and larger mid-lateral keel on peduncle; **gill rakers 25–31**; front of body with corselet of small thick scales; body behind corselet covered with minute scales; LL inconspicuous; swimbladder rudimentary, not apparent in small juveniles; jaws with row of small conical teeth. Head and **body dark blue-grey dorsally, white ventrally; dorsal and anal fins yellow, anal finlets dark; tail fin dusky, rear margin white**. Attains 1.3 m FL and 40 kg.

Worldwide in tropical and temperate waters.

Epipelagic and mesopelagic in offshore waters from surface to 600 m. Preys mainly on schooling fish such as anchovies, sardines and lanternfish (Family Myctophidae); also eats squid and zooplankton. Feeds near surface and also below thermocline in 100–600 m. Schooling species that migrates over great distances; tagged fish were found to travel 8 500 km in less than a year. Females mature at ~80 cm FL , males at ~90 cm FL (3–5 years); an albacore of 1.3 m is ~13–15 years old. Spawns in tropical waters twice a year.

Albacore (a.k.a. 'longfin tuna') are of great importance in commercial and sport fisheries. Caught all round our coast, but appears to be more common (perhaps just closer to shore) off west and south coasts. In the commercial fishery, albacore are taken with longlines, purse seines, trolling and by means of live-bait fishing. Good catches are made off Cape Point from November to April. IGFA all-tackle record: 40 kg fish from the Canary Islands.

YELLOWFIN TUNA
Thunnus albacares
(Bonnaterre 1788)

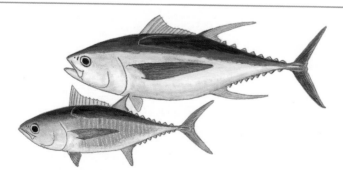

1.2 m FL adult
70 cm juvenile
(Australia)

Body robust, oblong, depth subequal to head length, 3.8–4.5 times in FL; eye diameter

more than half snout length; 1st dorsal fin with 12–14 spines, 1st spine much longer

than snout; 2nd dorsal fin rays 13–16 + 7–9 finlets; anal fin rays 13–15 + 8–10 finlets; pectoral fin rays 33–36, fin reaching almost to vertical at anal fin origin and longer than head; dorsal and anal fin lobes of adult greatly elongated; tail fin with 2 small fleshy keels on base of fin and larger mid-lateral keel on peduncle; gill rakers 27–32; front part of body with corselet of small thick scales; body behind corselet covered with minute scales; LL inconspicuous; swimbladder present; jaws with row of small conical teeth. Head and body dark blue dorsally, brassy yellow mid-laterally and pale silvery grey below; lower half of body with a broad, pale, bluish-grey swath from below pectoral fins to peduncle, this zone crossed by numerous narrow white bars or rows of small white spots; dorsal and anal fins and finlets yellow; finlets with black edges; tail and pelvic fins dusky yellow. Attains 2.2 m FL, 190 kg.

Worldwide in tropical and temperate waters.

Epipelagic and mesopelagic in offshore waters from surface to 600 m. Juveniles (5–20 kg) common off KZN. Feeds on broad spectrum of pelagic fish (including juvenile scombrids), crustaceans and squid. Prey are hunted in surface waters and also below thermocline in 100–600 m. Juveniles and adults congregate under floating *Sargassum* weed or other debris. Matures at ~0.9–1.0 m FL (2 years); a 2.0 m fish is at least 5 years old.

Yellowfin tuna ranks second in the world tuna fishery. Most yellowfin caught in South African waters are taken by foreign vessels using longlines or purse seines; other commercial fishing methods include gill-nets, pole-and-line (live bait) fishing, and trolling. IGFA all-tackle record: 176 kg fish from eastern Pacific, Revillagigedo Islands off Mexico.

FAMILY XIPHIIDAE ⬤ Swordfish

Body fusiform, but slightly compressed anteriorly; **snout and upper jaw greatly elongated, forming a flat double-edged bony sword**. In fish longer than 1 m, 1st dorsal fin short-based, erect, located just behind head, fin height greater than base; 2nd dorsal fin much smaller than 1st dorsal fin, located near tail fin; in small juveniles (<1 m from the eye to end of middle tail fin rays [eye–FL]) both jaws equally elongated, with minute teeth; skin covered with spiny scales; LL wavy; teeth, scales and LL absent in adults. In a 35 cm juvenile, the long dorsal fin is continuous, with 47 rays, fin height (length of anterior rays) greater than body depth; length of fin base ~70% eye-FL; with growth, most middle dorsal fin rays are resorbed, leaving a high short-based 1st dorsal fin above gill opening and a finlet near tail fin. Anal fin also continuous in juveniles, located on rear half of body, comprising 16–18 rays; in adults, anterior anal fin high and short-based, far removed from minute anal finlet, which is closer to tail than to anterior anal fin; pectoral fins well developed, falcate, with horizontal base, low on sides; tail fin large and lunate, with fleshy mid-lateral keel at base and running forwards onto peduncle; distinct notch on dorsal and ventral surfaces of peduncle just in front of tail fin lobes; **pelvic fins absent**; gill openings wide; branchiostegal membranes united far forward and free from isthmus; no gill rakers.

Epipelagic and mesopelagic in open ocean, usually in surface waters, but also to depths of 650 m. A single species. The genus name *Xiphias* is pronounced 'Ziff-ee-us'.

SWORDFISH
Xiphias gladius
Linnaeus 1758

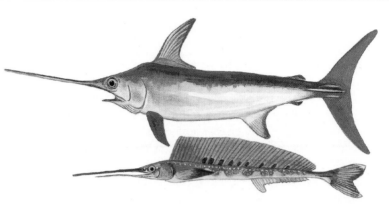

2.5 m adult
35 cm juvenile

Body robust, depth at dorsal fin origin about equal to head length (from tip of lower jaw to rear edge of operculum); body width distinctly more than half of depth at dorsal fin origin; bill length about half eye–FL. **Head and body blackish brown, dark grey, bronze or bluish black dorsally, paler below**. Attains 4.5 m (including bill) and at least 540 kg (females 12 years, males 9 years).

Tropical and temperate waters of all oceans, including the Mediterranean, Red Sea and North Sea.

Although swordfish tolerate a wide range of water temperatures (3–27° C), they are most often found in water of 13–22° C. Opportunistic predator that feeds during the day in deep (>200 m) water, and also at night (near surface) on a variety of pelagic and demersal fish. Over deep water, their prey includes epipelagic and mesopelagic fish: small tuna, dorado, flyingfish, barracuda, lancetfish, snake mackerel, snoek, myctophids, etc.; and squid. When foraging over the continental shelf and upper slope, swordfish take neritic fish: mackerel, sardines, anchovies, sauries, needlefish, etc. They also make excursions to the bottom where they feed on demersal fish: hake, cutlassfish, pomfrets, etc. The broad bill is used to strike and disable prey, especially squid and cuttlefish.

Migrates seasonally towards temperate areas in summer for feeding, and back towards tropical areas in winter for spawning. Males mature at ~1 m eye–FL (1 year), females mature at ~1.6 m eye–FL (5 years). Spawning lasts 6–7 months, during which swordfish spawn every 2 or 3 days. Spawning has been reported off Madagascar and near Réunion.

Important in longline fisheries and also caught by anglers fishing at night from ski-boats.

Swordfish and mako sharks are both at the top of the epipelagic food pyramid and well matched in speed and size as top predators. The struggle for survival of these two competitors sometimes includes a life-and-death battle, as pieces of swordfish are occasionally found in the shark's stomach, and some makos have been found with wounds and pieces of the sword embedded in their bodies. The swordfish is also a formidable antagonist for big game anglers, as this powerful fish sometimes charges a boat with such speed that the sword is driven right through the hull of the vessel.

Flesh excellent; though in the 1970s it was banned from sale in the USA due to high levels of mercury. Eaten raw as 'sashimi' (sliced, with soy sauce and 'wasabi' [green mustard]) or 'sushi' (sliced, with wasabi on vinegar-boiled rice balls), or cooked. Small swordfish are often cut transversely into 'steaks'.

FAMILY ISTIOPHORIDAE ■ Sailfish, Marlin & Spearfish

Body elongate, fusiform, somewhat compressed anteriorly; in adults, **snout and upper jaw greatly elongated, forming a bony spear-like pointed rostrum**, round in cross-section; in juveniles less than 30 cm SL, the jaws are equal; jaws with minute file-like teeth; 1st dorsal fin base longer than height of fin, and contiguous with short 2nd dorsal fin; 1st anal fin clearly separate from lower 2nd anal fin; tail fin lunate, with 2 short fleshy keels on each side of base; pelvic fins reduced, ribbon-like, with 1 spine and 2 fused soft-rays; 1st dorsal fin and anal and pelvic fins fold into grooves when fish is swimming rapidly. Branchiostegal membranes united, free from isthmus; no gill rakers. Body covered with small elongate embedded scales. Size range 2.3–4.5 m FL (including the bill).

Istiophorids (also known as billfish) are large swift voracious predators of the epipelagic zone of the open ocean. They feed mainly on a variety of pelagic fish, squid and crustaceans; some species also forage at the bottom, where they take demersal species. Prey are swallowed head-first, usually after being stunned or killed by a powerful blow from the bill. The long bony bill of the swordfish, marlin and sailfish is used to strike fish in order to impale, disable or kill the prey before eating it. Occasionally boats and other floating objects are accidentally impaled by billfish when they are chasing the small fish that congregate under these floating objects. The bill is also used in defence against mako and great white sharks. Billfish usually strike their prey with a lateral slashing movement of the bill, which is particularly effective in a tight school of bait fish.

Like the large tunas, some billfish maintain their body temperature several degrees above ambient water temperatures; this elevated body temperature increases the efficiency of the swimming muscles, especially during excursions into the cold water below the thermocline.

Istiophorids do not change sex and, except for size (females are usually larger), there are no obvious differences in the sexes. Spawning occurs in tropical and subtropical areas, often near shore; the eggs and larvae are pelagic.

Billfish are in great demand as food-fish in Japan and other Asian countries. They are eaten raw ('sashimi'), cooked or smoked, also marketed fresh, frozen or canned. In the commercial fishery, billfish are taken with drift nets and longlines; in the sport fishery, billfish are caught trolling a bait or lure at the surface.

The family is represented worldwide in tropical and temperate seas. Three genera and 11 species, 7 from our area.

Pacific sailfish

Black marlin

Pacific blue marlin

PACIFIC SAILFISH
Istiophorus platypterus
(Shaw 1792)

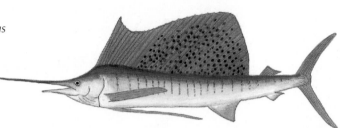

2.7 m adult

Body elongate, compressed; **1st dorsal fin high, sail-like, middle rays longest**, about twice depth of body at anus; 1st dorsal fin rays 42–49; pelvic fins longer than pectoral fins and nearly reaching anus; 1st anal fin rays 12–17; bill length 3.1–3.4 times in eye–FL. Head and body dark bluish violet dorsally, silvery below, with ~20 vertical series of pale blue spots on body; **1st dorsal fin dark blue, with numerous dark spots** on membranes of lower middle part of fin. Attains 3.4 m (including bill), 2.3 m eye–FL, 100+ kg (~15 years [based on tag return from a fish caught 10 years and 10 months after being tagged]).

> Widely distributed in tropical and temperate waters of Indo-Pacific, Red Sea, Persian Gulf to False Bay.

Epipelagic in open ocean, more common over continental shelf; usually above thermocline. Seasonal migrations show sailfish moving into temperate latitudes in summer and back to the tropics in winter. Opportunistic predator, feeding on a wide variety of fish (sardines, anchovies, mackerel, kingfish, dorado, bramids, stromateids, boxfish, gempylids, scombrids, ribbonfish, needlefish, triggerfish and puffers), and on squid and cuttlefish. Sailfish show co-operative 'pack-hunting' behaviour in capturing their prey. When a group of sailfish spot a school of prey fish, they start pursuit at half speed, with fins half-folded into their grooves; as swimming speed increases, the fins are folded completely down into their grooves; when the sailfish catch up with the prey, they

suddenly make sharp turns with their fins erected to startle and confuse the fish, and then rush into the school of prey, striking fish with rapid swings of their bills. The sailfish then turn about, catch the stunned or dead fish in their jaws and swallow them head-first.

Matures at ~1.4 m eye–FL (1–3 years). Spawns in batches all year in tropical and subtropical waters; spawns in pairs or with 2 or 3 males chasing 1 female.

In commercial fisheries, sailfish are caught mainly with longlines and gill-nets. Also popular with recreational anglers. Most billfish taken in South African waters are sailfish caught off KZN. Although prized as 'big game fish' for its size and leaping abilities when fighting on a line, the sailfish tires rapidly, and is not in the same league as a large wahoo or marlin when it comes to strength and endurance.

Flesh dark red and not as good as that of marlin, but fish caught in summer are good for sashimi or sushi. IGFA all-tackle record: 100 kg fish caught at the Galapagos Islands in 1947.

SIMILAR SPECIES

The Atlantic sailfish, *Istiophorus albicans* (Latreille 1804), is considered a separate species by some authors. Juvenile (<90 cm eye–FL) Atlantic sailfish are supposed to have longer pectoral and tail fins than Pacific sailfish, and Atlantic sailfish appear not to grow as large as the Pacific species (IGFA all-tackle record for Atlantic sailfish is a 64 kg fish from Angola).

425

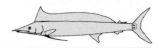

BLACK MARLIN
Makaira indica
(Cuvier 1832)

3 m adult
~2 cm postlarva

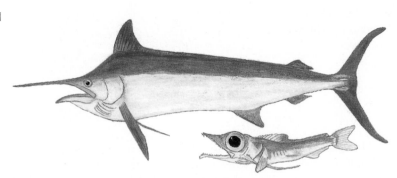

Body elongate, robust, width more than half body depth; nape distinctly elevated, greatest body depth just behind head; bill (snout plus upper jaw) long, round in cross-section and very sturdy; bill length (from front edge of eye) 3.1–3.4 times in eye–FL; 1st dorsal fin high anteriorly, its greatest height less than body depth or length of pectoral fins; 1st dorsal fin rays 34–43, 2nd dorsal fin rays 5–7; pectoral fins rigid, projecting at right angles to body and not capable of folding flat against body; pectoral fin rays 19–20, fin base horizontal; pelvic fins shorter than pectoral fins; 1st anal fin rays 10–14, 2nd anal fin rays 6–7; distance between upper and lower tail fin lobe tips contained 2.0–2.3 times in eye–FL; 2 fleshy keels on each side of tail fin base. Head and body dark blue dorsally, silvery white below; after death, colour changes to white (hence the Japanese name 'Shirokajiki' which means white marlin). Attains 4.5 m (including bill), 3.5 m eye–FL, and 710+ kg (females ~20 years, males ~13 years).

Tropical and temperate seas of Indo-Pacific, Red Sea, Oman to Cape Town; also known from all Indian Ocean islands north of 30° S latitude.

Based on records from Japanese commercial longliners, black marlin range to 45° S latitude in the Indian Ocean and occasionally migrate into the Atlantic via South Africa.

Atlantic records sparse, with no evidence of spawning. Epipelagic in open ocean, usually in waters of 15–30° C near islands and over continental shelf. As with other billfish, black marlin migrate to higher latitudes in summer and return to tropical waters in winter.

Feeds on pelagic and demersal fish (tunas, swordfish, bonito, gempylids, kingfish, boxfish, triggerfish, dorado, butterflyfish, puffers, etc.), cephalopods (squid, cuttlefish, octopus), crabs and lobsters. Demersal prey found in black marlin stomachs show that they sometimes forage near coral reefs. Spawns all year in tropical and subtropical waters, but no spawning areas have been located in Indian Ocean. Spawns in pairs, or with 2 or 3 males chasing 1 female. Matures at ~200 kg for females, ~50–80 kg for males.

The only predators of adult marlin are man and (rarely) killer whales. Juvenile marlin are prey for sharks, tuna, yellowtail, dorado and other billfish.

The huge blue and black marlin are rivalled only by the bluefin tuna for the heavyweight title of premier big game fish. The size, strength and endurance of these giant marlin command the awe and admiration of big game anglers all over the world. The IGFA all-tackle record is a 708 kg fish caught off Peru in 1953. Black marlin are more common than blue marlin off South Africa, and most catches by recreational

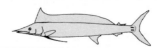

anglers occur in summer near the submarine canyons off Sodwana Bay. Although some black marlin are taken in tuna longline fisheries, there are no reliable catch statistics for this fishery off southern Africa.

The blue marlin are distinguished from the black marlin by their flexible pectoral fins, which can be folded flat against the body.

PACIFIC BLUE MARLIN
Makaira mazara
(Jordan & Snyder 1901)

2.5 m adult
~ 1 cm postlarva
~ 2 cm postlarva

Body elongate, robust, width more than half body depth; nape distinctly elevated, with greatest body depth just behind head; bill (snout plus upper jaw) long, round in cross-section and very sturdy; bill length (from front edge of eye) 3.4–3.8 times in eye–FL; 1st dorsal fin high anteriorly, its greatest height less than body depth or pectoral fin length; 1st dorsal fin rays 40–45, 2nd dorsal fin rays 6–7; **pectoral fins movable, folding flat against body**, with 20–23 rays; pectoral fin base oblique; 1st anal fin rays 12–17, 2nd anal fin rays 6–7; tail fin large, lunate, distance between upper and lower lobe tips about half eye–FL; 2 fleshy keels on each side of tail fin base; LL obscure in adults, forming mid-lateral chain of simple loops or straight lines in juveniles. **Head and body dark blue dorsally, silvery white below, with ~15 narrow pale blue bars or vertical series of spots**; fins dusky to black. Attains 4.5 m (including bill), 3.5 m eye–FL, 906+ kg (~21 years).

Tropical and temperate Indo-Pacific, Red Sea, Oman to Cape Town; known from all Indian Ocean islands north of 30° S latitude.

Epipelagic fish of the open ocean; an offshore species, rarely caught over the continental shelf or below the thermocline. Blue marlin migrate to higher latitudes in summer and return to tropical waters in winter. Opportunistic predator feeding on a wide variety of epipelagic squid and fish (mainly scombrids); occasionally makes forays to the bottom where it catches demersal fish.

One-year-old fish are mature at 1.3–1.4 m eye–FL for males, 2.0 m eye–FL for females. The age of a 337 kg blue marlin was estimated at 17 years. Females grow much faster and larger than males; an 8-year-old female already weighs 140 kg, while a 6-year-old male is only 52 kg. Maximum weight for males is a mere 150 kg, compared to 906+ kg for females.

In the South African recreational fishery, blue marlin are caught less frequently than black marlin. The catch of blue marlin in commercial fisheries (mainly the tuna longline fishery) off South Africa is not monitored. IGFA all-tackle record: 624 kg fish from Hawaii.

The Atlantic blue marlin, *Makaira nigricans* Lacepède 1802, has LL forming a reticulate pattern that extends over most of lateral body surface. This pattern is visible in juveniles, but obscured by skin and scales in adults. Maximum size for Atlantic blue marlin is ~680 kg; IGFA all-tackle record for Atlantic blue marlin: 636 kg fish from Brazil.

FAMILY STROMATEIDAE ■ Butterfish, Ruffs & Drift-fish

Body deep to elongate, with firm to soft musculature; dorsal fin continuous or partly divided, with 6–9 stiff spines, 19–33 soft-rays or 37–65 total dorsal fin rays (flexible spines + soft-rays); anal fin with 14–41 total rays; tail fin emarginate or shallowly forked; jaws with 1 row of small conical or flattened teeth; no teeth on roof of mouth or tongue; toothed pharyngeal sacs in oesophagus near last gill arch; scales moderate to small, usually cycloid, easily shed and extend onto base of median fins; head covered with small pores; no spines on opercle; preopercle with 9–20 small spines or weakly serrate. Size range 0.2–1.4 m FL.

Juveniles commonly associate with floating objects (jellyfish, *Sargassum* weed, etc.); adults usually near bottom in 10–500 m. Some species are good eating, others cause diarrhoea.

Worldwide in tropical and temperate seas. Ten genera and ~40 species, 11 in our area, but only 2 species of the Subfamily Centrolophinae are mentioned here.

SOUTHERN DRIFT-FISH
Schedophilus velaini
(Sauvage 1879)

56 cm
(Tristan da Cunha)

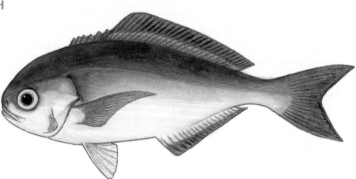

Body oblong, firm, greatest depth 2.6–3.1 times in SL; head length 3.2–3.8 times in SL; dorsal fin single with 6–8 weak spines, 26–29 rays, spines graduated in length posteriorly; anal fin with 3 weak spines (hidden at front margin of fin), 19–21 rays, fin base ~2/3 length of dorsal fin base; pectoral fins elongate (about equal to head) and pointed in adults, with 21–22 rays, the fin reaching vertical at anal fin origin; tail fin forked; pelvic fins well developed with 1 spine, 5 rays; dorsal head profile and inter-orbital area distinctly convex; preopercle edge with small spines; cheek and operculum scaly, except

lower margin of preopercle which is naked; snout and lower jaw naked; LL scales 90–110; gill rakers 6–7 / 17. **Adults dark olive-green dorsally, silvery below**; juveniles mottled. Attains 73 cm.

Southern Hemisphere: South Africa, St Helena Island, Vema Seamount, Tristan da Cunha, St Paul and Amsterdam Islands, Australia, Lord Howe Island, New Zealand, Rapa Island, Juan Fernandez Islands and Chile.

Generally an epibenthic species near bottom in 30–400 m, but occasionally feeds higher up in water column. Postlarvae and juveniles associate with flotsam, jellyfish and siphonophores in the open ocean. Feeds on salps, cephalopods and fish. Spawns at Tristan da Cunha in late summer.

Generally caught with trawls. Flesh excellent.

SIMILAR SPECIES

The southern drift-fish was previously confused with the North Atlantic and Mediterranean *Schedophilus ovalis* (Cuvier 1833), which has 21–23 anal fin rays.

The southern butterfish (Tristan bluefish), *Hyperoglyphe antarctica* (Carmichael 1819), has middle dorsal fin spines longest, 17–20 dorsal fin soft-rays, and 14–16 anal fin soft-rays. Good eating, maximum size at least 1.4 m FL and a weight of 36 kg. Worldwide in temperate waters of Southern Hemisphere.

FAMILY NOMEIDAE ▪ Drift-fish, Bluebottlefish & Fatheads

Body deep and compressed to elongate and cylindrical, with firm to soft musculature; dorsal fin divided to base or deeply notched before last spine, 1st part with 9–12 slender spines, longest spine at least as long as longest dorsal soft-ray; 1st dorsal fin folds into a groove; soft-rayed part with 1 spine, 13–31 rays; anal fin with 1–3 weak spines, 13–31 soft-rays; tail fin forked with pointed or rounded lobes; pelvic fins with 1 spine, 5 rays, fold into groove on belly; jaws with row of small conical or flattened teeth; vomer and palatines with or without minute teeth; toothed pharyngeal sacs present in oesophagus immediately behind last gill arch; scales moderate to small, thin, cycloid, easily shed and extend onto base of median fins; cheeks and operculum scaly; no spines on opercle; preopercle edge smooth. Size range 15 cm to 1 m FL.

Juveniles epipelagic; commonly associated with jellyfish, *Sargassum* weed and various flotsam; adults usually near bottom in 50–600 m.

Worldwide in tropical and temperate seas. Four genera with ~25 species, 13 in our area.

BLUEBOTTLEFISH
Nomeus gronovii
(Gmelin 1789)

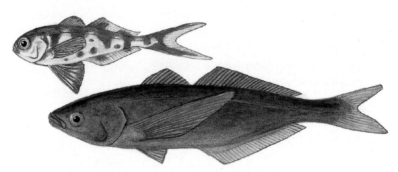

5 cm juvenile
~41 cm adult
(Gulf of Guinea)

Body compressed, oblong to elongate, **depth subequal to head length, 2.9–4.8 times in SL; dorsal fin with 10–13 weak spines, 24–28 soft-rays; anal fin 1–2 weak spines, 24–29 soft-rays; pelvic fins greatly enlarged in juveniles, inner ray attached along its full length to belly;** pectoral fins large with 19–24 rays; scales on top of head extend in front of eyes; teeth small, conical, similar in both jaws; gill rakers ~8 / 15–19. **Juveniles** striking: head and body **silvery white or bluish, with conspicuous blotches and spots of dark blue, turquoise or black;** 1st dorsal fin and front of 2nd dorsal fin dark blue or blackish; tail fin with base and upper and lower margins of fin lobes black or turquoise, contrasting sharply with hyaline inner (rear) margin of fin; pelvic fins blackish with silver streaks along rays. **Adults uniform brown.** Attains 42 cm.

Worldwide in tropical and warm temperate seas.

Found offshore all round our coast. Adults occur near bottom in 76–200 m. Juveniles at the surface in symbiotic relationship with *Physalia* spp, the pelagic bluebottle (a.k.a. 'Portuguese man-of-war'). In the open ocean, if you find a *Physalia* drifting at the surface, you will usually find one or more small *Nomeus* swimming amongst the long stinging tentacles hanging below. *Nomeus* have been observed to feed on the stinging tentacles of its host, but it also eats pelagic invertebrates (planktonic worms, crustaceans and molluscs.

Although *Nomeus* are able to tolerate 10 times the quantity of bluebottle venom that kills other fish, they are occasionally stung (and devoured) by their host. Like the anemonefish (*Amphiprion* spp) which are protected from the stinging tentacles of their anemone, the mucus on the skin of *Nomeus* may contain a chemical that inhibits discharge of the nematocysts of its host *Physalia* and they are also careful to avoid actual contact with the stinging tentacles of the siphonophore. *Nomeus* gain protection from predators by hiding amongst the stinging tentacles; and the bluebottles gain prey attracted by the fish's presence. When onshore winds drive bluebottles onto the beach, the bluebottlefish may also be stranded or carried into tide pools.

Four species of *Nomeus* have been described, but it appears they are all synonyms of a single worldwide species. The bluebottlefish is also known as 'man-of-war fish'.

SIMILAR SPECIES

Although other juvenile drift-fish (*Ariomma* and *Psenes* spp) often associate with jellyfish, these other nomeids have deeper bodies (depth 1.4–2.4 times in SL) and the pelvic fins are not broadly joined to the belly.

FAMILY BOTHIDAE ■ Lefteye Flounders

Head and body extremely compressed, normally with both eyes on left side of head (sinistral), but some bothids show reversals (both eyes on right side) and some species are indiscriminately either sinistral or dextral; dorsal fin origin above or in front of upper eye; **dorsal and anal fins separate from tail fin; pelvic fin base of eyed side elongate, situated on mid-ventral line of belly; no fin spines**; pectoral and pelvic fin rays unbranched; preopercle edge distinct; branchiostegal membranes united, free from isthmus. Size range 10–57 cm.

The bothid larva has an eye on each side of its head, but as the larva develops, the eye on the right side moves over the top of the head to lie on the left side with the other eye. Bothids (and other flatfish) spend most of their time on the bottom, resting on their blind side which is usually white or colourless; the pigmented (upper) side is coloured to match the substrate; and bothids are generally very difficult to see when they sit still on the bottom. Flounders often bury themselves in the sediment, with only their eyes and nostrils uncovered. The eyes of some species protrude from the head and can be moved independently.

Worldwide in tropical and warm temperate waters. The family comprises ~20 genera and ~161 species, 15 from our area.

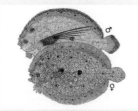

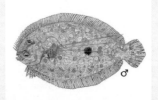

Peacock flounder   Leopard flounder

PEACOCK FLOUNDER
Bothus mancus
(Broussonet 1782)

47 cm male
20 cm female

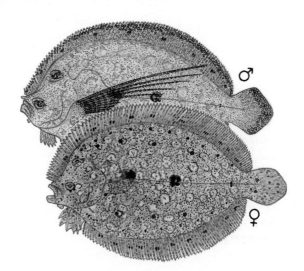

Body oval, depth 1.7–2.0 times in SL; head length 3.2–3.8 times in SL; **eyes far apart, inter-orbital width much greater than eye diameter and 2.5–3.1 times in head length**; snout projecting, its length greater than eye diameter; **anterior head profile concave**; dorsal fin rays 96–104, fin origin in front of lower eye; anal fin rays 74–81; pectoral fin rays 10–13, fin on eyed side of males greatly elongated, more than twice length of head; sexual dimorphism in specimens larger than 13 cm SL; adult males also have tentacles on eyes, a spine over each eye and on front of snout; scales on eyed side ctenoid; LL strongly arched over pectoral fin, LL scales 76–90; **lower gill rakers 9–11**. Head and body tawny, covered with pale blue spots, circles and irregular blue-edged white spots; usually

2 or 3 dark blotches on LL; median fins spotted like body; pectoral fin of eyed side on male dusky. Attains 47 cm.

> Indo-Pacific, Oman to Durban, juveniles to the Eastern Cape; not in Red Sea.

Sandy bottom, usually near coral or rocky reefs; also in tide pools; depth range 0–150 m. Feeds on fish, crabs and shrimp. The transparent pelagic larvae settle out of the plankton and take on juvenile pigmentation at ~30 mm SL.

SIMILAR SPECIES

May be confused with the leopard flounder which has a convex head profile, 1 spot on LL and 6–8 lower gill rakers.

LEOPARD FLOUNDER
Bothus pantherinus
(Rüppell 1830)

16 cm (Red Sea)

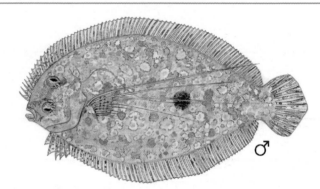

Body oval, depth 1.6–1.9 times in SL; head length 3.3–3.9 times in SL; **eyes far apart, inter-orbital width much greater than eye diameter**; snout shorter than eye diameter; anterior **head profile distinctly convex**, dorsal fin rays 84–97; anal fin rays 61–73; pectoral fin rays 9–12; adult males (>12 cm SL) with pectoral fin on eyed side elongated, more than twice length of head; tentacles on eyes, spine over each eye and on front of snout. Scales on eyed side ctenoid; LL strongly arched over pectoral fin, LL scales 74–87; **lower gill rakers 6–8**. Eyed side with dark

spots, blotches and rings on body and median fins; **dark blotch on straight part of LL**; pectoral fin of eyed side usually with narrow dark crossbars. Attains 30 cm.

> Indo-West Pacific, Red Sea, Persian Gulf to Port Alfred, juveniles probably farther south.

Sandy or silty sand bottom, sometimes near reefs; also in tide pools and estuaries; depth range 0–250 m. Feeds on fish, crabs and shrimp.

FAMILY PARALICHTHYIDAE ■ Sand Flounders

Head and body ovate, extremely compressed, normally sinistral (with both eyes on left side of head, but some paralichthyids show reversals [both eyes on right side] and some species are either sinistral or dextral); **dorsal fin origin above or in front of upper eye; dorsal and anal fins separate from tail fin; pelvic fins of equal size, symmetrically placed on each side of belly**; pectoral fins equally developed on each side of body; no fin spines; pectoral and pelvic fin rays branched; **preopercle edge distinct; LL with high arch above pectoral fin**; branchiostegal membranes united, free from isthmus. Size range 14–44 cm.

Larval development similar to that of bothids (see above). Like most flatfish, paralichthyids are well camouflaged to blend in with the bottom on which they are resting.

Worldwide in tropical and temperate waters. About 16 genera, ~185 species, 3 in our area.

LARGETOOTH FLOUNDER
Pseudorhombus arsius
(Hamilton 1822)

27 cm adult

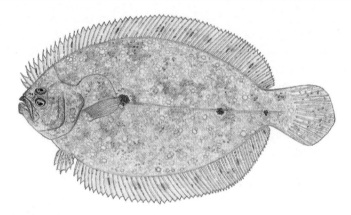

Body oval, depth 1.7–2.2 times in SL; head length 3.2–3.8 times in SL; upper jaw 2.2–2.4 times in head length, **maxilla extends to below rear half of lower eye**; eyes close together, inter-orbital width distinctly less than eye diameter; snout longer than eye diameter; anterior head profile slightly indented in front of upper eye; **dorsal fin rays 72–78, fin origin over anterior nostril or interspace between nostrils of blind side; anal fin rays 54–62**; pectoral fin rays 11–13; tail fin broadly wedge-shaped (>), with 10–13 branched rays; scales on eyed side ctenoid, cycloid on blind side; LL strongly arched over pectoral fin, **LL scales 67–81**; head scaly, snout and preopercle margin naked; gill rakers longer than broad, 4–8 / 9–13; upper jaw teeth small, closely spaced posteriorly, becoming widely spaced and enlarged anteriorly; **lower jaw teeth large, widely spaced, 8–18 on blind side of jaw**; both jaws with large canines anteriorly. Eyed side usually mottled brownish; vaguely defined black blotch (often edged with small pale spots) at origin of straight LL and 2 smaller dark spots near tail; median fins with faint dark spots; sometimes with tawny spots. Attains ~44 cm.

Indo-West Pacific, mainly continental, Red Sea to Algoa Bay.

Juveniles common in estuaries, adults from shore to 100 m on sandy or silty sand bottom. Juveniles in estuaries feed mainly on benthic crustaceans; adults in the sea eat fish, prawns, crabs and polychaete worms. Matures at ~20 cm SL (2 years); spawning occurs at sea in late spring in the northern Indian Ocean.

SIMILAR SPECIES

The smalltooth flounder, *Pseudorhombus natalensis* Gilchrist 1904, has 51–63 LL scales, 68–72 dorsal rays; lower jaw teeth closely spaced, 20–31 on blind side in adults; maxilla not reaching past middle of lower eye. Known only from Durban to Thukela River.

The ringed flounder, *Pseudorhombus elevatus* Ogilby 1912, has 15–19 lower gill rakers and a broad flap-like membrane joining proximal half of 1st dorsal fin ray to head above nostrils. Indo-West Pacific, Red Sea to Algoa Bay.

FAMILY PARALICHTHODIDAE ■ Measles Flounder

Head and body extremely compressed; **eyes on right side of head, well developed and well separated; dorsal fin origin anterior to eyes, above nasal organ on blind side; pectoral fin well developed on both sides of body**, middle rays branched; pelvic fins short-based, symmetrically placed, with 6 rays; tail fin with 16 rays, 12 branched, not attached to dorsal and anal fins; **no distinct peduncle**; anus on blind side above first anal fin ray; LL well developed on both sides of body, with high arch over pectoral fin; scales cycloid on both sides of body; maxilla exposed, reaching to below middle of eye; lower jaw projecting; preopercle edge distinct; large opening between left and right gill chambers.

Occurs over sandy and silty sand areas.

This family comprises a single species; apparently endemic to southern Africa.

Paralichthodes algoensis was previously included in the Family Pleuronectidae; however, it differs from pleuronectids in having the dorsal fin origin in front of the eyes, in lacking a distinct peduncle and in several osteological characters.

MEASLES FLOUNDER
Paralichthodes algoensis
Gilchrist 1902

22 cm

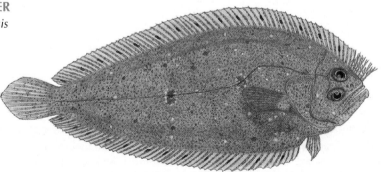

Body depth 2.3–2.5 times in SL; head length 3.8–4.5 times in SL; dorsal fin rays 67–74; anal fin rays 47–54; right pectoral fin rays 12–13, left 11; LL with distinct curve over pectoral fin, LL scales 110–125; inter-orbital width more than half eye diameter; gill rakers 8–9 / 19–21; jaws with short slender curved teeth; rear edge of front nostril flap extends past rear nostril. Eyed side brownish with dark spots; fins pale with dark spots; blind side white. Attains 50 cm.

Known only from Mossel Bay to Maputo.

Sandy or mud bottoms in 1–100 m.
   Good eating.

FAMILY CYNOGLOSSIDAE ■ Tonguefish

Head and body extremely compressed and elongate, depth 3.4–5.0 times in SL; eyes on left side of head; preopercle covered by skin and scales; dorsal fin origin over or anterior to eyes, above nasal organ on blind side; dorsal and anal fins joined to tail fin; pectoral fins absent; pelvic fins small with 4 rays; right pelvic fin absent in *Symphurus* spp; tail fin with 8–10 rays; anus on blind side above 1st anal fin ray; LL present (*Cynoglossus* and *Paraplagusia* spp) or absent (*Symphurus* spp); scales cycloid or ctenoid; mouth 'inferior' (hidden by large hooked snout) in *Cynoglossus* and *Paraplagusia*. Scales of middle LL are counted from the vertical branch on head. Size range 9–32 cm.

   Most species occur in shallow water or estuaries; common on sandy and mud bottom from shore to 1 900 m; 5 species known from rivers, and several species occur in estuaries. Adept at burrowing in sand, for which their very compressed bodies are well suited. Tongue-fish feed on small crustaceans, molluscs and worms.

Tropical and warm temperate areas of all oceans. Three genera, with ~110 species, 13 in our area.

REDSPOTTED
TONGUEFISH
Cynoglossus zanzibarensis
Norman 1939

32 cm adult

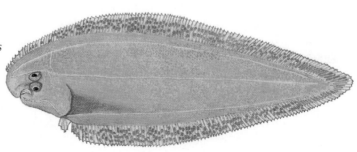

Body depth 3.5–4.6 times in SL; **dorsal fin rays 116–124; anal fin rays 92–103;** tail fin rays 10; left pelvic fin connected to anal fin; **1 nostril on eyed side; snout tip hooked, ends well before vertical line through nostril; lips not fringed;** inter-orbital width distinctly less than vertical eye diameter; **3 LLs on eyed side,** one near base of dorsal fin, one near base of anal fin and one of 80–95 scales along mid-lateral part of body; no LL on blind side of body. Juveniles (<15 cm) with ctenoid scales on both sides of body; adults (>20 cm SL)

with ctenoid scales anteriorly on blind side; scales elsewhere cycloid. Eyed side of head and body brown; **dorsal and anal fins covered with dark reddish orange spots**; blind side pale. Attains 32 cm (8 years).

Western Cape to Kenya.

Sandy or silty sand bottom in 10–430 m; juveniles occasionally in tide pools. Feeds on benthic invertebrates (isopods, amphipods, crabs and polychaetes) and fish. Females mature at 28 cm (2 years). Spawns small pelagic eggs throughout the year.

Eaten by many piscivores (sharks, bony fish and man). Common along our south coast and one of our best eating 'soles'.

Marketed as 'lemon sole' but affectionately known as 'sandrat' to fishermen. Taken mainly as by-catch in the hake and sole trawl fisheries.

SIMILAR SPECIES

None of the other species of *Cynoglossus* in our area have reddish spots on the median fins.

The roughscale tonguefish, *Cynoglossus lida* (Bleeker 1851), has 2 nostrils and usually 2 LLs on eyed side; snout curves round to below lower (ventral) eye. Indo-West Pacific, south to Durban.

The endemic sand tonguefish, *Cynoglossus capensis* (Kaup 1858), has 3 LLs; 1 nostril on eyed side; dorsal rays 103–110; anal rays 81–88. Attains 31 cm. Namibia to Thukela Bank.

The fringelip tonguefish, *Paraplagusia bilineata* (Bloch 1787), has lips on eyed side with fringe of short branched cirri; single nostril, 2 LLs on eyed side, no LL on blind side; left pelvic fin joined to anal fin; dorsal fin rays 99–110; anal fin rays 75–86; eyed side tawny, marbled with dark network enclosing pale patches. Attains 25 cm. Tropical Indo-Pacific, south to Durban.

FAMILY SOLEIDAE ■ Soles

Head and body extremely compressed, **body oblong to ovate, depth 2.0–3.8 times in SL; eyes on right side of head; preopercle covered by skin and scales**; no fin spines; dorsal fin origin over or in front of eyes; dorsal and anal fins joined to or separate from tail fin; pectoral fins well developed, rudimentary or absent; pelvic fins small with 2–5 rays; tail fin rays 11–18; anus on blind side above 1st anal fin ray; scales rough (distinctly ctenoid) or smooth (cycloid or weakly ctenoid); LL straight from above gill opening to base of tail fin; ribs absent; mouth terminal or 'inferior' (snout projecting slightly in front of mouth) or hidden by large hooked snout (*Heteromycteris capensis*). Size range 8–75 cm.

Soles are benthic fish occurring on the continental shelf and upper slope; most species on sandy or mud bottoms, from shore to 300 m; a few species occur on coral reefs. They feed on small crustaceans, molluscs, worms and brittlestars. In summer, many soles are speared by people wading in the sea and estuaries. Some species are of considerable economic importance as food-fish.

Tropical and temperate areas of the eastern Atlantic, Indian and Pacific oceans. About 30 genera, ~120 species; many genera and several species are not well differentiated; 17 species in our area.

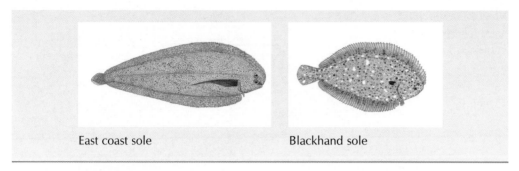

East coast sole   Blackhand sole

EAST COAST SOLE
Austroglossus pectoralis
(Kaup 1858)

26 cm

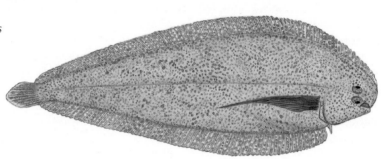

Body elongate, depth 3.2–3.8 times in SL; head small, its length ~6–7 times in SL; **pectoral fins well developed, right fin distinctly longer than head**; dorsal and anal fins joined to tail fin; dorsal fin rays 90–110; anal fin rays 80–95; pelvic fins rudimentary, with 4 unbranched rays; front nostril of eyed side tubular, rear nostril between front of eyes; body scales ctenoid. Eyed side **brown, with small dark spot at base of each scale; right pectoral fin blackish**. Attains 58 cm.

Endemic, Cape Point to KZN.

Sandy or silty sand bottom, from shore to 120 m. Feeds on benthic invertebrates. Once very abundant, but catches have declined markedly in recent years.

SIMILAR SPECIES

West coast sole, *Austroglossus microlepis* (Bleeker 1863), and all other soleids in southern Africa have the right pectoral fin shorter (less than head) and 48–78 anal fin rays.

Endemic, northern Namibia to False Bay.

The shallow-water sole, *Synaptura marginata* Boulenger 1900, has body depth about half SL; right pectoral fin pale (rarely dusky), fin much shorter than head. Colour uniform brown or with darker specks; dorsal, anal and tail fins with pale margin. Attains 50 cm. Hermanus to Durban, also reported from western Pacific.

The speckled sole, *Pardachirus marmoratus* (Lacepède 1802), has body depth about half SL; anal fin rays 48–55. Ground colour pale, the head, body and fins covered with blackish brown dots and ring-like larger dark brown marks. At the base of the dorsal and anal fin rays are a pair of sack-like mucous glands that produce a milky toxin that makes this species distasteful to predators; the toxin is secreted from pores on each (upper and lower) side of almost every dorsal and anal fin ray. Found in sandy areas associated with coral reefs. Western Indian Ocean, Red Sea, Persian Gulf to Durban in depths of 1–25 m.

BLACKHAND SOLE
Solea bleekeri
Boulenger 1898

2 cm

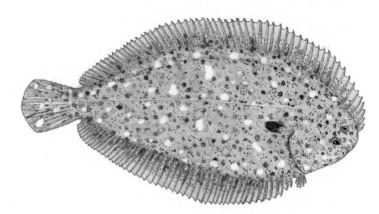

Body depth 1.9–2.7 times in SL; head length 5–6 times in SL; **front nostril of eyed side tubular, reaching rear nostril which is at front edge of lower (ventral) eye; pectoral fins small but distinct; basal half of last dorsal and anal fin rays joined to base of tail fin; dorsal fin rays 61–74; anal fin rays 46–59**; pelvic fins small with 5 rays; all fin rays branched except 2–4 upper and lower rays of tail fin; left and right paired fins about equal in size; body scales ctenoid. Eyed side brown with darker spots and specks; **right pectoral fin usually blackish**. Attains 17 cm.

False Bay to Zambezi Delta.

Found in 1–60 m. Common in turbid estuaries; juveniles abundant on shallow sand banks. Although not confined to estuaries, this sole spends much of its life there; tolerates a wide range of salinity, and spawns at the surface at dusk, either in the sea or in estuaries. Juveniles use estuaries as nursery areas, and adults are also common in this food-rich environment. In the estuary, the preferred food of adults is the siphon tip of *Solen cylindraceus*, a bivalve that lies buried in silty sand or mud, with just the tip of its siphon tube protruding from the substrate. The sole uses visual and olfactory cues to locate the siphons, and it nips off the siphon tip before the bivalve can retract it. Adults and juveniles also feed on crustaceans (mainly amphipods and tanaids).

No commercial value but an important component of estuarine ecology.

SIMILAR SPECIES

The lemon sole, *Solea fulvomarginata* Gilchrist 1904, has 75–81 dorsal fin rays, 60–69 anal fin rays; body brownish yellow, the yellow more intense on median fins. Attains 26 cm. Endemic, False Bay to the Eastern Cape in 1–50 m.

The Cape sole, *Heteromycteris capensis* Kaup 1858, has the snout distinctly hooked downwards over mouth; dorsal and anal fins separate from tail fin, fin rays unbranched, dorsal fin origin near tip of snout, and right pelvic fin on ventral midline of isthmus and joined to anal fin. Body and fins pale greyish brown with dark specks; 3 vague dark spots along LL. Attains 15 cm. Common in shallow water; juveniles abundant in estuaries. Endemic, Walvis Bay to Kei River.

FAMILY BALISTIDAE ■ Triggerfish

Head and body compressed, covered with strong, rough, interlocking plate-like scales in regular series; gill opening a small slit above and in front of pectoral fin base. **First dorsal fin with 3 spines, 1st spine large and strong, can be locked erect by 2nd spine**; 3rd spine usually insignificant; 2nd dorsal and anal fins similar, with branched rays; tail fin usually with 10 branched rays and 1 unbranched ray above and below; **pelvic fins reduced to tiny bony rudiment** at tip of long depressible pelvic bone on ventral midline of abdominal cavity; mouth small, with 8 outer teeth in each jaw and 6 small inner teeth in upper jaw. Size range 25–76 cm.

Generally near shore in relatively shallow water (usually in less than 100 m), but adults of some species are regularly found out in the open ocean. Triggerfish usually occur on coral reefs, where they often dart for shelter into crevices or holes, lock their stout dorsal fin spine erect, and depress their strong pelvic bone, thus making it impossible for a predator to dislodge them. When the 1st spine is erected, the 2nd spine is also pulled erect and functions like a cam to wedge the larger spine in a vertical position (see figure). The 1st spine cannot be folded down until the tip of the 2nd (trigger) spine is pulled posteriorly. The family name Balistidae is formed from the genus name *Balistes*, which is derived from the Latin *ballista*, another name for the Roman catapult, in allusion to the catapult-like mechanism of the dorsal fin spines.

Figure 41
Triggerfish dorsal fin spine locking mechanism
1. Fully erect
2. Partly erect
3. Depressed
(after Smith & Heemstra 1986).

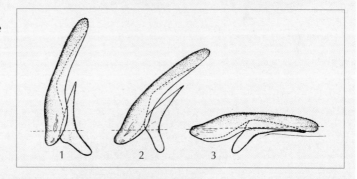

Most triggerfish swim using sinuous undulations of their soft dorsal and anal fins, only relying on their tail fin for rapid movement. Species with distinct lobes at the front of the soft dorsal and anal fins cruise by flapping the lobes synchronously from side to side like the ocean sunfish. Triggerfish have small mouths with powerful jaws and strong teeth that are able to shred their prey. They feed on sea urchins and other echinoderms, crustaceans, molluscs, tunicates, brittlestars, polychaete worms, hydrozoans, tips of branching coral, sponges and fish. They particularly enjoy the long-spined sea urchin, *Diadema*, which they flick over to expose the vulnerable (spineless) underside; the triggerfish then easily breaks the shell with its powerful jaws or by ramming the urchin against the substrate. Triggerfish also find small urchins, crabs and molluscs by picking up rocks or pieces of coral rubble in their mouths to expose the animals hiding beneath. Some triggerfish, especially the redtooth (*Odonus niger*) and species of the genera *Melichthys* and *Xanthichthys*, feed primarily on zooplankton.

Eggs demersal and placed in a depression excavated in the sand, where they are guarded by one or sometimes both parents. Divers should be wary of triggerfish guarding their nest, as they are aggressive and bite viciously. Although triggerfish are generally good eating, some large species are occasionally toxic.

The closely related filefish (Family Monacanthidae) are included in the Balistidae by some authors, as some filefish have a similar locking dorsal fin spine; but filefish have only 2 dorsal fin spines, all the dorsal, anal and pectoral fin rays are unbranched, and the scales have microscopic short spinules.

Worldwide in tropical and temperate waters. Twelve genera, ~37 species, 20 known in our area.

Orangestriped triggerfish

Clown triggerfish

Picasso triggerfish

ORANGESTRIPED TRIGGERFISH
Balistapus undulatus
(Park 1797)

*10 cm juvenile
(Comoros)*
~26 cm adult male

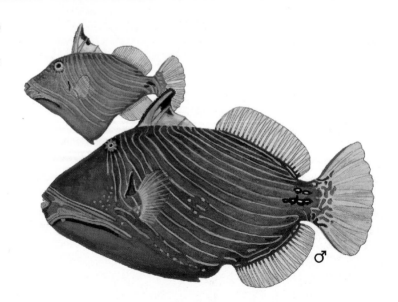

Body depth 1.8–2.0 times in SL; no groove on snout in front of eye; 3rd dorsal fin spine well developed; large bony plates behind gill opening; 6 large spines forming 2 rows on peduncle. **Head and body greenish with curved orange stripes**; adult males lack orange lines on snout; curved black line round underside of lower jaw; pectoral and tail fins golden orange; 1st dorsal fin with black margin between 1st and 3rd spines. Attains 30 cm.

Indo-central Pacific, Red Sea to Aliwal Shoal, juveniles to Port Alfred.

Adults usually on outer reef in 10–50 m; juveniles often hide in branching corals. A nest is constructed by the male lying on his side on the bottom and flapping his tail and median fins; this motion excavates a depression in the sand. Eggs transparent, 0.6 mm in diameter, adhesive, deposited in a cluster about 11 cm in diameter and attached to or weighted down by bits of coral rubble. During the day, the eggs are guarded by one or both parents to protect them from egg-eating fish (mainly wrasses). At night, the parents take refuge in holes or crevices in the reef and leave the nest unguarded, but no egg predation occurs.

SIMILAR SPECIES

The curved orange-striped colour pattern is unmistakable for this species.

CLOWN TRIGGERFISH
Balistoides conspicillum
(Bloch & Schneider 1801)

35 cm adult
~5 cm juvenile

Body robust, depth 1.8–2.0 times in SL; deep groove on snout in front of eye; cheek covered with scales; enlarged bony plates behind gill opening; 3rd dorsal fin spine small, not visible in lateral view; 2–4 longitudinal rows of large tubercles on peduncle; tail fin rounded. Adults with **dorsal** part of **head and body blackish** (some fish with yellow reticulum below spinous dorsal fin); **lower half of head and body with large round white blotches**; yellow or white band across snout in front of eyes; lips orange, bordered posteriorly by yellow line; tail fin yellow or white, with black base and wide black margin posteriorly. Small juveniles with white spots all over body; snout and broad area below spinous dorsal fin gold. Attains 50 cm.

Indo-West Pacific, Kenya to Aliwal Shoal; not known from Red Sea or northern Indian Ocean.

Adults usually on outer reefs in 5–75 m; juveniles rarely seen, because they are usually deeper than 25 m, hiding in caves and crevices.

Attractive aquarium fish, but needs a large tank of its own as it will attack most other fish.

The Titan or giant triggerfish, *Balistoides viridescens* (Bloch & Schneider 1801), is not at all similar in colour pattern, but it belongs in the same genus and shares other features (e.g. a groove in front of the eyes) with the clown triggerfish. The Titan triggerfish has head and body mostly greenish yellow; black mask with small orange spots over eyes and onto base of pectoral fins; median fins with blackish margin; dark green band over mouth and onto cheeks. Small juveniles tawny, covered with small black spots and 2 black blotches below dorsal fins. With a maximum size of 75 cm and a thick muscular body, the Titan or giant triggerfish is aptly named. This heavyweight triggerfish can strike a painful blow (when it rams you head-on), and its bite is even more to be feared. (Perhaps we should call it the 'Tyson triggerfish', after another heavyweight biter?) Not only does the Titan vigorously defend its nest, but some divers have found that it will also attack and bite without provocation. Nevertheless, the Titan is not all bad; as the major predator of the crown-of-thorns starfish, the Titan triggerfish plays a valuable role in the coral reef ecosystem. Indo-central Pacific, Red Sea to Aliwal Shoal.

PICASSO TRIGGERFISH
Rhinecanthus aculeatus
(Linnaeus 1758)

23 cm adult
5 cm juvenile
(Mauritius)

Enlarged bony plates behind gill opening; cheeks scaly, no naked areas or longitudinal groove before eye; teeth unequal, notched; 3rd dorsal fin spine minute, barely visible above dorsal edge of body; 3 rows of small black antrorse spines on peduncle. Head and body pale, with intricate markings as shown; note **yellow bridle stripe from mouth to pectoral fin base**. Attains 30 cm.

Tropical Indo-central Pacific, Kenya to Algoa Bay; also reported from tropical eastern Atlantic (Cape Verde Islands and west coast of Africa).

Reef flats, seagrass beds, inshore sand and rocks, often in silty areas with coral rubble. They dig their shelter under solid structures by lying on their side and flapping their tail to waft the sand away. Territorial species, but wary of divers. Sleeps on its side at night and makes a whirring noise when startled.

The common name alludes to the Spanish

artist who incorporated paintings of fish in some of his works.

SIMILAR SPECIES

The wedgetail triggerfish, *Rhinecanthus rectangulus* (Bloch & Schneider 1801), has a similar colour pattern, but it has 5 rows of small spines on the peduncle which is covered by a black wedge-shaped zone; a broad black swath from eye across pectoral fin to anal fin base; and no bridle stripe from mouth. Attains 25 cm. Indo-West Pacific, Kenya to East London.

FAMILY MONACANTHIDAE ■ Filefish

Head and body extremely compressed, covered with small embedded scales with dense layer of microscopic spinules that present a Velcro-like skin; gill openings restricted to a small slit above and in front of pectoral fin bases; **1st dorsal fin spine slender and weak in some species, or large and strong, and can be locked in upright position by the smaller 2nd spine; 2nd dorsal and anal fins similar**, with slender unbranched rays and transparent membranes; **pelvic fins reduced to tiny bony rudiment** at tip of the long depressible pelvic bone on ventral midline (inside) abdominal cavity. The body depth is increased when the pelvic bone is depressed, stretching the loose pelvic flap that joins the pelvic bone to the body; consequently body depth is measured at anal fin origin; mouth with 4–6 sharp outer teeth in each jaw and 4 smaller inner teeth in upper jaw only. Sexual dimorphism common; adult males of some species have 1st or 2nd dorsal fin ray elongated into a filament, or enlarged spines on side of peduncle, or a brush-like patch of conspicuous bristles on side of body; females of some species have a noticeably deeper body than males. Size range 3 cm to 1 m.

Figure 42
Filefish dorsal fin spine locking mechanism.

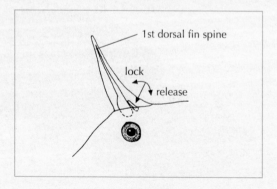

Filefish occur on coral reefs, shallow weed beds, and over sandy or mud bottoms to depths of 200 m; adults of some species associate with flotsam in the open ocean. They swim by undulations of soft dorsal and anal fins, and they use their tail fin only when they are in a hurry. Most species feed on benthic invertebrates, including crustaceans, molluscs, brittlestars, tunicates, polychaete worms, sponges, hydroids, tips of branching coral and small fish. The larger species are good eating and of commercial importance in Asia and Australia, (a.k.a. 'leatherjackets' in Australia). However, the males of some species taste unpleasant when they mature.

Worldwide in tropical and warm temperate waters. About 31 genera, ~99 species, 17 in our area.

The Monacanthidae are included as a subfamily in the Balistidae by some authors, and we don't doubt that these two groups are more closely related to one another than to any other family. Most filefish have a locking dorsal fin spine like that of triggerfish, but filefish have only 1 or 2 dorsal fin spines (3 in triggerfish), all dorsal, anal and pectoral fin rays are unbranched (mostly branched in triggerfish), and the scales are hidden by their covering of minute spinules, quite different from the obvious scales of triggerfish.

Whitespotted filefish   Blacksaddle mimic   Porky

WHITESPOTTED FILEFISH
Cantherhines dumerilii
(Hollard 1854)

24 cm adult
17 cm juvenile

Body depth contained 1.9–2.4 times in SL; dorsal fin rays 34–39; anal fin rays 28–35; pectoral fin rays 14–15 (not counting nubbin); **dorsal fin spine can be locked erect, like that of triggerfish, and it folds down into a deep groove along the back; dorsal and ventral profiles of head straight;** 2 pairs of antrorse spines on each side of peduncle, small and difficult to see in juveniles and adult females, enlarged and recurved in adult males. **Head and body brownish, usually with fine darker spotting on front half of body and 10–12 dark bars on rear half;** tail fin membranes and peduncular spines of male yellow-orange; lips pale; dorsal, anal and pectoral fin rays yellow; juveniles and small adults (<20 cm SL) with

white spots on head and body and some black spots on lower part of body. Attains 38 cm.

Indo-Pacific, Red Sea, Oman to Algoa Bay.

Coral and rocky reefs in 1–30 m; also in tide pools. Feeds on tips of branching corals, crustaceans, worms, sponges, echinoderms, molluscs and bryozoans. Eating these hard animals results in the front teeth of large fish having well worn rounded tips. Adults usually in pairs; wary of divers.

SIMILAR SPECIES

The honeycomb filefish, *Cantherhines pardalis* (Rüppell 1837), has 12–14 pectoral fin rays; no spines on peduncle, but there is a dense patch of bristles (resembling a toothbrush) in adult males. Three colour phases, and fish can change from one to another. The most common pattern is pale grey, body with numerous dark brown spots, the pale interspaces forming a pale greenish yellow honeycomb-like reticulum; head with several blue (or green) lines from eye and gill slit to mouth. The second phase is uniformly dark brown, and the third phase is pale greyish brown, mottled with dark brown. In all phases, there is usually a white (or silver) spot on the peduncle just behind the dorsal fin. Attains 21 cm. Indo-central Pacific, Red Sea, Oman to Mossel Bay.

The spectacled filefish, *Cantherhines fronticinctus* (Günther 1867), is yellowish brown or greyish, with vague longitudinal dark bands on side of body; dark band joining eyes across front of inter-orbital area and dark line at base of dorsal fin spine; broad white to yellowish zone round peduncle; tail fin yellowish with broad dark band along rear margin. Attains 23 cm. Indo-West Pacific, Tanzania to Durban, juveniles to Port Alfred.

BLACKSADDLE MIMIC
Paraluteres prionurus
(Bleeker 1851)

2 cm juvenile
(Comoros)
9 cm adult

Body depth contained 1.9–2.4 times in SL; dorsal fin rays 25–28; anal fin rays 22–25; pectoral fin rays 10–11; dorsal fin spine short, enveloped in loose skin; pelvic fin rudiment and belly flap absent; adult male with 2 pairs of antrorse spines on each side of peduncle and a patch of bristles extending above anal fin. Scales on body not covered with spinules. Head and body pale, **3 prominent black saddles**, usually present, but may coalesce in smaller fish; dark band joining eyes across top of head; head and middle of body with reticulum of irregular dark lines enclosing pale spots (spotting more obvious in juveniles); tail fin yellowish with curving submarginal dusky band, bright blue in adult male. Attains 11 cm.

Indo-West Pacific, Red Sea, Oman to Aliwal Shoal, juveniles to Algoa Bay.

Coral and rocky reefs in 1–30 m; also tide pools. Feeds on crustaceans, sponges, bryozoans, echinoderms, worms, molluscs and coral polyps.

SIMILAR SPECIES

The blacksaddle filefish is a mimic of the model toby (see p. 453) and when the filefish is swimming about, it usually keeps the dorsal and anal fins folded down to make itself look more like the pufferfish. The mucus on the skin of the conspicuous model toby contains a toxin that gives the fish a bad taste and predators have learned to avoid this fish. By copying the toby's colour pattern, blacksaddle filefish are also avoided by predators that mistake it for a model toby. Divers also mistake the mimic filefish for the model toby. They can be distinguished by the longer dorsal and anal fins of the filefish; the dorsal and anal fins of the toby are short and stubby.

The colour pattern of western Indian Ocean specimens of blacksaddle filefish differs slightly from eastern Indian Ocean and Pacific fish, which lack pale spots and may prove to be a different species.

PORKY
Stephanolepis auratus
(Castelnau 1861)

26 cm adult male

Body depth contained 1.7–1.9 times in SL; dorsal fin rays 28–34; anal fin rays 30–34; pectoral fin rays 13–14; 1st dorsal fin spine over rear half of eye; snout profile concave; pelvic fin rudiment movable, with small barbs, and belly flap convex; adult male has 2nd and sometimes 3rd dorsal fin rays elongated. Skin rough. **Head and body pale, with irregular dark blotches on side of body**. Males with blue spots and dashes at the base of the dorsal and anal fin rays. Attains 28 cm.

Western Indian Ocean, Somalia to False Bay and Madagascar.

Shallow sandy or rocky bottom to 18 m, also in seagrass beds in estuaries. Tiny juveniles often congregate under jellyfish in the open ocean.

SIMILAR SPECIES

The blackstriped filefish, *Paramonacanthus pusillus* (Rüppell 1829) [previously identified as *Paramonacanthus cingalensis* (Fraser-Brunner)], has belly flap straight to concave, with pelvic fin rudiment extending past flap, anal fin rays 24–29; skin velvety; body with 4 longitudinal dark bands. Attains 19 cm. Indo-West Pacific, southern Red Sea to Port Alfred.

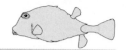

FAMILY OSTRACIIDAE ▪ Boxfish

Head and body enclosed in a hard bony carapace of modified polygonal scales fused to form a box-like armour. The carapace has openings for the mouth, eyes, gill slits, nostrils, anus, fins and the flexible peduncle. Mouth small, lips thick, a single row of small conical or incisiform teeth; no fin spines; no pelvic fins; most fin rays branched; dorsal and anal fins with 8–11 rays; pectoral fin rays 10–13; tail fin with 10 or 11 rays, 8 branched; LL inconspicuous. Size range 15–46 cm.

Generally solitary, on rocky and coral reefs, grass beds and over open sand to depths of 90 m. Omnivorous, feeding on molluscs, crustaceans, sponges, tunicates, worms, echinoderms, bryozoans and algae.

In cruising mode, boxfish swim with slow synchronous sculling movements of dorsal and anal fins; the tail fin is used when they want to go faster. Tail fin and peduncle increase in relative size with growth. Collecting boxfish for the aquarium is risky. When stressed, boxfish secrete a toxin that may be lethal to other fish kept in the same container. Even the boxfish may die, if there are not frequent changes of water in the container. Reproduction of the few species that have been studied involves a harem system, with a large male defending a large territory that includes several females and subordinate males. Boxfish spawn in pairs at dusk; eggs buoyant, larvae pelagic.

Worldwide in tropical and warm temperate waters. About 14 genera, ~34 species, 10 in our area.

Spiny cowfish

Boxy

SPINY COWFISH
Lactoria diaphana
(Bloch & Schneider 1801)

13 cm

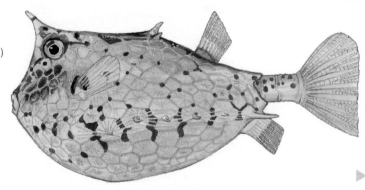

▶

447

Carapace with **small spine on dorsal midline**, ventral surface rounded (convex), and **short spine above each eye**. Dorsal and anal fins with 9 rays; pectoral fin rays 10–11. Colour as shown. Attains 25 cm.

Indo-Pacific, northern Mozambique to the Western Cape, occasionally round Cape Point to Swakopmund.

Shallow coral or rocky reefs; juveniles occasionally in estuaries or tide pools. Some pelagic juveniles mature at ~20 mm SL and live their entire life in the epipelagic realm; most spiny cowfish settle to the bottom and continue their life as a demersal fish. Adult demersal males have harems, defending a large territory that includes 3 or 4 females.

— SIMILAR SPECIES ——————————

The longhorn cowfish, *Lactoria cornuta* (Linnaeus 1758), has a long spine above each eye and a posterior carapace spine on each side of anal fin; tail fin of adults about half SL. Colour variable. Attains 46 cm. Indo-West Pacific, south to Mossel Bay.

The backspine cowfish, *Lactoria fornasini* (Bianconi 1846), has a strong ridge and spine on dorsal midline of carapace. Pale purple or reddish ring or spot on each carapace scale; scale mark can change colour in an instant. Courting males black and yellow, with brilliant blue stripes. Spawning occurs daily in pairs at dusk over a prominent feature of the reef. The spawning pair ascend several metres above the reef, and release of eggs and sperm is co-ordinated by a whining sound produced by the male. Attains 23 cm. Tropical Indo-West Pacific, south to Aliwal Shoal, occasionally to Algoa Bay.

BOXY
Ostracion cubicus
Linnaeus 1758

17 cm adult female
7 cm juvenile
~28 cm adult male

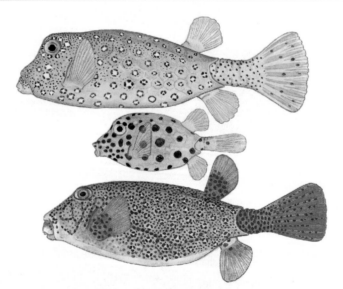

Body rectangular in cross-section; **no mid-dorsal ridge or spines on carapace**; snout and sides concave; carapace becomes more elongate with growth. **Juveniles and females bright yellow**, juveniles with black spots, females with black-ringed white or pale blue ocellus on each scale. Adult males pale bluish green, with pale (white on sides, blue

on back) spot on each scale, surrounded by numerous black dots; fins and peduncle blue with black spots. Large adults purplish brown, spots faint or absent on carapace. Attains 45 cm.

Indo-central Pacific, Red Sea, Oman to Knysna.

Shallow reefs; juveniles usually in branching corals or under ledges with sea urchins. Often washed ashore; when fresh from the water has an aromatic odour.

Juvenile and female whitespotted boxfish, *Ostracion meleagris* Shaw 1796, are black, covered with white spots; adult male has carapace dark brown or black dorsally, with white spots, rest of carapace blue, with yellow spots on sides and a gold stripe or series of gold spots along upper ridge of side and onto peduncle. Attains 20 cm. Indo-Pacific, south to Knysna.

FAMILY TETRAODONTIDAE ▪ Puffers (Blaasops), Tobies & Blowfish

Puffers (or blaasops) are named for their ability to take quantities of water (or air) into a distensible ventral sac connected to their stomach when alarmed. This defence mechanism causes their bodies to swell into a sphere (prickly in some species) to deter predators. When danger is past, the puffer slowly returns to its normal size. The alternative name 'blowfish' may refer to the habit of larger species of blowing a jet of water at the bottom to move sand from hidden prey. The unique expansion technique of puffers is facilitated by a tough flexible skin with scales (on species that still have them) reduced to scattered spinules, no pelvic fins or ribs, a slit-like gill opening, and the short-based dorsal and anal fins at the rear of the body near the tail fin. **Teeth fused forming a parrot-like beak with a median groove giving two 'teeth' in each jaw** (hence Tetraodon, meaning 'four-teeth'); tail fin usually with 11 rays, of which 8 are branched; no fin spines; dorsal fin over anus; dorsal and anal fin rays 6–15; pectoral fin rays 13–19. Size range 9–90 cm.

Most puffers occur near shore and are usually found singly near the bottom in shallow water, but some species have been taken in trawls at depths of 400 m; and a few puffers are typically encountered near the surface in the open ocean, far from land. They are opportunistic omnivores that feed on algae, detritus, sponges, corals, crustaceans, molluscs, tunicates, sponges, anemones, zooanthids, bryozoans, hydroids, foraminifera, tubeworms, brittlestars, sea urchins and starfish (including crown-of-thorns). Little is known regarding reproduction of tropical reef puffers. Eggs are probably demersal but the larvae are pelagic. In one species of Japanese puffer, eggs are deposited on the beach at high tide, with 2 to 4 males biting and hanging on to the female as they lie together on the sand.

The skin and viscera of most tetraodontids contain a potent toxin called tetrodotoxin. If the skin and viscera are carefully cut away from the fish, the flesh *may* be eaten safely; but errors in species identification or in preparation of the fish may be lethal. In Japan, puffers (a.k.a. 'fugu') are considered a delicacy, but only restaurants with specially trained chefs are allowed to sell fugu meals. Several deaths from fugu poisoning are reported each year in Japan from untrained people preparing their own fugu dishes. It is inexplicable that many fish predators (e.g. barracuda and tuna) often eat puffers and are unaffected by the puffers' toxin,

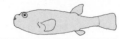
but the same puffer is poisonous to humans, cats and other mammals. A rotting puffer will also attract and kill the flies that feed on it.

Note from Margaret Smith in Smith & Heemstra (1986, p. 894): 'In northern Mozambique, the Macuas eat the flesh of puffers, if the fish is skinned while alive and contains no eggs. However, Abdula, a Macua sailor who assisted us [JLB and Margaret Smith] in Mozambique, said that he never ate puffers, because despite all the precautions, some people still died from eating these fish!'

Circumglobal in tropical and temperate waters; most species marine, but several enter estuaries and some live only in rivers. The taxonomy of this family is in need of revision, as several genera are poorly defined, and many species are difficult to distinguish. About 20 genera, ~125 species, ~32 known from our area.

Evileye puffer

Whitespotted puffer

Blackedged puffer

Blackspotted puffer

Model toby

EVILEYE PUFFER
Amblyrhynchotes honckenii
(Bloch 1785)

19 cm breeding female
8 cm juvenile

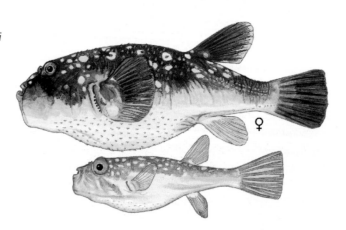

Body elongate, peduncle length 3.6–4.6 times in SL; mouth at or above horizontal line through upper end of pectoral fin base; chin prominent; nasal organs covered by small sac with 2 nostrils; gill opening extending below middle pectoral fin rays; cartilaginous spur on lower edge of gill opening more or less hidden by patch of long skin-covered spinules; lower side of peduncle with LL running along low ridge of skin; back and belly covered with minute spinules, each spinule embedded in a tiny scale-like skin lappet; dorsal fin rays 9–10; anal fin rays 8; pectoral fin rays 14–16. Dorsal surface **blackish brown with pale spots**; lateral surface often yellow; ventral parts white; pectoral, dorsal and tail fins dusky. Anal fin white, yellow in breeding female. Attains 25 cm.

Indo-West Pacific, mainly along continental shores from False Bay to Maputo.

Estuaries, seagrass beds, sandy and rocky bottom from shore to 400 m; juveniles occasionally in tide pools. Feeds on isopods, crabs, bivalves and fish. Often buries itself in sand, with only its eyes showing. Matures at 10 cm SL.

This puffer is adept at stealing bait from anglers' hooks, and the sharp tooth plates are also well suited for cutting fishing lines. JLB Smith (1949, p. 418) wrote: 'Highly poisonous, not touched by fishes or sea birds. Eaten by cats with rapidly fatal consequences and sometimes employed to end nocturnal disturbances. Hands should be washed after handling this fish.'

SIMILAR SPECIES

The slender puffer, *Torquigener marleyi* (Fowler 1929), has mouth below horizontal line through upper end of pectoral fin base, fewer spinules, belly with numerous longitudinal pleats, anal fin rays 7, pectoral fin rays 13–14. Endemic, known only from KZN, off the Thukela River.

Species of *Chelonodon* have nasal organs forming a depression with raised margin expanded fore and aft into pair of elongate flaps.

WHITESPOTTED PUFFER
Arothron hispidus
(Linnaeus 1758)

42 cm adult

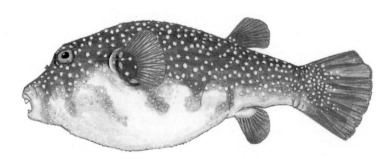

A big heavy-bodied globose puffer; peduncle depth subequal to its length, no lower LL or skin ridge on peduncle; **nasal organ a short fleshy bifurcate tentacle**, opposing surface of each branch with minute pits; inconspicuous spinules on head and body; dorsal and anal fin rays 10–11; pectoral fin rays 17–19. Head and body **greyish with numerous white spots**; juveniles with pale blue spots; underside pale; 2–3 irregular dark bars usually visible on lower part of head and another below pectoral fin base; pectoral fin base and gill opening blackish, with 1–2 white or yellow rings and/or spots. Attains 48 cm.

Indo-Pacific, Red Sea, Oman to Knysna.

Coral and rocky reefs or silty sand in 1–50 m; juveniles common in weedy areas.

Typical omnivore (see family account).

Superficially, the starry puffer, *Arothron firmamentum* (Temminck & Schlegel 1850), which is dark with numerous small white spots, is similar; but the body is more elongate and streamlined, the head and body are covered with distinct small spines, and the dorsal and anal fins are larger (dorsal rays 13–15, anal rays 14). The starry puffer is usually seen in schools (sometimes including several hundred fish), and it is a pelagic temperate water species; not known from South Africa before 1995, but in recent years, several specimens have been found between Algoa Bay and Cape Town in depths of 10–360 m. Also reported from Japan, South China Sea, Australia and New Zealand. Attains 80 cm in South African waters, 43 cm in Australia and 35 cm in Japan.

The guineafowl puffer, *Arothron meleagris* (Lacepède 1798), has 2 colour phases: one is dark brown to black, covered with tiny white or yellow spots; the less common phase is bright yellow with a few widely scattered small black spots, fins often with small white spots. No pale circle round pectoral fin base. Attains 50 cm; usually on coral reefs; feeds on tips of branching corals, molluscs and crustaceans. Indo-Pacific, south to Durban.

BLACKEDGED PUFFER
Arothron immaculatus
(Bloch & Schneider 1801)

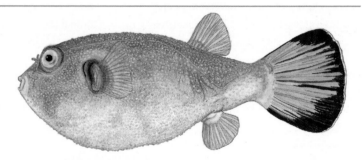

15 cm adult (Mauritius)

Nasal organ a short fleshy bifurcate tentacle, opposing surface of each branch with minute pits. Inconspicuous spinules on head and body; dorsal and anal fin rays 9–10; pectoral fin rays 16–17. Head and body pale brown dorsally, whitish below; pectoral fin base and area round gill opening usually blackish; fins dusky, **tail fin yellowish with black edges**. Attains 30 cm.

Indo-West Pacific, Red Sea, Oman to Knysna.

Shallow coral and rocky reefs; also trawled over sand or mud bottom to 50 m; juveniles common in mangroves and weedy areas of estuaries. Nocturnal, sleeps partly buried in silty sand areas during day. Matures at ~12 cm; spawns in shallow water in April – May. Blackedged puffers tolerate a salinity range of 8–38‰. Juveniles first enter estuaries at a length of 2 cm, and feed on zooplankton (primarily copepods). Larger juveniles and adults eat bivalves, gastropods and crustaceans.

As indicated by its name, the bellystriped puffer, *Arothron inconditus* Smith 1958, has dark lines from above anal fin to chin; black blotch round anus; pectoral fin base and gill opening in round black area, and short dark stripe below each corner of mouth. Endemic, Knysna to East London. Attains at least 40 cm.

BLACKSPOTTED PUFFER
Arothron nigropunctatus
(Bloch & Schneider
1801)

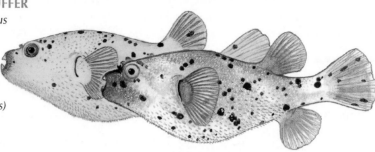

28 cm (2 colour morphs)

Snout profile concave in front of eyes; nasal organ a short fleshy bifurcate tentacle, the opposing surface of each branch with minute pits; inconspicuous spinules on head and body; dorsal fin rays 9–11, anal fin rays 10–12; pectoral fin rays 16–20. **Head and body pale grey to dark brown dorsally, with** few to many **scattered black spots of various sizes**; usually a pale band across snout in front of eyes; anus black. The less common yellow (xanthic) phase has scattered black specks and spots, black gill opening and dark brown to black round the mouth. Attains 30 cm.

Indo-West Pacific, Kenya to Algoa Bay.

Coral and rocky reefs in 2–35 m. Feeds on sponges, tips of branching corals, anemones, tunicates, molluscs and crustaceans.

The xanthic phase guineafowl puffer, *Arothron meleagris* (Lacepède 1798), can be distinguished from the xanthic blackspotted puffer by spots on the fins and the absence of the dark muzzle. Indo-Pacific, south to Durban.

The star puffer, *Arothron stellatus* (Bloch & Schneider 1801), also has numerous small black spots on head and body, but the spots are of more uniform size, close-set, extend onto median fins, but not on underside of body and head. Juveniles yellow to orange, with black spots on head and body except ventrally, where the spots are replaced by oblique dark stripes. Attains at least 90 cm. Indo-West Pacific, Red Sea, Oman to Knysna.

MODEL TOBY
Canthigaster valentini
(Bleeker 1853)

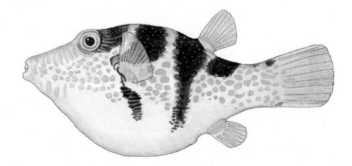

7 cm

Snout length more than half head length; single pore-like nostril on each side of snout; dorsal and anal fin rays 9; pectoral fin rays 16–17; no spinules on skin. **Colour pattern distinctive; note 1st black saddle blotch on body curves forward over gill opening and** runs down front of pectoral fin base to belly; tail fin yellow; males have blue lines radiating from eyes. Attains 9 cm.

Indo-central Pacific, Red Sea to Aliwal Shoal, juveniles to the Eastern Cape.

Coral and rocky reefs to 32 m. Feeds on algae and benthic invertebrates, including tunicates, corals, bryozoans, polychaete worms, echinoderms and molluscs. Reproduction is of the harem type, with a single dominant male defending a large territory that includes 4 to 7 females. The male spawns with a different female each day. Eggs are deposited in algae growing on coral rubble, and they are apparently not tended by the parents.

The mucus on the model toby's skin contains a toxin that gives the fish a bad taste, and predators have learned to avoid this distinctive species.

— SIMILAR SPECIES —

The blacksaddle mimic filefish (see p. 445) has a colour pattern very similar to that of the model toby, and predators will also avoid the filefish, as they perceive it as another bad-tasting toby.

The saddle toby, *Canthigaster coronata* (Vaillant & Sauvage 1875), has similar black saddle blotches on head and body, but the first 2 blotches do not extend below level of pectoral fin base (on the model toby these blotches continue down to the belly) and there are pale blue spots and stripes on the body (body of model toby with yellow to brown spots); tail fin pale grey with pale blue spots. The saddle toby also has a distasteful mucus that deters predators. The depth range (6–100 m) overlaps the 1–20 m depth range of the model toby. Indo-West Pacific, south to Aliwal Shoal, juveniles to Coffee Bay.

FAMILY DIODONTIDAE ■ Burrfish & Porcupinefish

Like the puffers, **porcupinefish can inflate their body by swallowing water (or air) to form an almost spherical spiny ball to deter predators. Also like the puffers, the scales are modified into sharp spines, but these conspicuous dermal spines are much larger than the tiny skin spinules of puffers**. Dermal spines either long and moveable (erectile, with 2 or 3 roots at base, porcupinefish *Diodon* and *Lophodiodon*) or short and fixed (with 3 or 4 roots at base, burrfish *Chilomycterus* and *Cyclichthys*). **Teeth fused into sharp dental plates**, but these tooth plates lack the median suture at front of jaws of puffers; so, instead of 4 tooth plates as in 'tetra-odontidae', we have 'di-odontidae' ('two-tooth' fish). No fin spines and no pelvic fins; dorsal and anal fins near tail fin, with 10–18 rays; pectoral fin rays 18–25; tail fin rays 9–10, 7–8 branched; LL inconspicuous. Size range 14–71 cm.

Adults generally demersal inshore fish, in mangrove areas, estuaries, and on coral or rocky reefs; some species taken in trawls to depths of 300 m. Epipelagic juveniles usually coloured differently from adults. Adults of the circumtropical pelagic porcupinefish, *Diodon eydouxii* Brisout de Barneville 1846, live in the open ocean far from land.

Although diodontids may be seen out and about by day, they are more active at night, when their favourite prey (sea urchins, gastropods and crustaceans) are also more available. During the day, most diodontids rest in caves or under ledges, or settle in a giant sponge for a nap. Eggs buoyant, larvae pelagic.

The pufferfish poison tetrodotoxin may be present in diodontids, but some fatalities attributed to eating diodontids may also be due to ciguatera, which is caused by a different toxin.

Circumglobal in tropical and warm temperate seas. Six genera with ~19 species, 8 in our area.

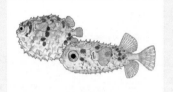

Birdbeak burrfish   Balloon porcupinefish

BIRDBEAK BURRFISH
Cyclichthys orbicularis
(Bloch 1785)

8 cm inflated juvenile
14 cm adult

Spines shorter than eye diameter, triangular to flattened in cross-section, all spines with 3 subdermal roots but no tentacles, spines on head erect, no spines wholly on peduncle; small movable spine below and behind corner of mouth; nasal organ a short tube with 2 openings; dorsal fin rays 11–13; anal fin rays 10–12; pectoral fin rays 18–21. Benthic fish brown to grey, with **black blotches or clusters of black spots on back and sides**; base of spines often in a pale spot. Pelagic stage covered with eye-sized or smaller black spots; transverse series of faint dark broken lines on all fins. Attains 15 cm.

Indo-West Pacific, Red Sea, Persian Gulf to Cape Town.

Usually on sand or coral rubble near reefs in 15–170 m. Adults nocturnal and solitary; often sleeps during day in a large vase sponge. Eats benthic invertebrates. Pelagic juveniles occasionally washed ashore.

— SIMILAR SPECIES

In yellowspotted burrfish, *Cyclichthys spilostylus* (Leis & Randall 1982), some spines on top of head have 4 subdermal roots. Pelagic juveniles (<10 cm) have long fleshy tentacles all over head and body, with base of each tentacle surrounding a dermal spine. On an 8 cm SL juvenile, the tentacles were 3–4 cm long; with growth, tentacles shrink, and on a 12 cm juvenile, the tentacles are reduced to little cirri (~3–4 mm), barely longer than

the spine to which they are attached. Juveniles bluish grey dorsally, sides and belly with scattered black pupil-size spots; adults have each spine of the flanks and belly in a black spot; dorsal spines in a white or yellow spot.

Attains 35 cm. Indo-Pacific, Red Sea, Oman to False Bay. Pelagic juveniles of yellow-spotted burrfish are known in our area, but adults have yet to be found here.

BALLOON PORCUPINEFISH
Diodon holocanthus
Linnaeus 1758

22 cm adult
5 cm juvenile

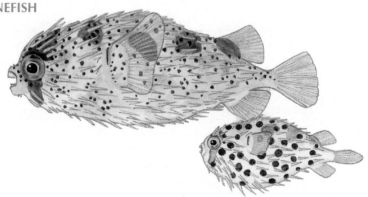

Spines longer than eye diameter, round in cross-section, and erectile (with 2 roots below skin), except for spines around gill opening and dorsal fin base; length of spines on forehead 3.6–7.7 times in SL; 12–15 spines along ventral midline from lower jaw to anus; no spines wholly on peduncle; dorsal and anal fin rays 13–15; pectoral fin rays 20–24; some fish with short tentacles over eyes on chin and body. Head and body pale olive to tawny dorsally, with **small black spots and several large dark blotches without pale borders, one over inter-orbital region, another across nape, large irregular dark blotch above and behind pectoral fin base and one at dorsal fin base; fins not spotted**. Pelagic juveniles (6–9 cm) with pupil-size spots, more prominent on belly. Attains 29 cm.

Tropical, subtropical and warm temperate waters of all oceans; apparently absent from central Pacific except for Hawaii and Easter Island; Namibia to Mozambique.

Coral and rocky reefs, also sandy or silty sand bottoms in 1–100 m. Feeds on molluscs, sea urchins, hermit crabs and crabs. Nocturnal species; usually solitary and hiding in caves or under ledges by day, but occasionally occurring in small groups, roaming about during the day. Spawns in pairs at dawn and dusk. Females display a distinctive white-sided pattern and hover a few metres above the bottom when they are ready to spawn. The male approaches and follows close behind the female, nudging her abdomen whenever she pauses. If she is receptive, the female rises, with the male close behind. Pressing his snout against her abdomen, the male begins to push her towards the surface. As they reach the surface, the female moves forward, releasing her eggs and vigorously splashing along the surface; the male follows closely and releases sperm to fertilise the eggs.

SIMILAR SPECIES

The spotfin porcupinefish, *Diodon hystrix* Linnaeus 1758, has 1–3 small spines on the dorsal surface of peduncle; adults with small dark spots on head, body and fins. Some fish also have dark blotches on body; dorsal and anal fin rays 14–17; pectoral fin rays 21–25; no tentacles on head or body. Attains 71 cm. Worldwide in warm waters.

Shortspine porcupinefish, *Diodon liturosus* Shaw 1804, have length of forehead spines 10–25 times in SL; may have small tentacles under chin and one over each eye; head and body with pale-edged dark blotches; black spot at base of each spine on flanks; no inter-orbital black blotch but there is one across the nape; black bar below eye and another in front of pectoral fin base; black blotch above and behind pectoral fin base, in middle of back and at base of dorsal fin; fins unspotted. Primarily on reefs. Attains 50 cm. Indo-central Pacific, Oman to Algoa Bay.

The blacklip porcupinefish, *Lophodiodon calori* (Bianconi 1854), has most spines on head and belly erectile with 2 roots, those on back and sides fixed with 3 roots; 2–4 antrorse spines between nostrils, short tentacle over each eye; dorsal and anal fin rays 10–12; pectoral fin rays 21–23. Pelagic juvenile white, covered with eye-size black spots. Adults tawny dorsally, white below; dorsal spines pale or in black spot; dark bar below eye, dark blotch (or cluster of small black spots) before and another behind pectoral fin base; lips black; fins uniformly pale grey. Attains 20 cm. Indo-West Pacific, Oman to False Bay.

FAMILY MOLIDAE ■ Sunfish

Body orbicular or elongate-oval, compressed, truncate posteriorly, as if the rear end were chopped off; tail fin resorbed during larval metamorphosis and replaced by a rudder-like structure called the 'clavus'; dorsal and anal fins long and stiff, with short base; pelvic fins absent; mouth very small; teeth fused to form a parrot-like beak in small juveniles (~25 mm); adults with row of minute teeth hidden behind thick lips; gill openings a small hole at base of pectoral fins. Swimbladder absent in adults. Size range 80 cm to 3 m.

Sunfish occur in the open ocean, usually near the surface and often far from land. In swimming, the dorsal and anal fins are flapped synchronously from side to side. Although this mode of propulsion seems clumsy and slow, sunfish can swim surprisingly fast. Juvenile molas (~1 m long and weighing 60 kg) have been seen leaping out of the water, so they must be capable of swimming fast when pursued by predators. Molids feed mainly on planktonic jellyfish, siphonophores, salps and occasionally (in shallow water) on benthic invertebrates such as sponges and worms.

Circumglobal in tropical and temperate seas. Three genera and 4 or 5 species, 4 in our area.

OCEAN SUNFISH
Mola mola
(Linnaeus 1758)

*1.4 m adult
(Indian Ocean)
5 cm juvenile*

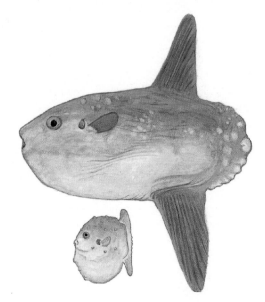

Body orbicular, truncate posteriorly, depth 0.8–1.8 times in length to clavus; clavus supported by 12 or 13 'rays', 8 or 9 of which (in adults) bear ossicles (small bony plates), **widely separated by skin which (in large adults) extends beyond the ossicles to form distinct lobes**; skin thick and tough, with small rough denticles; band of reduced (smooth) denticles between bases of dorsal and anal fins. Colour variable; usually bluish violet dorsally and posteriorly, whitish ventrally; clavus often with radiating white streaks. Attains 3 m, 2 tonnes.

Found in all oceans, but not in polar seas.

Generally epipelagic, occasionally to depths of 600 m; sometimes forages on continental shelf, but rarely seen near shore. Molas have been tracked with electronic tags diving frequently (20 dives per day) to frigid depths of 600 m to feed. Often seen drifting on their side at the surface, as if basking in the sun. Perhaps this behaviour helps the molas keep their muscle temperature and basal metabolism at a higher (more efficient) level. The fecundity of this giant fish is also prodigious: the ovary of a 1.5 m female was estimated to contain 300 million eggs.

Not good to eat, though Japanese fishermen are reported to relish the thick chewy blubber-like tissue under the skin, which they eat raw.

Mola, Latin for 'millstone', is the root of our word molar for teeth used for grinding.

SIMILAR SPECIES

The southern sunfish, *Mola ramsayi* (Giglioli 1883), has 16 'rays' supporting the clavus, 12 of which bear ossicles (in adults); ossicles broader than spaces between them, forming the smooth margin of clavus; no band of reduced denticles between dorsal and anal fins. The southern sunfish is also a giant, apparently growing as large as *Mola mola*. Southern Hemisphere, South Africa, Australia and New Zealand.

acronurus: the specialised larva of a surgeonfish.

acute: sharply pointed.

adherent: scales that are firmly attached.

adipose eyelid: a transparent fixed eyelid that covers or partially covers, protects and streamlines the eye of some fish (carangids, mullet, threadfins, sardines, herring, etc.).

adipose fin: a fleshy rayless median fin located on the back between the dorsal and tail fins of some fish.

a.k.a.: also known as.

allopatric: referring to species with disjunct (non-overlapping) geographic distributions; opposite of sympatric.

alpheid shrimp: small burrowing shrimp (Family Alpheidae) that lives commensally (sharing a burrow) with a goby (*Cryptocentrus* spp). Alpheid shrimps have an enlarged nipper that makes a loud cracking noise when it is snapped closed.

amphipod: a small aquatic crustacean with laterally compressed body.

ampullae of Lorenzini; ampullary organs: electro-receptor organs sensitive to the electric fields generated by living animals. They are connected with pores on the underside of the head of elasmobranchs.

anal fin: median fin on the underside of a fish behind the anus and in front of the tail fin.

anterior: on or towards the front (head) end of the fish.

anthozoan: animal of the Class Anthozoa; includes sea anemones, corals, sea fans, sea pansies, zooanthids and black corals.

anti-tropical distribution: found on both sides (north and south) of the tropics, but not in tropical areas.

antrorse: pointing towards the front (anterior) end of fish.

arrow-worm: small (3–10 cm) planktonic, carnivorous, torpedo-shaped worm.

ascidian: tunicate animal, e.g. red bait, sea squirt.

axil: the inner or posterior part of the fin base.

axillary process: scaly flap of skin at the base of the pelvic and pectoral fins of some fish.

barbel: fleshy tentacle-like sensory organ near the mouth of some fish.

basal: at or towards the base.

batch spawning: spawning of small batches of eggs daily, every few days or once a week, often throughout the year.

batoid: a flat elasmobranch fish, e.g. skate or ray, with pectoral fins fused to the sides of the head and with gill openings on the underside of the body.

benthic: on or situated near the bottom; demersal.

bicuspid: with two cusps or points.

bifurcate: split or divided into two parts.

bioluminescence: the ability of a living organism to produce light.

biserial: arranged in two series or rows.

bivalve: a mollusc with an external shell of two hinged valves (including oysters, clams, scallops, mussels, etc.); a.k.a. pelecypod.

branchial: pertaining to the gills.

branchiostegal membranes: membranes connecting the branchiostegal rays to close the gill cavity on the underside of the head.

branchiostegal rays; branchiostegals: strut-like bones supporting the branchiostegal membranes.

brittlestar: echinoderm with slender flexible 'arms' and soft central disc. Feeds on detritus and plankton.

broadcast spawner: shedding pelagic eggs and sperm simultaneously into the water where fertilisation takes place.

bryozoan: minute invertebrate animals of the Phylum Ectoprocta; form extensive colonies with numerous small pores and resemble encrusting sponges, calcareous branching algae, hydroids and corals. When the bryozoan is feeding, a miniature crown of ciliated tentacles is protruded through each pore to capture plankton.

canine: conical pointed tooth, usually larger than other teeth in the mouth.

carapace: the hard outer shell of an animal.

carnivore: predator that feeds on animals.

cartilage (*adj.* **cartilaginous**): skeletal tissue, usually soft and flexible; in bony fish it is mostly replaced by bone during the early growth stages.

caudal: pertaining to the tail or rear end of the fish.

caudal peduncle: see peduncle.

centrum (*pl.* **centra**): the cylindrical body of a vertebra; cartilaginous in sharks and rays, bony in bony fish.

cephalic: referring to the head.

cephalopod: a mollusc with 8 or 10 arms, large eyes and (usually) no external shell; includes octopuses, squid, cuttlefish, paper nautilus (*Argonauta*) and *Nautilus*.

cetacean: aquatic mammal of the Order Cetacea (whale, porpoise, dolphin, etc.).

cheek: area between the eye, upper jaw and the edge of the preopercle bone.

chiton: a flat oval mollusc with shell comprising 8 overlapping plates surrounded by a thick flexible girdle; usually attached to rocks in the intertidal zone.

chondrichthyan: cartilaginous fish (shark, ray, chimaera, etc.).

chromatophore: pigment cell responsible for the colour patterns of the skin.

ciguatera: unpredictable type of poisoning caused by a toxic benthic dinoflagellate eaten by herbivorous reef fish and concentrated in fish-eating predators.

circumtropical: distributed worldwide in the tropical zone.

cirrus (*pl.* **cirri**): small, slender, flexible, filamentous appendage.

CITES: Convention on International Trade in Endangered Species of Wild Fauna and Flora (www.cites.org).

cladoceran: minute crustacean which has the trunk enclosed in a horny carapace; includes the freshwater *Daphnia*; a.k.a. water flea.

claspers: see intromittent organ.

clupeoid fish: sardines, pilchards, herring, anchovies and wolfherring (Families Clupeidae, Engraulidae and Chirocentridae).

cnidarian: animal of Phylum Cnidaria (Coelenterata), including hydroids, jellyfish, sea anemones and corals.

coelenterate: see cnidarian.

commensal: referring to an association of two different organisms whereby one benefits by living with, on or within the other without harming it.

common name: see vernacular name.

compressed: flattened from side to side (laterally) so that the body is deeper than wide, like a butterflyfish.

continental shelf: the sea bottom from shore to 200 m.

continental slope: the sea bottom from 200– 2 000 m.

continuous: unbroken; usually referring to the dorsal fin in which the spinous part is joined to the soft-rayed part with no gap between the two; also refers to an unbroken lateral-line scale series.

copepod: tiny planktonic crustacean of major importance in marine food chains. Some parasitic species (known as 'fish lice') attach to the fins or gills of fish.

counter-shaded: a fish that is dark above (dorsally), and pale below (ventrally).

crepuscular: active at dawn and dusk, feeding or hunting in twilight.

crinoid: feather-like branching echinoderms of the Class Crinoidea; usually sessile, but they can also crawl or swim over the bottom using their arms; a.k.a. feather star.

crustacean: invertebrate animal with jointed external skeleton, e.g. crabs, prawns, krill, barnacles, mantis shrimp, copepods, isopods, amphipods, lobsters, etc.

ctenoid scale: a scale with minute spines (ctenii) on the rear margin.

ctenophore: transparent spherical animal resembling jellyfish, with two long fringed tentacles and iridescent, luminescent, radially arranged bands of cilia along the outer surface of the body.

cuneate: wedge-shaped.

cusp: a point or rounded projection on a tooth.

cycloid scale: a thin flexible scale with a smooth margin.

deciduous: scales that are easily shed or rubbed off.

demersal: on or near the bottom; benthic.

depressed: body flattened vertically, from top to bottom, like a stingray.

dermal: pertaining to the skin.

detritus: superficial layer of particulate matter on the bottom of aquatic habitats. Detritus comprises a mixture of decomposing organic matter, some fine inorganic sediment (sand, silt, mud) and various microscopic living organisms (bacteria, fungi and micro-algae, including dinoflagellates and diatoms).

diatom: microscopic unicellular algae that live in a transparent shell of silicon.

dichromatic: having two colour forms.

dimorphic: having two forms.

dinoflagellate: microscopic unicellular organism (protozoan) with two whip-like filaments (flagella); most are planktonic but a few are benthic.

distal: remote or away from point of attachment; opposite to proximal.

diurnal: active during day; feeding or hunting in daylight.

dorsal: on or towards the upper part of a fish.

dorsal fin: median fin on the dorsal surface of a fish; on fish with two or more dorsal fins, the fin closest to the head is called the 1st dorsal fin.

DW: disc width of skates, stingrays and other batoids.

echinoderm: mostly benthic marine animal (sea urchin, heart urchin, brittlestar, basketstar, sand dollar, starfish, crinoid and sea cucumber).

ectoparasite: external parasite.

edentate: without teeth.

elasmobranchs: cartilaginous fishes of the Subclass Elasmobranchii which includes sharks, rays, skates, guitarfish, sawfish, mantas, etc.

emarginate: with a slightly indented margin.

endemic: native; unique to a certain area.

endemism: the proportion of species restricted to an area.

epibenthic: above but close to the bottom.

epilithic: growing or living on the substrate.

epipelagic: oceanic zone from the surface to 200 m.

epithet: the second word of the species scientific name; usually a descriptive term.

esca: terminal lure or 'bait' of the anglerfish.

estuary: the wide lower tidal part of a river.

euphausiid: pelagic shrimp-like crustacean of the Order Euphausiacea. Most species live near the surface, occur in swarms and are commonly known as krill.

euryhaline: able to tolerate a wide range of salinity.

facultative: optional, incidental.

FADs: fish attracting devices; floating rafts or buoys usually anchored offshore to attract pelagic game fish.

falcate: sickle-shaped, crescentic.

finlet: small median fin or fins in a series behind 2nd dorsal fin and anal fin of scombrid fish (tunas and mackerels) and some kingfish.

fin ray: a slender, flexible, segmented, usually branched, cartilaginous or horny ray that supports the fins.

fin spine: an unsegmented unbranched supporting element of a fin, usually stiff with a sharp tip (some fish have slender flexible fin spines).

FL (fork length): fish length usually measured from the front end of the head to the tip of the middle tail fin rays (fork of tail fin).

foraminiferan: microscopic unicellular animal; most marine 'forams' live in multi-chambered limestone shells.

frenum: a connecting or restraining membrane.

fusiform: tapering towards each end; spindle-shaped.

gastropod: asymmetrical molluscs of the Class Gastropoda, including snails, whelks and sea slugs (nudibranchs).

genus (*pl.* **genera**): a group (taxonomic category) of closely related species.

gill: respiratory organ of fish and other aquatic animals.

gill arch: bony or cartilaginous arch bearing the gill filaments.

gill chamber: the space on each side of the head containing the gills.

gill filaments: soft red fleshy part of the gills; oxygen is taken into the blood from water flowing over the gill filaments.

gill lamellae: microscopic plate-like ridges on the gill filaments where gas (oxygen and carbon dioxide) exchange between blood and sea water takes place.

gill opening: posterior opening of the gill chamber where water flowing over the gills is expelled. Bony fish and chimaeras have only one gill opening on each side of the head; elasmobranchs (sharks and rays) have 5–7 pairs of gill openings (slits) on the head.

gill rakers: bony finger-like projections along the anterior (inner) edge of the gill arch; they are used to retain food organisms. Gill rakers vary greatly in number and length and are important in fish classification.

gill slit: see gill opening.

gonads: reproductive organs – ovary or testis.

gravid: pregnant; carrying unborn young.

gular region: area on underside of head between left and right lower jaw bones.

habitat: the place where a species usually lives.

herbivore: animal that feeds on plants.

hermaphrodite: a fish that changes sex (sequential hermaphrodite) or is simultaneously both male and female (synchronous hermaphrodite). See also synchronous hermaphrodite, protandrous and protogynous.

holothurian: elongate, cucumber or sausage-shaped echinoderms of the Class Holothuroidea; the body may be tough and muscular or thin and translucent; a.k.a. sea cucumber.

hyaline: transparent.

hydroid: polyp form of a hydrozoan coelenterate.

hydrozoan: cnidarian of the Class Hydrozoa. Usually occurring in colonies of low branching tree-like structures, bearing numerous small polyps with a ring of stinging tentacles around the mouth.

hyperostosis (v. **hyperossify**): hypertrophied bone growth that normally affects certain bones of some fishes and is characteristic for certain species (e.g. spotted grunter).

ichthyology: the study of fishes.

IGFA: International Game Fish Association (www.igfa.org).

incisor (adj. **incisiform**): tooth flattened at tip like a chisel.

Indian Ocean: distributed from Africa to Western Australia, including the Andaman Sea and western Indonesia.

Indo-central Pacific: distributed from western Indian Ocean to Pitcairn Islands in the South Pacific Ocean.

Indo-Pacific: distributed from the western Indian Ocean to the Americas.

Indo-West Pacific: distributed from the western Indian Ocean to the International Date Line (180° longitude) in the Pacific Ocean.

inferior mouth: mouth located on the underside of head.

interopercle: the lowest (ventral-most) opercular bone.

inter-orbital: area between the eyes, on top of head.

inter-spinous membrane: membrane between spines of a fin.

intertidal: between high and low tide marks on a shore.

intromittent organ: male copulatory organ.

invertebrate: an animal lacking vertebrae, e.g. jellyfish, crustacean, ctenophore, echinoderm, siphonophore, coral, sponge, mollusc, tunicate, worm, etc.

isopod: small dorso-ventrally flattened crustacean of the Order Isopoda.

isthmus: the part of the body that separates left and right gill chambers; the throat region of a fish.

junior synonym: a younger (more recent) scientific name for a species.

keel: narrow ridge on side of peduncle or base of tail fin.

krill: planktonic shrimp-like crustaceans that feed on phytoplankton and are eaten by mammals, fish and birds.

KZN: KwaZulu-Natal; province of South Africa (see map on inside front cover).

lamina (pl. **laminae**): thin plate or layer.

larva (pl. **larvae**): early life history stage between hatching and transformation to a juvenile, which is an immature miniature replica of the adult.

lateral: referring to or towards the side.

lateralis canal: the branch of the lateral-line system that continues onto the head.

lateral line (LL): system of minute perforated tubes or canals containing receptors sensitive to low-frequency sounds (vibrations) and water movements made by the motions of nearby animals and currents. The LL on the head divides into a network of branching lateralis canals, but on the body, it is usually a single tube along the mid-lateral region on each side from the head to the tail fin.

lateral-line scales: body scales perforated by tubes that connect with the lateral line.

lateral scale series (LSS): the oblique scale series from the gill opening to the base of the tail fin.

leptocephalus: the compressed transparent ribbon-like pelagic larva of eels, bonefish, tarpon and ladyfish.

lipid: organic chemicals including fats, oils and waxes.

littoral: marine intertidal zone between low and high water tide marks.

LL: see lateral line.

LSS: see lateral scale series.

lunate: crescent-shaped; used to describe a tail fin with deeply indented margin and narrow projecting lobes.

macro-zooplankton: large (visible to the naked eye; from ~5–200+ mm in length or diameter) animals of the plankton: krill, fish larvae, jellyfish, ctenophores, pelagic shrimp, arrow-worms, salps, etc.

Mascarene Islands: Réunion, Mauritius and Rodrigues.

maxilla (*pl.* **maxillae**): one of the two bones that comprise each half of the upper jaw.

MCM: Marine and Coastal Management; branch of the Department of Environmental Affairs and Tourism; conducts and funds research on the biology, ecology and utilisation of South African marine resources (www.environment.gov.za).

medial: on or towards the middle of the body.

median fins: the dorsal, anal and tail fins.

melanophore: a black pigment cell.

mesopelagic: the oceanic zone from 200–1 000 m.

mid-lateral: along the middle of the side of a fish.

midwater: middle of the water column.

mimic: a species that closely resembles another, usually unrelated organism and gains some advantage from this resemblance.

molar (*adj.* **molariform**): a blunt rounded tooth adapted for crushing food.

molluscs: animals of the Phylum Mollusca, includes chitons, gastropods (perlemoen, nudibranchs, limpets, whelks), cephalopods (cuttlefish, octopus, nautilus, squid) and pelecypods (mussels, oysters, clams, scallops).

morphology: the form and structure of organisms or the study of this subject.

mouth brood: to carry eggs in the mouth until they hatch (= oral incubation).

mucus: a slimy substance secreted by the skin.

mysids: small shrimp-like crustaceans; often occur in dense swarms near the bottom. Some species are demersal (burying in the sand) during the day and epibenthic or pelagic at night.

naked: without scales.

nape: the dorsal region at the rear of the head.

neritic: pelagic zone over continental shelf.

nictitans: a movable inner eyelid of some sharks.

nomenclature (zoological): system of names for animal species and the categories (taxa) of the hierarchical classification that expresses their hypothesised evolutionary relationships.

obligate: constrained.

oceanic zone: ocean realm beyond the continental shelf.

ocellus (*pl.* **ocelli**): an eye-like spot, usually ringed by another colour.

olfactory: pertaining to the sense of smell or nasal organs.

omnivore: animal that feeds on both plants and animals.

opercle: the large upper rear bone of the gill cover, the largest bone of the operculum.

operculum (*adj.* **opercular**): gill cover, comprising four bones – the opercle, preopercle, subopercle and interopercle.

oral incubation: see mouth brooding.

orbicular: round, disc-shaped, almost circular.

orbit: the dermal or bony socket for the eye.

organism: a living thing, plant (algae fungus, etc.) animal (jellyfish, coral, anemone, sponge, worm, mollusc, crustacean, echinoderm, tunicate, fish, mammal, human being, etc.), or protist (bacteria etc.)

ORI: Oceanographic Research Institute, Durban (www.ori.org.za).

ostracod: small planktonic crustacean with body enclosed in a bivalve-like carapace.

otolith: calcareous 'ear bone' or 'ear stone' in the ear capsule of fish.

oviparity (*adj.* **oviparous**): reproduction that involves release of eggs into the water column or depositing eggs on the bottom.

ovoviviparous: a type of viviparity in which the foetus is not provided with extra nutrients in addition to its own yolk supply.

paired fins: pectoral and pelvic fins.

palate: roof of the mouth (includes vomer, palatines and pterygoid bones).

palatines: paired bones on the roof of the mouth, lateral and posterior to the median vomer bone.

papilla (*pl.* **papillae**): a small fleshy protuberance.

PCL (precaudal length): a length measure for sharks from tip of snout to origin of upper tail fin lobe.

pectoral axillary fold: flap of skin at upper end of pectoral fin base.

pectoral fins: paired fins usually found on each side of fish behind gill openings. In primitive fishes, e.g. pilchards and anchovies, these fins are lower on the body than in more advanced forms. Some eels lack pectoral fins.

pedicellaria: small claw-like pincers of sea urchins.

peduncle: slender posterior part of body between rear end of dorsal and anal fin bases and the tail fin.

pelagic: of, inhabiting, or carried at the surface or in the water column in the open ocean.

pelecypod: bivalve mollusc.

pelvic fins: paired fins usually below or behind the pectoral fins. The pelvic fins are abdominal in primitive fish like pilchards and anchovies, but more anterior, closer to the pectoral fins, in spiny-rayed fish.

penaeid: shrimp of the Family Penaeidae.

peritoneum: skin lining the abdominal cavity.

phylogenetic order: supposed evolutionary sequence of families, whereby we start with the 'most primitive' (supposedly oldest) families (cartilaginous fish) followed by 'primitive' bony fish (coelacanths, ladyfish, bonefish, eels, sardines, anchovies, catfish, lizardfish, hake, kingklip), followed by 'more advanced' spiny-rayed fish (scorpionfish, rockcod, seabream, butterflyfish, wrasses, blennies, surgeonfish, tunas, soles, etc.), and finishing with the 'most advanced' families (triggerfish, puffers, porcupinefish and molas).

phytoplankton: microscopic single-cell organisms that float near the surace of the sea, e.g. dinoflagellates, diatoms and blue-green algae.

piscivore: fish-eating predator.

planktivore: animal that feeds on plankton.

plankton: small floating pelagic plants and animals that drift more or less passively with the ocean currents. Most plankton (e.g. copepods, fish larvae, arrow-worms) can swim but their movements are often random or co-ordinated with vertical migrations in the water column. Most plankton are less than 2 mm, but macro-zooplankton (krill, ostracods, ctenophores, salps, postlarvae of fish, etc.) are larger.

poison: a toxin that is eaten, causing stomach cramps, nausea, vomiting and sometimes, paralysis and death.

polychaete: segmented worm with bristles.

portunid: swimming crab of the Family Portunidae.

posterior: at or towards the rear end of a fish.

precaudal: region before the tail (caudal) fin.

precaudal length: see PCL.

predorsal scales: the line (series) of scales along the mid-dorsal line in front of the (1st) dorsal fin.

premaxilla: the more anterior (tooth-bearing) bone forming the upper jaw.

preopercle: boomerang- or L-shaped bone behind and below the eye, in front of the opercle and constituting the fore part of the operculum; its rear edge is usually free and may be serrated or smooth.

preorbital: bone or region below and in front of the eye.

procumbent: leaning or pointing forward (like the antrorse spine at the dorsal fin origin of rabbitfish) or lying in front of something (e.g. the small spine-like 'procumbent rays' at the front of the upper and lower edges of the tail fin).

protandry (*adj.* **protandrous**): sequential hermaphroditism in which a fish matures first as a male, and after spawning as a male for a year or more, changes sex (the testis transforming to an ovary) and spawns thereafter as a female. From the Greek *protos* – first, and *andros* – man, male.

protogyny (*adj.* **protogynous**): sequential hermaphroditism in which a fish matures first as a female, and after spawning as a female for a year or more, changes sex (the ovary transforming to a testis) and spawns thereafter as a male. From the Greek *protos* – first, and *gynos* – woman, female.

protrusile: capable of being thrust out or extended forwards.

proximal: towards the body or base of attachment.

pseudobranch: small gill-like organ on the inside of the operculum.

pterygiophore: bones supporting the fin spines and rays.

pterygoids: bones of the roof of the mouth posterior to the palatines.

pup: the prenatal or newly born young of sharks, rays and other chondrichthyans.

retrorse: pointing backwards (posteriorly).

rictus: corner of the mouth.

rostrum (*adj.* **rostral**): forward projection of the snout.

rotifer: microscopic zooplankton of the Phylum Rotifera.

SADSAA: South African Deep Sea Angling Association (www.fishingowl.co.za).

SAIAB: South African Institute for Aquatic Biodiversity (www.saiab.ru.ac.za).

salp: a pelagic colonial tunicate; more or less transparent, often forming long chains.

Sardine Run: Annual migration in May and June of huge schools of pilchards (and some other clupeoid fish) northwards from south coast, along the Eastern Cape coast, to KZN.

scientific name: the formal name of a taxon (phylum, class, order, family, genus or species). The scientific name of a species comprises the genus and species epithet. A species has only one valid scientific name.

scuba: self-contained underwater breathing apparatus.

scute: a modified (thickened) bony scale with a keel or a spiny point.

seine: fishing net for encircling fish.

semicircular canals: three curved inter-connected membranous tubes in the ear.

sexual dichromatism: having male and female of the same species with different colours.

sexual dimorphism: having differences in colour and/or morphology between male and female of the same species.

siphonophore: pelagic colonial coelenterate.

SL (standard length): length of fish, measured from front of upper jaw (or snout if it projects over jaw) to rear end of bones that support the middle rays of the tail fin.

soft-ray: a segmented, often branched, fin ray.

sp. (*abbrev.* **species**): usually denotes an unnamed (not formally described) species.

spawn; spawning: the simultaneous release of eggs by female fish and sperm by male fish to produce fertilised eggs.

species: a biological entity (plant, animal, bacteria, fungus), comprising individuals sharing a unique common gene pool and various anatomical (internal and external) features and colour patterns, enabling us to recognise and name these particular organisms. Species are the fundamental units of biological diversity and taxonomic classifications.

spine: a sharp projecting point; a fin ray that is not paired, unbranched and has no segments (cross-striations).

spinule: minute spine (not used to refer to fin spines).

spiracle: opening behind the eye of some sharks, rays and skates, leading into the gill cavity; may serve as an intake opening for water entering the gill chambers.

spp: two or more described or undescribed species.

standard length: see SL.

stomatopod: crustacean of the Order Stomatopoda; a.k.a. mantis shrimp.

subequal: approximately equal.

sublittoral: the continental shelf; from the intertidal (littoral) zone out to ~200 m.

subopercle: gill cover bone that lies below (ventral to) the opercle.

suborbital: beneath the eye.

substrate: the base or bottom of a habitat (e.g. sand, coral reef, mud, rocky reef, etc.).

subterminal: position of mouth slightly under tip of snout.

subtropical: near the tropics; on the east coast from Tropic of Capricorn, north of Inhambane, Mozambique, to Cape St Lucia, KZN.

supramaxilla: small bone on upper rear edge of maxilla.

supraoccipital: median bone at upper rear end of skull.

swimbladder: usually gas-filled sac attached to dorsal surface of body cavity; in some fish (e.g. coelacanths) the swimbladder is filled with fat; in a few (usually benthic) species it is rudimentary or absent. It provides buoyancy, enhances hearing and is used to make sounds in some species.

symbiosis (*adj.* **symbiotic**): the living together in close association of two dissimilar organisms (e.g. a prawn and goby that share a burrow).

sympatric: living together in the same geographic area.

symphysis: the median point or junction of the left and right halves of the jaws.

synchronous hermaphrodite: hermaphroditic fish with ovarian and testicular tissue active and functional at the same time.

synonym: different names given to the same species or taxon. The older (senior) synonym is usually the valid name.

tanaids: minute elongate crustaceans.

tapetum lucidum: reflective layer at the back of the retina in the eye of some fish.

taxon (*pl.* **taxa**): a formal taxonomic unit or category of organisms (genus, species, family, etc.).

teleost: a 'modern' (advanced) bony fish (not including the coelacanth and some other primitive fishes).

temperate southern ocean: pertaining to the circumglobal southern ocean between 30° and 40° S; includes parts of the South Atlantic, South Indian and South Pacific oceans.

temperate zone: in our area, Namibia to the Kei River, Eastern Cape.

tetrodotoxin: poison contained in the flesh, viscera and skin of some pufferfish, porcupinefish and boxfish. Causes illness and may be fatal.

thermocline: the abrupt interface (~3–4° C) between warm surface and cold deeper waters.

thoracic: the chest region (between the isthmus and belly or abdomen).

thorn: large scale or denticle on a skate or ray.

TL (total length): length of fish from front of head to rear end of tail fin.

tribe: a taxonomic category between the subfamily and genus.

tricuspid: with three cusps or points.

tropical: the region between the tropic of Capricorn or the tropic of Cancer and the equator. The tropical region of our area is north of 23° 27′ S latitude.

truncate: having the end square-cut or straight.

tunicate: generally a benthic sac-like attached animal; a.k.a. sea squirt, red bait or ascidian. See salp.

unicuspid: referring to teeth with a single cusp.

uniserial: aligned in a single row or series.

upwelling: occurs when strong winds blow from the land to the sea, pushing the warm surface water near the coast offshore and pulling deep colder water to the surface.

utriculus: central chamber attached to the semicircular canals in the ears of fish.

valid name: the correct scientific name for a taxon (species, genus, etc.).

veliger: the planktonic larval form of molluscs.

venom: a toxin introduced through the skin and into the muscle and blood stream by a wound (bite or sting), causing pain and in some cases, death.

ventral: on or towards the lower surface (underside) of the fish.

ventral fins: pelvic fins.

vernacular name: the 'common' name in a locally spoken language for a fish or other organism. This name often varies from place to place (Cape Town to Durban) or from one country to another (South Africa to Australia or the USA).

vertebrate: an animal with vertebrae (fish, amphibians, reptiles, birds and mammals).

villiform: hair-like; villiform teeth are very small and slender, resembling a short bristled toothbrush or having a velvet appearance.

villus (*pl.* **villi**; *adj.* **villose**): a soft hair-like filament.

viviparity: reproduction involving internal fertilisation of eggs, development of the foetus within the body of the mother and with few well developed young emerging from the oviduct at birth.

vomer: median bone at front of palate; often bears teeth.

warm temperate: in our area, from the Kei River, Eastern Cape, to Cape St Lucia, KZN.

western Indian Ocean: Indian Ocean west of 80° E (west coast of Sri Lanka) including the Red Sea and Persian Gulf. In this book Red Sea and Persian Gulf distributions are specified.

yolk sac: the bulb-like yolk-filled appendage of a larva or foetus.

zooantharian: animal of the Subclass Zooantharia; includes sea anemones and corals.

zooanthids: cnidarians of the Order Zoanthidea.

zooplankton: animals and larvae (mostly microscopic) that drift freely in the water column.

SYMBOLS USED IN TEXT

~   about

‰   parts per thousand, used to express salinity.

467

Allen GR, R Steene & M Allen. 1998. *A Guide to Angelfishes and Butterflyfishes*. Odyssey Publishing/Tropical Reef Research, Perth, Australia. 250 pp.

Branch GM, CL Griffiths, ML Branch & LE Beckley. 1994. *Two Oceans. A Guide to the Marine Life of Southern Africa*. David Philip Publishers, Cape Town, South Africa. 360 pp.

Compagno LJV, M Dando & S Fowler. 2004 (in press). *A Field Guide to the Sharks of the World*. HarperCollins, London, UK. 352 pp.

Cyrus DP & SJM Blaber. 1982. Mouthpart structure and function and the feeding mechanisms of *Gerres*. *South African Journal of Zoology* 18: 403–406.

Darwin C. 1859. *On the Origin of Species*. John Murray, London, UK. ix, 502 pp.

Davidson OG. 1998. *The Enchanted Braid: Coming to Terms with Nature on the Coral Reef*. John Wiley and Sons, Inc., New York, USA. 269 pp.

Debelius H. 1999. *Indian Ocean Reef Guide*. Ikan-Unterwasserarchiv., Frankfurt, Germany. 321 pp.

Gilchrist J. 1902. History of the local names of Cape fish. *Transactions of the South African Philosophical Society* 11(4): 207–232.

Gomon MF, CJM Glover & RH Kuiter. 1994. *The Fishes of Australia's South Coast*. State Print, Adelaide, Australia. 992 pp.

Henneman RM. 2001. *Sharks and Rays. Elasmobranch Guide of the World*. Ikan-Unterwasserarchiv., Frankfurt, Germany. 304 pp.

Jordan DS & B Evermann. 1896. The Fishes of North and Middle America, a descriptive catalogue of the species of fish-like vertebrates found in the waters of North America, north of the isthmus of Panama. *Bulletin of the US National Museums* (47), Part I: ix, 1–1240.

King D. 1996. *Reef Fishes & Corals, East Coast of Southern Africa*. Struik, Cape Town, South Africa. 128 pp.

King D & V Fraser. 2002. *More Reef Fishes & Nudibranchs, East and South Coast of Southern Africa*. Struik, Cape Town, South Africa. 136 pp.

Kuiter RH. 2002. *Fairy & Rainbow Wrasses and their Relatives. A Comprehensive Guide to Selected Labroids*. TMC Publishing, Chorleywood, UK. 208 pp.

Kuiter RH. 2002. *Butterflyfishes, Bannerfishes and their Relatives. A Comprehensive Guide to Chaetodontidae & Microcanthidae*. TMC Publishing, Chorleywood, UK. 208 pp.

Kuiter RH. 2003. *Seahorses, Pipefishes and their Relatives. A Comprehensive Guide to Syngnathiformes*. TMC Publishing, Chorleywood, UK. 237 pp.

Kuiter RH & H Debelius. 2001. *Surgeonfishes, Rabbitfishes and their Relatives*. TMC Publishing, Chorleywood, UK. 208 pp.

Last PR & JD Stevens. 1994. *Sharks and Rays of Australia*. CSIRO, Australia. 513 pp.

Lieske E & R Myers. 1994. *Collins Pocket Guide: Coral Reef Fishes*. HarperCollins, Johannesburg, South Africa. 400 pp.

Myers RF. 1999 (3rd edn). *Micronesian Reef Fishes*. Coral Graphics, Guam. 330 pp.

Paxton JR & WN Eschmeyer (eds). 1994. *Encyclopedia of Fishes*. Academic Press, San Diego, California, USA. 240 pp.

Pietsch TW & DG Grobecker. 1987. *Frogfishes of the World*. Stanford University Press, Stanford, California, USA. 420 pp.

Randall JE. 1995. *Coastal Fishes of Oman*. University of Hawaii Press, Honolulu, Hawaii, USA. 439 pp.

Randall JE. 2001. *Surgeonfishes of the World*. Bishop Museum Press, Honolulu, Hawaii, USA. 123 pp.

Rose JD. 2002. The neurobehavioral nature of fishes and the question of awareness and pain. *Reviews in Fisheries Science* 10: 1–38.

Smith JLB. 1931. New and little known fishes from the south and east coasts of Africa. *Records of the Albany Museum* 4(1): 145–160.

Smith JLB. 1939. A living coelacanthid fish from South Africa. *Nature* 143(March): 748–750.

Smith JLB. 1949. *The Sea Fishes of Southern Africa*. Central News Agency Ltd, South Africa. 550 pp.

Smith JLB. 1956. *Old Fourlegs: The Story of the Coelacanth*. Longmans, Green & Co., London, UK. 260 pp.

Smith JLB. 1956a. An extraordinary fish from South Africa. *Annals and Magazine of Natural History* (Series 12) 9: 54–57.

Smith MM & PC Heemstra (eds). 1986. *Smiths' Sea Fishes*. Macmillan South Africa, Johannesburg, South Africa. 1 047 pp. (Reprinted with 1995 additions and corrections by Struik, Cape Town, South Africa, 2003.)

Taylor L (ed.). 1997. *Sharks and Rays*. Time-Life Books, Melbourne, Australia. 288 pp.

Van der Elst R. 1981. *A Guide to the Common Sea Fishes of Southern Africa*. Struik, Cape Town, South Africa. 367 pp.

Weinberg S. 1999. *A Fish Caught in Time: The Search for the Coelacanth*. Fourth Estate, London, UK. 239 pp.

Whitfield AK. 1998. *Biology and Ecology of Fishes in Southern African Estuaries*. JLB Smith Institute of Ichthyology, Grahamstown, South Africa. 223 pp.

INDEX

487